Organic Farming: The Ecological System

Organic Farming: The Ecological System

Charles Francis, Editor

Agronomy Monograph 54

American Society of Agronomy   Crop Science Society of America   Soil Science Society of America

American Society of Agronomy, Inc.
Crop Science Society of America, Inc.
Soil Science Society of America, Inc.
677 South Segoe Road, Madison, WI 53711-1086 USA

Reprinted in 2010.

ISBN: 978-0-89118-173-6

Library of Congress Control Number: 2009909959

Cover design: Patricia Scullion

Cover photos: Images from the Center for Environmental Farming Systems, Raleigh; NC. Ken Wolf Photography, Raleigh, NC. Carrot photo, iStockphoto.com

Printed on recycled paper.
Printed in the United States of America.

Contents 🜂

Introduction • 1

1

Charles Francis
Justin Van Wart

2

Laurie E. Drinkwater

Systems Design • 49

3

Paul Porter

4

M. H. Entz
J. R. Thiessen Martens

5

E. Ann Clark

6

Kathleen Delate

Foreword

The science of crop production has advanced considerably with increased understanding of genetics, cellular biology, cellular physiology, soil plant interfaces, nutrient uptake, pest interactions, stress physiology, systems biology, ecology, soil water relations, economics, and basic soil and crop sciences. The application of this knowledge to organic crop production has been relatively limited in terms of years and volume of research, but significant new information has been obtained in the past 20 years as organically produced crops have increased to more than 2% of our food consumption in the United States.

Attention to organic farming practices and systems by state, federal, and nonprofit research groups has been welcomed by the organic farming community. Long dependent mainly on farmer experiences, those who produce organic crops and livestock are now working together with scientists to uncover mechanisms and better understand how nonchemical methods work. This collaboration of researchers with farmers is a good example of the potential for cooperative research that is important in advancing our knowledge in this emerging sector of the food system. The focus on ecology of farming is an essential foundation for understanding systems and improving production.

During the past five years the amount of research has increased considerably, with a significant increase in federal funding for organic research. We have seen an increased number of presentations and posters on organic research at the past several ASA–CSSA–SSSA meetings and more publications in our major journals. The Societies' Book and Multimedia Publishing Committee has observed this growth, and yet observed that there is no general reference work on organic production in the United States that is comprehensive and suitable as a college textbook that brings all the elements together. This led us to solicit an editor to develop such a reference. We appreciate the willingness of Dr. Charles Francis, of the University of Nebraska Agronomy and Horticulture Department, to take the lead and work with colleagues in this effort. His research and teaching in sustainable systems and special focus on organic production, along with his interactions with the organic farming community, make him an appropriate editor. The efforts by experts to develop the theme for each chapter and the excellent work by Society staff to transform the manuscript into an outstanding publication are easily recognized.

While much is controversial in the comparisons of organic and non-organic systems, those students, farmers, and scientists who are interested in learning more about the practices that lead to successful certification will find this new reference to be invaluable. For instructors offering courses in organic crop and animal production this would serve well as a textbook or reference book. A definitive work such as *Organic Farming: The Ecological System* will set the stage for research, extension, and education for many years to come.

David D. Baltensperger
Professor and Head of the Department, Soil and Crop Sciences, Texas A&M University
ASA–CSSA–SSSA Book & Multimedia Publishing Committee Chair

Preface 🧄

Agriculture is going through a profound revolution, one that rivals the industrial revolution of the 19th century and the green revolution in the 20th century. These previous changes transformed industries based primarily on local resources and principally serving local markets to more complex systems using high levels of technology. These have evolved to become more fossil fuel intensive, less efficient in output per unit energy input, and more global in their markets. Some people define current agricultural changes only in terms of specific technologies, such as transgenic crops and site-specific input use determined by GPS spatial methods. Yet there is a more profound change taking place mostly at the grass roots—a recognition that the resilience and sustainability of ecology and natural systems have much to teach modern agriculture. Organic farming systems are one manifestation of this new awareness.

Over the past decade, worldwide sales of organic crop and livestock products have expanded 10 to 20% per year (Lockie et al., 2006; Greene and Dimitri, 2007; Organic Trade Association, 2007), increasing interest in organic farming as a potentially profitable and more environmentally benign alternative to conventional production methods. Sales of organic products in 2006 exceeded $16 billion in the United States and reached $40 billion globally, with no drop in this market expected in the near future (U.N. Food and Agriculture Organization, 2007). Prices at the farm gate for organic products may be 10 to 300% greater than for conventional products. In spite of this price differential, sale of organic food continues to grow in the United States, Europe, Japan, and elsewhere. Matt Liebman and Adam Davis, co-authors of Chapter 8, provide a useful overview delving into this intriguingly counter-intuitive economic situation.

To participate in the current food system, it is imperative that agronomists and horticulturists master the practices, systems design, certification process, and details of that system's organic farming sector. The last American Society of Agronomy (ASA) book on organic farming was published more than two decades ago (Bezdicek and Power, 1984); to say that much has happened in research and development since that publication would be a gross understatement. Combining farmer experience and wisdom with the best that science has to offer can lead us to a better understanding of organic systems' mechanisms, as well as how we can design them to both meet human needs and preserve an environment where we would like to live. Beyond their production, economics, and environmental impacts, we are also learning that organic farming and food systems have potential to revitalize the rural landscape and its communities—areas that, as a result of industrial agriculture, are currently highly exploited, depopulated to some degree, and lacking in essential human and ecosystem services on which our long-term well-being depends.

In a series of integrated chapters by people in academic and nonprofit groups working on organic farming and food systems, we present a window on current research and development and a glimpse of a more desirable future for us all. We recognize up front that much of both innovation and application of organic farming methods have come from farmers, and that as researchers we build on this legacy in the United States, Europe, and elsewhere. This book represents a current look at what we know about organic farming practices and systems, primarily from the U.S. and Canadian perspectives.

A brief history of organic farming and an overview of the legal certification process in the U.S. are presented in Chapter 1 by Charles Francis and Justin Van Wart. The rapid standardization of products and their labeling were necessary steps in the growth of organic food markets, yet they introduce a number of challenges, since those efforts led much of our organic production and sales to resemble the industrial model. The ecological tone of the book is set by Laurie Drinkwater from Cornell University in Chapter 2, where she explores the importance of ecological knowledge as the foundation for not only organic farming but for sustaining food systems into the future. Studies of organic systems require holistic research strategies that can differ from traditional experimental design.

Careful systems design is essential for successful organic farming. One of the key practices that reflects the essential biodiversity needed in farming systems is crop rotation, whose principles and specific examples are described in Chapter 3 by Paul Porter from University of Minnesota. Natural systems are characterized by plants and animals, and the closest we can come in agriculture is to design crop–animal systems that are tightly integrated on the farm, a topic discussed in Chapter 4 by Martin Entz and J.R. Thiessen Martens from Manitoba. The essential role of forages in these complex farming systems is presented in Chapter 5 by E. Ann Clark of Guelph University in Ontario. How major grain, oil seed, and specialty crops are grown and marketed organically in the United States is described in Chapter 6 by Kathleen Delate of Iowa State University.

Specific organic practices are explored in the next section on soil fertility and pest management. Joseph Heckman of Rutgers University, Ray Weil of University of Maryland, and Fred Magdoff from University of Vermont are three of the best informed and most prolific authors on the subject of organic cropping and soil nutrient needs, a topic they present in Chapter 7. Innovative nonchemical methods for vegetation management in cropping systems are described in Chapter 8 by Matt Liebman of Iowa State University and Adam Davis of ARS/USDA in Urbana, Illinois. Understanding the biology of pests is critical to managing their impacts on crop plants; George Bird and colleagues from Michigan State University and Rodale Research Center provide an overview of pest classification and alternatives for pest management in Chapter 9.

Marketing of organic products is an essential part of the food chain or food web that will provide farm profits and lead to changes in the food system. In Chapter 10 Agricultural economist Hikaru Hanawa Peterson and horticulturist Rhonda Janke from Kansas State University describe the complexities and innovations that characterize the marketing of organic products in this fast-growing segment of the food industry. Sociologists Patricia Allen and Hilary Melcarek of U.C. Santa Cruz have published widely on the social impacts of alternative food systems and provide an overview of organic foods and food security in Chapter 11.

Organic research, teaching, and extension programs are new ventures for most of our land-grant universities, although they have been vital to informal education for decades. Nancy Creamer and colleagues describe in Chapter 12 the highly successful, integrated, and multi-institutional program in organic and sustainable agriculture research in North Carolina. Chapter 13, contributed by myself, Charles Francis from University of Nebraska, explores the growth of education and extension in organics, including the important roles played by farmers and by nonprofit organizations in the United States. Chapter 14, also contributed by myself, surveys the future of organic farming and the major challenges and changes we are seeing in this sector. Finally, a perspective on the overall structure of the agricultural industry and the future of the rural sector is envisioned in Chapter 15 by Fred Kirschenmann, a North Dakota farmer and active leader at Iowa State University.

These scholarly chapters describe the past, present, and future of organic farming in the U.S. and Canada. We recognize the parochial coverage of this important topic, as there are limited references to and no contributions from scientists and educators in Europe, from the Indian sub-continent, and other important centers of organic research and development. There are also many innovative consumer-driven marketing strategies, for example the large organic consumer network in Japan. Countries in the Nordic Region and some in northern Europe have set specific national goals to achieve a certain level of organic food by a specific year. There are also important advances being made in emerging economies, where in fact much of the farming is de facto organic due to the lack of chemical pesticide and fertilizer inputs. We recognize these initiatives and urge the serious reader to explore this wide range of activities through research or through travel and personal experience.

Organic Farming: The Ecological System provides a snapshot of programs and some history of development of this emerging part of local and global food systems. There will be many changes in the near future as a result of increasing economic pressures, growing appreciation of the impacts of chemicals on our food supply, livestock and human health, and understanding of how the structure of agriculture impacts the quality of life in the rural landscape and the ecosystem services available to us all. As a team of authors, we urge the American Society of Agronomy to continue to provide timely and relevant updates in this important area of agriculture.

Charles Francis, Editor

References

Bezdicek, D.F., and J.F. Power (ed.) 1984. Organic farming: Current technology and its role in a sustainable agriculture. ASA Spec. Publ. 46. ASA, CSSA, SSSA, Madison, WI.

Greene, C., and C. Dimitri. 2007. Organic agriculture: Consumer demand continues to expand. Available at http://www.ers.usda.gov/Briefing/Organic/Demand.htm (accessed 29 Nov. 2007, verified 2 Sept. 2009). USDA-Economic Research Service, Washington, DC.

Lockie, S., D. Halpin, and D. Pearson. 2006. Understanding the market for organic food. p. 245–258. *In* P. Kristiansen et al. (ed.) Organic agriculture: A global perspective. Comstock Publishing, Ithaca, NY.

Organic Trade Association. 2007. Organic Trade Association's 2007 Manufacturer Survey. Available at http://www.ota.com/pics/documents/2007ExecutiveSummary.pdf (accessed 29 Nov. 2007, verified 2 Sept. 2009). OTA, Greenfield, MA.

U.N. Food and Agriculture Organization. 2007. Report of the International Conference on Organic Agriculture and Food Security, Rome, Italy. 3–5 May 2007. Available at ftp://ftp.fao.org/docrep/fao/meeting/012/j9918e.pdf (accessed 29 Nov. 2007, verified 2 Sept. 2009). FAO, Rome.

Contributors ◖

Patricia Allen is Director of the Center for Agroecology and Sustainable Food Systems at the University of California–Santa Cruz. Her research interests include the political ecology of agrifood systems; alternative agrifood institutions; the social construction and relationships among nature, environment and society, race, class, and gender issues in the agrifood system; and the political economy of alternative modes of distribution and consumption and public health.

Ctr. for Agroecology and Sustainable Food Systems, Univ. of California, Santa Cruz, 1156 High St., Santa Cruz, CA 95064 (PatriciaAllen@ucsc.edu)

George Bird is Nematologist and Professor of Entomology at Michigan State University, where he also coordinates diagnostic services as an extension specialist. He has been Coordinator of the North Central Sustainable Agriculture Research and Education program, and served as National Coordinator of this program for the USDA. George also coordinates the IPM program at Michigan State and is on the board of directors of Rodale Institute.

Dep. of Entomology, Michigan State Univ., 38A Natural Sci., East Lansing, MI 48824 (birdg@msu.edu)

E. Ann Clark has teaching and research interests in pasture and grazing management, and in the design of ecologically sound production systems. She is Associate Professor in Plant Agriculture at the University of Guelph, Ontario, Canada. One of her prominent books is *The Contribution of Managed Grasslands to Sustainable Agriculture in the Great Lakes Basin*, published by Haworth Press in 1996.

Dep. of Plant Agriculture, Univ. of Guelph, Crop Science Bldg., 50 Stone Rd. E., Guelph, ON, Canada N1G 2W1 (eaclark@uoguelph.ca)

Nancy Creamer specializes in farming systems research, cover cropping and weed management in organic production systems, and community-based sustainable local food systems. She is Director of the Center for Environmental Farming Systems, a cooperative center organized in collaboration with North Carolina A&T and other groups, and currently a major source of education and research-based information on organic farming and sustainable agriculture. She is Extension Specialist and Professor of Horticulture at North Carolina State University.

Ctr. for Environmental Farming Systems, North Carolina State Univ., Campus Box 7609, Raleigh, NC 27695 (nancy_creamer@ncsu.edu)

Adam Davis is a weed ecologist with the USDA-ARS Invasive Weed Management Unit in Urbana, Illinois. His research centers on integrating empirical and theoretical approaches to multi-tactic management of weedy and invasive plant species. He is also Assistant Professor, Crop Sciences, and a member of the faculty of the Program in Ecology and Evolutionary Biology, University of Illinois.

USDA-ARS, Invasive Weed Management Unit, N-319 Turner Hall, Univ. of Illinois, 1102 S. Goodwin Ave., Urbana, IL 61801 (asdavis1@illinois.edu)

Kathleen Delate was appointed to the first land-grant university faculty position in organic agriculture in the U.S. in 1997. She is currently Associate Professor at Iowa State University in Horticulture and Agronomy Departments, where she is responsible for research, extension, and teaching in organic agriculture. Kathleen has farmed organically in Florida, Hawaii, California, and Iowa. She has degrees in agronomy, horticulture, and agricultural ecology.

Dep. of Agronomy and Horticulture, Iowa State Univ., 106 Horticulture Hall, Ames, IA 50011 (kdelate@iastate.edu)

Laurie Drinkwater is Agroecologist and currently Associate Professor in the Department of Horticulture, Cornell University. Her research focuses on nitrogen, carbon, and phosphorus biogeochemistry, and the ecology of agriculture and development of sustainable food systems. She has been engaged in ecological research on organic agriculture since the late 1980s.

Dep. of Horticulture, Cornell Univ., Plant Science Bldg., Rm. 124, Ithaca, NY 14853 (led24@cornell.edu)

Martin Entz is Professor of Cropping Systems at the University of Manitoba. He has education and research experience in crop physiology, agronomy, and organic agriculture. Included in his research are experiments on crop rotation benefits, long-term organic vs. conventional comparisons, cover crops, crop production energy efficiency, and integrated crop–livestock systems.

Dep. of Plant Science, Univ. of Manitoba, Winnipeg, MB, Canada, R3T 2N2 (m_entz@umanitoba.ca)

Charles Francis is Professor of Agronomy and Horticulture at University of Nebraska–Lincoln. His education and field experience in plant breeding and agronomy in the United States and in developing countries has led to research on crop rotations, genotype by systems interactions, multifunctional rural landscapes, and peri-urban farming. He has an appointment in research, teaching, and extension, and teaches agroecology, organic farming, and urbanization of rural landscapes, a course dedicated to education on the long-term impacts of urban sprawl.

Dep. of Agronomy and Horticulture, Univ. of Nebraska, 279 Plant Science, Lincoln, NE 68583-0915 (cfrancis2@unl.edu)

Matthew Grieshop is Assistant Professor of Entomology and Organic Pest Management Specialist in research and extension at Michigan State University. He specializes in integrated pest management and is active in the Fruit and Vegetable Area of Excellence teams in Cooperative Extension.

Dep. of Entomology, Michigan State Univ. 38A Natural Science, East Lansing, MI 48824 (grieshop@msu.edu)

Joseph Heckman is Professor of Soil Science at Rutgers University in the Department of Plant Biology and Pathology and has an interest in the history of organic agriculture. He grew up on an Ohio farm where his family began farming organically around 1949. He teaches courses in Soil Fertility and Organic Crop Production, and has research and extension programs with a focus on soil fertility management of agronomic and horticultural crops. He serves as Chair of the Committee on Organic and Sustainable Agriculture.

Dep. of Plant Biology and Pathology, Cook College, Rutgers, The State Univ. of New Jersey, 59 Dudley Rd., Foran Hall, New Brunswick, NJ 08901-8520 (heckman@AESOP.rutgers.edu)

Paul Hepperly is research and training director of the Rodale Institute in Kutztown, Pennsylvania. His background is in psychology, agronomy, and plant pathology, and his current research is focused on organic methods of pest management and carbon sequestration. His past experience includes work on temperate and tropical crops in Hawaii, India, Puerto Rico, and Chile, and he has also worked for the USDA and for commercial seed companies.

Rodale Research Inst., 611 Siegfriedale Rd., Kutztown, PA 19530-9320 (paul.hepperly@rodaleinst.org)

Laurie Hodges is Associate Professor of Agronomy and Horticulture at University of Nebraska–Lincoln. She has conducted research on the effects of microclimate on vegetable and cut flower crops and herbicide effects on root exudates and soil-borne pathogens. She works with large- and small-scale commercial producers on cultural practices to increase yield and profitability in high tunnel and field production systems. Her appointment is in extension and research with frequent invitations to speak with students and the public about her experiences with organic production systems and direct marketing.

Dep. of Agronomy & Horticulture, 279 Plant Science Bldg., Univ. of Nebraska, Lincoln, NE 68583-0910 (lhodges1@unl.edu)

Rhonda Janke is Associate Professor in the Department of Horticulture, Forestry, and Recreation Resources at Kansas State University, with research and extension experience in sustainable and organic cropping systems, weed ecology, whole farm planning, alternative crops, and soil quality. She currently teaches fruit crops, vegetable crops, sustainable agriculture, and organic farming systems. Her interest in local and organic food systems includes both extension activities and personal experience as a small-scale organic fruit and vegetable grower.

Dep. of Horticulture, Forestry, and Recreation Resources, Kansas State Univ., 2021 Throckmorton, Manhattan, KS 66506 (rrjanke@ksu.edu)

Fred Kirschenmann is former Director and currently Distinguished Fellow at the Leopold Center, Iowa State University, and President of the Stone Barns Center. He is one of the most articulate and highly recognized leaders in the U.S. in issues related to organic farming and sustainable agriculture and food systems. He is active in the Agriculture of the Middle initiative, which works to promote the future of mid-sized family farms, and he continues to own and co-manage a 3500-acre organic farm in North Dakota.

Leopold Ctr. for Sustainable Agriculture, 209 Curtiss Hall, Iowa State Univ., Ames, IA 50011-1050; Stone Barns Ctr. for Food and Agriculture, Pocantico Hills, NY (leopold1@iastate.edu)

Matt Liebman is Professor of Agronomy and the Henry A. Wallace Endowed Chair for Sustainable Agriculture at Iowa State University. His research, teaching, and outreach activities focus on reducing dependency on agrichemicals and fossil fuels through ecological processes. Included in his research are experiments focused on diversified cropping systems, organic soil amendments, and weed population dynamics.

Dep. of Agronomy, Iowa State Univ., 1401 Agronomy Hall, Ames, IA 50011-1010 (mliebman@iastate.edu)

Fred Magdoff is Professor Emeritus of Plant and Soil Science, University of Vermont and Adjunct Professor in the Department of Crop and Soil Sciences at Cornell University. For many years he taught and conducted research in the area of soil fertility. He was also a member of the National Small Farm Commission and Director of USDA's Northeast Region Sustainable Agriculture Research and Education Program. He is co-author of *Building Soils for Better Crops, a guide to ecological soil management*, SARE, 2000.

Dep. of Plant and Soil Science, Univ. of Vermont, Hills Bldg., Burlington, VT 05405 (fmagdoff@uvm.edu)

Hilary Melcarek has an interdisciplinary academic background in natural resource management and is currently studying urban agriculture in relation to urban social movements. She is a graduate student researcher and doctoral candidate in the Environmental Studies Department at the University of California–Santa Cruz.

Ctr. for Agroecology and Sustainable Food Systems, Univ. of California, Santa Cruz, 1156 High St., Santa Cruz, CA 95064 (melcarek@ucsc.edu)

Jeff Moyer is the Farm Director of the Rodale Research Institute near Kutztown, Pennsylvania. He has recently been appointed as chair of the USDA National Organic Standards Board, the official board that oversees the U.S. National Organic Program. As Farm Manager, Jeff has innovated with organic crop rotations and cover crops, as well as specialized equipment such as a roller-crimper to help manage cover crops before incorporation into the soil. He brings to the book years of farming knowledge, and a wide range of experiences with farmers converting to organic systems.

Rodale Research Inst., 611 Siegfriedale Rd., Kutztown, PA 19530-9320 (jeff.moyer@rodaleinst.org)

J. Paul Mueller has research and extension experience in applied grassland farming research with ruminant animals, including caprine silvo-pastoral systems and agricultural systems that integrate crops and livestock. He is interim Assistant Dean of International Programs, Sustainable Agriculture Coordinator for the College of Agriculture and Life Sciences, and Coordinator of the Farming Systems Research Unit, all at North Carolina State University.

Office of International Programs, College of Agriculture and Life Sciences, North Carolina State Univ., 319 Scott Hall, Campus Box 7608, Raleigh, NC 27695-7608 (Paul_Mueller@ncsu.edu)

John O'Sullivan has expertise in farm management, marketing, community-based food systems, and evaluation. He is coordinator of the Small Farm Unit at CEFS and a Farm Management and Marketing Extension Specialist. He is Adjunct Professor in the Department of Agricultural Economics at North Carolina Agricultural and Technical State University.

Ctr. for Environmental Farming Systems, North Carolina A&T State Univ., P.O. Box 21928, Greensboro, NC 27420 (Johno@ncat.edu)

Hikaru Hanawa Peterson is an agricultural economist whose research focuses on understanding marketing and risk management decisions in food and agriculture. Previous studies have examined marketing issues related to small-scale specialty crops, large-scale commercial crops, the dairy and livestock sectors, and the organic industry. She currently teaches agricultural marketing and agricultural finance at Kansas State University.

Dep. of Agricultural Economics, Kansas State Univ., 318 Waters Hall, Manhattan, KS 66506 (hhp@ksu.edu)

Paul Porter has research and education experience in agronomy in the United States, Zaire, and elsewhere, with a focus on crop rotation and the rotation effect, alternative cropping systems involving rye as a cover crop, and alternative crops. He is Professor of Agronomy and Plant Genetics at the University of Minnesota–St. Paul, with responsibilities in research and teaching, including a popular summer experiential learning course in agroecosystems analysis.

Dep. of Agronomy and Plant Genetics, Univ. of Minnesota, 411 Borlaug Hall, 1991 Buford Circle, St. Paul, MN 55108 (pporter@umn.edu)

Chris Reberg-Horton works on weed management in organic soybeans, introducing legume cover crops into corn–soybean–wheat rotations, reducing tillage in organic systems, allelopathic cover crops, and creating market opportunities for organic producers. He chairs the Organic Farm Panel, the Allelopathy Working Group, and the Organic Research Unit at the Center for Environmental Farming Systems and is an Assistant Professor and Organic Cropping Specialist at North Carolina State University.

Dep. of Crop Science, North Carolina State Univ., Campus Box 7620, Raleigh, NC 27695-7620 (chris_reberg-horton@ncsu.edu)

Michelle Schroeder-Moreno is an ecologist with interests in tropical biology and application of ecological principles in a variety of agricultural ecosystems. Her investigations have included examining how arbuscular mycorrhizal fungi mediate competition among crops in monocultures and polycultures and how phosphorus fertilizers reduce crop growth responses to arbuscular mycorrhizal fungi. She coordinates the Agroecology Program and teaches agroecology courses as Teaching Assistant Professor at North Carolina State University.

Crop Science Dep., North Carolina State Univ., 2406 Williams Hall, Campus Box 7620, Raleigh, NC 27695-7620 (michelle_schroeder@ncsu.edu)

Joanne Thiessen Martens is a Research and Extension Associate with the Organic Agriculture Centre of Canada, based at the University of Manitoba. She is involved in cover crop research, writing research papers and extension materials, and maintaining and developing the Natural Systems Agriculture Website. Her primary assignment involves facilitating the flow of information between organic researchers and organic producers.

Dep. of Plant Science, Univ. of Manitoba, Winnipeg, MB, Canada, R3T 2N2 (j_thiessen_martens@umanitoba.ca)

Justin Van Wart has academic study in agricultural economics and agronomy, and experience in linguistics and agricultural development in other countries. He is currently a graduate research assistant and doctoral candidate in the Department of Agronomy and Horticulture at University of Nebraska–Lincoln, working on biology and economics of energy relationships in biofuels, peri-urban agriculture, and organic farming systems.

Dep. of Agronomy and Horticulture, Univ. of Nebraska, 279 Plant Science, Lincoln, NE 68583-0915 (justin.vanwart@huskers.unl.edu)

Steve Washburn is a dairy scientist whose focus is reproductive management of dairy and beef cattle herds, seasonal breeding, crossbreeding in dairy cattle, estrous synchronization, and pasture-based and organic dairy production systems. He is Coordinator of the pasture-based Dairy Unit at CEFS and a Professor and Extension Specialist in the Animal Science Department at North Carolina State University.

Dep. of Animal Science, North Carolina State Univ., 211-C Polk Hall, Box 7621, Raleigh, NC 27695-7621 (Steve_Washburn@ncsu.edu)

Ray R. Weil is Professor of Soil Science in the Department of Environmental Science and Technology at University of Maryland. Since 1972 when he ran a 500-acre organic farm in North Carolina, he has been devoted to researching and promoting sustainable agricultural systems in both developed and developing countries. His research in collaboration with dozens of innovative farmers integrates management of soil organic matter, nutrient cycling, and alternative cropping systems to improve both the soil and the farmer's bottom line. Ray is best known as co-author of the classic soil science textbook, *The Nature and Properties of Soils*.

Dep. of Natural Resource Sciences and Landscape Architecture, Univ. of Maryland, H.J. Patterson Hall, Collegeville, MD 20742 (rweil@umd.edu)

Conversion Factors for SI and Non-SI Units

To convert Column 1 into Column 2 multiply by	Column 1 SI unit	Column 2 non-SI unit	To convert Column 2 into Column 1 multiply by
Length			
0.621	kilometer, km (10^3 m)	mile, mi	1.609
1.094	meter, m	yard, yd	0.914
3.28	meter, m	foot, ft	0.304
1.0	micrometer, μm (10^{-6} m)	micron, μ	1.0
3.94×10^{-2}	millimeter, mm (10^{-3} m)	inch, in	25.4
10	nanometer, nm (10^{-9} m)	Angstrom, Å	0.1
Area			
2.47	hectare, ha	acre	0.405
247	square kilometer, km² (10^3 m)²	acre	4.05×10^{-3}
0.386	square kilometer, km² (10^3 m)²	square mile, mi²	2.590
2.47×10^{-4}	square meter, m²	acre	4.05×10^3
10.76	square meter, m²	square foot, ft²	9.29×10^{-2}
1.55×10^{-3}	square millimeter, mm² (10^{-3} m)²	square inch, in²	645
Volume			
9.73×10^{-3}	cubic meter, m³	acre-inch	102.8
35.3	cubic meter, m³	cubic foot, ft³	2.83×10^{-2}
6.10×10^4	cubic meter, m³	cubic inch, in³	1.64×10^{-5}
2.84×10^{-2}	liter, L (10^{-3} m³)	bushel, bu	35.24
1.057	liter, L (10^{-3} m³)	quart (liquid), qt	0.946
3.53×10^{-2}	liter, L (10^{-3} m³)	cubic foot, ft³	28.3
0.265	liter, L (10^{-3} m³)	gallon	3.78
33.78	liter, L (10^{-3} m³)	ounce (fluid), oz	2.96×10^{-2}
2.11	liter, L (10^{-3} m³)	pint (fluid), pt	0.473
Mass			
2.20×10^{-3}	gram, g (10^{-3} kg)	pound, lb	454
3.52×10^{-2}	gram, g (10^{-3} kg)	ounce (avdp), oz	28.4
2.205	kilogram, kg	pound, lb	0.454
0.01	kilogram, kg	quintal (metric), q	100
1.10×10^{-3}	kilogram, kg	ton (2000 lb), ton	907
1.102	megagram, Mg (tonne)	ton (U.S.), ton	0.907
1.102	tonne, t	ton (U.S.), ton	0.907
Yield and Rate			
0.893	kilogram per hectare, kg ha⁻¹	pound per acre, lb acre⁻¹	1.12
7.77×10^{-2}	kilogram per cubic meter, kg m⁻³	pound per bushel, lb bu⁻¹	12.87
1.49×10^{-2}	kilogram per hectare, kg ha⁻¹	bushel per acre, 60 lb	67.19
1.59×10^{-2}	kilogram per hectare, kg ha⁻¹	bushel per acre, 56 lb	62.71

Table continued.

To convert Column 1 into Column 2 multiply by	Column 1 SI unit	Column 2 non-SI unit	To convert Column 2 into Column 1 multiply by
1.86×10^{-2}	kilogram per hectare, kg ha^{-1}	bushel per acre, 48 lb	53.75
0.107	liter per hectare, L ha^{-1}	gallon per acre	9.35
893	tonne per hectare, t ha^{-1}	pound per acre, lb acre^{-1}	1.12×10^{-3}
893	megagram per hectare, Mg ha^{-1}	pound per acre, lb acre^{-1}	1.12×10^{-3}
0.446	megagram per hectare, Mg ha^{-1}	ton (2000 lb) per acre, ton acre^{-1}	2.24
2.24	meter per second, m s^{-1}	mile per hour	0.447
Specific Surface			
10	square meter per kilogram, m^2 kg^{-1}	square centimeter per gram, cm^2 g^{-1}	0.1
1000	square meter per kilogram, m^2 kg^{-1}	square millimeter per gram, mm^2 g^{-1}	0.001
Density			
1.00	megagram per cubic meter, Mg m^{-3}	gram per cubic centimeter, g cm^{-3}	1.00
Pressure			
9.90	megapascal, MPa (10^6 Pa)	atmosphere	0.101
10	megapascal, MPa (10^6 Pa)	bar	0.1
2.09×10^{-2}	pascal, Pa	pound per square foot, lb ft^{-2}	47.9
1.45×10^{-4}	pascal, Pa	pound per square inch, lb in^{-2}	6.90×10^3
Temperature			
1.00 (K − 273)	kelvin, K	Celsius, °C	1.00 (°C + 273)
(9/5 °C) + 32	Celsius, °C	Fahrenheit, °F	5/9 (°F − 32)
Energy, Work, Quantity of Heat			
9.52×10^{-4}	joule, J	British thermal unit, Btu	1.05×10^3
0.239	joule, J	calorie, cal	4.19
10^7	joule, J	erg	10^{-7}
0.735	joule, J	foot-pound	1.36
2.387×10^{-5}	joule per square meter, J m^{-2}	calorie per square centimeter (langley)	4.19×10^4
10^5	newton, N	dyne	10^{-5}
1.43×10^{-3}	watt per square meter, W m^{-2}	calorie per square centimeter minute (irradiance), cal cm^{-2} min^{-1}	698
Transpiration and Photosynthesis			
3.60×10^{-2}	milligram per square meter second, mg m^{-2} s^{-1}	gram per square decimeter hour, g dm^{-2} h^{-1}	27.8
5.56×10^{-3}	milligram (H_2O) per square meter second, mg m^{-2} s^{-1}	micromole (H_2O) per square centimeter second, μmol cm^{-2} s^{-1}	180
10^{-4}	milligram per square meter second, mg m^{-2} s^{-1}	milligram per square centimeter second, mg cm^{-2} s^{-1}	10^4
35.97	milligram per square meter second, mg m^{-2} s^{-1}	milligram per square decimeter hour, mg dm^{-2} h^{-1}	2.78×10^{-2}
Plane Angle			
57.3	radian, rad	degrees (angle), °	1.75×10^{-2}

Table continued.

■ Conversion Factors for SI and Non-SI Units

To convert Column 1 into Column 2 multiply by	Column 1 SI unit	Column 2 non-SI unit	To convert Column 2 into Column 1 multiply by
Electrical Conductivity, Electricity, and Magnetism			
10	siemen per meter, S m^{-1}	millimho per centimeter, mmho cm^{-1}	0.1
10^4	tesla, T	gauss, G	10^{-4}
Water Measurement			
9.73 × 10^{-3}	cubic meter, m^3	acre-inch, acre-in	102.8
9.81 × 10^{-3}	cubic meter per hour, m^3 h^{-1}	cubic foot per second, ft^3 s^{-1}	101.9
4.40	cubic meter per hour, m^3 h^{-1}	U.S. gallon per minute, gal min^{-1}	0.227
8.11	hectare meter, ha m	acre-foot, acre-ft	0.123
97.28	hectare meter, ha m	acre-inch, acre-in	1.03 × 10^{-2}
8.1 × 10^{-2}	hectare centimeter, ha cm	acre-foot, acre-ft	12.33
Concentration			
1	centimole per kilogram, cmol kg^{-1}	milliequivalent per 100 grams, meq 100 g^{-1}	1
0.1	gram per kilogram, g kg^{-1}	percent, %	10
1	milligram per kilogram, mg kg^{-1}	parts per million, ppm	1
Radioactivity			
2.7 × 10^{-11}	becquerel, Bq	curie, Ci	3.7 × 10^{10}
2.7 × 10^{-2}	becquerel per kilogram, Bq kg^{-1}	picocurie per gram, pCi g^{-1}	37
100	gray, Gy (absorbed dose)	rad, rd	0.01
100	sievert, Sv (equivalent dose)	rem (roentgen equivalent man)	0.01
Plant Nutrient Conversion			
	Elemental	Oxide	
2.29	P	P$_2$O$_5$	0.437
1.20	K	K$_2$O	0.830
1.39	Ca	CaO	0.715
1.66	Mg	MgO	0.602

Introduction

History of Organic Farming and Certification

Charles Francis and Justin Van Wart
Department of Agronomy and Horticulture, University of Nebraska, Lincoln

The roots of organic farming probe deep into the soil of human agricultural history. We have depended on natural resources and ecological processes for 99% of the time since our ancestors moved from hunting and gathering to a sedentary habitation and organized production of plants and animals some 10,000 years ago (Table 1–1). During all this time, most of our crops depended on natural rainfall and stored moisture from winter snows in the temperate regions. Their nutrients came from soil organic matter, plant residues, animal manures, and small amounts from rainfall. Most pests were controlled by other organisms, by plant diversity in the system, and by natural genetic tolerance recognized by

Table 1–1. Relationship between time, the formation of the universe and Earth, appearance of humans, human population, agriculture, and crop rotation (from Bentley and Ziegler, 2006).

Timeline	Major events
~12,000,000,000 BCE	Big bang
5,000,000,000 BCE	Earth formed
24,000,000 BCE	Hominids first appear
2,500,000 BCE	*Homo erectus* first appear
300,000 BCE	*Homo sapiens* first appear
15,000 BCE	*Homo sapiens* appear worldwide
10,000 BCE	Agriculture begins
2,100 yr ago	Crop rotation written records first appear
200 yr ago	Industrial agriculture

Human population	Year	Years to add 1,000,000,000 people
million		
~4	~10,000 BCE	
5	5,000 BCE	
14	3,000 BCE	
50	1,000 BCE	
100	500 BCE	
500	1650 CE†	
1000	1804 CE	~300,000
2000	1927 CE	123
3000	1960 CE	33
4000	1974 CE	14
5000	1987 CE	13
6000	1999 CE	12
6300	2008 CE	

women who were the first plant breeders, and who harvested the best individual plants and saved their seeds. Since there were no chemicals used or transgenic crops (genetically modified organisms [GMOs]), except those that arose by natural crossing, these were de facto organic farming systems. The historical role of rotations and their potentials for sustaining soil fertility in agriculture in the face of rapidly expanding human population is described in Chapter 3 (Porter, 2009, this volume).

Although we do not present an exhaustive treatise on agricultural history here, we recommend further exploration of the linkages between the development of agriculture and ideas about organic practices and systems. A detailed history of organic farming was written by Conford (2001), and readers are referred to her book *The Origins of the Organic Movement* for a more in-depth treatment of how we arrived to where we are today. Another excellent resource is the recent book *Organic Farming: An International History* by longtime organic researcher and advocate Willie Lockeretz (2008).

It is intriguing to examine agricultural history and to see that parallel—and relatively disconnected—developments occurred in several parts of the world. The traditions of the Mediterranean basin, of East Asia, of Mesoamerica and the Andean Zone, and of northern Europe are explored briefly. This last tradition led to what we know today as organic farming in the United States. We also describe the roots of organic certification, which assures the production standards for organic food, and explain how organic farming is growing and permeating the U.S. food system today. A number of universities are now involved in classroom education and extension in organic farming, as described in Chapters 12 (Creamer et al., 2009, this volume) and 13 (Francis, 2009, this volume).

Finally, we present in Chapter 14 (Francis and Hodges, 2009, this volume) a brief discussion of the topics addressed in other chapters in the book as well as projections for the future of organic food, so that this chapter will be useful as a stand-alone primer for those who are unfamiliar with organic production and food systems. At 20% annual increase in sales, organic food is one of the most rapidly growing segments of the U.S. food sector, perhaps today even faster than fast food, due to growing concerns about obesity and food safety. Thus it is important to learn about its history and present activity, and to explore ways to plan for the future.

Multiple Traditions, Minimal Communication

Among the first agricultural systems were those developed in Mesopotamia and other regions along the great river system valleys, places where rainfall was adequate for cultivation, soils were alluvial and fertile, and water was available for some irrigation. Greek and Roman agricultural history is perhaps more accessible to western readers. From about 6000 to 5000 BP (years before present time) cropping and livestock systems developed in Greece and spread around the Mediterranean basin, as described by Isager (1992) in her book *Ancient Greek Agriculture*. By 4000 BP, the wooden plow came into use, and soon after that the wooden wheel was introduced into agricultural systems and society. Food was produced in essentially organic systems that persisted for millennia.

Roman agriculture was well chronicled by many, including the first-century writer Pliny the Elder (1991), whose 37 volumes were apparently a part of his *Historia naturalis* that may have originally consisted of more than 2000 volumes. He discussed crop plants and crop rotations, details on plowing and cropping practices, irrigation, and harvest techniques. The effects of application of animal manures and crop rotation were well known and practiced in Roman systems. This information spread with the Roman Empire to much of Europe, and their teachings seemed to influence biology and farming systems through the Middle Ages.

Agriculture in the Italian landscape, and how it was shaped over several millennia by topography and climate, was described by Sereni (1997). A family farm structure dominated this landscape since medieval time and created a close synergy between land and the people who lived there. Stable patterns of essentially organic farming were based on tradition and adapted to local conditions. Individual farms including field boundaries and crops, fodder crops and livestock, human labor and equipment were organized in a sustainable way in accord with both environmental and socioeconomic goals (Cuppari, 1862). The systems view of agriculture, one of the foundations of today's organic farming, was used to design farms in Tuscany. In his work *Principles of Physiology of the Farm*, Draghetti (1948) envisioned the farm as a whole composed of many parts harmoniously organized to achieve integrity of function and resulting sustainability. More recently, Caporali (1991) reported on this Italian tradition and how it relates to our current approach to systems under the term *agricultural ecology*. A summary of the history and tradition of education in organic farming in the Mediterranean region is found in Caporali et al. (2007).

Relatively unknown to most in western Europe throughout the 20th century was a parallel track of agricultural development in east Asia. An important western window into Asian organic systems was provided by F.H. King of the USDA, who traveled in 1905 through Japan, Korea, and China. Farmers were practicing multiple cropping, composting, application of manures including that from humans, integration of crops and animals, and efficient use of natural resources. Through these practices, farmers could produce enough food for the country's population on a very limited fertile land base. King (1915) included photos and provided careful notes about the systems that farmers were using in East Asia; this record was little known to our present generation until it was republished by Rodale Press a few decades ago.

Over this same period, a sophisticated agriculture was developing in the Andean Zone and Central America up to southern Mexico. Based on the indigenous crops of maize (*Zea mays* L.), dry bean (*Phaseolus vulgaris* L.), and many types of squash (*Curcubita* spp. L.), there were systems adapted to different rainfall regimes, topography, and soil conditions. The indigenous knowledge uncovered by Efraim Hernandez Xolocotzi (1987) and his students reveals a highly developed series of agricultural systems and sophisticated societies that depended on local food production. Specific intercropping systems including the three sisters (maize, bean, and squash) were common across the region (Plucknett and Smith, 1986). Many of the native varieties and some of the organic systems persist today where the green revolution technologies and improved varieties have not replaced those of the original peoples.

Parallel to the agricultural developments in the Mediterranean and borrowing from their traditions, farmers in northern Europe planted mixtures of cereals and used crop rotations to maintain soil fertility. Practical researchers interacted with farmers to establish a strong foundation for the organic farming systems we recognize today. Joseph Heckman's valuable history of organic farming (Heckman, 2006) chronicles the advances published by Albert Howard (1943, 1946) based on work in the United Kingdom and India (see Chapter 7, Heckman et al., 2009, this volume). Howard grew up on a farm in England, studied at Cambridge University, and had experience with soil fertility and farms in the West Indies and at Wye College, before his posting to India in 1905. He developed sophisticated systems for preparing compost and maintaining soil fertility with organic sources of nutrients. These were seminal experiences that prepared Howard for developing holistic ideas about soil fertility through composting and plant health through disease prevention and the creation of healthy soils. He was adamant that composting be based on both plant and animal residues.

Howard (1943) insisted that soil fertility be based on building up humus in the soil, recognizing that the soil was a living system dependent on microorganisms including bacteria and mycorrhizae. He was well aware of the research on soil chemistry by Sprengel, and later, von Liebig (van der Ploeg et al., 1999), but disagreed with their reliance on simple applications of the Law of the Minimum, which focused on macroelements N, P, and K that could be easily supplied by chemical fertilizers. Although this dogma is still alive today in many basic soil science textbooks and university courses, organic farmers have recognized the wisdom of Howard's position against chemical fertilizers and the need to build soil organic matter and natural sources of nutrients.

Contemporary with Howard were other organic farming advocates in England and Germany. Walter Northbourne (1940), in *Look to the Land,* discussed the importance of looking at the farm as a whole and may have been the first to use the term *organic* related to farming. His definition included reference to complexity of multiple factors in the organic farm and the important interactions among those factors that are similar to those in all living things. Results of the long-term Houghley experiments in Suffolk, UK, from 1939 to 1969 were published by the Soil Association in the United Kingdom through the writing of Evelyn Balfour (1976). In comparisons of organic systems, conventional mixed farming with animals, and stockless rotations, the organic systems had more earthworms, higher moisture retention, more organic carbon, and higher levels of major elements, as well as better soil structure.

Rudolph Steiner in Germany promoted what has been called *biodynamic agriculture,* a type of organic system that depends on natural methods of pest and fertility management, as well as use of special fermented *preparats* that catalyze microbial processes in soils and silage. These were described in Steiner's (1958) famous series of eight lectures that described the farm as a living organism, with closely interacting plants, animals, and soil organisms that provide most plant nutrition in a closed and recycling system on the farm. There is a spiritual dimension to biodynamic farming, called *anthroposophy,* which turns some people away from this holistic approach to farming. The certification of biodynamic farming is distinct from and more rigorous than organic rules.

Growth of Organic Farming in the United States

Just as in other parts of the world, essentially all agricultural production in the United States was de facto organic before the 20th century. Soil fertility depended on crop rotations, nitrogen fixed by legumes and from decaying green manure in the soil, and animal manure from the livestock present on most farms. Most pests were managed by crop rotations, diverse varieties with genetic tolerance or resistance, and small fields that provided harmful insects and pathogens with a varied host landscape where it was relatively difficult to succeed over a very large area. To feed horses and other livestock, diverse forages were an important component of the cropping patterns on most farms. It was only when mechanization brought a rapid expansion in tractor use that much of this forage was not needed. Specialization in a few crops and intensive feeding of grain to livestock further eroded the importance of grass and legume forage crops and pastures on farms. The importance of crop–livestock integration is described in Chapter 4 (Entz and Thiessen Martens, 2009, this volume), and the unique roles of forages in organic systems is discussed in Chapter 5 (Clark, 2009, this volume).

As chemical fertilizers and chemical pesticides were introduced in the United States in the first half of the 20th century, many farmers were reluctant to adopt them (Baker, 2005). When synthesized inputs such as dichlorodiphenyltrichloroethane (DDT) and urea first came into the marketplace, farmers and research scientists had many questions regarding their long-term impacts. Not until publication of Rachel Carson's (1962) *Silent Spring* decades later were many of their fears confirmed, and by then a massive change in mainstream agriculture had included the adoption of many chemical pesticide and fertilizer formulations.

Organic farming practices were supported in the United States in part due to the efforts of University of Missouri soil chemist William Albrecht (Walters, 1996) but largely as a result of practical ideas developed by innovative farmers. Their experiences were chronicled by the publisher and entrepreneur J.I. Rodale in his magazine *Organic Farming and Gardening*. Rodale, in Emmaus, PA, was a major force in establishing the legitimacy of organic farming, at least in the eyes of the public. Rodale had high respect for the United Kingdom's Albert Howard, and when Rodale's magazine first published in 1942, he named Howard as his consulting editor. Thus, the present-day seeds of organic farming in our country were planted in Germany and the United Kingdom, nurtured in India, and came to flower in the small town of Emmaus in southeastern Pennsylvania as well as on many organic and biodynamic farms across the country.

Yet research on nonchemical methods of plant nutrition had been in progress under the direction of Albrecht for some years. An energetic proponent of natural soil building, Albrecht took a different direction from most scientists working on soil fertility in the early years of chemical fertilizers. He insisted that proper plant nutrition came from soil organic matter and that adequate plant nutrition and a balance of macro- and micronutrients could be supplied by carefully designed crop rotations, plant and animal manures, composts, and field practices promoting a healthy soil (Walters, 1996). His work was virtually ignored by the mainstream but was published and distributed later, largely through the efforts of the publisher Acres U.S.A. Today we would call him a strong proponent of application of ecology in agriculture.

Among the early publications that linked practical farming experience with organic methods and with science were those of Louis Bromfield (1945, 1948), who studied agriculture at Cornell University and later became a journalist. He learned from experience and from his farm manager, a former county extension advisor, how to keep pastures fertile and both cattle and crops thriving without use of chemical fertilizers or pesticides. His is but one of many chronicles of the organic systems developed and used by farmers with limited reliance on technical support from universities or government research laboratories. Much of the practical information was published over the years by J.I. Rodale and his son Robert Rodale in their monthly magazines and many books from Rodale Press (e.g., Rodale, 1946) and later in *The New Farm* magazine, which is now available online (http://www.rodaleinstitute.org/new_farm, verified 22 June 2009).

One book that stands out because of its pragmatic descriptions of organic methods is *Future Harvest: Pesticide-Free Farming*, by Nebraska farmer Jim Bender (1994). There are many others. A comprehensive literature review of organic farming practices with more than 300 references was assembled by Don Lotter (2003) from the Rodale Institute. One of the most valuable and accessible resources today is the Website of the National Sustainable Agriculture Information Service in Fayetteville, Arkansas, and their resource center, Applied Technology Transfer to Rural Areas (ATTRA) (http://attra.org/organic.html, verified 22 June 2009). In fact, much of the information on this Website was generated by researchers at nonprofit centers, universities, and federal research stations, as described below.

Emergence of Research in U.S. Universities and Nonprofit Research Centers

A widely cited report by the USDA (Papendick et al., 1980) described the situation of organic farming and research in 1980. The report found growing concerns in this country about increasing fertilizer costs, decline in soil productivity, degradation of the environment, hazards to human and animal health as well as to food safety, and declining importance of the family farm and local markets. Among the conclusions were that organic farming included a range of practices designed to eliminate chemical fertilizers and pesticides, such as practical use of crop rotations, biological controls, and other nonchemical methods. Motivations of farmers included protecting soils, human and animal health, and food safety, as well as improving the environment. In general, farmers felt ignored by universities and USDA. The American Society of Agronomy (ASA) publication on organic farming was an exception to this general wisdom (Bezdicek and Power, 1984).

The Organic Farming Research Foundation provides a state-by-state summary of recent research in *State of the States, 2nd Edition: Organic Systems Research at Land Grant Institutions, 2001–2003* (Sooby, 2003). In sharp contrast to early assessments, the foundation found a marked increase in projects and activities in organic farming during the first few years of the 21st century. Further, a recent report on important research priorities was published by the Scientific Congress on Organic Agricultural Research (SCOAR), also indicating that there has been a large growth in research. However, much is still to be done (Sooby et al., 2007): the proportion of total research on organic systems and practices in the United States is still below the nearly 2% level of organic farming as a part of our total agriculture.

The following provides a brief overview of research and education by university and nonprofit experiment stations, including specific program illustrations. The treatment is not exhaustive, and there are numerous other references and descriptions of programs in the other book chapters, including focused reports on programs in California, Iowa, North Carolina, and other states in both the public and private sectors and a summary of key educational programs in Chapter 13 (Francis, 2009, this volume).

The Soil and Health Foundation was founded in 1947 by J.I. Rodale based on a model from the United Kingdom and with advice from Albert Howard, one of Rodale's early confidants and editors of organic publications. This foundation was the forerunner of the Rodale Institute; its research and education were later expanded by J.I.'s son Robert through purchase of a 333-acre farm near Kutztown in southeast Pennsylvania. (For a summary of the Rodale history, see http://www.rodaleinstitute.org/history, verified 22 June 2009). The institute has been a pioneer in organic farming research, often in collaboration with university researchers. Examples of its more recent work include the results of a long-term rotation study that showed that diverse organic crop sequences can be nearly as productive as conventional systems (Hepperly et al., 2006). There have also been comparisons of on-farm and experiment station methods used to study rotations (Drinkwater, 2002; Chapter 2, Drinkwater, 2009, this issue), and results have been similar.

An early university research program was started in 1967 at the University of California, Santa Cruz by Alan Chadwick on a wooded southwest-facing hillside in the heart of the redwoods. A charismatic speaker and tireless teacher in the field, Chadwick lacked the academic credentials needed in a mainstream university but attracted a following of dedicated students interested in biodynamic farming and French intensive planting methods. Chadwick's courage and dedication were rewarded with eventual support for an on-campus 25-acre organic farm for research and education that today is called the Center for Agroecology and Sustainable Food Systems. Nearly 1000 interns have experienced organic farming over the program's more than 30 years (MetroActive, 1997).

Michael Fields Institute, a prominent research and education center for biodynamic agriculture, was founded in Troy, WI, in 1984 to promote a more sustainable food system (see http://www.michaelfieldsaginst.org/, verified 22 June 2009). The Institute's original focus on hands-on training in farming and gardening practices has evolved to include programs on public policy education, cropping and farming systems research, and food systems. They openly embrace the political agenda in agriculture, recognizing that decisions made at the federal level strongly influence decisions on the farm. The staff of the Michael Fields Institute works closely with University of Wisconsin and with the Practical Farmers of Iowa on specific research projects, a pattern of cooperation that is duplicated in most of the organic research and education programs across the United States.

A committed group of University of Maine faculty and students, with strong support from the dean and other administrators, began in the 1980s what was to become an important sustainable agriculture program in a state with a small farming industry (http://sag.umaine.edu/, verified 22 June 2009). The university then introduced a bachelor's degree program in 1989 and initiated an organic farm for research and teaching in the 1990s. Continuing this history, a student-run community-supported agriculture (CSA) currently supplies organic food to families in the Orono community and surroundings. The program is recognized by farmers and agricultural industry in the state as an important contributor to new information for the food system (Liebman, 1997).

These are just examples of the many programs now in place in universities and those in the nonprofit sector that work closely with public education and research programs. They represent a geographic and subject-matter scope that is important to organic agriculture information generation; many other programs are cited in the chapters that follow.

Many Paths to Organic Farming and Certification

In 1972 the modest French magazine *Nature et Progrès* organized an international congress on organic agriculture in Versailles. "The Soil Association from Great Britain represented by Lady Eve Balfour, the Swedish Biodynamic Association with Kjell Arman, the Soil Association of South Africa in the person of Pauline Raphaely, Rodale Press from the U.S. whose representative was Jerome Goldstein and of course, *Nature et Progrès* with Roland Chevriot [urged] the diffusion and exchange of information on the principles and practises of organic agriculture of all schools and across national and linguistic boundaries. From the very beginning the need for information exchange between national and regional organic movements was seen necessary not only for the economically developed but also for developing countries" (Langman, 1998). This conference led to the formation of the International Federation of Organic Agriculture Movements (IFOAM) later in 1972.

Since that date, the emergence and evolution of certification of organic production practices, processing facilities, and products in the marketplace have been important steps in legitimizing and formalizing organic farming and foods. Begun in Europe, this process has been under the umbrella of the IFOAM since 1972, and this group provides overall guidance and rules to the many national and private certifying agencies. A recent modification of the IFOAM guidelines places emphasis on four guiding principles: health, ecology, fairness, and care. These principles are described in brief on their Website (http://www.ifoam.org/about_ifoam/principles/index.html; verified 22 June 2009):

Health: "Organic Agriculture should sustain and enhance the health of soil, plant, animal, human and planet as one and indivisible."

Ecology: "Organic Agriculture should be based on living ecological systems and cycles, work with them, emulate them and help sustain them."

Fairness: "Organic Agriculture should build on relationships that ensure fairness with regard to the common environment and life opportunities."

Care: "Organic Agriculture should be managed in a precautionary and responsible manner to protect the health and well-being of current and future generations and the environment."

All of the certification agencies, private and public, including nonprofits, in general ascribe to these principles, although many of the private certifiers and larger organic food corporations take a utilitarian approach that sees meeting the specific requirements for production and processing as simply a necessary step toward profits. There is concern that more social criteria as expressed in the new IFOAM principles be invoked in future certification decisions.

Before the 1980s in the United States, toward the beginning of the modern organic agriculture movement, certification was largely seen as unnecessary. Authentication of holistic practices was based on farmer-to-farmer and farmer-to-consumer relationships and peer-to-peer inspection and confirmation. As the industry has grown, the proportion of organic producers pursuing a time-consuming face-to-face marketing strategy has diminished. Moreover, a growing number of consumers are looking for organic products at conventional distribution sites such as supermarkets, grocery stores, mainstream restaurants, and megamarts (*les hypermarchets*) such as Carrefour, Super Target, Super Kmart, and Walmart (Duram, 2005). In addition to food, consumers have demanded health care products, cosmetics, housewares, and a variety of other merchandise be certified organic. The coordination necessary to supply these demands has led many suppliers to request independent third-party certification.

In the late 1980s, disagreements among certifiers, television specials about contaminated foods, and cases of organic certification fraud led organic advocates in the United States to seek federal regulation; consequently, the Organic Foods Production Act of 1990 (OFPA) was born (Kuepper, 2002). This act obligated the U.S. Secretary of Agriculture to establish a National Organic Program (NOP) to regulate certification and labeling. The original three requirements for organic certification in the OFPA were (i) no synthetic chemicals in production, (ii) no chemicals on the land for three years before harvesting, and (iii) abide by an organic production and handling plan between producers, handlers, processors, and retailers.

Once the OFPA was approved, the Secretary of Agriculture began compiling a national list of allowable and prohibited substances, with assistance from a National Organic Standards Board (NOSB) as stipulated in the OFPA. This board was composed of 15 members, each serving a five-year term: four organic farmers, two organic handlers, one organic retailer, three environmentalists, three from consumer interest groups, one scientist (ecology, biochemistry, toxicology), and one organic certifying agent. After the national list was established, any individual could petition the NOSB to prohibit or allow any substance. Items on the list received a review every five years and were not to be reviewed before another five years passed unless significant new information was determined. Any changes made to the national list are published in the federal registry for public comment (Agricultural Marketing Service, 2000).

The first draft of the organic allowables list from the NOP was released in 1997. It took most of the organic community by surprise to find irradiation, GMOs, and sewage sludge subtly allowed in the rule. Close to 280,000 people nationwide wrote to contest the inclusions, making this the most commented-on issue in USDA history (California Certified Organic Farmers, 2008) and the only time an industry fought for stricter standards for itself (Om Organics, 2008). In October 2002, after much deliberation and advocacy input, the NOP was implemented by the USDA.

It is difficult to discuss the philosophy and need for certification outside the context of the economics that have traditionally been unique to organic agriculture. Three economic issues stand out as significantly contributing to the need for verification of organic practices: the costs and benefits of going organic, price signaling, and industrial organization—that is to say, competition and fraud. Transitioning to an organic system from a conventional one presents interested farmers with a unique set of opportunity costs as their farm undergoes a period of soil building before organic yields will resemble the historical conventional levels. For ideological, social, and political reasons, consumers or governments are often willing to pay a premium to offset these costs and to encourage the transition.

The difficulty becomes how to signal to consumers and governments that organic production methodology was undertaken by the producer and to unify what that production methodology entails. Anyone can claim to use a holistic approach and attempt to raise the price. While advocates of price signaling may avow the ability of price to capture and represent all relevant information, one number is not enough in today's highly preferential producer and consumer world. Producers and consumers are interested in attributes of quality, size, quantity, nutrition, and methods of production, and price cannot adequately or sufficiently represent each of these simultaneously. A second difficulty is determining what qualifies as organic. Because organic is based on building soil, it will look very different on sandy versus clayey soils, whereas conventional agriculture looks the same everywhere. Without a common standard, consumers who hear the word *organic* don't know what to think.

Although consumers are often willing to pay more for these qualities, it would be too costly for each producer and consumer to verify organic status or sift through every verification agency's claims of organic certification. Both consumers willing to pay higher prices and perceived superior quality attract fraud from every level of the supply chain. Cheaters are a part of most industrial games where there can be winners and losers, and organic agricultural production is unfortunately no different. Human nature seems to necessitate policing. All of these factors contribute to the need for independent third-party certification. Drawn from publicly transparent, national standards, certification provides producers with access to price premium benefits after paying the costs of access. Consumers also receive more comprehensive signals, and fraud is made much more difficult and severely restricted. A unified, verifiable concept of organics also makes exporting, mass production, and mass transport more feasible.

But not everyone is enthusiastic about organic certification. Many who have been with the modern organic movement since its beginning see certification as undermining the holistic roots of organic production. They claim that true organic products should be sold locally and should be especially attractive to the small independent farmer, not the factory farm. They maintain that certification puts up barriers of paperwork, costs, and bureaucracy that can prevent otherwise interested farmers from going organic. They fear degradation of the standards used in certification is inevitable as big business lobbyists, provided a legal framework to work in, slowly erode and make allowances in the standards to meet their special interests and gain market share. Many also feel the standards do not go far enough, often because there is no mention of fair and equitable employment practices or local community social justice issues and because of the allowance of certain synthetic chemicals (Duram, 2005). These and other reasons have led many to request a "beyond organic" certification standard or an elimination of certain certification standards.

In the United States, there is currently a complex system that includes state certification in a few places, a number of nonprofit certification agencies, and a growing number of private certifiers. Each must use standards that meet the minimum specified by the NOP, but most have higher standards—that is, stricter rules—to help farmers market their organic products in specific places. For example, the export market must meet the specific requirements of Japan, of the European Union, or of the strictest rules of all for Switzerland. Most organic farmers who decide to certify will examine the rules of these various options in their state and will determine which markets are most appropriate and choose a strategy for certification that helps them meet their goals. Some farmers who use completely organic practices forego the formal certification process if their customers are all local, and they essentially use their personal credibility and proximity of the farm to consumers to market their products. This opens a larger issue of the value of local production versus organic production, a topic that is considered in several chapters of this book, and in Chapter 14 (Francis and Hodges, 2009, this volume) on the future of organic production and foods.

Summary and Conclusions: A Look at the Future

This introduction to the history of organic farming and what led to our current certification programs provides a prelude to the chapters that follow. Together, the authors explore and elaborate on how organic farming has stimulated an ecologically based research agenda, a far-reaching change that is now permeating our national agricultural research agenda (Chapter 2, Drinkwater, 2009, this volume). It is difficult to quantify the impacts that organic farmers and organic farming research have made on mainstream agriculture. We are becoming more aware of the unintended consequences of many of our current fertilizer and pesticide practices, as farmers struggle to meet USEPA requirements for water quality and as farm program compliance for federal payments continues to put pressure on mainstream agriculture. These emergent properties of high-tech agriculture help us to realize the importance of a systems perspective to research, one that considers production and economics but also the environmental and social impacts of alternative agricultural strategies. All of these factors lead us toward research that takes into account the ecological processes on which agriculture depends and compels us to use an improved understanding of ecosystem dynamics in planning future, sustainable production and food systems.

The second section of the book deals with system design, especially the application of ecological principles of biodiversity and crop–animal integration in choice of enterprises and the spatial and temporal planning of how these fit into the farm, field, and rural landscape. Crop rotations and spatial diversity are keys to soil fertility and crop protection, and these are central to design of organic systems (Chapter 3, Porter, 2009, this volume). Most proponents of organic farming consider the design of efficient and profitable crop–animal mixed farming systems to be essential due to the need for forages and the increased potentials for nutrient cycling compared to stockless systems (Chapter 4, Entz and Thiessen Martens, 2009, this volume). The central role of forages as perennial components of organic systems, along with the multiplicity of ecosystem services they provide, is explored in depth (Chapter 5, Clark, 2009, this volume). How the principles and practices of organic major cereal and pulse crop farming have evolved in the U.S. heartland, and why all organic crops should be considered "specialty crops" because of their unique marketing, is described as one route for farmers who seek more profitable alternatives to mainstream farming (Chapter 6, Delate, 2009, this volume). From these discussions, it has become clear to us that there is in fact a large impact of organic research and practices on what is happening today in what is called conventional agriculture, although it is difficult to quantify.

In the third section, on production practices, we explore details about how organic farmers design diverse mixed farming strategies and crop rotations to increase soil fertility and achieve pest management in systems using no chemical fertilizers or pesticides. Building and maintaining soil fertility can be accomplished in many ways in organic systems, including use of green manure crops, composts, animal manure, and rotations (Chapter 7, Heckman, et al., 2009, this volume). The emerging field of weed ecophysiology is providing direction to managing weed pests in field crops, including a strategy—called *many little hammers*—that combines a number of weed suppression measures, an especially important technique in organic systems (Chapter 8, Liebman and Davis, 2009, this volume). Integrated pest management (IPM) research has many lessons for organic farming; this complex strategy, which combines genetic resistance and tolerance with carefully designed cultural practices, can guide decisions on control strategies, maintaining pest populations at acceptable levels in organic production systems (Chapter 9, Bird, G.W. et al., 2009, this volume).

Organic farmers are faced with more than production challenges. They must also design a marketing strategy that meets both the demands of consumers and the requirements of organic certification (Chapter 10, Peterson and Janke, 2009, this volume). Many people in the organic farming community share concerns about food security and equity in the organic sector as well as the entire U.S. food system and wonder whether organic food will become a product only for the elite or whether it will be widely available for all (Chapter 11, Allen and Melcarek, 2009, this volume). The history of sales of certified organic food through farmers markets, specialty shops, and direct delivery to customers and its current entry into mainstream marketing raise large questions about the future of this unique food source. Over half of all organic food in the United States is currently sold through large, conventional supermarkets; it is not clear that this approach meets the social goals of many traditional growers of organic foods.

The cycle is not complete until farming practices from research reach the farmer and food reaches the consumer. In the final section, we describe how mainstream research has developed in the land-grant universities through a specific case study on organic systems research at North Carolina State University (Chapter 12, Creamer et al., 2009, this volume). How this information reaches farmers, students, and consumers is of vital interest to those doing research, and the number of universities and nonprofit groups involved in outreach in organic farming is growing (Chapter 13, Francis, 2009, this volume). The future of organic farming and certification, and how this is likely to continue to impact the U.S. farm sector is also explored as a conclusion to the technical information provided throughout the book (Chapter 14, Francis and Hodges, 2009, this volume). In an eloquent conclusion, an organic farmer from North Dakota examines the current structure of farming in the United States and looks at the ethics and values behind organic farming and focuses on the disappearing family farms. He maintains that the strong family farm and social system currently in decline is the heart of our country's food production and security and that without farmers who are committed to stewardship and to their rural communities, the U.S. food system is not sustainable (Chapter 15, Kirschenmann, 2009, this volume).

It has been more than two decades since the publication of *Organic Farming: Current Technology and Its Role in a Sustainable Agriculture* by the American Society of Agronomy (Bezdicek and Power, 1984). Although a number of research papers, posters, and symposia have been found in the annual meetings of the American Society of Agronomy, Crop Science Society of America, and Soil Science Society of America, it is only now that they have brought together the current state of research and application of organic practices and systems. In a field of intense research interest and with growing concern about the sources and safety of food, organic farming and food systems will continue to capture the attention of farmers, processors, marketers, and consumers in the United States and elsewhere. We provide here a window on this dynamic system that is shaping the profile of food in this country.

Discussion Questions

1. How is the history of organic farming useful to us in designing systems for today's economic and environmental challenges?

2. Describe at least two non-Internet sources where you could go to learn about specific organic agricultural management practices. How do you assess their validity?

3. Describe the profile of a farmer who should definitely go organic, and describe a scenario for him or her to achieve certification and economic success. In what sort of situation should a producer not consider conversion to organic?

4. Some people claim that organic agriculture is a completely ideologically based system with no founding in good management. What evidence from the history of organic agriculture could be used to support these claims, and what evidence is there to refute them?

5. Based on its history, in what ways does organic agriculture seem like a way of agriculture only from the past, and in what ways does it offer promise as a valid direction for the future, and why?

6. What would you suggest that needs to happen to strengthen the certification regulations and process for conversion? What should be done to relax some of the requirements? Why should each of these be considered?

7. Where have the most substantial contributions to organic agriculture research and education come from, and how has this changed over the past two decades?

8. Organic agriculture is often referred to as a "movement." Why do you think that organic farming is singled out for this type of description? In what ways to you agree and/or disagree with this idea?

9. Who were the most influential people or organizations in the organic agriculture movement in the United States and in the global picture, and in what ways were they important?

References

Agricultural Marketing Service. 2000. Submission of petitions for evaluation of substances for inclusion on or removal from the National List of Substances Allowed and Prohibited in Organic Production and Handling. USDA. 13 July 2000. Fed. Regist. 65(103):43259–43261.

Allen, P., and H. Melcarek. 2009. Organic agriculture and food security: Saving the environment, feeding the world? p. 235–252. *In* C. Francis (ed.) Ecology in organic farming systems. Agron. Monogr. 54. ASA, CSSA, and SSSA, Madison, WI. (This volume.)

Baker, B. 2005. Brief history of organic farming and the National Organic Program. *In* B. Baker et al. (ed.) Organic farming compliance handbook: A resource guide for western region agricultural professionals. Available at http://www.sarep.ucdavis.edu/organic/complianceguide/ (verified 22 June 2009). Western Region SARE, Logan, UT.

Balfour, E.B. 1976. The living soil and the Haughley experiment. Universe Books, New York.

Bender, J. 1994. Future harvest: Pesticide-free farming. Univ. of Nebraska Press, Lincoln.

Bentley, J.H., and H.F. Ziegler. 2006. Traditions and encounters: A global perspective on the past. 3rd ed. McGraw-Hill, New York.

Bezdicek, D.F., and J.F. Power (ed.) 1984. Organic farming: Current technology and its role in a sustainable agriculture. ASA Spec. Publ. 46. ASA, Madison, WI.

Bird, G.W., P. Hepperly, M. Grieshop, and J. Moyer. 2009. Climbing Mt. Organic: An ecosystem approach to pest management. p. 197–214. In C. Francis (ed.) Ecology in organic farming systems. Agron. Monogr. 54. ASA, CSSA, and SSSA, Madison, WI. (This volume.)

Bromfield, L. 1945. Pleasant valley. Harper Bros., New York.

Bromfield, L. 1948. Malabar Farm. Harper Bros., New York.

Caporali, F. 1991. Ecologia per l'agricoltura: Teoria e pratica. Utet-libreria, Torino, Italy.

Caporali, F., G. Lieblein, P. Von Fragstein, and C. Francis (ed.) 2007. Integration of research and education in agroecology and organic farming. In Proc. ENOAT Workshop, Pieve Tesino, Italy. 29 Aug.–2 Sept. 2007. Dep. of Plant Production, Univ. of Tuscia, Viterbo, Italy.

California Certified Organic Farmers. 2008. The history of CCOF. Available at http://www.ccof.org/history_mr.php (verified 22 June 2009). California Certified Organic Farmers, Santa Cruz, CA.

Carson, R. 1962. Silent spring. Houghton Mifflin, Boston, MA.

Clark, E.A. 2009. Forages in organic crop–livestock systems. p. 85–112. In C. Francis (ed.) Ecology in organic farming systems. Agron. Monogr. 54. ASA, CSSA, and SSSA, Madison, WI. (This volume.)

Conford, P. 2001. The origins of the organic movement. Floris Books, Glasgow, Scotland.

Creamer, N.G., J.P. Mueller, J. O'Sullivan, C. Reberg-Horton, M. Schroeder-Moreno, and S. Washburn. 2009. Center for Environmental Farming Systems: Designing and institutionalizing an integrated sustainable and organic agriculture program. p. 255–282. In C. Francis (ed.) Ecology in organic farming systems. Agron. Monogr. 54. ASA, CSSA, and SSSA, Madison, WI. (This volume.)

Cuppari, P. 1862. Saggio di ordinamento dell'azienda rurale. Cellini, Firenze, Italy.

Delate, K. 2009. Organic grains, oilseeds, and other specialty crops. p. 113–136. In C. Francis (ed.) Ecology in organic farming systems. Agron. Monogr. 54. ASA, CSSA, and SSSA, Madison, WI. (This volume.)

Draghetti, A. 1948. Principi di fisiologia dell'azienda agrarian. Istituto Edizioni Agricole, Bologna, Italy.

Drinkwater, L. 2002. Cropping systems research. HortTechnology 12:355–361.

Drinkwater, L.E. 2009. Ecological knowledge: Foundation for sustainable organic agriculture. p. 19–48. In C. Francis (ed.) Ecology in organic farming systems. Agron. Monogr. 54. ASA, CSSA, and SSSA, Madison, WI. (This volume.)

Duram, L. 2005. Good growing: Why organic farming works. Univ. of Nebraska Press, Lincoln.

Entz, M.H., and J. R. Thiessen Martens. 2009. Organic crop–livestock systems. p. 69–84. In C. Francis (ed.) Ecology in organic farming systems. Agron. Monogr. 54. ASA, CSSA, and SSSA, Madison, WI. (This volume.)

Francis, C. 2009. Education in organic farming and food systems. p. 283–300. In C. Francis (ed.) Ecology in organic farming systems. Agron. Monogr. 54. ASA, CSSA, and SSSA, Madison, WI. (This volume.)

Francis, C., and L. Hodges. 2009. Human ecology in future organic farming and food systems. p. 301–324. In C. Francis (ed.) Ecology in organic farming systems. Agron. Monogr. 54. ASA, CSSA, and SSSA, Madison, WI. (This volume.)

Heckman, J. 2006. A history of organic farming: Transitions from Sir Albert Howard's War in the Soil to the USDA National Organic Program. Renewable Agric. Food Syst. 21:143–150.

Heckman, J., R. Weil, and F. Magdoff. 2009. Practical steps to soil fertility for organic agriculture. p. 139–172. In C. Francis (ed.) Ecology in organic farming systems. Agron. Monogr. 54. ASA, CSSA, and SSSA, Madison, WI. (This volume.)

Hepperly, P., D. Douds, and R. Seidel. 2006. The Rodale Institute farming systems trial 1981 to 2005: Long-term analysis of organic and conventional maize and soybean cropping systems. p. 15–31. In J. Raupp, C. Pekrun, M. Oltmanns, and U. Köpke (ed.) Long-term field experiments in organic farming. Verlag Dr. Koester, Berlin.

Hernandez Xolocotzi, E. 1987. Xolocotzia: Obras De Efraim Hernandez Xolocotzi. Revista de Geografia Agricola, Univ. Autonoma de Chapingo, Mexico.

Howard, A. 1943. An agricultural testament. Rodale Press, Emmaus, PA.

Howard, A. 1946. The war in the soil. Rodale Press, Emmaus, PA.

Isager, S. 1992. Ancient Greek agriculture: An introduction. Routledge, London.

King, F.H. 1915. Farmers of forty centuries. Rodale Press, Emmaus, PA.

Kirschenmann, F. 2009. Farming in the middle: An ethical imperative. p. 325–342. In C. Francis (ed.) Ecology in organic farming systems. Agron. Monogr. 54. ASA, CSSA, and SSSA, Madison, WI. (This volume.)

Kuepper, G. 2002. Organic farm certification and the National Organic Program: Marketing technical note. ATTRA Publ. IP222. Available at http://attra.ncat.org/attra-pub/organcert.html (verified 22 June 2009). NCAT, Fayetteville, AR

Langman, M. 1998. Memories and notes on the beginning and early history of IFOAM. p. 10–12. In B. Geier (ed.) 25 years of IFOAM. Ecology and Farming Special Issue 17. IFOAM, Theley, Tholey, Germany.

Liebman, M. 1997. Consortium news. Consortium Sustain. Agric. Res. Educ. 14 (June–July): 5–6.

Liebman, M., and A.S. Davis. 2009. Managing weeds in organic farming systems: An ecological approach. p. 173–196. In C. Francis (ed.) Ecology in organic farming systems. Agron. Monogr. 54. ASA, CSSA, and SSSA, Madison, WI. (This volume.)

Lockeretz, W. 2008. Organic farming: An international history. CABI, London.

Lotter, D. 2003. Organic agriculture. J. Sustain. Agric. 21:59–128.

MetroActive. 1997. Fire in the garden. 1997. Available at http://www.metroactive.com/papers/cruz/10.02.97/chadwicks-garden-9740.html (verified 22 June 2009). Metro Publishing, Santa Cruz, CA.

Northbourne, W.J. 1940. Look to the land. Dent, London.

Om Organics. 2008. History of organics. Available at http://www.omorganics.org/page.php?pageid=82 (verified 22 June 2009). Om Organics, San Francisco, CA.

Papendick, R.I., L.L. Boersma, J.M. Kla, C.A. Kraennzle, P.B. Marsh, A.S. Newman, J.F. Parr, J.B. Swan, and I.G. Youngberg. 1980. Report and recommendations on organic farming. USDA, Washington, DC.

Peterson, H.H., and R.R. Janke. 2009. Organic marketing. p. 217–234. In C. Francis (ed.) Ecology in organic farming systems. Agron. Monogr. 54. ASA, CSSA, and SSSA, Madison, WI. (This volume.)

Pliny the Elder. 1991. Historia naturalis. 37 vol. Harvard Univ. Press, Cambridge, MA.

Plucknett, D.R., and N. Smith. 1986. History of multiple cropping systems. In C.A. Francis (ed.) Multiple cropping systems. Macmillan, New York.

Porter, P. 2009. Crop rotations in organic production systems. p. 51–68. In C. Francis (ed.) Ecology in organic farming systems. Agron. Monogr. 54. ASA, CSSA, and SSSA, Madison, WI. (This volume.)

Rodale, J.I. 1946. Pay dirt. Rodale Press, Emmaus, PA.

Sereni, E. 1997. History of the Italian agricultural landscape. Princeton Univ. Press, Princeton, NJ.

Sooby, J. 2003. State of the states, 2nd edition: Organic farming research at land grant institutions, 2001–2003. Organic Farming Research Foundation, Santa Cruz, CA.

Sooby, J., J. Landeck, and M. Lipson. 2007. National organic research agenda, 2007. Organic Farming Research Foundation, Santa Cruz, CA.

Steiner, R. 1958. Agriculture: A course of eight lectures. Biodynamic Agric. Assoc., London.

van der Ploeg, R.R., W. Böhm, and M.B. Kirkham. 1999. On the origin of the theory of mineral nutrition of plants and the law of the minimum. Soil Sci. Soc. Am. J. 63:1055–1062.

Walters, C. (ed.) 1996. The Albrecht papers. Vol. 1. Foundation concepts. Acres U.S.A., Metairie, LA.

2

Ecological Knowledge: Foundation for Sustainable Organic Agriculture

Laurie E. Drinkwater
Department of Horticulture, Cornell University, Ithaca, New York

The expansion of organic agriculture increases the need for science-based research to improve production systems. This presents an opportunity as well as a challenge to traditional agricultural research institutions and scientists. Organic agriculture is fundamentally different from industrial, conventional agriculture in terms of (i) origins and development, (ii) the guiding management paradigm, which is based on a systems view, and (iii) goals that are the basis for this distinct management approach. Research on organic agriculture should apply interdisciplinary systems approaches, but what exactly does this mean? How can agricultural scientists, who have focused largely on research to support industrial agriculture, adjust their research to include organic systems? What approaches are most effective in advancing organic agriculture? Application of ecological knowledge is used to address these three key questions. This perspective was given only minor attention in the last ASA book on organic farming (Bezdicek and Power, 1984), although it was relatively prominent in the chapter by Hardy Vogtmann (1984) from Witzenhausen, Germany.

Science and Practice of Organic Agriculture

Agricultural science and the practice of organic agriculture have evolved independently for many decades. The organic agriculture movement emerged in the 1940s, largely as a reaction to the industrialization of agriculture that was occurring at a rapid pace (Heckman, 2006). The theory of organic farming as it was originally articulated was strongly influenced by systems thinking and grounded in the philosophy of holism. Early proponents of organic agriculture viewed the farm as a complex system, analogous to an organism, governed by interacting processes linking soil organic matter and soil organisms to crop, animal, and human health (Paull, 2006). This perspective was contrary to the dominant thinking in agricultural science, which was embracing reductionism and focused on simplifying agricultural systems into component parts that could be studied in separate, factorial experiments (Keller and Brummer, 2002). Since the formative decades of the 1940s and 1950s, organic agriculture has continued to be influenced by social forces such as environmental and consumer movements and economics, as well as progress in the agricultural sciences and ecology (Vos, 2000; Klonsky, 2000). Heckman (2006) outlines key events signaling the gradual recognition and incorporation of organic agriculture into the larger agricultural scientific community and government policy arena where it is currently viewed as one variant of "alternative" agriculture.

As the demand for organic food has increased, the regulatory infrastructure has grown. Scientific and social forces have strongly influenced the legal definition of organic agriculture and the practices that organic farmers commonly use. The practice of organic agriculture now encompasses a broad range of agricultural management strategies, including (i) farming systems that reflect the early ideas of the farm as a complex, interacting system and incorporate more recent ecological knowledge, (ii) input substitution approaches, and (iii) narrowly defined systems such as biodynamic or veganic, which are more restrictive than organic (Buck et al., 1997; Ingram, 2007; Letourneau and Bothwell, 2008). Food production systems based on any of these approaches can meet the legal definition of *certified organic* as long as they adhere to the federal organic standards (USDA, 2009), which largely entail the avoidance of synthetic inputs of fertilizers and pesticides. The focus of this chapter follows the first typology, closely linked to the roots of organic farming and contemporary ecological theory. This approach holds the most potential for achieving sustainability.

Unique Features of Organic Systems That Impact Research

Three fundamental characteristics of organic agriculture have important ramifications for research. First, organic agriculture evolved through a grass roots–based, farmer-dominated process. Next, organic farming systems apply an integrated, systems-based management strategy that differs from the command-and-control approach that has dominated industrial agriculture. Finally, the goals of farmers practicing organic agriculture are multidimensional and go beyond simply maximizing yield or economic return.

Unique Role of Organic Farmers

The significant role of organic farmers in developing organic production systems requires special attention. Organic farming systems were developed outside the mainstream of the land-grant system and national agricultural research infrastructure. Indeed, there were decades of hostility directed at organic agriculture from within the agricultural scientific community (Heckman, 2006). Existing organic cropping systems were developed by farmers, and as a result, the role of organic farmers in research targeting their systems differs fundamentally from the farmer–researcher relationships that predominate in the industrial agriculture realm (Nerbonne and Lentz, 2003). Scientists in institutions that are primarily focused on research for an industrial agricultural model need to recognize this difference and learn about organic management systems before launching into a new research direction. Many organic growers are eager to use scientific information in optimizing their farming systems; however, research that is not informed by the experience of organic farmers and their models of successful production is often flawed. Farmer participation can be incorporated into the research process in a variety of ways, and the specific level of involvement will vary depending on the research goals (Lilja and Ashby, 1999). Even the most basic research that aims to contribute primarily to scientific knowledge about organic systems rather than to improve management or solve problems is of little value if it is conducted in an agroecosystem that is inappropriately designed or lacking in production integrity. Therefore, it is important that farmer knowledge is incorporated into organic agricultural research at the planning and design stage.

Integrated, Ecosystem-Based Management Requires Systems Research Approaches

We need to consider the ramifications of the systems-based management strategy, which is the basis of organic agriculture, and its consequences for research and experimental design. Research on organic agriculture should apply systems thinking, and some insist that interdisciplinary systems approaches are necessary (Francis et al., 2003; Sooby et al., 2007). But what exactly does this mean? To help answer this question, it is important to first consider conventional agriculture and the research methods that have been successful in developing high-yielding, industrial systems.

The theory guiding conventional agricultural management is based on a "command-and-control" approach that emphasizes the simplification of natural systems as a way to modify the system to achieve desired outcomes (Holling and Meffe, 1996; Meffe et al., 2002). Thus, research on conventional systems has emphasized deconstructing cropping systems into specific components, which are studied in isolation using many separate, short-term factorial experiments (Drinkwater, 2002). These experiments are seldom linked to processes occurring over time frames longer than two growing seasons (Gardner and Drinkwater, 2009) or scales larger than the plot or field in which they are conducted. In conventional agriculture, command-and-control thinking has led to the development of practices and inputs aimed at simplifying and reducing variation in agricultural systems, a strategy that has been extremely successful in elevating yields and homogenizing fields to achieve a monoculture-based agriculture. Furthermore, yield and short-term profits have been the main criteria used to evaluate the success of farming practices and systems. The limitations of command and control are evident when we consider that many of the problems we are facing today are the unforeseen consequences or *emergent properties* of applying this approach (Meffe et al., 2002).

In contrast, the use of systems thinking and integrated management strategies is fundamental to organic agriculture. Organic agricultural theory requires that complex ecological interactions among organisms, their environment, and each other are understood and then managed to influence processes that support soil and crop health and plant productivity (see, e.g., Lewis et al., 1997, Carter et al., 2004). Furthermore, many cultural practices used in organic production systems are intentionally multifunctional. For instance, cover crops play multiple roles related to soil fertility and weed and arthropod pest management, while also providing biological N fixation and forages.

This approach to agroecosystem management used in organic farming is comparable to natural resource management approaches that emerged at the grassroots level in the early 1980s (Meffe et al., 2002). By the 1990s, this approach, known as ecosystem management, adaptive management, landscape-level conservation, community-based conservation, or integrated natural resource management, was being widely adopted by government agencies and institutions engaged in natural resource management. Dale et al. (2000) defined ecosystem management as "the process of land-use decision making and land-management practice that takes into account the full suite of organisms and processes that characterize and comprise the ecosystems and . . . includes a primary goal of sustainability of ecosystems structure and function, recognition that ecosystems are spatially and temporally dynamic, and acceptance of the dictum that ecosystem function depends on ecosystem structure and diversity."

The application of adaptive, ecosystem-based management that is the hallmark of organic agricultural practice can only be supported by research that is grounded in a similar conceptual framework based on systems thinking. Through the application of systems theory to natural systems, ecologists have developed a conceptual framework that pertains to managed as well as unmanaged ecosystems (Golley, 1993). Ecological theory, the principles and ideas that can be generally applied to natural systems, can be used to organize and understand the biocomplexity that is inherent to all natural systems as well as agroecosystems. Because of the central role played by ecological interactions and cascading, ecosystem-based processes in organic agricultural systems, there is much to be gained by situating organic research within an ecological framework. To move organic agriculture forward, we must continue to develop a theoretical basis for organic agriculture that goes beyond the original theory proposed nearly 70 years ago. The role of science is to develop general principles that can provide a foundation for practice.

Multifunctionality: Yield Is Only One of Many Goals for Organic Farming

A third aspect in designing agricultural research is the multifunctional goals of organic agriculture. In contrast to the productivist agricultural paradigm, focused primarily on yields and serving as the basis for industrial agricultural systems, farmers practicing organic agriculture since its inception have been concerned with outcomes beyond simply maximizing yields (Conford, 2001). Achieving adequate yields is certainly an important goal for organic farming; however, other goals relating to food quality, human and animal health, and environmental stewardship are viewed as central to organic farming. Thus, organic agriculturalists have been explicit about the multifunctionality of agriculture long before this idea began to influence mainstream visions for agricultural landscapes. Recently, the idea that agricultural systems must contribute to multiple ecosystem-level processes has emerged from discussions of sustainable management of the earth's ecosystems (Daily, 1997; Keller and Brummer, 2002).

While primary productivity and the ensuing agricultural goods are considered to be the primary function of agroecosystems, other ecosystem functions such as nutrient cycling, circulation of water, and soil formation are also crucial to sustainable agroecosystems (Power et al., 2008). Ecosystem functions have been referred to as *ecosystem services* when they are evaluated from the perspective of their relationship to human communities (Costanza et al., 1997; Daily, 1997). This approach of defining the goal of multifunctionality in agricultural landscapes as services to society provides a list of tangible outcomes resulting from ecological processes that can be understood by a broader community of stakeholders, and in some cases these can be evaluated in economic terms. Some ecosystem services occur at temporal and spatial scales that do not coincide with our interests in field or farm-level production of food and fiber. The contributions of agricultural systems to water flows and quality, for example, must often be considered within the context of a watershed rather that at a field or farm scale. Thus, attention to these multiple functions in agricultural systems helps to define the scales that should be considered in conducting research and developing sustainable organic systems. For this reason, developing a capacity to evaluate ecosystem services across different organic farming systems is integrally linked to the application of ecological theory that provides a framework for dealing with the full range of relevant spatial and temporal scales.

Ecosystem services can be classified as follows: (i) *provisioning services* supply ecosystem goods including food, fodder, and building materials; (ii) *supporting services* sustain the integrity of the agroecosystem via soil function and cross-trophic processes (e.g., conserve soil structure, nutrient cycling, beneficial species–species interactions such as biological control of pests); (iii) *regulating services* ensure desirable outcomes to ecosystems outside of agricultural fields (e.g., generation of groundwater, quality of ground and surface water, atmospheric composition, climate regulation); and (iv) *cultural services* relate to broader outcomes beyond the field scale and include aesthetic beauty, recreation, tourism, and wild diversity of flora and fauna (Power et al., 2008).

The ecosystem services framework has much in common with goals that have long been espoused by organic farmers and can help move these ideals forward by providing a tangible basis for evaluating the success of organic agricultural systems in meeting broader goals. To fulfill the intention of organic farmers, involved researchers cannot focus solely on yield-related outcomes but must also target multidimensional goals. Ultimately, the sustainability of agricultural systems will depend on successful implementation of farming systems that provide the full range of ecosystem services.

Survey of Recent Organic Research in North America

To assess how well these aspects of organic agriculture are being addressed in contemporary organic research, I conducted a quick assessment of organic literature published between 2003 and 2007. A search for all papers mentioning the term *organic* adjacent to relevant nouns (e.g., *agriculture, cropping system, crop, food, production, farm, management*) extracted those with words in the title, abstract, or key words. A subset consisting of only those papers published by researchers located in the United States, Canada, or Mexico was chosen and a random sample of 20% taken for closer examination. I scored these papers for experimental design, subject area, stakeholder involvement, linkage to ecological theory, and multifunctionality.

Although organic agriculture is now accepted as a viable approach to food production, and research is expanding rapidly (Fig. 2–1A), research that explicitly targeted organic systems only accounted for 2 to 3% of the published journal articles (Fig. 2–1B). No doubt, many more published articles address ecological processes in agricultural systems and are relevant to organic systems. However, this chapter is focused on the subset that explicitly targeted organic agriculture.

The sample consisted of both biophysical and social science studies, with 30% of the papers addressing social processes such as farmer knowledge or farmer attitudes. Sixty percent characterized differences between organic and

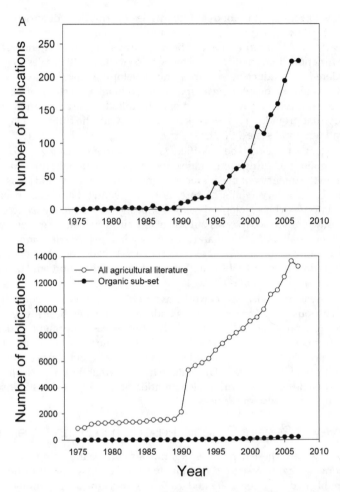

Fig. 2–1. Journal articles published by authors in North American institutions on organic agriculture and agriculture in general. Note difference in the *y* axis scale. **(A)** Publications explicitly addressing organic production have increased rapidly since the mid-1990s. **(B)** Compared to the total agricultural literature, organic research only accounts for 2% of the publications.

conventional systems (or farmers), and one-third focused on improving organic production systems. Only 10% of the research explicitly addressed some aspect of processes occurring during the transition from conventional to organic management. Research on crop yields (25%) and soil processes (25%) dominated, while studies of weeds, pathogens, insects, and livestock health each accounted for about 10% of the biophysical studies. About half of the biophysical research was conducted in replicated plots located at a single site, providing weaker conclusions about field-scale processes due to pseudoreplication (Hurlbert, 1984). The average length of the biophysical studies was two years, with 15% reporting on research spanning four or more years. The social science studies used a diverse range of methodologies including surveys, focus groups, and ethnographic interviews; about half of them were descriptive.

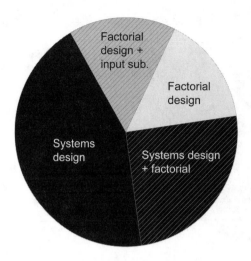

Fig. 2–2. Experimental designs used in the organic biophysical research. Systems approaches predominated either as the sole approach used or in combination with factorial experiments. Reductionist factorial designs accounted for 30% of the studies, of which half applied an input substitution framework.

How Well Did Research Meet Three Key Criteria?

When the on-farm and field-station research are combined, 60% of the biophysical studies were informed by knowledge drawn from organic farmers. Forty-five percent of the biophysical research engaged organic farmers simply by virtue of being conducted on working organic farms. In addition, some of the research station studies explicitly mentioned seeking farmer input or used practices that reflected local organic farming systems. The value placed on organic farmer expertise is also evident in the social science articles, with many studies investigating organic farmer knowledge and attitudes. However, the fact that none of the biophysical studies specifically described the role of organic farmers is indicative of obstacles that restrain the participation of farmers as true partners in production-oriented research.

Experimental designs based on the application of systems thinking predominated, although research questions were rarely linked to contemporary ecological concepts. Of the papers targeting biophysical processes, the distribution among systems experiments, hybrids (use of factorial experiment embedded within a system), and a factorial design alone was 45, 25, and 30%, respectively (Fig. 2–2). While an impressive amount of research was situated within systems-based design (70%), few studies (15%) were framed with any reference to ecological theory, and authors of only two studies explicitly discussed their results in terms of specific ecological mechanisms. The majority of biophysically oriented studies lacked any reference to ecology or ecological processes relevant to the research. Instead, the research questions were situated exclusively within the practice of organic agriculture. An even smaller proportion used an ecological conceptual framework to organize the research questions or interpretation of the results. For example, less than 10% considered interactions either among components or across temporal and spatial scales. As a result, a majority of the research in this sample is lacking a clear, systems-based conceptual framework that could be used to support a broader application of the research findings to organic agriculture. Furthermore, although some of these studies acknowledged the importance of ecological interactions to organic agroecosystems in the introduction to the article, results were

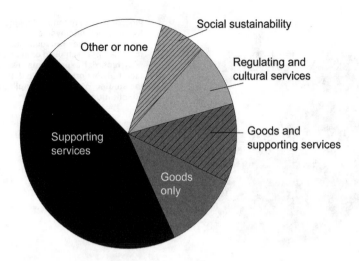

Fig. 2–3. Frequency of studies addressing various ecosystem services. A large proportion of studies (45%) focused on supporting ecosystem services (internal services that support yields and the production of goods) without reporting any yield-related outcomes.

rarely interpreted within the ecological context that was mentioned in the introduction. Of the 30% that did not apply systems thinking, half could be classified as using an "input substitution" approach. Lastly, although few studies included more than one discipline, the opportunity to conduct interdisciplinary research targeting interactions among components (e.g., weeds and insects or soil processes, weed populations and yields) was not fully realized since 25% of these component studies were associated with larger, interdisciplinary studies.

Finally, the sample scored well in terms of addressing the multiple goals of organic agriculture, although explicit acknowledgment of agroecosystem multifunctionality or ecosystem services as a conceptual framework was rare. Studies that focused only on ecosystem goods (yields or product-related outcomes) accounted for only 10% of the sample, while nearly 45% addressed supporting ecosystem services such as nutrient cycling, disease suppression and regulation of pest populations (Fig. 2–3). A smaller proportion (9%) evaluated organic systems in terms of external ecosystem services such as erosion reduction, wild biodiversity, and prevention of antibiotic resistance in microorganisms, and another 11% evaluated both goods (yields) and ecosystem services simultaneously. Interestingly, a small number of social science studies went beyond concepts related to environmental sustainability and assessed characteristics associated with social aspects of sustainability, such as social justice, access to resources, and quality of life. Lastly, studies that integrated across social and biophysical processes in organic production systems were extremely rare (2%). This is neither surprising nor unique to agroecological research. Synthetic, interdisciplinary research addressing linkages between humans and the environment is unusual in the world of mainstream agricultural research and natural resource management, as well as in applied ecology. However, solving the many complex environmental challenges we are facing requires greater understanding of the interplay between social and environmental processes, and research that tackles these questions is on the rise (Clark and Dickson, 2003; Turner et al., 2003). The scientific community is becoming more aware of ecosystem services and the potential economic and other rewards for promoting this dimension in evaluation of new farming systems.

Strengths and Weaknesses of Current Research

This brief assessment of the current organic agriculture literature indicates that scientists in public research institutions have made some adjustments to accommodate the unique aspects of organic agricultural systems. A majority of research included some level of organic farmer expertise. This progress in increasing participation of farmers and other stakeholders in the research arena needs to continue. Most researchers understand that organic farming needs to be studied as an intact system, with attention to interactions. Much research was focused on understanding how to manage the ecological processes that support internal ecosystem services such as nutrient cycling, pest suppression, and natural enemy dynamics. Relatively little research was based on the conventional industrial paradigm of input substitution.

The weakest aspect of organic agricultural research relates to the application of an ecological framework to organize research questions, design, and interpretation. Awareness of ecological interactions as an important mechanism for managing organic production is clearly evident in many publications. Use of experimental designs that study intact agroecosystems suggests that many in the organic research community are committed to a systems-based paradigm compatible with the practice of organic agriculture. However, limited use of ecological concepts indicates that knowledge of basic tools that can be used to organize biocomplexity in intact agroecosystems may be a limiting factor. The remainder of this chapter highlights key ecological concepts essential for developing scientific understanding of organic agricultural systems and provides examples of successful research approaches.

Application of Ecological Concepts to Organic Research

Ecology is an interdisciplinary, synthetic field of science that is focused on the interactions among organisms and between organisms and their environment. The discipline is strongly influenced by general systems theory. The field of ecology is vast, and to cover all concepts that can be applied to agroecosystems is beyond the scope of this chapter. I focus on six major concepts that represent the core of the ecological knowledge system and are broadly applicable to agroecosystems. In each case, there are specific examples of how the concept has been applied and discussion of relevance to organic agriculture.

Organizational Hierarchy of Ecological Processes

The conceptual framework of ecology is organized based on different biotic levels of processes occurring in natural systems. This classic perspective reflects the evolution of the discipline during the past century as the scale of research questions expanded to reflect new knowledge about ecological processes. Biotic units begin with individual organisms and extend to the ecosystem. Ecological processes occurring at the level of the *organism* include individual responses

to environmental stresses, environmental adaptations, and life-cycle regulation. Individuals of the same species living in the same area form *populations*,
whose characteristics such as density, age structure, and genetic composition are
governed by processes occurring within populations, such as reproduction, dispersal, mate selection, and intraspecific competition, as well as those occurring
across populations, such as interspecific interactions. *Communities* consisting of
interacting populations are characterized by structure, diversity, and abundance.
They are regulated by interactions among species such as herbivory, predation,
mutualism, and competition but also reflect biotic processes occurring at all three
levels: the organism, population, and community. An *ecosystem* is composed of
many interacting communities and their environment. Emphasis on integrating
organisms and their environment has transformed ecological thinking in recent
decades. All the biotic interactions discussed above occur in a specific place and
are influenced by that environment. At the same time, organisms influence their
environment. For example, nitrogen-fixing plants tend to increase soil nitrogen
levels over time, and earthworms alter soil structure and hydrological properties
through their burrowing.

A nested hierarchy of ecological processes based on the scale of the biotic unit
(organism, population, community, ecosystem) is a useful starting point for fram-
ing research in organic agricultural systems. Hierarchies of scale are widely used
in agroecological research, although researchers may not explicitly situate their
research in this framework. Agroecosystems differ from unmanaged ecosystems
in that dominant plant populations as well as plant community composition are
determined by management decisions. Successful organic systems are dependent
on many processes governed by the community of organisms both within the
field and farm and across the surrounding landscape (Marino and Landis, 1996;
Cronin and Reeve, 2005). Understanding ecological processes within and across
populations, communities, and ecosystems is the key to organic management.

As a first step in undertaking research to improve organic farming systems, it
is useful to ask, "What kind of processes are involved in this particular problem?"
For example, a goal for organic farming systems is to reduce insect pest problems
by targeting several distinct mechanisms: (i) temporal plant diversity (rotations)
is managed to minimize the carryover of pest populations from one season to
the next via reproduction (a population level process), (ii) plant temporal and
spatial biodiversities are managed to enhance pest suppression through interspecific interactions such as predation and parasitism (community processes),
and (iii) soil health (ecosystem-level functions) can increase plant vigor and pest
resistance of crops. The importance of these processes differs from one insect
species to another, but in most cases successful management of insect pests will
likely result from a combination of these processes (Letourneau, 1997). Successful
organic weed management schemes also rely on processes occurring at many levels and require knowledge of physiological ecology (seed dormancy regulation),
population ecology (number of generations per year), and community ecology
(herbivores or pathogens that attack particular weed species). This multifaceted
approach to weed management is referred to as "many little hammers" (Liebman
and Gallandt, 1997; Westerman et al., 2005; Chapter 8, Liebman and Davis, 2009,
this volume). Understanding the processes that govern desired outcomes will
contribute to a research design that situates an experiment within the agroecosystem and enables the optimization of ecologically based management regimes.

Ecosystem Concept

The term *ecosystem* was proposed by Arthur Tansley in 1935 to emphasize the importance of interactions between communities and their environment, and it has been the subject of much discussion and controversy in part because the term has multiple meanings (O'Neill, 2001). In common usage, it is a noun, as in "the temperate forest ecosystem" or "the tallgrass prairie ecosystem." This implies that an ecosystem exists as a specific object and can be defined by a fixed, geographic boundary. More comprehensively, the term is used to convey a *concept*, and in the science of ecology, the "ecosystem concept" represents a way of thinking about natural systems.

Ecologists have spent the past several decades developing a cohesive conceptual framework that can be applied to any ecosystem, natural or managed, that encompasses the full range of ecological processes occurring at widely varying spatial and temporal scales (Golley, 1993). Key characteristics and concepts drawn from general systems theory are used to more specifically define all ecosystems. For example, ecosystems are conceptualized as a nested hierarchy of interacting subsystems that impact one another across spatial and temporal scales. The scales or boundaries of an ecosystem can vary, depending on the processes being studied or the research questions being addressed (Odum, 1953; Holling, 1992; Golley, 1993; Chapin et al., 2002). Thus, time and space are used to organize the myriad ecological processes in natural systems.

The ecosystem concept has undergone substantial modifications since the 1940s when ecologists first used the "organism" analogy (Golley, 1993) which was applied to organic agricultural systems. Now most research conducted at the scale of individuals, populations, and communities is cast within an ecosystem framework that links biotic interactions with environment. Use of this framework has contributed significantly to understanding how natural systems function and to development of organic agriculture. The ecosystem framework provides a flexible systems approach that can be used to understand complex, dynamic interactions among organisms and environment that characterize agroecosystems. In the 1980s, ecosystem concepts were used by scientists applying systems thinking to agriculture (Odum, 1984; Lowrance et al., 1984; Conway, 1985, 1987). As new discoveries are made, theories of how natural systems function are being revised. Studies of agroecosystems now contribute to the development of ecosystem theory. Concepts discussed below are drawn from ecosystem theory and provide a more detailed framework that can be used to conceptualize organize agroecosystems research.

Structure Determines Function

The role of structure in determining system function is fundamental to systems theory and is applied across a wide range of disciplines, from engineering to medicine to biology. In ecology, the relationship between ecosystem structure and function serves as a framework to explain characteristics of natural systems and for comparing and contrasting a diverse array of ecosystems. Properties defining *ecosystem structure* include both the physical environment, beginning with Jenny's state factors (Jenny, 1941) and the organisms living in that environment. Examples of structural attributes include precipitation regime, soil type, elevation, and species composition and diversity of the soil and plant communities. In agroecosystems any human-initiated intervention or management decision is a major factor shaping ecosystem structure. *Ecosystem functions* are those processes that result from interactions between organisms and their physical environment in an integrated system and include net primary productivity (NPP), crop yields, nutrient cycling, soil aggregation, and organic matter formation and decomposition. When ecosystem functions are related to human societies, they are called *ecosystem services* and described in ways that reflect human concerns rather than the actual mechanisms (Power et al,. 2008). For example, atmospheric composition and climate regulation are considered key regulatory ecosystem services. However, numerous ecosystem processes such as decomposition, aggregation, organic matter formation, and denitrification contribute to these services.

The relationships between ecosystem structure and function have received major attention in recent years due to concerns about the rate of species extinctions and possible consequences for the ecological integrity of ecosystems (Loreau et al., 2001; Hooper et al., 2005). Understanding this relationship is important for conserving ecosystem functions that maintain earth's biosphere and for optimizing management of ecological processes in agroecosystems. In agriculture this can be used as a basis for developing hypotheses that explicitly link management practices to ecosystem processes or functional outcomes. The concept serves to formalize thinking about management and promote transdisciplinary communication. This is particularly useful in organic agricultural systems where management strategies are designed to impact multiple ecological processes that support production and broader environmental goals.

The original hypothesis that increased biodiversity supports ecosystem function has been modified to recognize the role different species play in ecosystem processes. It is now clear that simply increasing the number of species does not always lead to improved ecosystem function (Hooper et al., 2005). Instead, species' functional characteristics determine ecosystem properties. Experiments have demonstrated that community composition rather than simply number of species present in a given community plays a major role in determining functional outcomes such as productivity and soil carbon sequestration (Loreau et al., 2002; Li et al., 2007; Fornara and Tilman, 2008). In agroecosystems, biodiversity studies have emphasized differences in species richness rather than functional diversity (Letourneau and Bothwell, 2008); however, intentional management of functional diversity has tremendous potential to contribute to sustainable organic systems (Jackson et al., 2007a, 2007b).

Using Spatial and Temporal Scales to Understand Ecological Interactions

The ecological processes governing agroecosystems occur at multiple spatial scales ranging from microscale processes that determine the fate of solutes in soil to landscape-level processes such as wind erosion, seed dispersal, and immigration. Processes occurring at one scale affect to varying degrees what happens at every other scale, and ecological processes also occur at varying temporal scales. Processes such as decomposition of labile organic matter or population changes due to predator–prey interactions occur within a single growing season (Letourneau, 1997; Puget et al., 2000), while others such as detectable changes in soil organic matter or the evolution of resistance to herbicides occur over time spans of years to decades (Aref and Wander, 1998; Vila-Aiub et al., 2007). Temporal and spatial scales used to organize ecological processes into a logical structure are fundamental to developing a coherent set of principles that are compatible with ecological science and can guide research and management in organic agricultural systems.

The spatial scales we must consider range from microns to kilometers and encompass processes occurring at microbial, plant, farm, foodshed, community, and regional scales. These spatial scales are nested within one another, so that at any level we can situate our research within this hierarchy and identify the processes that must be considered. Furthermore, we can use this hierarchy of nested scales to understand agroecosystem dynamics resulting from cross-scale interactions (Ludwig et al., 2007). The concept helps to explain how cross-scale interactions account for the nonlinear behavior of populations, communities, and ecosystems, with applications to agricultural systems (Carpenter and Turner, 2000; Cronin and Reeve, 2005; Viglizzo et al., 2005; Ludwig et al., 2007). Cronin and Reeve (2005) reviewed numerous studies illustrating how landscape-level characteristics impact parasitoid host interactions. Larger-scale landscape characteristics also interact with field-scale management to impact weed diversity (Gabriel et al., 2006) and soil erosion rates (Ludwig et al., 2007). Research in disturbed forests illustrates how the processes regulating N cycling vary, depending on scale (Smithwick et al., 2005). These examples demonstrate the importance of considering processes at multiple scales in agricultural systems, as we attempt to optimize ecological control of system functions. See "Using Spatial Scale to Organize Research Questions" on the next page for an example illustrating how systemic analysis of processes at different scales and their interactions can be used in planning experimental design and subsequently interpreting the results.

Recognizing that processes occur at differing time scales is also a useful organizing principle (Carpenter and Turner, 2000). Temporal dynamics are more complex that those across spatial scale for two reasons. First, they are a function of both the *flux* (rate of a process, i.e., grams of CO_2 respired per day) and pool size (a *pool* can be a nutrient reservoir, a population, a community, or an ecosystem). Together these two pieces of information are used to estimate turnover times or mean residence times. Second, the rate of temporal processes is usually linked to a spatial scale (grams of CO_2 respired per day per square meter) or to a specific compartment (milligrams of CO_2 respired per day per grams of microbial biomass C). These concepts are fundamental to understanding many processes that change over time such as soil organic matter cycling, population dynamics that regulate seed bank composition, and migration dynamics and community interactions that change species richness and abundance over multiple seasons.

Generally speaking, the spatial and temporal scales of ecological processes are closely linked. Small-scale or local processes are often ephemeral and rapid, but they interact with slower processes and impact ecosystem scale functional traits (Carpenter et al., 2001). Going back to the rock P example given in "Using Spatial Scale to Organize Research Questions," microscale transformations controlled by microorganisms such as P solubilization and nutrient uptake by a single fine root occur rapidly and can be highly variable in space and time. In aggregate, these very dynamic processes interact with slower processes such as abiotic weathering and erosion to determine net P flows at the field scale.

Awareness of temporal dynamics is particularly important for studies focusing on the initial years of organic management because legacy effects from previous conventional management interact with newly imposed organic practices. For

Using Spatial Scale to Organize Research Questions

Research evaluating the use of rock phosphate as a source of P may involve processes occurring at the micron, plant, and field scales that directly or indirectly impact P solubilization (see Fig. 2–4). Using a conceptual model to outline the various processes governing plant access to a sparingly soluble P source can help to ensure that the experimental design is well suited to the specific questions being addressed.

The background soil environment and climate affect the biotic processes occurring at every level including the management decisions that may alter the impact of rock P additions. Assuming that P is a limiting factor in this field, plant productivity will be impacted by field-scale management decisions and the resulting rate of P solubilization. So, by using rock P as a fertility source, we are aiming to modify the solubilization of P, a microscale process that is mediated by microorganisms and plant species as well as their interactions with the soil environment of the particular field. At the scale of microbially mediated processes, the addition of a C substrate or inoculation with a microbe that facilitates P solubilization can enhance the impact on P solubilization and plant access to this P. In addition to these strategies that target the microbial contribution to solubilization, the impact of rock P additions will be influenced by rotation and plant species decisions. Use of a mycorrhizal cash crop or a rotations using a cover crop species known to access sparingly soluble pools will increase access to rock P additions.

Interactions across these scales impact one another, that is, field management impacts the plants and soil microbes, and P solubilization influences plant productivity and creates a feedback because increased productive capacity increases the ability of the plant to stimulate P solubilization through direct and indirect means. Adding rock P in conjunction with planting a legume can be particularly effective because legumes are able to access sparingly soluble P. If rock P were added without consideration of plant species or use of an additional C source (such as compost or manure) to support microbial P solubilization, then it is possible that there may not be a detectable improvement in crop yields in the first growing season because microbial activity is limited by access to C (energy), not P.

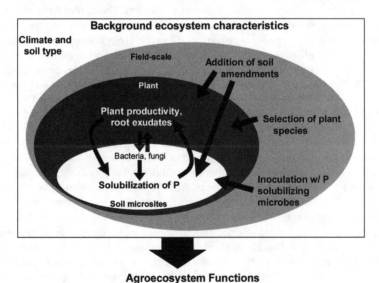

Fig. 2–4. Processes occurring at multiple scales must be considered in nutrient management decision making.

example, there are major differences in the process rates and the flux through various soil organic matter pools (Jenkinson and Parry, 1989; Schimel and Bennett, 2004). As a result, the mean residence times of relevant nutrient pools range from minutes for transient inorganic N forms such as nitrite to centuries for humified pools of soil organic matter. Differences in rates of population and community processes also impact species richness and abundance during transition from conventional to organic agriculture. For example, the weed seed bank reflects previous management history rather than the current management of a particular growing season (Davis et al., 2005; Brainard et al., 2006). During the initial years of organic management the weed community is strongly determined by this legacy (Davis et al., 2005). With each successive year of organic management, as the soil environment changes and selection pressures resulting from a different management regime act on weed populations, the composition of the weed community and the soil seed bank gradually changes to reflect different conditions (Davis et al., 2005).

Most agricultural research has emphasized time-scales of one field season or one to two years of a crop cycle or rotation (Drinkwater, 2002; Menalled et al., 2003; Gardner and Drinkwater, 2009). However, many organic agricultural goals such as soil restoration result from slow changes that accrue over decades rather than years and represent the sum of many shorter-term processes and events (Drinkwater and Snapp, 2007; Wander et al., 2007). This difference in the timeframe of processes supporting internal ecosystem services underscores the need for long-term research. Furthermore, it is these slower processes that are critical to many ecosystem services and the long-term sustainability of agroecosystem production (Carpenter et al., 2001). To better understand mechanisms of systems, one often moves to a smaller spatial or temporal level of scale, while to understand context it is necessary to move to larger or longer levels of scale.

Open versus Closed Systems: Flows of Materials, Organisms, and Genes

Another principle drawn from systems theory is the concept of open versus closed systems. Agroecosystems are open systems and therefore have inputs and outputs. These transfers across system (or subsystem) boundaries provide insights into the functional characteristics of ecosystems. For example, nutrient and energy flows are key ecosystem-scale attributes. To efficiently gauge the impact of farm management on longer-term soil fertility and sustainability, it is crucial to consider the flow of nutrients across boundaries of management units as well as the larger landscape in which they are embedded (see "Constructing Simple Nutrient Budgets"). Populations can be open (free migration in and out) or closed (in isolated islands or fields), or they can consist of a series of spatially discrete local populations linked together by migration. In the latter case, the linked populations are called a *metapopulation* (Hanski, 1998), which functions as a closed system while the local populations are open systems (Roughgarden and Iwasa, 1986). Fluxes of nutrients, genes, or organisms across boundaries are viewed in terms of source–sink fluxes, posing questions such as, Where do the flows originate and where are they going? Use of this concept has proven useful in studying many ecological processes essential to organic agricultural systems including regulation of pests and beneficials (Rosenheim, 2001; Cronin, 2007; Hirao and Murakami, 2008), agroecosystem plant diversity (Cousinsa and

Constructing Simple Nutrient Budgets

To analyze the movement of nutrients across field and farm boundaries, net flows of nutrients can be estimated by constructing nutrient budgets. This approach is used in ecosystem ecology to compare fluxes into and out of a defined compartment, which can be as small as a patch of organic residue in the soil (Hodge, 2004) or as large as the entire atmosphere (Schlesinger, 2005) to find out whether the balance of these fluxes (inputs–outputs) are positive or negative. Over the last 10 years, the value of nutrient budgeting as a tool for analyzing nutrient flows in agroecosystems and agricultural landscapes has become apparent and the approach has been widely applied at a variety of scales. Depending on the questions being addressed, the scale of land unit used can be individual fields, farms, watersheds, or even whole regions and countries.

In agricultural systems, the simplest nutrient budgets emphasize the flow of nutrients that are controlled by the manager such as fertility inputs and harvested exports because these fluxes are usually the dominant flows that regulate the transfer of nutrients into and out of a field or farm. Construction of a field-scale mass balance entails calculating the difference between inputs and harvested exports over the course of a rotation cycle (Drinkwater et al., 1998). All fertilizers, soil amendments and N-fixing crops must be accounted for as inputs. One of the most challenging aspects of using this budgeting approach is determining N inputs from leguminous cover crops. A common practice for legumes is to measure N in standing biomass for green manures as an estimate of N from biological N fixation and to consider no net gain or loss of N for leguminous grain crops (Drinkwater et al., 1998). The exports are all harvested crops or animals, including grains, forages, or crop residues removed and manure or animal biomass removed.

This simple budgeting method can be very useful as an indicator of directional change and the relative efficiency of divergent nutrient management strategies (Drinkwater et al., 2008). Negative balances indicate that deficits are accruing, and if management practices are not modified, soil fertility will continue to be depleted and production will decline. Chronic surpluses may indicate overapplication; to fully determine the fate of these surpluses, however, additional analysis of soil stocks and internal cycling processes is needed. In some cases, such as sloping fields, additional potential loss pathways such as erosion will need to be evaluated. These simple mass balances also provide a starting point for understanding the dynamics of smaller-scale, internal processes that are regulating the fate of nutrients in agroecosystems.

Lindbor, 2008), weed seed dispersal (Thomson, 2007), and nutrient cycling (Dalal, 1998; Drinkwater et al., 1998; Bationo et al., 2007).

Life-cycle analysis (LCA) is a special case developed in industrial ecology where multiple input–output flows are used to analyze the environmental impacts of a product or process. Landis et al. (2007) used LCA to evaluate the consequences of corn (*Zea mays* L.)–soybean [*Glycine max* (L.) Merr.] feed in terms of energy, C emissions, N and P flows, pesticides, and air pollutants. This analysis is one of many ecosystem-based approaches being used to evaluate the environmental impacts of agricultural systems and could prove to be useful in evaluating how well organic systems meet environmental goals (van der Werf et al., 2007).

Directional Change and Steady-State Conditions

Ecosystems can reach *steady-state conditions* when the relationship between inputs and outputs and community composition does not indicate directional change (Chapin et al., 2002). Even under steady-state conditions, ecosystems are dynamic and can exhibit significant spatial and temporal variation. Directional change in elemental cycles, nutrient reservoirs, populations, or community composition are indicative of non–steady-state conditions. Steady-state conditions are not "all-or-none" phenomena. Ecological processes are occurring at different spatial and temporal scales, so it follows that smaller-scale, faster processes will be more sensitive to change compared to slower processes. As ecosystems move toward a steady state, small-scale components that are regulated by fast processes may reach steady-state conditions before larger components that change more slowly. For example, increases in NPP would support a larger soil microbial biomass before a change in total soil organic C storage can be detected. As a result, the decomposers may track shifts in NPP quickly so that the average annul microbial biomass is at steady-state conditions while the larger, slow-cycling soil organic matter pools are still showing directional changes.

When a major change in agroecosystem management is implemented, such as a shift from conventional to organic management or from conventional tillage to no-till, we say that the cropping system is *in transition* (Liebhardt et al., 1989). The transition from conventional to organic management can be thought of as analogous to succession in plant communities. Both reflect a period of directional change during which the ecosystem is shifting from one dynamic steady state to another, distinct steady state. During this transition period, differences in flows and subsequent changes in nutrient pools or communities provide clear signs of directional change. For instance, in the case of organic transitions, increased weed competition and shifts in C and N cycling have been reported (Wander et al., 1994; Liebhardt et al., 1989).

Implementing Effective Organic Agricultural Research

The initial stages of research planning and experimental design are key steps in the research process that ultimately determine the quality of the information produced. Scientists, farmers, and extension educators would likely all agree that while interdisciplinary research is essential, the collaborative process is challenging. There is a growing body of literature that specifically addresses the collaborative process in science, one that is highly relevant to organic research. Specifically, the use of conceptual models can support the collaborative process and provide a framework for integrating ecological concepts and agricultural management. Second, the major attributes of an experimental plan, that is, location of the research and application of systems versus factorial designs, are major determinants of the potential for research to contribute to understanding organic agroecosystems. The role of on-farm versus field-station research is often hotly debated. Some scientists believe that real research, that is, quantitative studies aimed at testing hypotheses and system mechanisms, cannot be conducted on working farms. On the other hand, some organic proponents believe that all research needs to be conducted on organic farms. Also, the distinct contributions that can be made by systems-level comparisons versus factorial experiments conducted within a systems context is an important aspect of experimental design. We need to rigorously apply the full spectrum of research approaches to study the full range of ecological and social processes that are important for the development of sustainable organic agricultural food systems.

Planning Collaborative Agroecological Research

A first step in conducting any research is to clearly identify goals for the experiment. To carry out effective, interdisciplinary research, however, it is necessary to plan research and develop goals collaboratively. This presents unique challenges. There are currently many resources documenting successful strategies to enhance research partnerships that include farmer participation and interdisciplinary collaboration (Lilja and Ashby, 1999; Heemskerk et al., 2003; Boulton et al.,

2005; Gonsalves et al., 2005; Lele and Norgaard, 2005; Warner, 2006). In particular, the use of conceptual models or concept mapping has proven to be a useful tool for facilitating communication and planning in groups with diverse perspectives (Heemskerk et al., 2003). A conceptual model is a visual representation of the system to be studied. Conceptual models are particularly useful in planning interdisciplinary agricultural systems research because they require the team to graphically represent the problem to be addressed within a larger, systems context. Ideally, to be useful as a planning tool, a conceptual model should do the following:

- Describe a system that encompasses the research questions and management issues but has clear boundaries.
- Explicitly define the components of the system and how they interact with one another; for example, it should identify the factors that directly or indirectly contribute to production, environmental outcomes, or nutrient flows.
- Provide a logical framework for the problems or questions to be addressed.
- Be simple enough to be understood by scientists from a variety of disciplines and stakeholders.
- Be developed and agreed on by all stakeholders and researchers.

Diagrams of agroecosystems processes such as predator–prey interactions, competition, or nutrient flows can serve as a vehicle for achieving several outcomes that are prerequisites for successful ecologically based research and its application to organic agriculture. This process is important for three reasons:

1. Facilitating information exchange. Communication ensures that farmers and researchers have an agreed-upon understanding of the system to be studied and the processes that are important to consider. It also helps scientists to share information about ecological processes with farmers and provides an opportunity for farmers to give researchers feedback on their concept model when they verify that the diagram reflects their practical experience.

2. Organizing a complex system. By laying out the relationships among the interacting processes using an ecological framework that is structured to include processes occurring at different spatial and temporal scales, trade-offs and linkages between management strategies become apparent.

3. Moving the organic knowledge system forward. The process of agreeing on a diagram that represents diverse perspectives helps to identify knowledge gaps and promotes the incorporation of innovations and new information into the shared knowledge structure that reflects ecological and agricultural paradigms.

Experimental Designs to Support Ecosystem-Based Management

Research on organic agricultural systems can be conducted in simulated cropping systems located on a research station or by using intact agroecosystems on actual farms and agricultural landscapes as study sites. To support ecosystem-based management strategies, it is desirable to use a hybrid approach that includes research sites that encompass the full range of ecological scales over the long term. Choosing the location(s) is probably the most important decision about experimental design and one that will have wide-ranging consequences for the application of results. Often this decision is made before the research goals have been clearly established, and as a result, the choice of location, research station or on-farm, drives the research questions that can be addressed. Instead, the appropriate venue should be dictated by the research goals and the questions that have been identified by the research team.

Research Using Farm Sites or Agricultural Landscapes

Research projects that aim to answer questions about farms or agricultural landscapes must be conducted in appropriate intact agroecosystems. Over the long term, research programs targeting organic agricultural systems often need to include on-farm research at some point, particularly because it may be difficult to accurately reproduce the farm environment on an experiment station. On-farm research has the advantage of avoiding transition effects encountered when experimental treatments that differ from the past management history are imposed in cropping systems experiments, almost always the situation on experiment stations. Some examples of questions that are more easily addressed by studying working, intact agroecosystems and landscapes include the following:

- Farmer decision making, marketing practices, farm enterprise budgets, and other social questions
- Processes that operate at scales too large to be accommodated on research stations, such as economics and other social system processes; questions focused on highly mobile pests or beneficial insects; any landscape-level ecological processes
- Processes that change very slowly (20 to more than 100 years), such as some soil organic matter pools, soil weathering processes, and weed evolutionary biology that can be addressed if the right chronosequence of farms can be found
- Interactions between environmental variation (soil textural or topographical location) and management
- Specific management practices that require a high degree of skill not available on the research farms or that are site specific
- Systems that are already in place on working farms and would require time, money, and perhaps a new skill set to re-create on-station

Among the variety of possible methods and designs used in conducting studies of agroecosystems in the real world, the appropriate approach will depend on the goals of the project and the questions of interest. Some sample designs for research based on working farms are described here.

- Case studies are used when in-depth, qualitative information is desired. The approach is used more heavily in the social sciences but has proven useful in providing a holistic overview of specific farms. The results from case studies can prove to be useful as educational materials (Mikkelsen, 1995), particularly for educating researchers about management systems that are less commonly encountered. They can also serve as the basis for generating hypotheses and lead to new discoveries about how particular management systems function on working farms.
- Comparison of farm pairs is the most common method used to study different farming systems on working farms, with a comparison of multiple paired farm sites under the assumption that confounding variation can be eliminated by carefully matching pairs. This design considers each pair as

a replication for statistical analysis, and common statistical analyses can be applied (Lockeretz et al., 1981; Reganold et al., 1993). The strategy works fairly well if the study is limited to one or two disciplines or takes place in agricultural landscapes where the distribution of farm types is well suited for the questions to be addressed. However, as the number of disciplines involved in the study increases, it can become extremely difficult to reach agreement on how to designate farm pairs because the number of criteria used in matching the pairs increases. The feasibility of this approach also depends on the distribution of farms in the landscape.

- Comparison of groups of farms can be used where pairing farms is not an option; groups of farms can be compared using multivariate statistical techniques (Drinkwater et al.,1995; Wander and Bollero, 1999). Multivariate analyses make it possible to examine relationships between many variables simultaneously. As a result, groups of farms, defined either in terms of specific environmental variables or management types, can be compared to address the question of interest. Farms are selected so that the confounding variables have similar distributions in each of the groups. This approach allows for greater flexibility in terms of the farms that can be included in the study. A variation on this approach is to identify a set of farms that form a continuum (in terms of environmental or management characteristics) rather than contrasting groups (Steenwerth et al., 2002). For example, the use of a chronosequence of farms that have implemented a new management system can provide useful information about how quickly the agroecosystem responds to changes in management.

- In-depth study of a single site or a pair of farms provides sites for mechanistic studies of small-scale processes such as microbially mediated processes. In this case, the questions are not focused on the effects of management practices on field-scale processes. Instead these studies usually focus on interactions within a farming system that has already been well characterized by previous research (Steinheimer et al., 1998; Kramer et al., 2006).

- Larger-scale studies are useful for agroecosystem research that addresses questions targeting processes occurring at scales larger than a field or farm. Examples of these studies include comparisons of watersheds (Sovell et al., 2000; Napier and Tucker, 2001) or studies that aim to understand how land management varies across regions or through time (Auclair, 1976). This approach is useful in studying the impacts of organic farming on ecosystem services occurring at larger scales (Gabriel et al., 2006).

- Mother–baby trials provide a hybrid method that combines the use of farm sites with the use of experimental plots located on the research station (Snapp et al., 2002). It is extremely powerful for developing improved management options because it allows researchers to test a wide variety of management options across varying farm environments and in a replicated field-station design in a single experiment. It is also appealing to farmers, which usually makes it relatively easy to recruit farmer participation.

Research Using Simulated Agroecosystems Experiments

All cropping-systems experiments are based on the premise that it is possible to create simulations of agroecosystems on research farms that mimic the behavior of real farming systems managed by farmers. The success or failure of these experiments depends on the integrity of their constructed cropping systems and the quality of management. To be valid, these studies must include cropping systems that represent realistic management systems either currently in use in the landscape or likely to be adopted by farmers as an improvement. During the design phase and throughout implementation of simulated systems experiments, researchers need to be clear about exactly what systems are being represented by each treatment included in the experiment. For this reason, it is important to involve practitioners in the design process to ensure that viable management systems form the basis of the experiment. Researchers must remember that any new management scheme that differs from the previous management history will undergo a transition phase and will require time to reach a new relatively steady state that reflects current management practices. Topics that are more easily addressed in well-designed cropping systems experiments on field stations include the following:

- How transition to organic management impacts ecological processes at micro- to small field scales, but not landscape level or large farm scale
- Microbially mediated soil processes such as nutrient cycling, decomposition, and aggregation
- Processes that respond to management in time frames of less than 1 year to 20 years.
- New or innovative organic management systems that are not currently used by organic farmers
- Ecological mechanisms that require extensive monitoring, use of stable isotopes, or use of other substances that are not approved for certification or that pose a risk to organic farming for some other reason

Currently, a large number of ongoing cropping-systems comparisons are in progress, with widely varying goals and designs (see, e.g., Temple et al., 1994; Mueller et al., 2002; Peterson et al., 1999; Robertson, 2008; Mohler, 2008). These systems experiments include some that compare organic and conventional systems such as the Rodale Institute Farming Systems Trial (Liebhardt et al., 1989; Drinkwater et al., 1998) and more recent experiments that focus largely on optimizing organic cropping systems management (Mohler, 2008). It can be highly advantageous to become familiar with these existing experiments before launching your own. Each has unique design features reflecting the regional environment, farming practices, and research priorities. Virtually all these experiments have some capacity to generate both practical outcomes relevant to organic farmers and new knowledge of ecological processes.

Using Factorial Experiments within a Systems Context

The controversy over experimental design and the role of systems versus factorial experiments is another issue that should be resolved based on research goals and the questions that are being asked. The vast majority of agricultural research is conducted in reductionist, factorial experiments. A major reason for this is that the guiding paradigm in agricultural science has been based on the command-and-control approach to management. Factorial experiments permit the deconstruction of a complex system so that specific components can be isolated and cause–effect relationships can be identified. Factorial experiments are excellent for studying isolated components and mechanisms; however, they cannot predict the performance of intact agroecosystems unless they are conducted within an agroecosystem context (Drinkwater, 2002).

Research on organic cropping systems needs to be conducted to address both the systemic characteristics and the underlying specific mechanisms or cause–effect relationships. For example, many of the systems comparisons that have been conducted address questions about how ecosystem processes differ across production systems. Questions about yields, nutrient cycling, crop damage, or crop quality across differing systems are just a few examples of systems-level questions. Hypotheses about agroecosystem functions can be tested with scientific rigor and analyzed using a number of quantitative and statistical methods (Drinkwater et al., 1995, 1998; Ray et al., 2006; Smith and Chaney, 2007).

The use of factorial experiments within a systems context to test specific cause–effect hypotheses and shed insight on agroecosystem function is a powerful research approach. To interpret the results from factorial experiments in terms of their implications for the intact system requires experimental designs that can account for processes occurring at larger scales and longer time frames. Thus, a common approach to reductionist research questions within agroecosystems is to embed factorial experiments into the larger systems. For example, microplots have been used within larger cropping systems experiments to manipulate a single factor and test specific, mechanistic hypotheses about underlying ecological processes within a given management history (Harris et al., 1994, Puget and Drinkwater, 2001; Kramer et al., 2002, 2006). The recent literature contains many examples of studies that used factorial designs within an agroecosystems context (Mueller et al., 2002; Berkelmans et al., 2003; Brainard et al., 2006; Maxwell et al., 2007; Murphy et al., 2007; Wander et al., 2007). Increased use of experimental designs that integrate systems thinking and test specific, mechanistic hypotheses has much to contribute to organic agriculture.

Conclusions

An organic research community is still in the early stages of development and is emerging within publicly funded research institutions that have not served the organic farming community in the past. In general, the literature suggests that scientists are aware of the unique characteristics of organic farming and are attempting to adjust their research approaches to reflect these differences. The organic research literature is distinct from traditional agricultural research in that studies of organic agriculture commonly include farmer participation, use systems-based research approaches, and investigate ecological processes.

Future research must build on past farmer participation by recognizing farmers as research partners and by explicitly documenting the contributions of organic farming knowledge to research. In addition, more consistent application of an ecosystem conceptual framework will enable organic researchers to successfully study important ecological processes occurring at the full range of spatial and temporal scales. The increased use of ecological concepts will also support the development of organic agricultural theory that is science based and compatible with the holistic management approach used by organic farmers. A formalized conceptual framework will also enable a systematic documentation of the full range of ecosystem services that can be provided by organic food systems.

Ultimately, the development of sustainable organic agricultural systems will depend on changes in food culture, government policies that impact food systems and natural resource management, and application of ecological knowledge to agricultural management. The widespread application of current ecological understanding to the design of organic agricultural systems will provide the scientific expertise to promote sustainable food systems that can supply a wide range of necessary ecosystem services.

Discussion Questions

1. Compare and contrast agroecosystems and nature ecosystems in terms of structural characteristics, nutrient and energy flows, biodiversity, and ecosystem services. What are the key similarities and differences between these ecosystems?

2. What are the strengths and limitations of reductionist science and factorial experimental designs? Compare reductionist and systems-based experimental designs and discuss how these two approaches can be used concurrently to address research questions in organic farming systems.

3. Compare and contrast command-and-control and ecosystem-based management approaches. Do you think ecosystem-based management approaches could be applied to conventional farming systems? Explain your rationale.

4. How can ecological theory and systems thinking be used to design research that is appropriate for improving organic farming systems? Design some examples of experiments that could be done on farm and some that could be done on experiment stations to improve productivity and economic returns from organic systems.

5. Organic farming systems are often described as meeting multiple objectives of the farmer and family; give some examples of positive environmental and social outcomes of organic systems that would be valued by the family. Provide some examples of ways that society could reward this type of multifunctional agriculture and the ecosystem services that they provide.

6. Why are spatial hierarchies important in ecological study of organic farming systems and mechanisms, and how does the researcher choose the appropriate level of scale for application of treatments and collection of data? At what levels of scale can the results of experiments be applied?

7. Are there research results from studies of organic farming systems that could be applied to conventional agricultural systems? Provide examples of ecological processes that could play a role in conventional systems. Can you think of ecological processes that cannot play a role in conventional systems?

8. Define ecosystem structure and ecosystems functions and explain how they are related to one another. Give some examples of structure–function relationships in organic farming systems.

9. Describe the open and closed aspects of natural ecosystems, as well as human-managed agroecosystems. What lessons can we learn from natural systems that help in the design of agroecosystems, and how can we use them?

10. What types of questions are most appropriately addressed on the experiment station, and what questions are more adequately addressed on farms? In what key ways can the farmer be a participant in both types of research?

11. Describe a number of experimental strategies or methods that can be used on farms in the rural landscape. Provide examples of where each would be appropriate.

12. What is the relationship among organic farming, agroecology, and sustainable agriculture, and why are their definitions important?

References

Aref, S., and M.M. Wander. 1998. Long-term trends of corn yield and soil organic matter in different crop sequences and soil fertility treatments on the Morrow plots. Adv. Agron. 62:153–197.

Auclair, A.N. 1976. Ecological factors in development of intensive-management ecosystems in midwestern United States. Ecology 57:431–444.

Bationo, A., J. Kihara, B. Vanlauwe, B. Waswa, and J. Kimetu. 2007. Soil organic carbon dynamics, functions and management in west African agro-ecosystems. Agric. Syst. 94:13–25.

Berkelmans, R., H. Ferris, M. Tenuta, and A.H.C. van Bruggen. 2003. Effects of long-term crop management on nematode trophic levels other than plant feeders disappear after 1 year of disruptive soil management. Appl. Soil Ecol. 23:223–235.

Bezdicek, D.F., and J.F. Power (ed.) 1984. Organic farming: Current technology and its role in a sustainable agriculture. ASA Spec. Publ. 46. ASA, Madison, WI.

Boulton, A.J., D. Panizzon, and J. Prior. 2005. Explicit knowledge structures as a tool for overcoming obstacles to interdisciplinary research. Conserv. Biol. 19(6):2026–2029.

Brainard, D.C., A. DiTommaso, and C.L. Mohler. 2006. Intraspecific variation in germination response to ammonium nitrate of Powell amaranth (Amaranthus powellii) seeds originating from organic vs. conventional vegetable farms. Weed Sci. 54:435–442.

Buck, D., C. Getz, and J. Guthman. 1997. From farm to table: The organic vegetable commodity chain of northern California. Sociol. Ruralis 37:3–20.

Carpenter, S.R., and M.G. Turner. 2000. Hares and tortoises: Interactions of fast and slow variables in ecosystems. Ecosystems 3:495–497.

Carpenter, S., B. Walker, J.M. Anderies, and N. Abel. 2001. From metaphor to measurement: Resilience of what to what? Ecosystems 4:765–781.

Carter, M.R., S. Andrews, and L.E. Drinkwater. 2004. System approaches for improving soil quality. p. 261–281. In P. Schjonning, B.T. Christensen, and S. Elmholt (ed.) Managing soil quality: Challenges in modern agriculture. CAB Int., Oxford, UK.

Chapin, F.S., III, P.A. Matson, and H.A. Mooney. 2002. Principles of terrestrial ecosystems ecology. Springer, New York.

Clark, W.C., and N.M. Dickson. 2003. Sustainability science: The emerging research program. Proc. Natl. Acad. Sci. USA 100:8059–8061.

Conford, P. 2001. The origins of the organic movement. Floris Books, Edinburgh, Scotland.

Conway, G.R. 1985. Agroecosystem analysis. Agric. Admin. 20:31–55.

Conway, G.R. 1987. The properties of agroecosystems. Agric. Syst. 24:95–117.

Costanza, R., R. d'Arge, R. deGroot, S. Farber, M. Grasso, B. Hannon, K. Limburg, S. Naeem, R.V. O'Neill, J. Paruelo, R.G. Raskin, P. Sutton, and M. van den Belt. 1997. The value of the world's ecosystem services and natural capital. Nature 387:253–260.

Cousinsa, S.A.O., and R. Lindbor. 2008. Remnant grassland habitats as source communities for plant diversification in agricultural landscapes. Biol. Conserv. 141:233–240.

Cronin, J.T. 2007. From population sources to sieves: The matrix alters host–parasitoid source–sink structure. Ecology 88:2966–2976.

Cronin, J.T., and J.D. Reeve. 2005. Host–parasitoid spatial ecology: A plea for a landscape-level synthesis. Proc. R. Soc. London, Ser. B 272:2225–2235.

Daily, G.C. (ed.) 1997. Nature's services: Societal dependence on natural ecosystems. Island Press, Washington, DC.

Dalal, R.C. 1998. Soil microbial biomass- what do the numbers really mean? Aust. J. Exp. Agric. 38:649–665.

Dale, V.H., S. Brown, R.A. Haeuber, N.T. Hobbs, N. Huntly, R.J. Naiman, W.E. Riebsame, M.G. Turner, and T.J. Valone. 2000. Ecological principles and guidelines for managing the use of land. Ecol. Appl. 10:639–670.

Davis, A.S., K.A. Renner, and K.L. Gross. 2005. Weed seedbank and community shifts in a long-term cropping systems experiment. Weed Sci. 53:296–306.

Drinkwater, L.E. 2002. Cropping systems research: Reconsidering agricultural experimental approaches. HortTechnology 12:355–361.

Drinkwater, L.E., D.K. Letourneau, F. Workneh, A.H.C. Vanbruggen, and C. Shennan. 1995. Fundamental differences between conventional and organic tomato agroecosystems in California. Ecol. Appl. 5:1098–1112.

Drinkwater, L.E., M. Schipanski, S.S. Snapp, and L.E. Jackson. 2008. Ecologically based nutrient management. p. 159–209. In S.S. Snapp and B. Pounds (ed.) Agricultural systems: Agroecology and rural innovation. Elsevier, Amsterdam.

Drinkwater, L.E., and S.S. Snapp. 2007. Nutrients in agroecosystems: Rethinking the management paradigm. Adv. Agron. 92:163–186.

Drinkwater, L.E., P. Wagoner, and M. Sarrantonio. 1998. Legume-based cropping systems have reduced carbon and nitrogen losses. Nature 396:262–265.

Fornara, D.A., and D. Tilman. 2008. Plant functional composition influences rates of soil carbon and nitrogen accumulation. J. Ecol. 96:314–322.

Francis, C., G. Lieblein, S. Gliessman, T.A. Breland, N. Creamer, L. Harwood, L. Salomonsson, J. Helenius, D. Rickerl, R. Salvador, M. Wiedenhoeft, S. Simmons, P. Allen, M. Altieri, C. Flora, and R. Poincelot. 2003. Agroecology: The ecology of food systems. J. Sustain. Agric. 22:99–119.

Gabriel, D., I. Roschewitz, T. Tscharntke, and C. Thies. 2006. Beta diversity at different spatial scales: Plant communities in organic and conventional agriculture. Ecol. Appl. 16:2011–2021.

Gardner, J., and L.E. Drinkwater. 2009. The fate of nitrogen in grain cropping systems: A meta-analysis of ^{15}N field experiments. Ecol. Appl. (in press).

Golley, F.B. 1993. A history of the ecosystem concept in ecology: More than the sum of the parts. Yale Univ. Press, New Haven, CT.

Gonsalves, J., T. Becker, A. Braun, D. Campilan, H. de Chavez, E. Fajber, M. Kapiriri, J. Rivaca-Caminade, and R. Vernooy (ed.) 2005. Participatory research and development for sustainable agriculture and natural resource management: A sourcebook. Vol. 1–3. CIP-UPWARD, IDRC, Ottawa, ON, Canada.

Hanski, I. 1998. Metapopulation dynamics. Nature 396:41–49.

Harris, G.H., O.B. Hesterman, E.A. Paul, S.E. Peters, and R.R. Janke. 1994. Fate of legume and fertilizer nitrogen-15 in a long-term cropping systems experiment. Agron. J. 86:910–915.

Heckman, J. 2006. A history of organic farming: Transitions from Sir Albert Howard's war in the soil to USDA National Organic Program. Renewable Agric. Food Syst. 21:143–150.

Heemskerk, M., K. Wilson, and M. Pavao-Zuckerman. 2003. Conceptual models as tools for communication across disciplines. Conserv. Ecol. 7(3):8.

Hirao, T., and M. Murakami. 2008. Quantitative food webs of lepidopteran leafminers and their parasitoids in a Japanese deciduous forest. Ecol. Res. 23:159–168.

Hodge, A. 2004. The plastic plant: Root responses to heterogeneous supplies of nutrients. New Phytol. 162:9–24.

Holling, C.S. 1992. Cross-scale morphology, geometry, and dynamics of ecosystems. Ecol. Monogr. 62:447–502.

Holling, C.S., and G.K. Meffe. 1996. Command and control and the pathology of natural resource management. Conserv. Biol. 10:328–337.

Hooper, D.U., F.S. Chapin, J.J. Ewel, A. Hector, P. Inchausti, S. Lavorel, J.H. Lawton, D.M. Lodge, M. Loreau, S. Naeem, B. Schmid, H. Setala, A.J. Symstad, J. Vandermeer, and D.A. Wardle. 2005. Effects of biodiversity on ecosystem functioning: A consensus of current knowledge. Ecol. Monogr. 75:3–35.

Hurlbert, S.H. 1984. Pseudoreplication and the design of ecological field experiments. Ecol. Monogr. 54:187–211.

Ingram, M. 2007. Biology and beyond: The science of "back to nature" farming in the United States. Ann. Assoc. Am. Geogr. 97:298–312.

Jackson, L.E., U. Pascual, L. Brussaard, P. de Ruiter, and K.S. Bawa. 2007a. Biodiversity in agricultural landscapes: Investing without losing interest. Agric. Ecosyst. Environ. 121:193–195.

Jackson, L.E., U. Pascual, and T. Hodgkin. 2007b. Utilizing and conserving agrobiodiversity in agricultural landscapes. Agric. Ecosyst. Environ. 121:196–210.

Jenkinson, D.S., and L.C. Parry. 1989. The nitrogen-cycle in the Broadbalk wheat experiment: A model for the turnover of nitrogen through the soil microbial biomass. Soil Biol. Biochem. 21:535–541.

Jenny, H. 1941. Factors of soil formation. McGraw-Hill, New York.

Keller, D.R., and E.C. Brummer. 2002. Putting food production in context: Toward a post-mechanistic agricultural ethic. Bioscience 52:264–271.

Klonsky, K. 2000. Forces impacting the production of organic foods. Organic farming and the politics of nature. Agric. Human Values 17:233–243.

Kramer, A.W., T.A. Doane, W.R. Horwath, and C. van Kessel. 2002. Short-term nitrogen-15 recovery vs. long-term total soil N gains in conventional and alternative cropping systems. Soil Biol. Biochem. 34:43–50.

Kramer, S.B., J.P. Reganold, J.D. Glover, B.J.M. Bohannan, and H.A. Mooney. 2006. Reduced nitrate leaching and enhanced denitrifier activity and efficiency in organically fertilized soils. Proc. Natl. Acad. Sci. USA 103:4522–4527.

Landis, A.E., S.A. Miller, and T.L. Theis. 2007. Life cycle of the corn-soybean agroecosystem for biobased production. Environ. Sci. Technol. 41:1457–1464.

Lele, S., and R.B. Norgaard. 2005. Practicing interdisciplinarity. Bioscience 55:967–975.

Letourneau, D.K. 1997. Plant–arthropod interactions in agroecosystems. p. 239–290. In L.E. Jackson (ed.) Ecology in agriculture. Academic Press, San Diego, CA.

Letourneau, D.K., and S.G. Bothwell. 2008. Comparison of organic and conventional farms: Challenging ecologists to make biodiversity functional. Frontiers Ecol. Environ. 8:430–438.

Lewis, W.J., J.C. van Lenteren, S.C. Phatak, and J.H. Tumlinson. 1997. A total system approach to sustainable pest management. Proc. Natl. Acad. Sci. USA 94:12243–12248.

Li, L., S. Li, J. Sun, L. Zhou, X. Bao, H. Zhang, and F. Zhang. 2007. Diversity enhances agricultural productivity via rhizosphere phosphorus facilitation on phosphorus-deficient soils. Proc. Natl. Acad. Sci. USA 104:11192–11196.

Liebhardt, W.C., R.W. Andrews, M.N. Culik, R.R. Harwood, R.R. Janke, J.K. Radke, and S.L. Riegerschwartz. 1989. Crop production during conversion from conventional to low-input methods. Agron. J. 81:150–159.

Liebman, M., and A.S. Davis. 2009. Managing weeds in organic farming systems: An ecological approach. p. 173–196. In C. Francis (ed.) Ecology in organic farming systems. Agron. Monogr. 54. ASA, CSSA, and SSSA, Madison, WI. (This volume.)

Liebman, M., and E.R. Gallandt. 1997. Many little hammers: Ecological management of crop–weed interactions. p. 291–343. In L.E. Jackson (ed.) Ecology in agriculture. Academic Press, San Diego, CA.

Lilja, N., and J.A. Ashby. 1999. Types of participatory research based on locus of decision making. Participatory Research and Gender Analysis Working Document 6. Consultative Group on International Agricultural Research. CIAT, Cali, Colombia.

Lockeretz, W., G. Shearer, and D.H. Kohl. 1981. Organic farming in the corn belt. Science 211:540–547.

Loreau, M., S. Naeem, and P. Inchausti (ed.) 2002. Biodiversity and ecosystem functioning: Synthesis and perspectives. Oxford Univ. Press, Oxford, UK.

Loreau, M., S. Naeem, P. Inchausti, J. Bengtsson, J.P. Grime, A. Hector, D.U. Hooper, M.A. Huston, D. Raffaelli, B. Schmid, D. Tilman, and D.A. Wardle. 2001. Biodiversity and ecosystem functioning: Current knowledge and future challenges. Science 294:804–808.

Lowrance, R., B.R. Stinner, and G.J. House (ed.) 1984. Agricultural ecosystems: Unifying concepts. John Wiley, Toronto, Canada.

Ludwig, J.A., R. Bartley, A.A. Hawdon, B.N. Abbott, and D. McJannet. 2007. Patch configuration non-linearly affects sediment loss across scales in a grazed catchment in north-east Australia. Ecosystems 10:839–845.

Marino, P.C., and D.A. Landis. 1996. Effect of landscape structure on parasitoid diversity and parasitism in agroecosystems. Ecol. Appl. 6:276–284.

Maxwell, B.D., R.G. Smith, and M. Brelsford. 2007. Wild oat (*Avena fatua*) seed bank dynamics in transition to organic wheat production systems. Weed Sci. 55:212–217.

Meffe, G., L. Neilsen, R.L. Knight, and D. Schenborn. 2002. Ecosystem management: Adaptive, community-based conservation. Island Press, Washington, DC.

Menalled, F.D., A.C. Costamagna, P.C. Marino, and D.A. Landis. 2003. Temporal variation in the response of parasitoids to agricultural landscape structure. Agric. Ecosyst. Environ. 96:29–35.

Mikkelsen, R.L. 1995. Swine waste disposal dilemma: A case study. J. Nat. Resour. Life Sci. Educ. 24:169–172.

Mohler, C. 2008. Organic cropping systems project—Organic agriculture for the future: Designing farms for better soil and pest management. Available at http://www.organic.cornell.edu/ocs/ (verified 23 June 2009). Dep. of Horticulture, Cornell Univ., Ithaca, NY.

Mueller, J.P., M.E. Barbercheck, M. Bell, C. Brownie, N.G. Creamer, S. Hu, L. Kin, H.M. Linker, F.G. Louws, M. Marra, C.W. Raczkowski, D. Susko, and M.G. Wagger. 2002. Implementation of long-term agricultural systems studies: Challenges and opportunities. HortTechnology 12:362–368.

Murphy, K.M., K.G. Campbell, S.R. Lyon, and S.S. Jones. 2007. Evidence of varietal adaptation to organic farming systems. Field Crops Res. 102:172–177.

Napier, T.L., and M. Tucker. 2001. Factors affecting nutrient application rates within three midwestern watersheds. J. Soil Water Conserv. 56:220–228.

Nerbonne, J.F., and R. Lentz. 2003. Rooted in grass: Challenging patterns of knowledge exchange as a means of fostering social change in a southeast Minnesota farm community. Agric. Human Values 20:65–78.

O' Neill, R.V. 2001. Is it time to bury the ecosystem concept? (With full military honors of course!). Ecology 82:3275–3284.

Odum, E.P. 1984. Properties of agroecosystems. p. 5–11. In R. Lowrance, B.R. Stinner, and G. House (ed.) Agricultural ecosystems: Unifying concepts. John Wiley & Sons, New York.

Odum, E.P. 1953. Fundamentals of ecology. W.B. Saunders, Philadelphia, PA.

Paull, J. 2006. The farm as organism: The foundational idea of organic agriculture. Elementals J. Bio-Dynamics Tasmania. 80:14–18.

Peterson, C., L.E. Drinkwater, and P. Wagoner. 1999. The farming systems trial: The first fifteen years. Rodale Inst., Kutztown, PA.

Power, A., M. O'Rourke, and L.E. Drinkwater. 2008. Ecosystem services from agroecosystems. In S. Levin (ed.) Guide to ecology. Princeton Univ. Press, Princeton, NJ.

Puget, P., C. Chenu, and J. Balesdent. 2000. Dynamics of soil organic matter associated with particle-size fractions of water-stable aggregates. Eur. J. Soil Sci. 51:595–605.

Puget, P., and L.E. Drinkwater. 2001. Short-term dynamics of root and shoot-derived carbon from a leguminous green manure. Soil Sci. Soc. Am. J. 65:771–779.

Ray, K.A., L.D. Warnick, R.M. Mitchell, J.B. Kaneene, P.L. Ruegg, S.J. Wells, C.P. Fossler, L.W. Halbert, and K. May. 2006. Antimicrobial susceptibility of *Salmonella* from organic and conventional dairy farms. J. Dairy Sci. 89:2038–2050.

Reganold, J.P., A.S. Palmer, J.C. Lockhart, and A.N. Macgregor. 1993. Soil quality and financial performance of biodynamic and conventional farms in New Zealand. Science 260:344–349.

Robertson, R.P. 2008. The KBS LTER site: Long-term ecological research in row crop agriculture. Available at http://lter.kbs.msu.edu (verified 23 June 2009). Kellogg Biological Station Long-Term Ecological Research Program, Michigan State Univ., East Lansing.

Rosenheim, J.A. 2001. Source–sink dynamics for a generalist insect predator in habitats with strong higher-order predation. Ecol. Monogr. 71:93–116.

Roughgarden, J., and Y. Iwasa. 1986. Dynamics of a metapopulation with space-limited subpopulations. Theor. Popul. Biol. 29:235–261.

Schimel, J.P., and J. Bennett. 2004. Nitrogen mineralization: Challenges of a changing paradigm. Ecology 85:591–602.

Schlesinger, W.H. 2005. Biogeochemistry. Elsevier, Amsterdam.

Smith, H.A., and W.E. Chaney. 2007. A survey of syrphid predators of *Nasonovia ribisnigri* in organic lettuce on the Central Coast of California. J. Econ. Entomol. 100:39–48.

Smithwick, E.A.H., M.C. Mack, M.G. Turner, F.S. Chapin, J. Zhu, and T.C. Balser. 2005. Spatial heterogeneity and soil nitrogen dynamics in a burned black spruce forest stand: Distinct controls at different scales. Biogeochemistry 76:517–537.

Snapp, S., G. Kanyama-Phiri, B. Kamanga, R. Gilbert, and K. Wellard. 2002. Farmer and researcher partnerships in Malawi: Developing soil fertility technologies for the near-term and far-term. Exp. Agric. 38:411–431.

Sooby, J., J. Landeck, and M. Lipson. 2007. National organic research agenda: 2007. Organic Farming and Research Foundation, Santa Cruz, CA.

Sovell, L.A., B. Vondracek, J.A. Frost, and K.G. Mumford. 2000. Impacts of rotational grazing and riparian buffers on physicochemical and biological characteristics of southeastern Minnesota, USA, streams. Environ. Manage. 6:629–641.

Steenwerth, K.L., L.E. Jackson, F.J. Calderon, M.R. Stromberg, and K.M. Scow. 2002. Soil microbial community composition and land use history in cultivated and grassland ecosystems of coastal California. Soil Biol. Biochem. 34:1599–1611.

Steinheimer, T.R., K.D. Scoggin, and L.A. Kramer. 1998. Agricultural chemical movement through a field-size watershed in Iowa: Subsurface hydrology and distribution of nitrate in groundwater. Environ. Sci. Technol. 32:1039–1047.

Temple, S.R., D.B. Friedman, O. Somasco, H. Ferris, K. Scow, and K. Klonsky. 1994. An interdisciplinary, experiment station-based participatory comparison of alternative crop management systems for California's Sacramento Valley. Am. J. Alternative Agric. 9:64–71.

Thomson, D.M. 2007. Do source–sink dynamics promote the spread of an invasive grass into a novel habitat? Ecology 88:3126–3134.

Turner, B.L., R.E. Kasperson, P.A. Matson, J.J. McCarthy, R.W. Corell, L. Christensen, N. Eckley, J.X. Kasperson, A. Luers, M.L. Martello, C. Polsky, A. Pulsipher, and A. Schiller. 2003. A framework for vulnerability analysis in sustainability science. Proc. Natl. Acad. Sci. USA 100:8074–8079.

USDA. 2009. National organic standards. Available at http://ecfr.gpoaccess.gov/cgi/t/text/text-idx?type=simple;c=ecfr;cc=ecfr;sid=4163ddc3518c1ffdc539675aed8efe33;region=DIV1;q1=national%20organic%20program;rgn=div5;view=text;idno=7;node=7%3A3.1.1.9.31 (verified 20 July 2009).

van der Werf, H.M.G., J. Tzilivakis, K. Lewis, and C. Basset-Mens. 2007. Environmental impacts of farm scenarios according to five assessment methods. Agric. Ecosyst. Environ. 18:327–338.

Viglizzo, E.F., A.J. Pordomingo, D. Buschiazzo, and M.G. Castro. 2005. A methodological approach to assess cross-scale relations and interactions in agricultural ecosystems of Argentina. Ecosystems 8:546–558.

Vila-Aiub, M.M., M.C. Balbi, P.E. Gundel, C.M. Ghersa, and S.B. Powles. 2007. Evolution of glyphosate-resistant Johnsongrass (*Sorghum halepense*) in glyphosate-resistant soybean. Weed Sci. 55:566–571.

Vogtmann, H. 1984. Organic farming practices and research in Europe. p. 19–36. *In* D.F. Bezdicek and J.F. Power (ed.) Organic farming: Current technology and its role in a sustainable agriculture. ASA Spec. Publ. 46. ASA, Madison, WI.

Vos, T. 2000. Visions of the middle landscape: Organic farming and the politics of nature. Agric. Human Values 17:245–256.

Wander, M.M., and G.A. Bollero. 1999. Soil quality assessment in Illinois. Soil Sci. Soc. Am. J. 63:961–971.

Wander, M.M., S.J. Traina, B.R. Stinner, and S.E. Peters. 1994. Organic and conventional management effects on biologically-active soil organic-matter pools. Soil Sci. Soc. Am. J. 58:1130–1139.

Wander, M.M., W. Yun, W.A. Goldstein, S. Aref, and S.A. Khan. 2007. Organic N and particulate organic matter fractions in organic and conventional farming systems with a history of manure application. Plant Soil 291:311–321.

Warner, K.D. 2006. Extending agroecology: Grower participation in partnerships is key to social learning. Renewable Agric. Food Syst. 21:84–94.

Westerman, P., M. Liebman, F.D. Menalled, A.H. Heggenstaller, R.G. Hartzler, and P.M. Dixon. 2005. Are many little hammers effective?- Velvetleaf (*Abutilon theophrasti*) population dynamics in two- and four-year crop rotation systems. Weed Sci. 53:382–392.

Systems Design

Crop Rotations
in Organic Production Systems

Paul Porter

Department of Agronomy and Plant Genetics, University of Minnesota, St. Paul

Although humans have been practicing agriculture for approximately 12,000 years (Rindos, 1984), documentation of the value of fallowing cropped land and of rotating crops does not date back that long. In his seminal book *Crops and Man*, Harlan (1975) devoted a chapter to views on the origins of agriculture, elaborating on domestication for religious reasons, domestication by crowding, agriculture by discovery, agriculture as an extension of gathering, and the concept of the geography of plant domestication. It is now believed that agriculture originated in multiple locations around the world over a short time frame relative to the formation of the earth and the appearance of *Homo sapiens* (Chapter 1, Francis and Van Wart, 2009, Table 1–1, this volume). Soils have had a long time to develop, and time is one of the five factors along with climate, organisms, parent material, and topography that impact soil development (Froth, 1990). Without soil, it can be argued, humans would have never occupied this planet.

The human population on earth at the time agriculture began was only about 4 million compared with more than 6300 million today. With such a small population in earlier times, there was little pressure on the land to produce. Once cropped land became less productive, it is quite probable that the early agriculturalists simply farmed neighboring, more productive land. Often this involved cutting the existing vegetation and burning it, a practice referred to as slash and burn agriculture (Cornell and Miller, 2007). Burning results in the deposition of plant nutrients back into the soil. After growing crops and removing some of the plant nutrients, farmers observed that soil fertility generally decreased. Additional factors negatively influencing soil productivity include increased erosion due to tillage of the soil and increased weed pressure if these pests are not adequately controlled. Still today, slash and burn agriculture practiced in tropical regions is a form of crop rotation whereby soil is fallowed from cropping for a period of time in order for it to regain productivity.

It is probably no coincidence that written records of crop rotation first appear as human population began its exponential growth (Fig. 3–1). Over a 4000-year span, from about 5000 to 1000 BCE, the human population expanded tenfold to 50 million people. It took about 2650 years, from about 1000 BCE to the year 1650, for it to again expand tenfold to 500 million people. Another tenfold expansion,

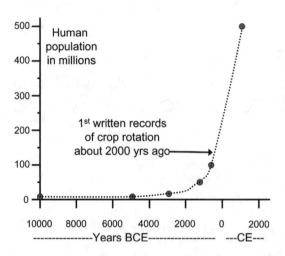

Fig. 3–1. Written records of crop rotation first appear as human population growth became exponential. Today's population is more than 6600 million, or 13 times the scale on the y-axis, which goes to only 500 million (see Chapter 1, Francis and Van Wart, 2009, Table 1–1, this volume, for more detailed numbers.)

to 5000 million people, occurred in just 337 years, from 1650 to 1987. Current estimates do not predict another twofold expansion in human population to over 10,000 million people. Instead the population is expected to peak at about 9500 million people within the next 50 years (Cohen, 2003). Clearly, the need for adequate land for agricultural production to feed the massive increase in human population has changed dramatically in the last 2000 years.

The Chinese recognized the value of crop rotations using legumes more than 2000 years ago (Pieters, 1927). At about the same time in Italy, Virgil wrote of the virtues of rotating small grains with legumes and of fallowing land from continuous cropping in the Mediterranean region (Gladstones, 1976). A Roman text written 2100 years ago noted that "some crops are to be planted not so much for the immediate yield as with a view to the following year" (Varro, 1913). Begun in the mid-1700s, the four-year Norfolk rotation, which consisted of wheat (*Triticum* spp.)–turnip (*Brassica rapa* subsp. *rapa*)–barley (*Hordeum vulgare* L.)–red clover (*Trifolium pratense* L.), contributed to more than doubling wheat yields in England (Pearson, 1967).

From the above discussion, it appears crop rotation came about by necessity. It was practiced for the benefits it provided. If these benefits are not seen or if they are achieved by other means, it should not be surprising if crop rotation is not practiced. In the case of modern, industrial agriculture, there was the belief that the need for crop rotation would evaporate as farmers controlled factors such as fertility, erosion, and weed management, thereby mitigating the necessity for crop rotation (Melsted, 1954). This has been more challenging than anticipated, and still today yield increases associated with crop rotation referred to as the *rotation effect* (Pierce and Rice, 1988) and *monoculture yield declines* (Sumner et al., 1990) are not well understood. Although widespread use of synthetic fertilizers and pesticides has occurred only for a short time segment in our agricultural history, this approach dominates current agricultural practices in industrialized countries. Organic producers, however, rely on crop rotations, and these practices are a mainstay of organic cropping systems.

Definition of Crop Rotation

A *cropping system* describes what crop or crops are grown in a particular location as well as how and why they are grown. A particular cropping system may be applied to an extensive geographic area, such as a semiarid region, or to a more restricted area, such as a single farm operation or field. Crop rotation constitutes one part of a cropping system; the precise pattern of rotation is determined only after the overall system has been defined (Chapman and Carter, 1976).

Crop rotations have both spatial and temporal dimensions. Reeves (1994) defined crop rotation as "a systematic or recurrent sequence of crops grown over a number of cropping seasons." Cropping seasons, rather than years, are considered the unit of time since in some areas the length of the growing season allows for more than one crop per year. Troeh et al. (1980) stated that "two or more crops grown in a repetitive sequence on the same land constitute a crop rotation." One problem with these definitions is that more often than not, a crop rotation as practiced by farmers is neither systematic nor repetitive.

While a strict definition of crop rotation may be elusive, the concept of crop rotation is easily distinguished from that of a monoculture, or the practice of growing the same crop on the same piece of land over multiple growing seasons. With annual plant species, there are few examples where monocultures have been sustainably practiced over the course of centuries. Probably the best exception to that statement is rice (*Oryza sativa* L.) grown in certain areas of Asia (Lu and Li, 2006). With perennial plant species, the concept of crop rotation is not normally discussed since crops such as grapes (*Vitis vinifera* L.) or olives (*Canarium* L.) can be grow for over a century on the same land, although systems may be diversified through planting of cover crops or intercropped annuals.

Crop rotations used by farmers are generally determined by a combination of ecology and economics. Ecological factors include the crop's suitability to edaphic, biotic, and climatic factors. In a given environment at a given point in time, there are often one or two crops that offer the greatest comparative advantage relative to other crops, and the comparative advantage is mainly a function of economic principles (Pearson, 1967). Before the 1950s and widespread use of the tractor, it was necessary to grow crops to feed animals that assisted with farming operations. This required the production of crops for both human and animal usage. For example, in the early 20th century in Louisiana, it was necessary to plant 0.8 ha (2 acres) of hay crops to feed the draft animals required to produce cotton on 0.4 ha (1 acre) of land. Since that time, agriculture has become much more specialized, draft animals have all but left the farm, and crop rotations have been simplified. By the 1990s, it was estimated that only 5 to 10 rotations were being used on over 80% of the cropland in the United States (Daberkow and Gill, 1989). These included the maize (*Zea mays* L.)–soybean [*Glycine max* (L.) Merr.] rotation in the Corn Belt; soybean rotated in a double-cropping system with winter wheat (*Triticum aestivum* L.) in the Piedmont and eastern Upland region; wheat and wheat–fallow rotation in the northern Great Plains; and rice–soybean rotation in the Mississippi Delta region. Reeves (1994) pointed out that "the role of government farm programs in creating comparative advantage for a crop to the point of discouraging crop rotation is illustrated by the fact that on farms enrolled only in the cotton commodity program, over 75% of the cotton (*Gossypium hirsutum*) is grown continuously." In the Midwest, maize and soybean production is so

% Land in Maize and Soybeans 1998

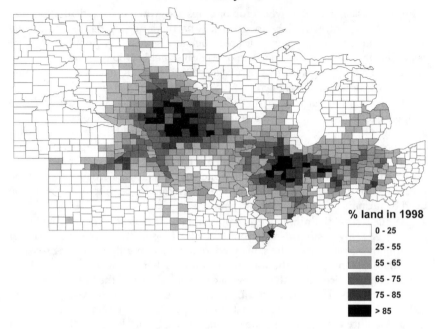

Fig. 3–2. Certain counties in the U.S. Midwest are so dominated by maize and soybean production that the infrastructure to produce other crops has diminished. (Source: modified data from USDA National Agricultural Statistics Service, 2008.)

pervasive that in some counties well over 75% of the total land area of the county is planted to one of these crops (Fig. 3–2), leaving little area for other crops or livestock alternatives.

Crop Rotations and the National Organic Standards

In "Subpart A—Definitions, § 205.1 Terms Defined" of the USDA National Organic Program (NOP) standards (USDA Agricultural Marketing Service, 2002), *crop rotation* is defined as "The practice of alternating the annual crops grown on a specific field in a planned pattern or sequence in successive crop years so that crops of the same species or family are not grown repeatedly without interruption on the same field. Perennial cropping systems employ means such as alley cropping, intercropping, and hedgerows to introduce biological diversity in lieu of crop rotation."

It is interesting to note the requirement for a "planned pattern." Accredited certification agencies require proper record keeping of the planned sequence of crops in each identified field. The farmer is not strictly required to adhere to the planned sequences; leeway is given in cases where changes to the planned sequences are justified. Examples include drought or other climatic conditions causing crop failure in one season or financial considerations whereby one small grain crop is substituted for another.

It is also interesting that the NOP standards do not specify requirements for crop rotation length or what specific sequence of crops constitutes an acceptable crop rotation. The NOP standards leave further definition up to the discretion of the accredited certification agencies, except to state in "Subpart C—Organic Crop, Wild Crop, Livestock and Handling Requirements, §205.205 Crop Rotation Practice Standard":

> The producer must implement a crop rotation including but not limited to sod, cover crops, green manure crops, and catch crops that provide the following functions that are applicable to the operation:
> (a) Maintain or improve soil organic matter content;
> (b) Provide for pest management in annual and perennial crops;
> (c) Manage deficient or excess plant nutrients; and
> (d) Provide erosion control. (USDA Agricultural Marketing Service, 2002)

The intent of the NOP standards is to promote crop rotations that improve the soil, minimize weed and other pest problems, and provide for erosion control. It is up to the accredited certification agency to determine that the farmer is implementing a sound crop rotation on the land that is farmed. Typically the crop rotation is assessed on a field-by-field basis. The standards do not state how frequently a crop can appear in the rotation. Also, the standards do not state that a farmer must include a cover crop or green manure crops in the rotation. Such practices may not be advisable in certain situations, as in dry years on the Great Plains of western Nebraska. However, these farming practices would be applicable to the farming operation in areas of higher rainfall only several hundred kilometers to the east, and hence the need for accredited certification agencies to have a flexible interpretation of the NOP standards. As demonstrated in the next section, there are valid reasons for the organic farmer to utilize appropriate crop rotations. Often failure to pay close attention to the crop rotation one uses can result in future frustrations with issues related to soil fertility, weed and pest management, and/or crop performance.

Importance of Proper Crop Rotation

Many useful articles have been written on crop rotations for conventional systems (Daberkow and Gill, 1989; Karlen et al., 1994) and for sustainable and organic production systems (Francis and Clegg, 1990; Kuepper and Gegner, 2004; Magdoff and Van Es, 2000). The importance of proper crop rotation in organic production systems cannot be overemphasized, as it can strongly influence the sustainability of the farming operation.

Some of the more important beneficial effects that can be obtained from a well-planned crop rotation include the following:

- improved soil fertility
- improvements in soil tilth and aggregate stability
- soil water management
- reduction of soil erosion
- reduced insect and disease problems
- reduction of allelopathic or phytotoxic effects

Cover Crops

The benefits of managing cover crops in the crop rotation have been well summarized (Clark, 2007). Cover crops are grown primarily for future contributions to the system. These functionalities can include improved weed management (e.g.., through increased weed seed depravation, increased nutrient and light competition), improved soil quality (e.g., reduced soil compaction due to cover crop root systems, modified nutrient cycling and/or availability, reduced surface runoff), and improved water use efficiencies (e.g., reduced evaporation from soil surface, increased transpiration through carbon fixation).

Cover crops frequently are used to provide interim soil cover in the cropping sequence. They are usually planted when the main cash crops are not grown, such as fall or winter, but occasionally are interplanted with the cash crops. The cover crop may be grazed or returned to the soil as green manure. Rye (*Secale cereale* L.), wheat, clover (*Trifolium* spp. and other), vetch (*Vicia* spp.) and Austrian winter pea (*Pisum sativum* L.) are common cover crops. Cover crops are best suited to humid areas or where irrigation is available. Cover crops are less suitable for drier regions because they consume water needed for the following main cash crop.

Soil Nitrogen

Legumes in the rotation can be used to increase the available soil nitrogen. Symbiotic nitrogen-fixing bacteria called *rhizobia* form nodules on the roots of legume plants and convert or fix atmospheric nitrogen to plant-available organic nitrogen. The amount of nitrogen fixed varies with species, available soil nitrogen, and many other factors. Fixed nitrogen not removed during plant harvest becomes available to succeeding crops as the legume tissues undergo microbial decomposition. A legume is typically followed by a high N-demanding crop such as maize or wheat. Legumes may be used less in lower rainfall areas or on vegetable farms that have access to animal manures.

Soil Tilth and Structure

Many farmers who rotate crops notice the improvement in tilth or friability of soil following alfalfa (*Medicago sativa* L.) or other sod crops. Increased aggregate stability reduces the tendency of the soil to puddle or crust, increases rate of water infiltration under certain conditions, and can also reduce wind erosion.

Soil Moisture

Crop rotation can lead to greater overall efficiency in soil water utilization. Spring-seeded small grains usually deplete soil water a meter deep. In contrast, sunflower (*Helianthus* spp.), safflower (*Carthamus tinctorius* L.), maize, and sugar beet (*Beta vulgaris* L.) are deep-rooted crops that can deplete soil water to depths as much as 2 m. Therefore, deep-rooted crops such as sunflower following small grains can take advantage of the extra reserve of deep moisture and also any nitrogen that was positionally unavailable to a shallow-rooted crop. Alfalfa and some clovers, also deep-rooted crops, can be used to dry up saline seeps and other wet areas. Depletion of soil water in saline areas prevents the accumulation of salts on the surface, permits movement of the salts downward by leaching, and allows recropping to a cash crop such as wheat. Deep- and shallow-rooted crops are often rotated because it is felt that this practice improves nutrient scavenging and use efficiency. Even where erosion is not a serious hazard, organic farmers avoid continuous row cropping.

Soil Erosion

Crop rotations combined with recommended tillage practices can play an important role in reducing wind and water erosion. Solid seeded crops such as small grains provide more protection against water erosion than row crops. Permanent crops such as hay or pasture provide even more protection against erosion. Management of crops to provide sufficient residue throughout the year is essential for satisfactory control of both wind and water erosion. No-till or minimum-till farming is highly desirable as a conservation practice, but crop rotation must be used to reduce the buildup of pests, including insects, pathogens, and weeds.

Insect Control

Some insects can be controlled entirely or in part with a proper crop rotation. Insect populations and associated problems can become greater within a region where only one or two crops are continuously grown, in contrast to a region where several crops are grown in rotation. Some insects such as the European corn borer [*Ostrinia nubilalis* (Hübner)], certain weevils (many species), and others readily migrate to nearby or distant fields. Therefore, only partial control can be obtained by rotation. Increasing field isolation from fields seeded to the same crop the previous year will often increase the effectiveness of crop rotation as an insect control method.

Disease Control

Crop rotation has tremendous potential for reducing and often preventing the transmission of disease. Care must be taken in selecting crop sequences that avoid successive crops that are susceptible to the same pathogens.

Advantages and Disadvantages of Crop Rotations

Advantages of a proper crop rotation are multiple, and this is why they are required for certification in organic farming. Among the advantages, a proper cropping sequence can help:

- maintain soil fertility,
- reduce soil erosion,
- control insect and mite pests,
- reduce pest build-up,
- prevent diseases, and
- control weeds

A major negative of a crop rotation may include forcing the farmer to grow crops that are not profitable in the short term. In addition, some crops in the rotation may take more time, money, and skill than the farmer is willing to invest. These limitations should not be underestimated. Proper crop rotations require additional planning and management skills, increasing the complexity of farming. Often farmers transitioning into organic production do not have the knowledge or equipment necessary to grow certain crops. They may not know the markets for those crops, or those markets may be less defined and reliable than for other crops that are more familiar.

General Crop Rotation Principles

Magdoff and Van Es (2000) provide an excellent list of general principles to consider when designing a crop rotation:

- Reduce the likelihood of insects, diseases, and nematodes becoming a problem; don't grow the same annual crop or a closely related species in the same field in succession.
- Follow a legume forage crop (alfalfa or clover) with a high nitrogen demanding crop (maize) to take advantage of the fixed nitrogen.
- Grow less nitrogen demanding crops (small grains) in the second or third year after the legume forage crop.
- Use crop sequences that aid in controlling weeds; over time, change up early-planted cool-season crops with later-planted warm-season crops. Also, sequence widely spaced row crops with drilled crops, and annual crops with perennial crops that are mowed or grazed.
- Respect farm-site specificity, especially on sloping land or highly erosive soils, and emphasize perennial crops in these sites.
- Alter crop root depth over time: use certain deep-rooted crops such as alfalfa and sunflower to scavenge the subsoil for nutrients and water.
- Include crops such as maize and sorghum (*Sorghum bicolor*) that leave a significant amount of residue on the soil.
- Include cropping sequences that alter the tillage required such as drilled soybean into rye.
- When growing a wide mix of crops—such as on vegetable farms—group plant families into blocks and/or plant early-season crops together.

  Other useful tips in planning crop rotations include the following:
- Know the characteristics of your crops to make sure that each crop in a sequence belongs to a different family than the previous one.
- Make a list of the crops you want to grow by also taking into consideration the market demand for the produce.
- Grow legumes before grains or cereals.
- Practice green manuring with cover crops.
- Always keep good farm records.

Designing a Crop Rotation

We would like to think that the sequence of crops in a rotation is fixed and repetitive and thus can be projected as many years into the future as desired. Rotations can be designed to allow the farmer to grow approximately the same area of each crop each year from a constant number of hectares. This can be achieved by dividing their farmland into as many parts as there are years in the rotation. A four-year rotation, for example, requires four fields or groups of fields of fairly equal size and productive capacity. The example below highlights the challenges and limitations a farmer faces when implementing an effective crop rotation.

Let us look at the practical implications of trying to design an effective crop rotation on a typical, yet simplified, farm in the U.S. Midwest that has no livestock. Assume the farm has a total of 128 ha (320 acres) consisting of a quarter section (64 ha or 160 acres), an "80" (32 ha or 80 acres) and two "40s" (16 ha or 40 acres each). These land area measures are used as it was common at time of European settlement to acquire a "quarter section" or multiple thereof in the Midwest. In this example, it is easy to define with two-crop and four-crop rotations where each crop can be grown (Table 3–1). In the two-crop rotation, each crop is planted on 64 ha, and in the four-crop rotation, each crop is planted on 32 ha. It is considerably less convenient to define the three-crop and five-crop rotations. With these rotations, one must either plant more than one crop in a portion of various fields or resort to planting an unequal number of hectares to each crop. As shown in Table 3–1, for the three-crop rotation, crop 1 is planted on double the number of hectares as crops 2 and 3; for the five-crop rotation, crops 1 and 2 are planted on double the number of hectares as crops 3, 4, and 5. In certain situations, having twice as many hectares of certain crops compared with other crops may not be desirable. This will depend on prices each year as well as the biology of fields and positive reasons for a specific rotation sequence.

Generally, two-crop rotations are not allowed as an acceptable organic sequence under the NOP standards. Thus, the commonly practiced maize–soybean rotation does not qualify as an acceptable organic system when these two crops are the only ones in the succession. A three-crop rotation consisting of soybean–maize–small grain is an allowed rotation, as it incorporates a solid-seeded crop with two row crops. A four-crop rotation of a three-year maize–soybean–oat (*Avena sativa* L.)/alfalfa rotation, a four-year maize–soybean–oat/alfalfa–alfalfa rotation, and a five-year maize–soybean–oat/alfalfa–alfalfa–alfalfa rotation are all acceptable rotations. One could ask if a three-crop, two-year rotation of maize/ rye–soybean is an acceptable rotation when practiced in succession. The answer is site specific and depends on the rules and regulations of the accredited certification agency. Most accredited certification agencies would advise a broader rotation—one that would have no one crop grown more frequently than 50 to 60% of the time. In the five-year maize–soybean–oat/alfalfa–alfalfa–alfalfa rotation, alfalfa is in the field in 6 of 10 years, whereas in the two-year maize/rye–soybean rotation both maize and soybean are grown five times in 10 years.

In the first few years of the NOP standards, some accredited certification agencies had restrictions on the frequency of certain types of crops in a rotation. They would require, for example, that having row crops more frequently than every two of three years would not be allowed, or that continually growing one crop with a fallow season in between would not be allowed. Such requirements are not spelled out in the NOP standards and thus are no longer allowed by the NOP. The accredited certification agencies can provide these statements as suggested guidelines to aid farmers in thinking through functional rotations. What the accredited certification agencies require is that there is an ongoing plan that

Table 3–1. Examples of crop rotations on a 128-ha (320-acre) farm with two to five crops (labeled 1–5).

Field	Field size	Crops			
		2-crop rotation	3-crop rotation	4-crop rotation	5-crop rotation
	ha				
A	64	1	1	1, 2	1, 2
B	32	2	2	3	3
C	16	2	3	4	4
D	16	2	3	4	5

shows that the farmer is addressing the soil building functions intended by the NOP standards. As one inspector stated, "Crop rotation is one of the greyest areas, yet it is one of the most important areas in terms of managing weed and fertility challenges that organic producers face" (Jim Boots, personal communication, 2007).

Crop Rotations: Three Case Studies

In this section three certified organic farms in Minnesota and their crop rotation histories over a five-year time span are examined. None of the three farms has a major livestock component, and thus they do not represent the broad spectrum of organic operations. However, the three farms are perhaps typical organic farms in that they show how diverse certified operations can be even within a relatively small geographical area. Annual precipitation typically ranges from 60 to 80 cm; however, it is not uncommon for it to be half or double those amounts.

Farm A is located in north-central Minnesota and has been certified organic for 10 years. The farm has no livestock, and until it converted to organic, the primary cash crop was sugar beet followed distantly by small grains (Tables 3–2 and 3–3). A number of factors contributed to the decision of the farm family to convert

Table 3–2. Field size and crops grown on Farm A in north-central Minnesota from 2003 through 2007.

Field	Field size		Crop 2003	2004	2005	2006	2007
	ha (acres)	%					
1	62 (153)	12.8	Wheat	Soybean	Buckwheat/rye†	Soybean	Barley/rye
2	93 (231)	19.3	Soybean	Wheat	Soybean	Wheat	Soybean
3	61 (150)	12.5	Alfalfa	Wheat	Soybean	Wheat/popcorn†	Wheat
4	31 (76)	6.4	Soybean	Wheat	Buckwheat/rye	Soybean	Bar/rye
5	62 (153)	12.8	Soybean	Maize	Alfalfa	Alfalfa	Alfalfa
6	25 (63)	5.3	Fallow	Soybean	Oat	Soybean	Wheat
7	61 (150)	12.5	Alfalfa	Alfalfa	Alfalfa	Maize	Soybean
8	62 (153)	12.8	Wheat	Soybean	Wheat	Pea/rye	Soybean
9	27 (67)	5.6	Popcorn	Soybean	Oat/rye	Soybean	Fallow
Total	484 (1196)	100					

† "/" indicates the following crop was relay cropped (in the case of rye) with the cash crop.

Table 3–3. Percentage of land devoted to specific crops on Farm A in north-central Minnesota from 2003 through 2007. Over the five years, the farm averaged 35% of land in grasses, 36% in soybean, 18% in alfalfa, and 11% in fallow (or a buckwheat or rye cover crop).

Crop	% of farmer's land 2003	2004	2005	2006	2007	Avg.
Maize	5.6	12.8	0	12.5	0	6.2
Soybean	38.5	36.5	31.9	30.0	44.6	36.3
Wheat	25.6	38.2	12.8	19.3	17.8	22.7
Barley	0	0	0	0	19.1	3.8
Oat	0	0	10.9	0	0	2.2
Alfalfa	25.1	12.5	25.3	12.8	12.8	17.7
Fallow or gm†	5.3	0	19.1	25.3	5.6	11.0
Buckwheat	0	0	(19.1)	0	0	(3.8)
Rye	0	0	(24.7)	(12.8)	(19.1)	(11.4)
Total	100	100	100	100	100	100

† gm, green manure. In 2006 in Field 3 the wheat crop and a subsequent popcorn crop were green manured due to poor stands.

to organic production strategies, including disease pressure buildup on the sugar beet land and concern over pesticide use. Farmer A grows crops on 484 ha of certified organic land and has an additional 8 ha of cropped buffer land. Most of the land farmed is owned, and what is not owned is cash rented on a stable long-term basis. All fields are located within 20 km of each other. The predominant crops grown in the area include small grains, some sugar beet and maize, and an increasing amount of soybean. Soil fertility is inherently high, but cropping concerns include years in which spring operations are delayed due to cold, wet soils. Most of the family income is from the farm.

Farm B is located in southwest Minnesota and has been certified organic for over 25 years. This farm is managed by a committed organic farmer who is a spokesman for the organic community. The farm is partially dependent on outside employment to sustain the family. In addition, some of the farm income is derived from a conventional confinement hog operation in cooperation with a relative. Farmer B grows crops on 129 ha of certified organic land that he owns. All fields are located within 5 km of each other (Tables 3–4 and 3–5). The predominant crops grown in the area include maize and soybean. Of the three farms discussed, this one is the most prone to summer droughts due to geographic location and soil types.

Farm C may not be considered by some to be a farm at all. It is Cornercopia, the Student Organic Farm, a student-run operation associated with the Minnesota Agricultural Experiment Station of the University of Minnesota (Ashling et al., 2006; http://sof.cfans.umn.edu/). Farm C consists of about 0.5 ha of land (Table 3–6). It is located in the center of Minneapolis–St. Paul, a metropolitan area of more than 2 million people. The land has been farmed for over a century, but in

Table 3–4. Field size and crops grown on Farm B in southwest Minnesota from 2003 through 2007.

Field	Field size		2003	2004	2005	2006	2007
	ha (acres)	%					
1	7.3 (18)	5.6	Oat	Alfalfa	Alfalfa	Alfalfa	Soybean & pea†
2	12.1 (30)	9.4	Soybean	Wheat	Barley & flax	Flax & soybean	Pea
3	5.7 (14)	4.4	Soybean	Wheat	Flax	Alfalfa	Alfalfa
4	14.6 (36)	11.3	Alfalfa & soybean	Wheat & alfalfa	Maize	Soybean & oat	Bar & soybean
5	10.1 (25)	7.8	Maize	Soybean	Oat/alfalfa‡	Maize	Soybean
6	4.0 (10)	3.1	Maize	Oat/alfalfa	Soybean	Maize	Oat/clover
7	7.3 (18)	5.6	Alfalfa	Maize	Soybean	Pea/clover	Maize
8	9.3 (23)	7.2	Maize	Soybean	Barley/alfalfa	Alfalfa	Alfalfa
9	7.7 (19)	6.0	Wheat/clover	Maize	Soybean	Oat/alfalfa	Alfalfa
10	13.0 (32)	10.0	Maize & flax	Soybean	Bar/alfalfa	Pea/clover	Maize
11	12.1 (30)	9.4	Soybean	Maize	Pea & barley/ alfalfa	Soybean	Barley & oat
12	10.1 (25)	7.8	Soybean	Oat/alfalfa	alfalfa	Alfalfa	Alfalfa
13	15.8 (39)	12.2	Alfalfa	Alfalfa	Alfalfa	Maize & soybean	Soy & flax
Total	129.1 (319)						

† "&" indicates the field was split and two crops were grown on that acreage.

‡ "/" indicates the following crop was either underseeded (in the case of clover and alfalfa) or relay cropped (in the case of rye) with the cash crop.

Table 3–5. Percentage of land devoted to specific crops on Farm B in southwest Minnesota from 2003 through 2007. Over the five years, the farm averaged 44% of land in grasses, 25% in soybean, 5% in pea with unharvested underseeded cover crops grown on 16% of the land (alfalfa and clover).

Crop	% of farmer's land					
	2003	2004	2005	2006	2007	Avg.
Oats	5.6	11.0	7.8	11.6	7.8	8.8
Soybean	36.7	25.1	14.7	25.7	22.6	25.1
Alfalfa	23.5	23.5	25.7	25.1	25.4	24.8
Maize	23.2	21.0	11.3	17.2	15.7	17.6
Wheat	60	19.4	0	0	0	5.0
Flax	5.0	0	9.1	4.7	6.0	5.0
Barley	0	0	26.6	0	10.3	7.5
Peas	0	0	4.7	15.7	12.2	6.6
Total	100	100	100	100	100	100
Underseeded cover crop						
Alfalfa	23.5	11.0	30.1	6.0	9.4	11.3
Clover	6.0	0	0	15.7	3.1	5.0

Table 3–6. Some of the crops grown since 2004 on the 0.5-ha Farm C. The rotations with these crops are detailed in the text.

Vegetables

Azuki bean (*Vigna angularis*)	Garlic (*Allium sativum*)	Pumpkin (*Cucurbita pepo*)
Beans (*Phaseolus* sp.)	Gourds (*Cucurbita* sp.)	Purslane (*Portulaca oleracea*)
Beets (*Beta vulgaris*)	Kohlrabi (*Brassica oleracea*)	Radish (*Raphanu sativus*)
Bok choy (*Brassica chinensis*)	Leeks (*Allium ampeloprasum*)	Soybean (*Glycine max*)
Broccoli (*Brassica oleracea*)	Lettuce (*Lactuca sativa*)	Spinach (*Spinacia oleracea*)
Cabbage (*Brassica oleracea*)	Melons (*Citrullus* sp.)	Squash (*Cucurbita* sp.)
Carrot (*Daucus carota*)	Mushrooms (*Laccaria* sp.)	Sunflower (*Helianthus annuus*)
Cauliflower (*Brassica oleracea*)	Onion (*Allium* sp.)	Sweet corn (*Zea mays*)
Cucumber (*Cucumis sativus*)	Parsnip (*Pastinaca sativa*)	Swiss chard (*Beta vulgaris*)
Dandelion (*Taraxacum* sp.)	Peas (*Pisum sativum*)	Tomato (*Lycopersicon esculentum*)
Eggplant (*Solanum melongena*)	Pepper (*Capsicum* sp.)	Turnip (*Brassica rapa*)
Fava bean (*Vicia faba*)	Potato (*Solanum tuberosum*)	Zucchini (*Cucurbita pepo*)

Perennial guild

Apples (*Malus domestica*)	Grape (*Vitis* sp.)	Rhubarb (*Rheum rhabarbarum*)
Asparagus (*Asparagus officinalis*)	Raspberry (*Rubus* sp.)	Serviceberry (*Amelanchier* sp.)
Blackberry (*Rubus* sp.)	Strawberry (*Fragaria* sp.)	Chokecherry (*Prunus virginiana*)

Cover crops and green manures

Alfalfa (*Medicago sativa*)	Clovers (*Trifoliumm* sp.)	Rye (*Secale cereale*)
Buckwheat (*Fagopyrum esculentum*)	Oats (*Avena sativa*)	Wheat (*Triticum aestivum*)

Cut flowers

Amaranth (*Amaranthus* sp.)	Iris (*Iris* sp.)	Marigold (*Calendula* sp.)
Cone flower (*Echinacea* sp.)	Larkspur (Delphinium sp.)	Zinnia (*Zinnia* sp.)

Herbs and spices

Basil (*Ocimum basilicum*)	Cilantro (*Coriandrum sativum*)	Oregano (*Origanum vulgare*)
Chives (*Allium schoenoprasum*)	Dill (*Anethum graveolens*)	Sage (*Salvia* sp.)

2004 it began the transition to becoming a certified organic operation. Prior to that, it was typically planted to research plots of maize, soybeans, or small grains. It has a history of receiving a large amount of composted animal manure and has elevated P and K levels.

By evaluating the cropping patterns on these three farms, we can begin to understand the complexity of designing a crop rotation—in fact, we will see that perhaps it is a misnomer to refer to "a crop rotation." From the accredited certification agency's and the farmer's perspectives, Farm A consists of 9 fields that range from 25 to 93 ha in size, Farm B consists of 13 fields that range from 4 to 16 ha in size, and Farm C consists of 1 field of 0.5 ha. In evaluating the crops grown on these different fields over the past five years, we realize that there is no distinct pattern of crop rotation common among the 9 fields of Farm A, the 13 fields of Farm B, or within the 1 field of Farm C.

Over a five-year period from 2003 to 2007, Farm A grew maize, soybean, wheat, barley, oat, and alfalfa as cash crops. Soybean, the main cash crop, was grown on 36% of the acreage and was planted on all nine fields over the five-year period. Wheat and alfalfa were grown on 23 and 18% of the acreage and were grown on six and three of the nine fields, respectively. Small grains were grown on seven of the nine fields, and maize, which accounted for 6% of the acreage, was grown on three fields. The maize and most of the soybeans are grown on 76-cm row widths, while all other crops are either drilled or broadcast seeded. None of the nine fields had similar crop rotations. The largest field, Field 2, was planted to soybean–wheat–soybean–wheat–soybean and was the only field that was planted to this cropping sequence. Over the five-year period, 11% of the acreage was fallowed or green manured. Twice, Farmer A bare-fallowed fields, primarily to manage a heavy weed pressure due to a weather-related lack of timely weed control (too wet). Once a field planted to wheat, then popcorn, was green manured due to weather-related poor stands. On two fields, buckwheat (*Fagopyrum esculentum* Moench) was planted as a green manure plow-down—in part to cycle nutrients and in part to help control weeds. Since 2005 rye was fall-planted as a cover crop after either a cash small-grain crop or the buckwheat green manure. Farmer A has been successful with drilling soybeans directly into the rye cover crop then shredding the standing rye once it reaches anthesis. No subsequent weed control, such as cultivation, was done in the drilled soybeans, which constituted almost a third of the total soybean acreage. For a more detailed description of this practice, see Porter et al. (2005).

Over a five-year period from 2003 to 2007, Farm B grew eight cash crops: maize, soybean, alfalfa, field peas (*Pisum* spp.), wheat, oats barley, and flax (*Linum usitatissimum* L.). Clover and alfalfa were also grown as companion green manure crops. Similar to Farm A, maize and soybean were grown on 76-cm row widths, and all other crops were drilled or broadcast seeded. Soybean, the main cash crop, was grown on 25% of the acreage and was planted on all 13 fields over the five-year period. Alfalfa was grown on 25% of the acreage and was grown on 12 of the 13 fields. Small grains (wheat, oats, and barley) were grown on 11 of the 13 fields, maize on 9 fields, flax on 4 fields, and peas on 5 fields. Small grains, maize, flax, and peas constituted 21, 18, 5, and 6% of the acreage, respectively. Farmer B never bare-fallowed any of his fields. None of the 13 fields had similar crop rotations over the five-year period. Complicating the farming practices even further, each year at least 1 of the 13 fields was split and two crops were grown on that particular field—effectively meaning Farmer B managed more that 13 parcels of land each year.

The one field in Farm C began its transition to certified organic production with a fall-planted rye cover crop in September 2004. Previously, the land had been maintained with conventional agronomic practices and was planted to soybean in 2003 and a canola (*Brassica napus*) green manure crop in 2004. In 2005 about a third of the acreage was planted to a large number of vegetables, about a third was converted to a "perennial guild," and on the remainder of the acreage the rye was harvested as grain. On the acreage planted to vegetables, elaborate plans were made to grow plant families in 42 beds approximately 1.2-m wide by 18-m long with mowed rye alleyways of approximately 0.5 by 18 m. The practice was a modification of Eliot Coleman's eight-year rotation (Coleman, 1995; Kuepper and Gegner, 2004) with a seven-year rotation of these plant families: nightshades, root crops, maize, leafy greens, brassicas, cucurbits, and legumes. During the 2005 harvest, it was realized that the harvest of the various vegetables was complicated by the fact that they were planted in multiple locations and thus difficult to harvest efficiently. In 2006 the portion of land devoted to vegetable production expanded and the concept of family blocks was initiated, where each family block was approximately 12 by 18 m. In 2007 the basic seven-year rotation was still followed, and chickens in cages approximately 2 by 4 m were included in the weedy fallow–green manure sections of the rotation. The perennial guild is described in more detail by Westmoreland (2006). As its motto "Growing to learn, learning to grow" (Ashling et al., 2006) suggests, Farm C has a strong educational component, and it struggles with the need to balance producing only a relatively few crop species of high monetary value with the need to plant and grow a larger number of crops with a multiple of techniques for the benefit of learning about those species and techniques.

In summary, it is difficult to easily describe the rotation each of the three case study farms uses. Each uses a multitude of rotations based on the site-specific nature of the fields within the farms. Farm A and Farm B both focus on soybeans and alfalfa with small grains or maize in their rotations, but the exact rotations used vary from field to field. Farm C is a vegetable operation whose manager tries to rotate crops based on crop families, but because it is still relatively new and has multiple objectives, the crop rotations it uses is still evolving.

Crop Rotations during Transition

Crop rotation is perhaps the most important management technique or strategy available to the organic farmer because it helps address soil fertility as well as pest management issues. Often the biggest challenges during transition are maintaining an adequate supply of nitrogen for optimum crop growth and keeping weeds under control while at the same time minimizing economic hardships associated with the transition. It is important to carefully plan how to accomplish the goals of effectively using crops and green manures in a rotation.

The transition period is typically 36 months from the last application of a prohibited substance (USDA Agricultural Marketing Service, 2002). Depending on timing of harvest, the transition period may be fulfilled in the second or the third cropping year. In either case it is critical to know which crop will be the first that can be marketed as certified organic and thus qualified to receive an associated price premium. It is not uncommon for farmers transitioning to organic to grow crops that they have never before grown or grew many years ago. Often it is necessary to learn about the marketing of these crops and at the same time to learn about their agronomics.

As pointed out in *Transitioning to Organic Production* (Sustainable Agriculture Network, 2007), there are several approaches farmers can take when changing to this new production system, and each approach has its appeal. Some farmers prefer to transition one field at a time while others prefer to go "cold turkey" with their entire farm. Farmers transitioning a field at a time into organic production have the advantage of going through the initial years of transition with a perennial crop such as alfalfa, whereas the farmers going cold turkey probably should not be planting their entire area to just one crop. The downside of transitioning a field at a time into organic production is that it requires a considerably longer time to convert the entire farm to organic. Regardless of approach, it is necessary to have a well-planned crop rotation strategy for each field that will be transitioned.

Some farmers begin the transition years with cash crops that require less nitrogen and can be effectively managed to control weeds. Studies have shown that with proper weed management, soybeans can be planted in the first year of a transition with no declines in yields. Maize, on the other hand, is not as good a transition crop because it requires high levels of nitrogen and more timely weed management (Sustainable Agriculture Network, 2007). Avoiding consecutive years of row cropping during the conversion to organic production could prevent weed outbreaks and maintain system productivity. Grass–legume mixtures provide good cover and supply nitrogen, but if the soils are low in organic matter, it may be advisable to incorporate the mixtures instead of cutting them for hay.

Conclusions

During the transition years, it is important to strive for balance between maintaining soil health and producing economically profitable yields. Other considerations for the rotation employed during transition include the following:

- Does the rotation match the crop needs for fertility? It is important to have crops with differing root depths so they can access different nutrient zones in the soil profile.
- Does the rotation have sufficient diversity so that risks will be minimized? Risks include the transition to nonchemical pest management that must utilize systems design as a major strategy.
- Does it provide adequate weed management? It is important to plan enough diversity and high-enough planted crop density to suppress major weed species and allow for cultivation at appropriate states.

A final piece of advice for those considering what rotations to use during the transition to organic production is to keep the rotation as simple as possible and to think in whole farm terms. There is no need for an elaborate crop rotation that includes many new crops not familiar to the farmer. Crop rotation, as with life, is a journey—not a destination. Experience leads to the best crop sequence for a given farm and field and in a larger sense, for meeting the goals of the farm family. This represents an ecological approach to design of rotations, including the social dimensions and needs of people, a key species in the agroecosystem.

Discussion Questions

1. Agriculture is thought to have begun about 12,000 years ago, but the first evidence of crop rotation is slightly over 2000 years ago. List several reasons why they did not occur concurrently.

2. Why do accredited certification agencies have a flexible interpretation of the National Organic Program (NOP) standards with respect to crop rotation? Who decides what is acceptable and why?

3. Explain several benefits of a proper crop rotation, giving details on the mechanisms that are involved in soil fertility, weed and other pest management, and economic resilience.

4. Explain several disadvantages of crop rotation, including biological, economic, and environmental concerns.

5. Explain why a crop rotation a farmer practices often are found to be neither systematic nor repetitive.

6. What are rotation effects and why are the mechanisms of this phenomenon so difficult to research and understand? What are the most likely causes of a rotation effect? Can this effect be either negative or positive, and why?

References

Ashling, J., C. Tchida, A. Markhart, and P. Porter. 2006. Origin of Cornercopia, the University of Minnesota Student Organic Farm. J. Hunger Environ. Nutr. 1:27–42.

Chapman, S.R., and L.P. Carter. 1976. Crop production: Principles and practices. W.H. Freeman, San Francisco, CA.

Clark, A (ed.) 2007. Managing cover crops profitably. 3rd ed. Available at http://www.sare.org/publications/covercrops/covercrops.pdf (verified 24 June 2009). Handbook Series Book 3. Susatinable Agriculture Network, Beltsville, MD.

Cohen, J.E. 2003. Human population: The next half century. Science 302:1172–1175.

Coleman, E. 1995. The new organic grower: A master's manual of tools and techniques for the home and market gardener. Chelsea Green, White River Junction, VT.

Cornell, J., and M. Miller. 2007. Slash and burn. Available at http://www.eoearth.org/article/slash_and_burn (verified 24 June 2009). In C.J. Cleveland (ed.) Encyclopedia of Earth. Environmental Information Coalition, National Council for Science and the Environment, Washington, DC.

Daberkow, S., and M. Gill. 1989. Common crop rotations among major field crops. p. 34–40. In Agricultural resources: Inputs situation and outlook report. AR-15. USDA, Economic Research Service, Washington, DC.

Francis, C.A., and M.D. Clegg. 1990. Crop rotations in sustainable production systems. p. 107–122. In C.A. Edwards, R. Lal, P. Madden, R.H. Miller, and G. House (ed.) Sustainable agricultural systems. Soil and Water Conservation Soc., Ankeny, IA.

Francis, C., and J. Van Wart. 2009. History of organic farming and certification. p. 3–18. In C. Francis (ed.) Ecology in organic farming systems. Agron. Monogr. 54. ASA, CSSA, and SSSA, Madison, WI. (This volume.)

Froth, H.D. 1990. Fundamentals of soil science. 8th ed. John Wiley & Sons, New York.

Gladstones, J.S. 1976. The Mediterranean white lupin. J. Agric. West. Aust. 17:70–74.

Harlan, J.R. 1975. Crops and man. ASA, Madison WI.

Karlen, D.L., G.E. Varvel, D.G. Bullock, and R.M. Cruse. 1994. Crops rotations for the 21st century. Adv. Agron. 53:1–45.

Kuepper, G., and L. Gegner. 2004. An overview of organic crop production: Planned crop rotation. Available at http://attra.ncat.org/attra-pub/organiccrop/tools2.html (verified 24 June 2009). ATTRA Publ. IP170. Appropriate Technology Transfer for Rural Areas, Fayetteville, AR.

Lu, J., and X. Li. 2006. Review of rice–fish-farming systems in China: One of the globally important ingenious agricultural heritage systems (GIAHS). Aquaculture 260:106–113.

Magdoff, F., and H. Van Es. 2000. Crop rotations. p. 99–108. *In* Building soils for better crops. 2nd ed. Handbook Series Book 4. SARE Outreach, Beltsville, MD.

Melsted, S.W. 1954. New concepts of management of Corn Belt soils. Adv. Agron. 6:121–142.

National Agricultural Statistics Service. 1998. USDA.

Pearson, L.C. 1967. Principles of agronomy. Reinhold, New York.

Pierce, J.J., and C.W. Rice. 1988. Crop rotation and its impact on efficiency of water and nitrogen use. p. 21–42. In W.L. Hargrove (ed.) Cropping strategies for efficient use of water and nitrogen. ASA Spec. Publ. 51. ASA, Madison, WI.

Pieters, A.J. 1927. Green manuring principles and practices. John Wiley & Sons, New York.

Porter, P., G. Feyereisen, J. De Bruin, and G. Johnson. 2005. No-till organic soybean production following a fall-planted rye cover crop. p. 26–30. *In* U. Köpke, U. Niggli, D. Neuhoff, P. Cornish, W. Lockeretz, and H. Willer (ed.) Proc. of the 1st Scientific Conf. of the Int. Soc. of Organic Agriculture Research (ISOFAR): Researching Sustainable Systems, Adelaide, Australia. 20–23 Sept. 2005. International Society of Organic Agriculture Research, Bonn, Germany.

Reeves, D.W. 1994. Cover crops and rotations. p. 125–172. *In* J.L. Hatfield and B.A. Stewart (ed.) Advances in soil science: Crop residue management. CRC Press, Boca Raton, FL.

Rindos, D. 1984. The origins of agriculture: An evolutionary perspective. Academic Press, Orlando, FL.

Sumner, D.R., G.J. Gascho, A.W. Johnson, J.E. Hood, and E.D. Treadgill. 1990. Root diseases, populations of soil fungi, and yield decline in continuous double-crop corn. Plant Dis. 74:704–710.

Sustainable Agriculture Network. 2007. Transitioning to organic production. Available at http://www.sare.org/publications/organic/organic.pdf (verified 24 June 2009). Sustainable Agriculture Network, Beltsville, MD.

Troeh, F.R., J.A. Hobbs, and R.L. Donahue. 1980. Soil and water conservation for productivity and environmental protection. Prentice Hall, Englewood Cliffs, NJ.

USDA Agricultural Marketing Service. 2002. National Organic Program. Available at http://www.ams.usda.gov/AMSv1.0/nop (verified 9 July 2009). USDA Agricultural Marketing Service, Washington, DC.

USDA National Agricultural Statistics Service. 2008. Quick stats: Agricultural statistics data base. Available at http://www.nass.usda.gov/Data_and_Statistics/Quick_Stats/index.asp (verified 9 July 2009). USDA National Agricultural Statistics Service, Washington, DC.

Varro. 1913. De rerum rusticarum. p. 122. *In* Roman farm management: The treatises of Cato and Varro. Macmillan, New York.

Westmoreland, P. 2006. Online database of plant communities helps Upper Midwest farmers. p. 14–18. *In* Minnesota Department of Agriculture (ed.) GreenBook 2006: Sustainable agriculture. Minnesota Dep. of Agric., St. Paul, MN.

4

Organic Crop–Livestock Systems

M. H. Entz and J. R. Thiessen Martens
Department of Plant Science, University of Manitoba, Winnipeg, Manitoba, Canada

> Sustainability today depends in part on reintegrating animals and crops—S.R. Gliessman, *Agroecology: The Ecology of Sustainable Food Systems,* p. 269.

> Welcome the animals of the field to your farm. Let them live amongst you like brethren and sister. Be kindly to them—Kaysing, *First-Time Farmer's Guide,* p. 183.

Agricultural systems that combined animals and crops were developed 8 to 10 millennia ago. Today, the principle role of livestock in a farming system is recognized as the ability to convert biomass from leys or pastures, which is otherwise unusable, to economically viable products and to increase flow rates of nutrients (Schiere et al., 2002). Integration also represents an ecological approach to production of both crops and livestock. It is important to examine the role of crop–livestock systems since they are indispensible to organic farming and were virtually ignored in the previous ASA book on organic farming (Bezdicek and Power, 1984).

Until recently, most farms in developed countries included both crops and livestock animals. Before widespread use of inorganic fertilizer and pesticide inputs, integration of crops and livestock has been seen as a way to increase food production for an expanding human population (Granstedt, 2000). Similar attitudes exist in places where these inputs are not available today (Powell et al., 2004). Over a hundred years ago, western Canadian scientists concluded that mixed farming was important for "permanence" (Janzen, 2001). However, their pronouncements were not heeded as farmers opted rather to use fallow methods that exploit the soil resource. Thoughtful observers of agriculture today are envisioning crop–livestock integration as an important principle in the development of sustainable food production systems.

The separation of crops and livestock (Fig. 4–1) has been seen as a disintegration of agriculture (Clark and Poincelot, 1996). Farmer-philosopher Wendell Berry (1977) described the process of crop and livestock specialization as "[taking] a solution and [dividing] it neatly into two problems." Clark and Poincelot (1996) concluded that cheap fossil fuel energy was ultimately responsible for marginalizing pasture and that by deemphasizing pasture in beef and dairy production, we have "abandoned the one real advantage that ruminants had over other classes of livestock." Schiere et al. (2002) pointed out that as the degree of integration between crops and livestock declines, the need for fossil fuel energy in the agricultural system increases. While separation of crops and livestock is widespread

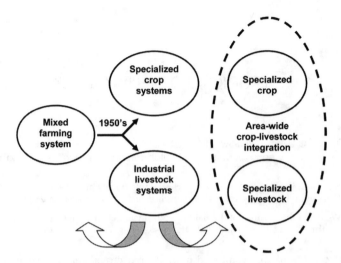

Fig. 4–1. A state-and-transition model describing the evolution of integrated crop–livestock systems. Curved arrows represent the two directions of integration.

in modern conventional cropping systems that use synthetic nitrogen fertilizers, organic farming systems also reflect this dominant trend. Patriquin (1999) suggested that livestock are underutilized in organic systems and that organic codes have been weak in regard to integrating livestock into farms.

From Diversification to Integration

Crop–livestock integration involves more than raising both crops and livestock on the same farm. Clark and Poincelot (1996) identified an integrated farm as one in which livestock are incorporated to perform tasks and services to other enterprises, not just to produce a marketable product. "Integration of function rather than mere diversification" should be the goal of such systems (Schiere et al., 2002). On diversified farms, success of one component can compensate for failure of another, while in integrated systems the components rely on one another through their ecological interactions. Agroecologists are trained to understand integration; it is time that agronomists learn to design integrated systems.

A number of questions arise that are key to this process. First, to what extent have organic farmers adopted crop–livestock integration? In Denmark, for example, farmers converting to organic systems increased grassland area by 20% and increased livestock production by 6% (Langer, 2002). Second, does integration on organic farms occur more at the local or on-farm scale, or also at the regional scale with areawide integration? Langer (2002) concluded that diversification with livestock was greatest on smaller farms, indicating that farmers have gone to mixed farming systems (Fig. 4–1) and suggested that the synergies between crops and livestock production may be better satisfied on small rather than large farms.

In the northern Great Plains of North America, only some organic farms are integrated (Entz et al., 2001). Only 12% of organic fields in the region receive manure on a regular basis (Knight and Shirtliffe, 2003). Where soils are fertile, many organic farms appear not to be integrated with livestock, with farmers choosing instead to use green manuring with legumes for soil building (Entz et al., 2001). Some farmers rely on the exploitative practice of summer fallow as a means of mineralizing soil nutrients and controlling weeds. Therefore, our challenge is similar to that of scientists in 1906—to convince farmers that integration is important for "permanence" (Janzen, 2001).

Local vs. Areawide integration: The Case of Nutrients

Perhaps the most important reason for crop–livestock integration is to allow for *nutrient sharing* between crop and livestock systems and to accelerate the nutrient cycling process. While N is the primary limiting nutrient in organic systems (Watson et al., 2002), P is of special concern since it cannot be fixed through symbiosis in the same way that N is fixed, and organic farming tends to deplete soil P reserves (Mäder et al., 2002). A survey of stockless organic grain farms in Manitoba and North Dakota showed very low soil P levels (<7 mg kg^{-1}) on fields farmed organically for over 30 years (Entz et al., 2001). Even lower available P has been recorded on organic farms in Australia (Cornish, 2007).

Integration on a mixed farm can create a semiclosed system (Pearson, 2007). In a survey of 15 long-term organic dairy farms in Ontario with one animal unit per hectare, Lynch (2006) found that whole farm nutrient balance averages for N, P, and K were +75, +1, and +11 kg ha^{-1} yr^{-1}, respectively. N$_2$ fixation with legumes accounted for 60% of total farm N inputs. About one-fourth of survey farms imported little P as feed or feed supplements; these farms had a small negative farm P balance (–1.5 kg P ha^{-1} yr^{-1}). Cornish (2007) reported positive P balances (0.69 to 7.15 kg P ha^{-1} yr^{-1}) for some biodynamic dairy operations in Australia. These results indicate that mixed farms that use local integration (Fig. 4–1) can be sustainable from a nutrient balance perspective; however, stock density must be sufficient.

Specialized crop or livestock systems require areawide integration for nutrient sharing. Even some mixed farms require additional P (Cornish, 2007). Animal-based P is often the best source since rock P is largely unavailable due to high soil pH and low water availability. Areawide integration for nutrients can take many forms. The most common form is movement of composted manure from larger-scale poultry or dairy farms to stockless organic farms. Some organic certification bodies allow long-distance manure transport, while others do not. A less-common form of integration is to move certified organic livestock to the stockless farm on a short-term basis. This system mimics the "night-time corralling" used in West Africa (Powell et al., 2004).

Proximity of crop and livestock operations is key to the success of areawide integration. Hoshide et al. (2006) examined regional integration between potato (*Solanum tuberosum* L.) and dairy producers in Maine, where manure is applied to land where it had not been applied previously. Limitations to this arrangement were distance between farms (ideally <25 km) and basic trust between individuals, which required lengthy relationships. Schiere et al. (2002) demonstrated that as the distance between specialized crop and livestock production units increases, labor and energy costs of any integration also increase. Further, while specialized production results in more by-products that may be consumed by livestock, on-farm availability of bran and oilcakes is likely to decrease particularly on small farms due to increasingly centralized grain and oilseed processing. For organic

Fig. 4–2. Implement for applying very low rates of composted manure to organic fields, designed and built by a Quebec organic farmer. Photo: M. Entz.

farms, the issues of proximity and availability of by-products are important since the number of organic farms in a given area is generally relatively small.

Knowledge of manure nutrient concentration and crop-specific nutrient requirements is critical for efficient use of animal manure compost, especially since the manure is typically in short supply and manure transport is expensive. Using compost as a N source leads to overapplication of P, as well as potential for N leaching. Using manure to replace P means applying low rates of compost. Some farmers have built special machines that enable low rates of compost to be applied uniformly to land (Fig. 4–2).

A future issue may be to include humans in the areawide nutrient integration. Should this be considered if human waste can be kept separate from industrial wastes? Sir Albert Howard thought so. Pearson (2007) argued that human waste must be considered in future "semiclosed" agricultural systems.

Examples of Integrated Crop–Livestock Systems

The literature abounds with cases of how crops and livestock can be integrated (Schiere et al., 2002), although there are fewer reports on integrated systems in organic agriculture. The examples of organic crop–livestock integration range from simple to complex. Common organic crop–livestock systems in North America are beef–forage–grain and dairy–forage–grain (Table 4–1). Other examples involving ruminants and crops sometimes focus on different goals. For example, in Java, small ruminants are confined and offered forage in excess of animal requirements with the goal of producing large quantities of high-quality manure compost (Table 4–1).

Being omnivores, pigs offer many options as a component of integrated farming systems. Nation (2005) described a system from 1916 where pigs were used as followers behind ruminants and would eat the cows' manure (Table 4–1). At Polyface Farm in Virginia, Joel Salatin uses pigs to compost beef cattle manure; the pigs are enticed into the beef manure pack with sweet wood chips and cereal grains. Similar systems are used in Germany in organic pig and beef cattle systems. Livestock have been used for millennia in agroforestry systems. Systems

Table 4–1. Examples of crop-livestock integration used in organic production.

Type of integrated system	Animal species	Plant species	Reference
1. Mixed farming with beef cattle, Ontario, Canada	Beef cattle	Alfalfa (*Medicago sativa* L.) hay, cereal, perennial pasture	Clark and Poincelot (1996)
2. Mixed farming with dairy cattle, Germany	Dairy cows	Alfalfa hay, cereal, perennial pasture	Haas et al. (2007)
3. *Dehesa* system, Spain	Pigs, beef cattle	Oak (*Quercus* spp.) trees, natural herbaceous cover	Gliessman (2007)
4. Polyface farm, Joe Salatin, Virginia	Pigs, beef cattle, chickens	Forage hay, corn (*Zea mays* L.), wood chips (perennial trees), barley (*Hordeum vulgare* L.), rye (*Secale cereale* L.), oat (*Avena sativa* L.)	Pollan (2006); www.polyfacefarms.com
5. Chicken–orchard systems, California and Denmark	Chickens	Walnut trees (*Juglans regia* L.), apples (*Malus* Mill.), fall-planted cover crop	Gliessman (2007); Hermansen et al. (2004)
6. Cut-and-carry system for manure production, Upper Java	Small ruminants	Herbaceous perennial	Tanner et al. (2001)
7. Mixed grazing	Beef, pigs	Perennial pasture	Nation (2005); Sehested et al. (2004)
8. Central Italy	Sheep	Perennial pasture, cereals, hazelnut (*Corylus* L.), vineyard	Ronchi and Nardone (2003)
9. Integrated farming system, India	Ducks, dairy cows, fish, goats	Rice (*Oryza sativa* L.), azolla (*Azolla* spp.), vegetables	Jayanth (2006)

that include chickens and tree fruit or nut production can be found in different parts of the world. In Spain, pigs actually consume seasonally produced acorns in native oak stands. Highly integrated and complex crop–livestock systems come from places like India and Vietnam, where farmers combine animals with fish and various plants (Jayanth, 2006). Even mushrooms (fungi) and azolla (*Azolla* spp.) (N-fixing fern) are parts of these systems. Animal manures in these systems are sometimes used in biogas production.

Managing Integrated Crop–Livestock Systems

Managing integrated crop–livestock systems requires consideration of a wide range of components, including animals, crops, soil, buildings, and landscape, as well as the expected weather patterns. Important also are the relationships among these components (Fig. 4–3). Organic production standards requiring animals to have outdoor access and opportunity for social interaction present new challenges as well as opportunities for disease and parasite management, especially in poultry and pigs. Therefore, special consideration must be given to keeping animals healthy, and new health care approaches are needed. The integration must also allow services from animals to the land and the landscape to be captured and applied. All of this presents new and interesting challenges for farmers and researchers.

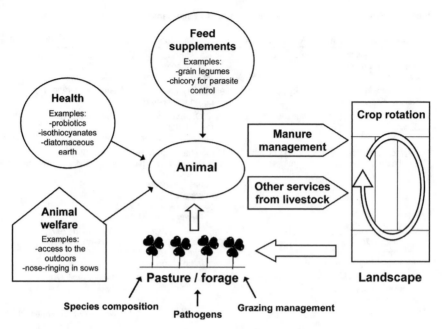

Fig. 4–3. The major components of integrated crop–livestock production systems.

Central Role of Leys within Crop Rotations

Benefits of crop–livestock integration are to a large extent due to perennial N_2–fixing plants that are included in the rotation (Campbell et al., 1990; Entz et al., 1995; Schiere et al., 2002). Perennial legumes improve soil quality, reduce salinization, and add more N to the soil than annual legumes (Entz et al., 2002). Perennial legumes can supply 60% of total farm N inputs into organic dairy farms, for example (Lynch, 2006). When these perennial plants are grazed instead of hayed, fewer nutrients are removed from the soil system (Baron et al., 2002), and hence nutrient management can be controlled through animal management. Due to their perennial habit and cutting regime, alfalfa (*Medicago sativa* L.) hay crops provide excellent control of some of the worst weeds on organic farms—wild oat (*Avena fatua* L.), Canada thistle [*Cirsium arvense* (L.) Scop.], and wild mustard (*Sinapis arvensis* L. ssp. *Arvensis*) (Entz et al., 1995, 2001). Nitrate leaching is a serious risk when a legume-intensive rotation and/or animal manure is used (Drinkwater et al., 1998), but long-term field experiments show that periodic planting of deep-rooted alfalfa in the rotation eliminates the leaching risk (Campbell et al., 1994). Perennial pastures sequester more soil C than annual plant systems and also place the C deeper in the soil profile (Gentile et al., 2005). This ability of perennial plants to increase soil organic matter is critical for long-term sustainability of organic systems, as it represents an investment in the future (Schiere et al., 2002).

Grazing Management

Grazing management based on knowledge of climate, soil, and animal requirements is fundamental to ecological organic livestock production. Conversion of small and large ruminant production systems from conventional to organic is less difficult than for pigs and poultry, in large part due to their adaptability to grazing. Organic beef and dairy production involves significant pasturing. In Canada, 70% of cattle finished on high-quality grass–alfalfa pasture met the standards for finished beef according to the Canadian standard (McCaughey and Cliplef, 1995).

Pasture botanical composition is important for animal productivity and health. Tannin-containing legumes (e.g., *Lotus corniculatus* L.) can be particularly important since condensed tannins, such as polyphenolic proanthocyanidins, reduce parasitism in young ruminants (Heckendorn et al., 2007). Häring et al. (2007) found that tannin concentration in sainfoin (*Onobrychis viciifolia* Scop.) averaged 5 to 9% (dry matter basis) and increased with leaf age. Red clover (*Trifolium pratense* L.) contains formenonetin, which has been shown to inhibit *Escherichia coli* (Duncan et al., 2000).

Disease prevention in grazing animals should be based on the principles of prevention—moving uninfected animals to a clean grazing area; evasion—moving infected animals to a clean grazing area; and dilution—alternate-species or mixed-species grazing (Barger, 1997). Hence, rotational and mixed-species grazing, and perhaps even refuge areas, are important in organic systems. Parasite control in sheep can be achieved by rotational grazing and special forage crops (Ronchi and Nardone, 2003). Since free-living parasites often live in soils, control of grazing height is important so that animals are not eating too close to the soil surface.

In Denmark, sows are typically on pasture all year (Hermansen et al., 2004) and can obtain up to 50% of their energy from grazing (2–2.5 kg sow^{-1} d^{-1}) (Sehested et al., 2004). Grower pigs on pasture can consume 20% of their daily dry matter intake needs from forage (Carlson et al., 1999). These authors also observed that the proportion of forage in the diet decreases to 2 to 8% when supplemented with ad libitum concentrate. Pig growth rate in outdoor systems can be comparable with indoor systems, although feed conversion is typically lower (Sather et al., 1997), especially in winter (Stern and Andresen, 2003). Working in Denmark, Hermansen et al. (2004) found that pastured pigs fed a restricted ad libitum diet (70% of expected up to 80-kg pig weight) had a similar feed conversion as indoor pigs, and average daily gain was reduced only 10 to 15%. A concern for outdoor pig production is maintenance of the grass stand since pigs tend to root out plants. Factors contributing to maintenance of the sward are low stocking rate, nose ringing, and use of supplementary paddocks (Sehested et al., 2004).

Pasturing broilers and laying hens using floorless cages has received a great deal of attention and is now practiced by organic producers (Pollan, 2006). Some research has been conducted on management of hen yards for egg production. Steps such as landscaping the yard (Hermansen et al., 2004), increasing the yard size (Hirt et al., 2000), and adding cockerels to the flocks (Odén et al., 1999) were positive to hen performance and flock health.

Mixed-species grazing holds promise for increasing pasture productivity and reducing parasites. Cattle avoid dung pats, but sheep graze the grass around the pat. Chickens will pick insects out of the pat, while pigs simply eat the whole dung pat (Nation, 2005). The limited literature on mixed-species grazing points to many advantages of such systems. For example, cograzing sows with heifers reduced the parasite (*Ostertagia ostertagi*) burden in heifers and increased overall pasture productivity compared with alternate grazing of sows and heifers in separate paddocks (Sehested et al., 2004). In addition, the mixed-species grazing system required less management than alternate grazing of heifers and pigs in separate paddocks.

Supplemental Feeding Strategies

Although pasture is a major feed source in integrated organic systems, supplemental feeding may also be required. Adding protein crops to the diet of organic pigs and poultry is important since the availability of protein feeds and sources of essential amino acids are main limiting factors in organic monogastric production (Fig. 4–3). These supplements can be provided ad libitum on pasture. Spoolder et al. (2007) reported that diets with 10% low alkaloid lupins (*Lupinus luteus* L.) or 20% low-tannin faba beans (*Vicia faba* L.) were found to provide as much protein as soybean [*Glycine max* (L.) Merr.]. Quinoa (*Chenopodium quinoa* Willd.) was also tested, although its protein level is low by comparison. Grain legume protein crops have the additional advantage of adding N to the land through symbiotic N fixation. Purchasing supplemental feed off-farm provides an opportunity to import limiting nutrients onto the farm (e.g., P and K) in a form that will be more available to plants than rock P (Gordon et al., 2002). There is considerable annual variation in amino acid content of grain legumes (Böhm et al., 2007), and it is strongly suggested that these protein sources be tested before use.

Ruminants grazing high-protein forages are typically protein sufficient. Velik et al. (2007) reported that corn (*Zea mays* L.) silage improved the protein supply for dairy cows kept on grassland. Ruminants can consume cropping by-products such as straw and grain chaff. Collection of chaff during the threshing process is also an effective way to remove weed seeds from the land and reduce the spread of weed patches in arable fields (Shirtliffe and Entz, 2005).

Prospects for Environmentally Adapted Animal Breeds

As animal housing, feeding, and health care approaches are substantially different on organic farms than conventional farms, it is possible that conventionally bred genotypes may not perform as well on organic farms (Boelling et al., 2003). Genetic variation is known to exist in all animal classes, although currently only small ruminants have significant genetic diversity in conventional production. Genotype × environment interactions have been observed in suitability of pigs to outdoor housing, in feather pecking and ability to forage in poultry, and in dairy cattle performance (Boelling et al., 2003). Ronchi and Nardone (2003) reported genetic variation in resistance to nematodes between and within animal breeds. Gerber and Krogmeier (2007) did not observe a genotype × environment interaction in dairy cow performance but suggested further research. Organic dairy farmers in Ontario have identified grazing, fertility, and health longevity traits for future breeding programs, and Rozzi et al. (2007) proposed a strategy of scoring conventional bulls for desirable traits in organic dairy systems. Selection of meat and dairy animals for increased performance on pasture is possible (Bapst, 2001).

Hermansen et al. (2004) pointed out that conventional poultry has been bred for productivity, not social relations. Gauly et al. (2002) observed significantly higher fecal egg outputs in white laying hens than in brown hens; they estimated significantly high heritabilities for fecal egg counts to allow for selection for helminth (*Ascaridia galli*) resistance in chickens.

Although the potential for developing animal breeds for organic production appears to exist, there is some debate as to the practicality of such breeding programs. Breeding programs for cattle may not be practical due to the small population size (Rozzi et al., 2007). However, breeding programs may be feasible for organic poultry due to the short generation length (Boelling et al., 2003) and growing demand for organic products. Heritage livestock breeds may be well suited to organic production systems, but there has been little research on this topic.

Health Supplements and Animal Health

Some animal health supplements are more important to integration than others. For example, probiotic treatments (live microbial cultures) based on lactic acid bacteria can reduce the risk of gastrointestinal disease in organic pigs (Spoolder et al., 2007). Modesto et al. (2007) found that *Bifidobacterium animalis* subsp. *lactis* Ra18 administered to weaning piglets reduced their susceptibility to *salmonella* but not to *E. coli*. There is a growing literature that shows positive effects of supplementation with probiotics as an alternative to antibiotics. Homeopathic treatments have been used to treat mastitis in dairy cows, resulting in similar ($P > 0.05$) effectiveness as chemotherapeutic treatments in one recent study (Werner et al., 2007). This treatment is now recommended for conventional dairy cows as a way to reduce antibiotic use (Fidelak et al., 2007).

Herbs and plant additives represent supplements that are important to crop–livestock integration. For example, diets containing significant amounts of nitrate and/or isothiocyanates from *brassicas* also increase the antimicrobial activity of the stomach acid (Fig. 4–3). These plants can be consumed through grazing or in feed supplements, and *Brassica* cover crops are popular for late-season grazing. Chicory (*Cichorium intybus* L.) roots have been found to be effective against pig endoparasites (Spoolder et al., 2007), while feeding herbs to pigs for suppression of mild roundworm (*Ascaris suum*) infection can also be effective (Spoolder et al., 2007).

Animal Welfare

While animal welfare is often equated with animal health in conventional production, organic standards require consideration of animal welfare to also include animals' need for social interaction and other natural behaviors. Therefore, animal welfare issues are sometimes different in organic than in conventional agriculture. Crop–livestock integration can offer opportunities to meet the welfare requirements of livestock and can also present challenges. For example, nose ringing, which keeps sows on pasture from rooting, has been disallowed in several European countries. Other strategies to keep pigs from rooting are now being tested (Hermansen et al., 2004). Sometimes, mixed farms can result in poorer animal health and welfare due to farmers' time constraints (Hovi et al., 2003).

Welfare of ruminants is very much a function of their life in the outdoors, which means that ruminant animal welfare is strongly affected by the nature of the crop–livestock integration. For example, the desire to finish beef cattle on pasture in the northern Great Plains usually means calving in June compared with March—a time when calves can be born on pasture and risk of ear freezing and diarrhea is reduced.

In poultry and to a lesser extent pig production, only some animal welfare issues directly involve crop–livestock integration. For example, management strategies to prevent feather pecking and cannibalism in poultry mostly include poultry management per se, such as including cockerels in flocks (Hermansen et al., 2004), barn design, and small flock size (Keppler et al., 2007). However, the quality of the outdoor run (pasture) in poultry production can influence animal health and welfare. For example, Spoolder et al. (2007) reported that extensive runs with tall grass had less *Ascaridas galli* compared with overused poultry runs. They also reported a series of strategies for organic pig production including directing dunging behavior so that contact with infected fecaes is minimized. This example also points to the need for a "rotational housing system" that could in fact utilize pasture.

Manure Management

Even though organic farms often produce a smaller nutrient surplus than do conventional farms (Granstedt 2000; Gordon et al., 2002; Haas et al., 2007), nutrient pollution remains a concern in organic ruminant and monogastric production, especially if animals are allowed to graze near water bodies. For example, Hermansen et al. (2004) determined that the current organic regulations in Denmark (1250 chickens ha^{-1}) result in accumulation of approximately 200 kg N ha^{-1} in 100 days. Unless chicken production areas are rotated, N losses could occur. This illustrates an important principle in organic livestock management—rotating livestock.

Challenges in outdoor pig production include vegetation destruction, which exacerbates nutrient losses. Nitrogen and P accumulation in outdoor organic pig production can be mitigated by restricting concentrates, avoiding fodder loss, optimizing crop rotation, moving huts and troughs, and changing paddocks often (Quintern and Sundrum, 2006). Hermansen et al. (2004) observed complete vegetation destruction when pigs were kept outside from 20- to 100-kg live weight at a stock density of 100 m^2 per outdoor pig. By controlling leaching below the farrowing huts (using biomembranes), the system would be more sustainable. Sehested et al. (2004) found that N-leaching potential from sows on pasture was reduced when they were cograzed with heifers. One important source of nutrient loading in beef production is the winter feeding area (Flaten, personal communication, 2007). Farmers must rotate the winter feeding areas even though infrastructure costs will likely increase.

Other Services from Livestock

Crop–livestock integration can provide services at many levels. Research in Scandinavia provides evidence that pigs can be integrated into a rotation with grain crops. The natural inclination of sows and even feeder pigs to root can be used for land cultivation (Andresen et al., 2001) and also for quackgrass [*Elymus repens* (L.) Gould] control. Stern and Andresen (2003) observed the greatest rooting and grazing when pregnant sows and growing pigs were given 3 to 6 m^2 of new area daily. As supplemental feeding decreased, rooting increased. Also, animals tended to defecate and urinate on these new areas, thereby spreading manure across the field over time. These examples show that integrated pig–grain–pasture systems add diversity and functionality to the crop rotation.

Hermansen et al. (2004) compared ducks, geese, and chickens in a combined fruit–livestock system in Denmark. They found that ducks were better than chickens in weed control but that the grazing action of the ducks together with chickens resulted in less nutrient buildup in the soil than chickens alone. Pedersen et al. (2002) observed significant reduction in apple sawfly (*Hoplocampa testudinea* Klug) (50–75% reduction) where portable chicken cages were placed in the apple (*Malus* Mill.) orchard, but with no significant effect on apple yield or quality. In an apple orchard with intercropped potatoes, weeding by geese resulted in higher potato plant yield and insect predation by chickens reduced insect pest populations (Clark and Gage, 1996). Use of floorless, movable chicken cages was suggested as a way to reduce apple drops on the orchard floor (Clark and Gage, 1996).

The Sunshine Farm project in Kansas demonstrated that many traditional practices, including organic management and livestock integration are essential features of energy-efficient systems (Bender, 2002). In a 12-year Canadian study, Hoeppner et al. (2005) found that energy efficiency of organic crop–livestock systems was 12% greater than specialized cropping systems (11.9 vs. 10.4 energy out/ energy in), and total energy production was three times higher in the integrated system. On the other hand, Kumm (2002) reported that when land is in short supply, land-intensive systems such as beef production become energy inefficient because land could instead be used for other purposes such as energy forestry. Therefore, under land-restricted conditions, integrated organic systems will have to become more intensive, perhaps including more species diversity (see example 9 in Table 4–1).

Organic agriculture offers biodiversity benefits over conventional farming at all scales within the agroecosystem (Hole et al., 2005), and "preservation of mixed farming" was cited as one important reason for this higher biodiversity. Kuo and Chiu (2006) promoted small-scale organic farming as an opportunity for ecoagriculture tourism. Schiere et al. (2002) pointed out that integration provides labor opportunities and income for rural areas.

Farm Management Skills

Integrated systems require more farm management and a wider range of skills than do specialized systems (Entz et al., 2005). Time constraints on mixed farms, for example, may contribute to animal health and welfare problems (Hovi et al., 2003). Skills and knowledge most important in organic farming may also be most deficient as people with limited or no prior knowledge and experience start farming because of ideals (Younie, 2000). In Italy, barriers to integration with small ruminants include not only inadequate technical knowledge of the farmer but poorly organized marketing (Nardone et al., 2004). These constraints need to be addressed through extension and education.

Conclusions

Integrated crop–livestock systems are essential to sustainability of organic farming. The nature of the integration will depend on local conditions and farmer experience and interests. There is a growing body of scientific knowledge about these integrated systems, and it will be important for extension workers and educators to bring this knowledge to students and farmers. Farmer knowledge must be valued; farmers have developed most of the integrated systems on their own with little help from the mainstream agricultural community. More organic farming systems research and education is also needed. This work should remain largely holistic, not falling into the reductionism trap.

It is essential that crop–livestock integration be given greater importance by organic certifiers and consultants and that constraints to integrated crop–livestock systems, whether at the regional or national level, be researched and mitigated. There is a large potential for increased food production through more diverse crop–animal systems, and much of this potential is yet to be realized.

Discussion Questions

1.   What are the major causes of separation of crops from livestock on most farms, and what are the consequences for organic farmers?

2.   Describe the potential integration efficiencies of crop and livestock enterprises on the same farm, and how specific crop and animal species could complement each other on an integrated, mixed farm.

3.   What are the specific advantages of different livestock species in an integrated crop–livestock farm, and how would choice of crops influence their success?

4.   What are the unique requirements for raising livestock on an organic farm, and how would integration of crops and livestock help the organic farmer meet these rules?

5.   What are the advantages of incorporating ley fields (pastures) in a long-term rotation with crops on an integrated farm?

6.   Describe the factors that contribute to efficient grazing management, including maintaining health of both livestock and crops.

7.   What are the environmental benefits of maintaining all or a part of a farm in perennial pastures or hay crops, compared with annual crop production?

8.   Describe the nutrient cycling potentials of an integrated crop–livestock farm compared with a farm that is all-livestock or all-crop production.

9.   What are some examples of multispecies grazing systems, and what are the advantages of such a management strategy?

References

Andresen, N., P. Ciszuk, and L. Ohlander. 2001. Pigs on grassland: Animal growth rate, tillage work, and effects in the following winter wheat crop. Biol. Agric. Hortic. 18:327–343.

Bapst, B. 2001. Swiss experiences on practical cattle breeding strategies for organic dairy herds. p. 44-50. In M. Hovi and T. Baars (ed.) Breeding and Feeding for Animal Health and Welfare in Organic Livestock Systems: Proc. of the 4th NAHWOA Workshop, Wageningen, the Netherlands. 24–27 March 2001. Network for Animal Health and Welfare in Organic Agriculture, Reading, UK.

Barger, I.A. 1997. Control by management. Vet. Parasitol. 72:493–506.

Baron, V.S., E. Mapfumo, A.C. Dick, M.A. Naeth, E.K. Okine, and D.S. Chanasyk. 2002. Grazing intensity impacts on pasture carbon and nitrogen flow. J. Range Manage. 55:535–541.

Bender, M.H. 2002. Energy in agriculture: Lessons from the Sunshine Farm Project. In Proc. of the 3rd Biennial Int. Workshop, Advances in Energy Studies: Reconsidering the Importance of Energy, Porto Venere, Italy. 24–28 Sept. 2002.

Berry, W. 1977. The unsettling of America: Culture and agriculture. Sierra Club Books, San Francisco, CA.

Bezdicek, D.F., and J.F. Power. 1984. Organic farming: Current technology and its role in a sustainable agriculture. ASA Spec. Publ. 46. ASA, Madison, WI.

Boelling, D., A.F. Groen, P. Sorensen, P. Madsen, and J. Jensen. 2003. Genetic improvement of livestock for organic farming systems. Livest. Prod. Sci. 80:79–88.

Böhm, H., K. Aulrich, and A. Berk. 2007. Content of protein and amino acids in grain legumes and cereals. (In German, with English abstract.) p. 569–572. In S. Zikeli, W. Claupein, S. Dabbert, B. Kaufmann, T. Müller, and A. Valle Zárate (ed.) Zwischen Tradition und Globalisierung: Beiträge zur 9. Wissenschaftstagung Ökologischer Landbau, Univ. of Hohenheim, Germany. 20–23 March 2007. Verlag Dr. Köster, Berlin.

Campbell, C.A., G.P. Lafond, R.P. Zentner, and Y.W. Yame. 1994. Nitrate leaching in a Udic Haploboroll as influenced by fertilization and legumes. J. Environ. Qual. 23:195–201.

Campbell, C.A., R.P. Zentner, H.H. Janzen, and K.E. Bowren. 1990. Crop rotation studies on the Canadian prairies. Agriculture Canada, Ottawa, ON, Canada.

Carlson, D., H.N. Lærke, H.D. Poulsen, and H. Jørgensen. 1999. Roughages for growing pigs, with emphasis on chemical composition, ingestion and faecal digestibility. Acta Agric. Scand. Sect. A. Anim. Sci. 49:129–136.

Clark, E.A., and R.P. Poincelot (ed.) 1996. The contribution of managed grasslands to sustainable agriculture in the Great Lakes Basin. Food Products Press, New York.

Clark, M.S., and S.H. Gage. 1996. Effects of free-range chickens and geese on insect pests and weeds in an agro-ecosystems. Am. J. Alternative Agric. 11:39–47.

Cornish, P.S. 2007. Phosphorus management on "extensive" organic farms with infertile soils. p. 231–234. In U. Niggli, C. Leifert, T. Alföldi, L. Lück, and H Willer (ed.) Improving Sustainability in Organic and Low Input Food Production Systems: Proc. of the 3rd Int. Congress of the European Integrated Project Quality Low Input Food (QLIF), Univ. of Hohenheim, Germany. 20–23 Mar. 2007. Research Inst. of Organic Agriculture FiBL, Frick, Switzerland.

Drinkwater, L.E., P. Wagoner, and M. Sarrantonio. 1998. Legume-based cropping systems have reduced carbon and nitrogen losses. Nature 396:262–264.

Duncan, S.H., I.R. Booth, H.J. Flint, and C.S. Stewart. 2000. The potential for the control of Escherichia coli O157 in farm animals. J. Appl. Microbiol. 88 (Suppl.):157S–165S.

Entz, M.H., V.S. Baron, P.M. Carr, D.W. Meyer, S.R. Smith, Jr., and W.P. McCaughey. 2002. Potential of forages to diversify cropping systems in the northern Great Plains. Agron. J. 94:240–250.

Entz, M.H., W.D. Bellotti, J.M. Powell, S.V. Angadi, W. Chen, K.H. Ominski, and B. Boelt. 2005. Evolution of integrated crop–livestock production systems. p. 137–148. In D.A. McGilloway (ed.) Grassland: A global resource. Wageningen Academic, Wageningen, the Netherlands.

Entz, M.H., W.J. Bullied, and F. Katepa-Mupondwa. 1995. Rotational benefits of forage crops in Canadian Prairie cropping systems. J. Prod. Agric. 8:521–529.

Entz, M.H., R. Guilford, and R. Gulden. 2001. Crop yield and soil nutrient status on 14 organic farms in the eastern portion of the northern Great Plains. Can. J. Plant Sci. 81:351–354.

Fidelak, C., A. Peinecke, C. Merck, P. Klocke, and J. Spranger. 2007. The extend of reducing antibiotics in therapy of clinical mastitis by homeopathy. (In German, with English abstract). p. 617–620. In S. Zikeli, W. Claupein, S. Dabbert, B. Kaufmann, T. Müller, and A. Valle Zárate (ed.) Zwischen Tradition und Globalisierung: Beiträge zur 9. Wissenschaftstagung Ökologischer Landbau, Univ. of Hohenheim, Germany. 20–23 March 2007. Verlag Dr. Köster, Berlin.

Gauly, M., C. Bauer, R. Preisinger, and G. Erhardt. 2002. Genetic differences of Ascaridia galli egg output in laying hens. p. 1–4. In Proc. of the 7th World Congress on Genetics Applied to Livestock Production, Montpellier, France. 19–23 August 2002. Institut National de la Recherche Agronomique, Paris.

Gentile, R.M., D.L. Martino, and M.H. Entz. 2005. Influence of perennial forages on subsoil organic carbon in a long-term rotation study in Uruguay. Agric. Ecosyst. Environ. 105:419–423.

Gerber, A., and D. Krogmeier. 2007. Investigations on the suitability of Simmental bulls of different genetic potential for milk yield for organic dairy farms. (In German, with English abstract.) p. 485–488. In S. Zikeli, W. Claupein, S. Dabbert, B. Kaufmann, T. Müller and A. Valle Zárate (ed.) Zwischen Tradition und Globalisierung: Beiträge zur 9. Wissenschaftstagung Ökologischer Landbau, Univ. of Hohenheim, Germany. 20–23 March 2007. Verlag Dr. Köster, Berlin.

Gliessman, S.R. 2007. Agroecology: The ecology of sustainable food systems. 2nd ed. CRC Press, Boca Raton, FL.

Gordon, S.H., A. Bhogal, and A.W. Walker. 2002. Integration of organic poultry in whole farm systems: Manure nutrient budgets. p. 237–242. In J. Powell et al. (ed.) UK Organic Research 2002: Proc. of the COR Conference, Aberystwyth, Ceredigion, Wales. 26–28 March 2002. Organic Centre Wales, Inst. of Rural Sciences, Univ. of Wales Aberystwyth, Ceredigion, Wales.

Granstedt, A. 2000. Increasing the efficiency of plant nutrient recycling within the agricultural system as a way of reducing the loan to the environment: Experience from Sweden and Finland. Agric. Ecosyst. Environ. 80:169–185.

Haas, G., C. Deittert, and U. Köpke. 2007. Farm-gate nutrient balance assessment of organic dairy farms at different intensity levels in Germany. Renewable Agric. Food Syst. 22:223–232.

Häring, D.A., D. Suter, and A. Lüscher. 2007. The optimal time for harvesting tanniferous forage plants. (In German, with English abstract.) p. 533–536. In S. Zikeli, W. Claupein, S. Dabbert, B. Kaufmann, T. Müller, and A. Valle Zárate (ed.) Zwischen Tradition und Globalisierung: Beiträge zur 9. Wissenschaftstagung Ökologischer Landbau, Univ. of Hohenheim, Germany. 20–23 March 2007. Verlag Dr. Köster, Berlin.

Heckendorn, F., D.A. Häring, V. Maurer, W. Langhans, and H. Hertzberg. 2007. Effect of sainfoin (Onobrychis viciifolia) silage and hay against gastrointestinal nematodes in lambs. p. 645–648. In S. Zikeli, W. Claupein, S. Dabbert, B. Kaufmann, T. Müller, and A. Valle Zárate (ed.) Zwischen Tradition und Globalisierung: Beiträge zur 9. Wissenschaftstagung Ökologischer Landbau, Univ. of Hohenheim, Germany. 20–23 March 2007. Verlag Dr. Köster, Berlin.

Hermansen, J.E., K. Strudsholm, and K. Horsted. 2004. Integration of organic animal production into land use with special reference to swine and poultry. Livest. Prod. Sci. 90:11–26.

Hirt, H., P. Hödegen, and E. Zeltner. 2000. Laying hen husbandry: Group size and use of henruns. p. 363. In T. Alföldi, W. Lockeretz, and U. Niggli (ed.) Proceedings 13th International IFOAM Scientific Conf., Basel, Switzerland. 28–31 Aug. 2000. Int. Federation Organic Agriculture Movements, Bonn, Germany,

Hoeppner, J.W., M.H. Entz, B.G. McConkey, R.P. Zentner, and C.N. Nagy. 2005. Energy use and efficiency in two Canadian organic and conventional crop production systems. Renewable Agric. Food Syst. 21:60–67.

Hole, D.G., A.J. Perkins, J.D. Wilson, I.H. Alexander, P.V. Grice, and A.D. Evans. 2005. Does organic farming benefit biodiversity? Biol. Conserv. 122:113–130.

Hoshide, A.K., T.J. Dalton, and S.N. Smith. 2006. Profitability of coupled potato and dairy farms in Maine. Renewable Agric. Food Syst. 21:261–272.

Hovi, M., A. Sundrum, and S.M. Thamsborg. 2003. Animal health and welfare in organic livestock production in Europe: Current state and future challenges. Livest. Prod. Sci. 80:41–53.

Janzen, H.H. 2001. Soil science on the Canadian prairies: Peering into the future from a century ago. Can. J. Plant Sci. 81:489–503.

Jayanth, C. 2006. Integrated farming systems: A path to sustainable agriculture. Tamil Nadu Agricultural Univ., Coimbatore, India.

Kaysing, B. 1971. First-time farmer's guide. Straight Arrow Books, San Francisco, CA.

Keppler, C., V. Weigand, M. Staack, W. Achilles, and U. Knierim. 2007. How laborious is organic pullet rearing? A comparison of labour demands between conventional and organic rearing systems of laying hens. (In German, with English abstract.) p. 497–500. In S. Zikeli, W. Claupein, S. Dabbert, B. Kaufmann, T. Müller, and A. Valle

Zárate (ed.) Zwischen Tradition und Globalisierung: Beiträge zur 9. Wissenschaft-stagung Ökologischer Landbau, Univ. of Hohenheim, Germany. 20–23 March 2007. Verlag Dr. Köster, Berlin.

Knight, J.D., and S. Shirtliffe. 2003. Saskatchewan organic on-farm research: Part I. Farm survey and establishment of on-farm research infrastructure. Project 20010016. Final Report. Submitted to Saskatchewan Agriculture, Food and Rural Revitalization, Agriculture Development Fund, Regina, SK, Canada.

Kumm, K.-I. 2002. Sustainability of organic meat production under Swedish conditions. Agric. Ecosyst. Environ. 88:95–101.

Kuo, N., and Y. Chiu. 2006. The assessment of agritourism policy based on SEA combination with HIA. Land use policy 23:560–570.

Langer, V. 2002. Changes in farm structure following conversion to organic farming in Denmark. Am. J. Alternative Agric. 17:75–82.

Lynch, D. 2006. Integrated nutrient management for organic dairying in Ontario. Available at http://www.omafra.gov.on.ca/english/research/new_directions/projects/2003/sr9126.htm (verified 25 June 2009). Ontario Ministry of Agriculture, Food and Rural Affairs, Guelph, ON, Canada.

Mäder, P., A. Fließbach, D. Dubois, L. Gunst, P. Fried, and U. Niggli. 2002. Soil fertility and biodiversity in organic farming. Science 296:1694–1697.

McCaughey, W.P., and R.L. Cliplef. 1995. Carcass and organoleptic characteristics of meat from steers grazed alfalfa/grass pastures and finished on grain. Can. J. Anim. Sci. 76:149–152.

Modesto, M., I. Stefanini, and M.R. D'Aimmo. M, Mazzoni, P. Trevisi, C Tittarelli, P. Bosi, and B. Biavati. 2007. Effect of probiotic inocula on the population density of lactic acid bacteria and enteric pathogens in the intestine of weaning piglets. p. 370–374. *In* U. Niggli, C. Leifert, T. Alföldi, L. Lück, and H Willer (ed.) Improving Sustainability in Organic and Low Input Food Production Systems: Proc. of the 3rd Int. Congress of the European Integrated Project Quality Low Input Food (QLIF), Univ. of Hohenheim, Germany. 20–23 Mar. 2007. Research Inst. of Organic Agriculture FiBL, Frick, Switzerland.

Nardone, A., G. Zervas, and B. Ronchi. 2004. Sustainability of small ruminant organic systems of production. Livest. Prod. Sci. 90:27–39.

Nation, A. 2005. Grassfed to finish: A production guide to gourmet grass-finished beef. Green Park Press, Ridgeland, MS.

Odén, K., K.S. Vestergaard, and B. Algers. 1999. Agonistic behaviour and feather pecking in single-sexed and mixed groups of laying hens. Appl. Anim. Behav. Sci. 62:219–231.

Patriquin, D.G. 1999. Farms as ecosystems. p. 25–32. *In* Wordstream Associates (ed.) Exploring organic alternatives: Meeting the challenges of agriculture, health, and community. Univ. Extension Press, Univ. of Saskatchewan, Saskatoon, SK, Canada.

Pearson, C.J. 2007. Regenerative, semiclosed systems: A priority for twenty-first-century agriculture. Bioscience 57:409–418.

Pedersen, H.L., A. Olsen, K. Horsted, B. Pedersen and J. Hermansen. 2002. Combined production of broilers and fruit. *In* NJF Seminar 346: Organic Production of Fruit and Berries, Ärslev, Denmark. 21–22 Oct. 2002. Danish Inst. of Agricultural Sciences, Dep. of Horticulture, Årslev, Denmark.

Pollan, M. 2006. The omnivore's dilemma. Penguin Press, New York.

Powell, J.M., R.A. Pearson, and P.H. Hiernaux. 2004. Crop–livestock interactions in the west African drylands. Agron. J. 96:469–483.

Quintern, M., and A. Sundrum. 2006. Ecological risks of outdoor pig fattening in organic farming and strategies for their reduction: Results of a field experiment in the centre of Germany. Agric. Ecosyst. Environ. 117:238–250.

Ronchi, B., and A. Nardone. 2003. Contribution of organic farming to increase sustainability of Mediterranean small ruminants livestock systems. Livest. Prod. Sci. 80:17–31.

Rozzi, P., F. Miglior, and K.J. Hand. 2007. A total merit selection index for Ontario organic dairy farmers. J. Dairy Sci. 90:1584–1593.

Sather, A.P., S.D.M. Jones, A.L. Schaefer, J. Colyn, and W.M. Robertsen. 1997. Feedlot performance, carcass composition and meat quality of free-range reared pigs. Can. J. Anim. Sci. 77:225–232.

Schiere, J.B., M.N.M. Ibrahim, and H. van Keulen. 2002. The role of livestock for sustainability in mixed farming: Criteria and scenario studies under varying resource allocation. Agric. Ecosyst. Environ. 90:139–153.

Sehested, J., K. Söegaard, V. Danielsen, A. Roepstorff, and J. Monrad. 2004. Grazing with heifers and sows alone or mixed: Herbage quality, sward structure, and animal weight gain. Livest. Prod. Sci. 88:223–238.

Shirtliffe, S.J., and M.H. Entz. 2005. Chaff collection reduces seed dispersal of wild oat (Avena fatua) by a combine harvester. Weed Sci. 53:465–470.

Spoolder, H.A.M., H.E. Mejer, H.M. Vermeer, B.G. Meerburg, M. van Krimpen, and H.A. Kijlstra. 2007. Prevention and treatment of parasitic infections in organic pigs. p. 327–332. In U. Niggli, C. Leifert, T. Alföldi, L. Lück, and H Willer (ed.) Improving Sustainability in Organic and Low Input Food Production Systems: Proc. of the 3rd Int. Congress of the European Integrated Project Quality Low Input Food (QLIF), Univ. of Hohenheim, Germany. 20–23 Mar. 2007. Research Inst. of Organic Agriculture FiBL, Frick, Switzerland.

Stern, S., and N. Andresen. 2003. Performance, site preferences, foraging and excretory behaviour in relation to feed allowance of growing pigs on pasture. Livest. Prod. Sci. 79:257–265.

Tanner, J.C., S.J. Holden, E. Owen, M. Winugroho, and M. Gill. 2001. Livestock sustaining intensive smallholder crop production through traditional feeding practices for generating high quality manure-compost in upland Java. Agric. Ecosyst. Environ. 84:21–30.

Velik, M., A. Steinwidder, R. Baumung, W. Zollitsch, and W.J. Knaus. 2007. Optimization of the protein supply through maize silage on organic dairy farms in grassland regions. (In German, with English abstract.) p. 537–540. In S. Zikeli, W. Claupein, S. Dabbert, B. Kaufmann, T. Müller, and A. Valle Zárate (ed.) Zwischen Tradition und Globalisierung: Beiträge zur 9. Wissenschaftstagung Ökologischer Landbau, Univ. of Hohenheim, Germany. 20–23 Mar. 2007. Verlag Dr. Köster, Berlin.

Watson, C.A., H. Bengtsson, M. Ebbesvik, A.K. Loes, A. Myrbeck, E. Salomon, J. Schroder, and E.A. Stockdale. 2002. A review of farm-scale nutrient budgets for organic farms as a tool for management of soil fertility. Soil Use Manage. 18:264–273.

Werner, C., A. Sundrum, and A. Sobiraj. 2007. Recommendations for using the homeopathic treatment strategy in the case of bovine clinical mastitis. (In German, with English abstract.) p. 609–612. In S. Zikeli, W. Claupein, S. Dabbert, B. Kaufmann, T. Müller, and A. Valle Zárate (ed.) Zwischen Tradition und Globalisierung: Beiträge zur 9. Wissenschaftstagung Ökologischer Landbau, Univ. of Hohenheim, Germany. 20–23 Mar. 2007. Verlag Dr. Köster, Berlin.

Younie, D. 2000. Integration of livestock into organic farming systems: Health and welfare problems. In M. Hovi and R. Garcia Trujillo (ed.) Proc. of the NAHWOA 2nd Workshop, Cordoba, Spain. 9–11 Jan. 2000. Network for Animal Health and Welfare in Organic Agriculture, Reading, UK

5

Forages in Organic Crop–Livestock Systems

E. Ann Clark
Plant Agriculture, University of Guelph, Guelph, Ontario, Canada

The reintegration of forages into arable agriculture is a prerequisite to sustained land use. Forages have traditionally been viewed as a vehicle for soil improvement, livestock feed, nitrogen, and most recently, bioheat (Samson et al., 2005). A more holistic view would encompass the broader range of services through which forages support the whole farm and the broader ecosystem. Weed management and greenhouse gas abatement will be profiled in this chapter as local and global examples of the additional services offered by forages. While equally applicable to conventional and organic farming, examples are presented to demonstrate the particular relevance of forages as a holistic management tool for organic farms. Recent reviews calling for more systems-oriented, forage-based research include those by Entz et al. (2002), Russelle et al. (2007), and Sulc and Tracy (2007).

Why Forages?

What are forages and why do we grow them? Why have forages disappeared from so many farms, including some organic farms, and does it really matter?

Definition of Forages

The term *forages* commonly used in North America is equivalent to *grass* or *herbage* in New Zealand and the United Kingdom, where a forage stand is also referred to as a *sward*. Broadly defined, *forage* is herbaceous, high-fiber vegetation that may be consumed by grazers such as cattle and sheep, in contrast to woody vegetation, which is typically more appealing to browsers, such as goats and deer. Forage could include weeds, annual grains (Maloney et al., 1999), immature maize (*Zea mays* L.) (Karsten et al., 2003), and residual cereal stubble or stalks, as well as sown species. Such an encompassing use of the word reveals the scope for forages to connect crop and livestock enterprises to each other and to the land.

The rationale for growing forages on organic farms ranges from the dogmatic, dating back at least to the deductive experience of Sir Albert Howard in the early 20th century, to more contemporary awareness of the ecological and agronomic services performed by forages.

An Organic Farming Dogma

Traditional organic farming was mixed crop and livestock farming, with livestock providing an economic justification for growing the forages needed to sustain the land and provide other benefits. In the words of Sir Albert Howard, widely regarded as the father of the organic movement: "Mother Earth never attempts to farm without live stock; she always raises mixed crops; great pains are taken to preserve the soil and prevent erosion; the mixed vegetable and animal wastes are converted into humus; there is no waste; the processes of growth and the processes of decay balance one another; ample provision is made to maintain large reserves of fertility; the greatest care is taken to store the rainfall; both plants and animals are left to protect themselves from disease" (Howard, 1943, p. 4).

Biodynamic organic practitioners, who follow the integrated spiritual and agronomic precepts of Rudolph Steiner, are required to integrate livestock, and hence forages, with their crops (Steiner, 1929, cited in Padel et al., 2004). In a commentary on contemporary European agriculture, Allan Nation, editor of *Stockman Grass Farmer*, described "the planned rotation of crop and leguminous pasture to maintain soil organic matter" and then asked rhetorically, "Is North America the only continent that doesn't do this?" (Nation, 2008).

Given the prominence of stockless organic as well as conventional farming today, how strong is the evidence that livestock and forages are essential to sustain agriculture? A three-year survey of 14 organic farmers in Ontario, half with and half without livestock, found that all livestock farms grew forages and field crops (e.g., Field Crop farms), while stockless farms grew horticultural crops (e.g., Hort Crop farms) as well as forage, grain, and other service crops (e.g., Pasture farms) (Clark and Maitland, 2004; Table 5–1). Up to three crop types, spring grain, winter grain, and soybean [*Glycine max* (L.) Merr.] or broccoli (*Brassica oleracea*), carrot (*Daucus carota*), and potato (*Solanum tuberosum* L.), were sampled and analyzed on each farm in each year (Table 5–1). Pasture was present on some farms and was sampled and analyzed as a separate farm type (e.g., pasture farm). Horticultural and field crop farmers averaged 10 years as certified organic producers at the start of the study.

The soil parameters measured in this study do not support the hypothesis that the presence of livestock on a farm enhances soil quality and hence sustainability (Table 5–1). Both types of arable cropping reduced soil organic matter and some nutrient levels, relative to pasture. However, both types of arable cropping also maintained adequate to high levels of soil organic matter and soil nutrients, based on crop-specific provincial standards (OMAFRA, 2002, 2008).

Table 5–1. Summary of farm type effects on soil nutrients, pH, and soil organic matter (SOM) in three contrasting sets of farm fields (*n* = no. of fields) (Clark and Maitland, 2004).

Farm type	P	K	Ca	Mg	pH	SOM
	—————————— mg L soil^{-1} ——————————					%
Hort crop (*n* = 30)	15 a†	88 b	2193	262 b	7.6 a	4.1 b
Field crop (*n* = 39)	23 a	102 b	2340	220 b	7.4 a	3.8 b
Pasture (*n* = 5)	27 a	182 a	2496	394 a	7.6 a	6.3 a
Mean (*n* = 74)	20 ns‡	102**	2291 ns	248**	7.5**	4.1**

** Significant at the 0.01 probability level.

† Numbers in each column followed by same letter do not differ significantly among farm types.

‡ ns, not significant at the 0.05 probability level.

Despite the absence of livestock, the horticultural farms nonetheless depended integrally on livestock, either as a source of imported manure or as a buyer for the exported grain or forage service crops, or both, in their rotations (Clark and Maitland, 2004). Only 2 of the 14 farms (1 horticultural and 1 field crop) used neither perennial forages nor compost; one farm imported yard waste from a landscaping business, and the other was on land with a long history of livestock production. Horticultural farms allocated an average of 6 out of 10 years to growing service crops—mainly forages—either for direct plowdown or for sale. The willingness of organic farmers to forego horticultural crop income 6 out of 10 years reflects their obligate dependence on the services performed by forages and other service crops. Thus, the influence of livestock was prominent on virtually all farms, either directly or indirectly, supporting the hypothesis that livestock and the crops that nourish livestock are necessary to sustain agriculture in this region.

An Ecological Fit

The ecological parallels between forage and native vegetation facilitate harnessing natural processes to perform agricultural services. In the temperate continental forest region of North America, which includes much of the eastern half of the United States and the most productive land in Ontario and Quebec in Canada (Forest Resources Assessment, 2001), perennial forages are the closest agricultural surrogate to the mixed woodlands native to the region. Of all agricultural land uses, perennial forages best approximate such ecological functions as

- supporting biodiversity,
- sustaining year-round groundcover to protect soil and maintain a tight nutrient sink,
- accumulating soil organic matter, which enhances soil structure, biotic health, water infiltration, and nutrient storage, and
- cycling nutrients when forages are utilized on-farm.

Thus, Howard's beliefs that integrated crop and livestock farming, including forages, best approximates nature and sustains agricultural land use are supported by contemporary ecological reasoning.

System Services

Forages, including cover crops, have long been valued as system service crops. The four-crop Norfolk rotation of turnip (*Brassica rapa* subsp. *rapa*), barley (*Hordeum vulgare* L.), clover (*Trifolium* spp.), and wheat (*Triticum aestivum* L.) dates from the 18th century (McConkey, 1952). Beneficial effects of forages on soil, nutrient, and water management were reviewed by Clark and Poincelot (1996), with broader system impacts reviewed by Clark (2004) and others. Other system services afforded by forages include N fixation (Russelle and Birr, 2004), weed and pest control (Abawi and Widmer 2000), and creation of an aesthetic landscape (Fales et al., 1993). Recent additions to forage services include bioheat (Samson et al., 2005) and medicinal and bioactive properties (Ramírez-Restrepo and Barry, 2005). A wider perspective on forages as service providers reveals novel solutions to pending crises, from mounting weed resistance to herbicides to food shortages, land degradation, peak oil, and global warming.

In sum, forages are an ecologically sound management tool to connect agriculture and nature, plant and soil, and crops and livestock. Broadly defining forages as high-fiber, herbaceous vegetation consumed by domesticated livestock—whether sown or unsown, leaves or stems, and juvenile or mature tissues—profiles the range of services by forages.

Overview of Forage Crops

Barnes et al. (2007) and Rayburn (2007) ably discussed individual forage species and mixtures. Thus, the focus here will be on forages in organic production systems. The versatility of forages derives in part from the enormous range in growth habit and adaptation of many types of forage species.

Forage Species

Forage species include summer annuals, winter annuals, biennials, and perennials, although coverage here will emphasize perennials. They may be native to North America, as in big bluestem (*Andropogon gerardii* Vitman) in the western prairies, or introduced or nonnative, as in the ubiquitous dairy species alfalfa (*Medicago sativa* L.).

Species may also be grouped by plant functional traits into such categories as "rhizomatous, dense sod-forming, cool-season perennial grasses," versus "warm season perennials" and "species productive on imperfectly drained soils," as reviewed by Clark et al. (2006b). The abundant diversity of forage species is the foundation from which agronomic and ecological services derive.

Forage Mixtures

Forages are typically sown in species mixtures of varying complexity, generally including both forbs and grasses. Although advocates of perennial ryegrass (*Lolium perenne* L.) in western Europe and New Zealand or alfalfa in much of North America might disagree, no single species can do everything. Unlike grain crops, it is common to sow forage mixtures where adaptive traits are distributed among species rather than being bred into elite varieties of a single species.

Particularly under low-input conditions, diverse species adaptations tolerate stress and achieve performance goals, prolonging sward life and enhancing profitability. On an organic farm, effectively suppressing a perennial sward without herbicides consumes time during the growing season as well as scarce energy resources. Sustaining productive sward life also enables the progressive successional enrichment of soil nutrients and organic matter in agroecosystems, as in nature.

Forage Sward Stratification

Regardless of sown mixture complexity, sward composition is quickly enriched with other species derived from the soil seedbank and seed rain. Encroachment by wind-blown species, such as dandelion (*Taraxacum* sp.) and Canada thistle (*Cirsium arvensis* L.), is encouraged by simple mixtures of nonspreading hay species, such as alfalfa and timothy (*Phleum pratense* L.), which expose considerable bare soil after harvest (Fig. 5–1). Furthermore, despite uniform seeding, the sward gradually becomes stratified in space, with different communities distributed along ecological gradients, as reviewed by Clark (2001) and Clark et al. (2006b).

Fig. 5–1. Bare soil left after hay harvest is vulnerable to encroachment by windblown weed seed.

Small differences in species adaptation result in progressive differentiation of communities on the basis of soil type, internal drainage, exposure, previous land use history, and many other factors.

Stratification in a forage stand can be a problem for haymaking, as species differences in growth, maturity, and drying rates affect windrow density and uniformity of moisture content. For pastures, diversity and stratification can be promoted by sowing more complex mixtures and then fencing to separate and strategically graze the stratified swards (Clark et al., 2006a). A complex mixture supplies adapted sward genetics to occupy more niches and minimize invasion by undesirable species. In the absence of herbicides, biodiversity is particularly important for organic producers.

In sum, forages are the only modern crop type that includes genetic diversity both within and among species in the same field at the same time. Although forage species are bred and evaluated in monoculture, and are often sown in simple mixtures, swards diversify and stratify over time to create mixtures that are diverse in space and in time. Sward heterogeneity reflects the cumulative effect of diverse growing conditions on sward composition. Sward diversity can either be avoided by frequent but costly reseeding or be channeled to agricultural use through seeding of complex mixtures and strategic fencing and grazing (Clark et al., 2006b).

Uses of Forages

Traditional uses of forages include livestock feed, soil and water conservation, and N fixation and retention. Each use is reviewed in terms of specific relevance to organic farming.

Forages for Livestock

Nourishing livestock is one of the reasons for growing forages. In contrast to cereals and grain legumes, which produce primarily energy and protein, forages also provide the high-fiber roughage needed to sustain ruminant digestion. However, the role of forages in livestock feeding differs among regions, as well as with farming philosophy. In Great Britain, Frame (1992) noted that grasslands accounted for 60 to 65% of the diet of dairy cows, 70 to 75% of the diet of beef cattle, and 90 to 95% of that for sheep. In Ontario, maize and maize silage typically account for the majority of a dairy cow ration, while a recommended ration for growing out beef calves (from 317 to 407 kg) might be composed almost entirely of maize: 15 kg of maize silage, 3.5 kg of maize and cob meal, and 2 kg of maize gluten, as fed (Martin, 2005). Thus, annual rather than perennial forages have come to account for a majority of the feed energy consumed by conventionally managed ruminants.

In contrast, organic standards mandate forage-based rations, with an emphasis on pasture, for both ruminants and non-ruminants.

- For herbivores, Canadian organic standards (National Standard of Canada, 2006) require that "a substantial proportion of dry matter in daily rations consists of roughage, fresh/dried fodder, or silage." For pigs and poultry as well, roughage and fresh or dried fodder or silage are required in daily rations.

- The U.S. National Organic Program (USDA, 2008) specifies "access to pasture for ruminants." *Pasture* is defined as "land used for livestock grazing that is managed to provide feed value and maintain or improve soil, water, and vegetative resources" to distinguish it from a simple drylot or yard.

- Denmark requires 60% of the dairy cow ration to come from forage (Sehested et al., 2003).

- In Norway, concentrates can account for up to 30% of the energy in organic dairy rations, with pasture, silage, and root crops making up the balance (Reksen et al., 1999).

Compliance with forage-based regulations is evident in on-farm practice. Based on organic farmer focus groups in each country, Haring (2003) reported that 50% of fat-corrected milk comes from forage in Denmark compared with 57% in Italy, 65% in the United Kingdom, and 76% in Germany. In a comparison of 30 pairs of conventional and organic dairy farms in Wisconsin, cows on 15 of the 30 conventional dairies had either no grazing or only access to an exercise yard with little grazing (Sato et al., 2005). In contrast, cows on 15 of the 30 organic dairies utilized grazing as their primary source of nutrition in the summer. Thus, forage and pasture use for livestock feeding differs, with organic farmers mandated to emphasize perennial forage, including pasture, in livestock rations.

Dependence on forage-based rations, especially pastures, is intended to do more than support healthy digestive processes. Among the benefits to whole farm management are livestock health and welfare and internalized nutrient cycling.

Animal Health and Welfare

Alroe et al. (2001) suggested that the principles of organic farming engender a distinctive set of criteria for animal welfare centering on "naturalness, harmony, integrity, and care." When surveyed in meetings held between 2000 and 2002, organic producers in the United States ranked animal healthcare as their top priority for organic livestock research (Sooby et al., 2007). As noted by Clancy (2006b), the obligation for forage-based nutrition specifically pastures, on organic farms minimizes the adverse effects on animal health and welfare, on food quality and safety, and on human health that may derive from high-density confinement feeding.

Pasture enables livestock to express their natural behaviors, whether grazing or rooting or scratching, and to distribute themselves in space, thus enhancing health and welfare. Emphasis on natural behavior features in the national organic standards of many jurisdictions. In Canada, "Under a system of organic production, livestock are provided with living conditions and space allowances appropriate to their behavioral requirements, and organically produced feed. These practices strive to minimize stress, promote good health and prevent disease" (National Standard of Canada, 2006).

Forages also sustain livestock health directly. The high grain diets which have become the norm in conventional dairies and confinement operations can create a range of metabolic problems in ruminants, such as acidosis and liver abscesses. Liver dysfunction can lead to a cascade of other illnesses, including secondary photosensitization (McGuirk and Semrad, 2005).

Owing to their high-fiber content, forages are a more dilute source of nutrition than grain. As a result, mandating a high-forage content in the ration reduces milk yield. High milk production is often associated with increased incidence of mastitis. Vaarst et al. (2003) reported that treatment of mastitis is the single largest consumer of antibiotics in Danish dairies, consistent with evidence cited by Zwald et al. (2004) and Sato et al. (2005) for U.S. dairies. The ubiquity of antibiotic use in contemporary livestock agriculture (Mellon et al., 2001) has led some in the veterinary sector to assume that organic livestock would suffer from the prohibition on antibiotic use. In a comparison of 30 pairs of organic and conventional dairies in Wisconsin, Sato et al. (2005) found that the organic cows yielded 15% less milk (20.2 vs. 23.7 kg d^{-1}), with a 12.5% lower incidence of clinical mastitis (27.7 vs. 32 per 100 cow years; not significant), and an 8% lower bulk tank somatic cell count (262,000 v. 285,000 mL^{-1}; not significant). In Sweden, Hamilton et al. (2006) compared mastitis and related parameters in 26 organic herds visited three times in a year with that from 1102 conventional herds drawn from official records. Mean milk yield was 18% lower (6213 and 7572 kg per cow), while mean bulk milk somatic cell count was 10% lower (173,000 and 191,000 cells mL^{-1}) for organic compared to conventional herds, respectively. Estimated incidence of clinical mastitis was lower in organic than conventional herds (9.1 vs. 14.7 per 100 cows). Greater dependence on forages in the organic ration was identified as the main factor distinguishing udder health in organic and conventional herds (Hamilton et al., 2006).

Within-Farm Nutrient Cycling

Nutrient export from the farm differs for crop and livestock commodities. Whole plant crops, such as hay or silage, represent the greatest losses if they leave the farm, followed by vegetables such as potatoes and field crops as maize or barley. Lowest nutrient export comes from livestock products. Based on European data, Spedding et al. (1981) calculated that crude protein (CP) production by livestock enterprises ranges from 53 to 292 kg CP ha^{-1} yr^{-1}, equal to the export of 8 to 22 kg N ha^{-1} yr^{-1}, with cow–calf, stockers, and sheep at the low end and pigs, dairy, and meat chickens at the high end. In contrast, crop enterprises produced from 350 to 2100 kg CP ha^{-1} yr^{-1}, equal to 56 to 336 kg N ha^{-1} yr^{-1}, with grain crops at the low end and hay at the high end. Thus, nutrient exports are much greater for hay than for grain crops, and grain exports are much greater than for livestock products.

Multiplying average Ontario yields over the last four years (OMAFRA, n.d.) with typical nutrient data for field crops (Natural Resources Conservation Service, n.d.) reveals that N export in alfalfa hay, oat (*Avena sativa* L.), and barley would be 137, 43, and 60 kg ha^{-1}, with 13, 8, and 12 kg ha^{-1} for P, and 104, 9, and 16 kg ha^{-1} for K, respectively. Thus, exporting hay would remove two to three times as much N, somewhat more P, and many times as much K as exporting either oat or barley. Of these, only N can be generated on-farm through growing leguminous crops. In organic systems, other macro- and micronutrients have to be replaced either with permitted substances, such as greensand and kelp, imported feedstuffs, or manure.

Particularly on organic farms, where exported nutrients are difficult or costly to replace, nutrient management encourages export of livestock products first, followed by field crop, and then vegetable crop products. Whole plant crops such as hay should be grown for on-farm use.

The mandated use of forages in organic rations serves these multiple purposes. Forages provide the high-fiber diet to which ruminants are uniquely adapted, avoiding a range of adverse outcomes associated with more concentrate-rich diets. Pasturing also enables the expression of natural behaviors precluded by cement floors and confined housing systems, rendering unnecessary the use of antibiotics on organic farms. Marketing forages in the form of meat, milk, and eggs also minimize linear nutrient export in preference to cycling of nutrients on the farm.

Utilization of Forages

Forages may be grazed as a standing pasture crop, in winter as well as in summer, or mechanically harvested and conserved for later feeding.

Pasture

The trend in recent years has been toward managed grazing, particular on organic farms where pasture use is required. Methods for controlling grazing by free-ranging livestock are discussed in a variety of forage texts (Rayburn, 2006; Barnes et al., 2007) as well as popular press (Murphy, 1999; Gerrish, 2004; Nation, 2004).

Grazing on an organic farm may differ in some respects from that on most conventional farms. For example, health and welfare of livestock may be the explicit goal. Dairy cattle may be offered a shade paddock, with trees to provide shade in the heat of the summer (Fig. 5–2). Swards may also be intentionally diverse, both sown and naturalized, to capitalize on perceived medicinal benefits of species such as caraway (*Carum carvi* L.) or chicory (*Cichorium intybus* L.) (Smidt and Brimer, 2005). However, Sato et al. (2005) found that cows on organic dairies carried a higher worm burden in both March and September, with a significantly higher worm burden and lower milk yield from cows under intensive grazing. In a review of 22 studies, Lund and Algers (2003) concluded that health and welfare of dairy cows on organic farms was as good or better than on conventional farms, with the exception of parasite-related disease.

On organic farms, livestock grazing may also be viewed not simply as a way to support livestock but also as a way to provide services such as pest or weed control. Effective organic farming reduces costs and increases ecological benefit by capturing enterprise synergies. The prohibition against synthetic biocides makes grazing to manage pests in other farm enterprises particularly valuable for organic farmers. For example, on the McQuail Farm in Lucknow, ON, sheep are used to consume downed apples (*Malus domestica*) and to graze off residual herbage in an organic orchard in the fall. Such an approach reduces overwintering habitat for both codling moth (*Cydia pomonella* L.), a serious pest of organic apples, and for rodents that would otherwise girdle the trees (Fig. 5–3). Sheep

Fig. 5–2. Intentionally sown tree line provides shade for organic dairy cows on Pronkdale Farm, Harriston, ON, Canada.

Fig. 5–3. Strip grazing by sheep removes downed apples and keeps grass under control, Meeting Place Farm, Lucknow, ON, Canada.

grazing protects the apple trees, while the apple orchard affords grazing and nutrition. On the Reid Farm in Abbotford, BC, rotationally grazing organic laying hens serve not simply as a source of commercial scale egg production but also as weed control in commercial raspberry (*Rubus idaeus* L.) fields (Fig. 5–4). Reid (2002) reported that as creatures of the "edge" between forest and grassland, chickens preferentially scratch out weeds at the base of raspberry rows, which they perceive as an edge. In parallel with a natural ecosystem, the chickens perform a service for the raspberries, which in turn affords the layers herbage and especially the opportunity for expression of natural behaviors. Nonruminant species such as pigs (Fig. 5–5) or chickens may feature more prominently as grazers on organic farms, both on grass and in arable crop rotations (Clancy, 2006a).

Thus, grazing on organic farms uses many of the same strategies, methodologies, and approaches as on conventional farms, but with an intentional focus on animal health. A broader range of species may also be grazed to produce meat, milk, and eggs, as well as achieve other system goals.

Conserved Feeds

Forage conservation, as dry hay or ensiled haylage, baleage, or silage (Fig. 5–6 and 5–7), is needed to provide feed during the "dead season". Detailed information on machinery and methods may be found in Barnes et al. (2007) and Rayburn (2007).

Fig. 5–4. Managing chickens as rotational grazers manages weeds on the Reid Farm in Abbotsford, BC, Canada.

Fig. 5–5. Tamworth pigs graze rotationally at Whole Circle Farm in Rockwood, ON, Canada.

Fig. 5–6. Dry bale basket at Kingsholm Farm, Campbellford, ON, Canada.

Fig. 5–7. Bale wrapping to make ensiled baleage.

The role of conserved feeds on an organic farm differs in at least three respects: the preference for dry hay rather than ensilage, the retention of the conserved crop for on-farm use, and an emphasis on feed self-reliance.

Ensiled forage may be the fallback position in regions, such as the United Kingdom, that do not have sufficient good drying weather to enable reliable hay production. Nonetheless, a full feed diet of silage is not recommended, in part because of the tendency toward fat yellowing from β-carotene content. In Canadian organic standards, "for ruminant animals, when silage is fed, dry roughage is provided" (National Standard of Canada, 2006). The preference for dry rather than ensiled feeds may also relate to carryover effects on milk or cheese quality. Martin et al. (2005) reviewed the impact of different herbage species and conservation methods on cheese attributes. Feeding a diet of ensiled maize, in contrast to either dry or ensiled perennial grasses, results in characteristic effects on the firmness, texture, color, and flavor of cheese and butter.

While cash-crop hay is becoming more common in conventional agriculture, organic farmers grow forage largely for on-farm use, with manure recycled back out to the land. Soil nutrient balance is of specific interest to organic farmers not simply for nutrient replacement but also to promote crop health and reduce vulnerability to pests. Organic farmers believe that healthy soils lead to healthy plants, healthy livestock, and healthy people, and thus, they monitor and balance soils to avoid pest and pathogen problems.

The traditional belief that healthy, balanced soils help plants avoid pest problems is supported by current literature. Phelan et al. (1996) compared egg-laying preference of European corn borer [*Ostrinia nubilalis* (Hübner)] (ECB) on sweet maize grown on soils from a pair of neighboring farms, one organic and one conventional. In greenhouse studies with controlled release of ECB adults, egg laying was significantly lower on maize grown on organic soils. They concluded that mineral balance affected susceptibility to ECB and that organic soils provided more balanced nutrition, making plants less attractive to ECB. In a later study from the same laboratory, Beanland et al. (2003) varied the ratio of boron, zinc, and iron in hydroponic culture and monitored how three insect pests grew when fed leaves from the various treatments. They observed significant effects of nutrient balance on insect as well as on plant growth. In Maine, Alyokhin et al. (2005) amended soil with manure, fertilizer, or both in various rotations and tested effects on Colorado potato beetle [*Leptinotarsa decemlineata* (Say)] (CPB) density. Tissue concentrations differed dramatically in N, Ca, Mg, P, Al, B, Cu, Fe, Mn, and Zn. They concluded that 40 to 57% of the variation in CPB populations could be accounted for by the mineral content of the potato leaves.

As part of whole farm management, feed self-reliance means not simply retaining conserved feed on the farm but also minimizing purchased feed inputs. Organic livestock farming is often referred to as *land-based* to distinguish it from concentrated feeding systems that rely predominantly on imported feed and that, in turn, externalize the ramifications of overapplication of manure on site. In Ontario, Stonehouse et al. (2001) reported that organic dairy producers were almost wholly self-reliant in feedstuffs, whereas conventional dairies depended more on purchased feed. In a comparison of 32 organic and 99 conventional dairy herds in Michigan, Minnesota, New York, and Wisconsin, Zwald et al. (2004) reported that just under half of the organic dairies purchased feed, and the only feed purchased was whole soybean and soy meal, products that were purchased for 91% of conventional herds, along with other inputs. The adequacy of organic approaches to nutrient management can be questioned, however, as demonstrated for phosphorus by Lynch et al. (2006) in Canada and Oehl et al. (2002) in Switzerland.

Except for a stronger emphasis on dry hay, equipment and approaches for feed conservation are similar on organic and conventional farms. Organic farmers' reliance on home-grown feed reflects holistic concerns, including the cost and difficulty of obtaining replacement nutrients as well as the pivotal role of soil nutrient balance on crop health and pest management.

Soil and Water Conservation

Forages have long been valued for replenishing and rejuvenating soil, as well as enabling an economic return from marginal land. Sites unsuited to arable cropping can be left as permanent pasture or hay crops, to minimize risk of erosion or degradation.

As agriculture has become more polarized, with annual grain and silage crops displacing perennial forages and livestock production spatially separate from production of feedstuffs, marginal land is often the only place where forages remain in the landscape. In place of forages, conservation tillage became a substitute that allowed continuous cash cropping in the absence of livestock. But considering the diverse contributions of forages to soil and water conservation, conservation tillage is at best a partial proxy. As a solution to erosion and degradation issues, conservation tillage has created or compounded other difficulties, ranging from facilitated denitrification (Aulakh et al., 1984) to greater dependence on herbicides for weed control, coupled with the externalized cost of dealing with the windblown seed of dandelion and other perennials that proliferate in conservation tillage systems. Key reasons for the prominence of forages on organic farms, and on sustainable farms in general (Bird et al., 1995), are to conserve but still make economic use of marginal land, to sustain soil structure and biological activity, and ultimately to promote plant health.

Nitrogen Fixation

Forage legumes are used primarily for biological fixation of on-farm N but may also influence immobilization and retention. Forage legumes, including cover crops such as red clover (*Trifolium pratense* L.) and hairy vetch (*Vicia villosa* Roth), are a significant source of biologically fixed N. With no synthetic fertilizers on organic farms, leguminous crops feature prominently in crop rotation design and nutrient supply. Forages are also valued as N scavengers, to temporarily immobilize labile N for subsequent release to subsequent grain crops. For this purpose, nonleguminous cover crops, such as sorghum-sudangrass (*Sorghum bicolor* × *S. bicolor* var. *sudanense*) or annual ryegrass [*Lolium perenne* L. ssp. *multiflorum* (Lam.) Husnot], may be preferred, although alfalfa (Russelle et al., 2001) and native grass species (Entz et al., 2001) are also excellent N scavengers.

Rates of N fixation in temperate legume–grass pastures in trials spanning 20 years ranged from 66 to 152 kg N ha^{-1} yr^{-1} (Ledgard, 2001). According to Russelle and Birr (2004), alfalfa in the Mississippi River basin fixes an average of 152 kg N ha^{-1}, which accounts for 79% of total alfalfa N uptake. In contrast, soybean in the same region fixes an average of 84 kg N ha^{-1}, or 57% of total soybean N uptake. Much of the N from both crops is destined to support production of maize, a crop that uses N inefficiently, leading to significant losses through leaching and denitrification. Large-scale losses of N result in part from the uncoupling of C and N cycles, which Tonitto et al. (2006) consider to be "a defining trait of human-dominated systems."

Nitrogen Retention

Rejoining C and N cycles within living tissues is one of the reasons for cover cropping, whether to generate biologically fixed N or to conserve labile N in the soil. Tonitto et al. (2006) conducted a meta-analysis comparing yield in continuous cash grain rotations using cover crops as a source of N and N retention. Cover crops providing from 110 to 180 kg N ha^{-1} supported subsequent grain yields that did not differ from those of fertilized crops. However, when cover crops fixed 80 to 110 kg N ha^{-1}, subsequent grain yield was 15% lower than that of fertilized crops. Berry et al. (2002) demonstrated that insufficient N is constraining typical arable crop yields on organic farms.

Nitrogen retention is of particular importance on organic farms because of the time and effort needed to generate in situ N within crop rotations. Clark et al. (2006a) compared several leguminous and nonleguminous cover crops sown after winter cereal harvest for their ability to immobilize soil N in the fall. In two successive years, sorghum–sudan accumulated 122 and 143 kg N ha⁻¹, compared with 26 and 48 kg N ha⁻¹ for buckwheat (*Fagopyrum esculentum* Moench) and 25 and 44 kg N ha⁻¹ for oilseed radish (*Raphanus sativus* L.). In a three-year study of an arable crop rotation on sandy soil in the Netherlands, Vos and van der Putten (2004) demonstrated that without cover crops, the concentration of nitrate N in soil water consistently exceeded the EU standard of 11.3 mg L⁻¹. Including fall rye (*Secale cereale* L.) and oilseed radish cover crops reduced average nitrate N concentration to near or below this level. Thus, grasses and nonleguminous forbs may be better suited to immobilizing potentially labile N.

Grazing systems may be particularly prone to leaching losses from urine, depending on the balance between C and N in the herbage on-offer, the link between forage protein content and livestock demand, and the fraction of rumen bypass versus rumen degradable protein (Hoekstra et al., 2007). Because labile N can also be vulnerable to loss as a greenhouse gas (GHG), ensuring an effective balance between N supply and demand is needed not simply to retain a scarce and valuable nutrient but also to reduce both groundwater contamination and GHG emission.

Dalgaard et al. (1998) reported that organic farming had the potential to use N more efficiently and reduce N leaching losses from Danish dairies, but at the expense of lower stocking rates, and lesser production per hectare. They compared 14 organic and 16 conventional pilot farms, with mean stocking rates of 1.1 and 1.5 livestock units (LSU) ha⁻¹, and mean milk yields of 5600 and 8200 kg ha⁻¹ yr⁻¹, respectively. Nitrogen surplus, or N vulnerable to loss, averaged 124 and 240 kg N ha⁻¹ and 22 and 29 kg N t milk⁻¹, for organic and conventional dairies, respectively. Nitrogen surplus increased linearly with stocking rate at a rate of 117 kg N surplus ha⁻¹ LSU⁻¹ for conventional farms and at 33 kg N surplus ha⁻¹ LSU⁻¹ for organic farms. Increasing dependence on fodder in the ration reduced N surplus on conventional farms. Factors that may have resulted in the lesser rate of increase in N surplus with livestock density on organic farms could include greater fodder-feeding intensity and lesser dependence on imported feed.

Prevention of Leaching

System management can also influence leaching risk, as shown in studies with outdoor rearing of organic pigs on sandy loam soils in Denmark. Set stocking of individual sows in single (not rotated) 10- by 35-m paddocks, equivalent to 29 sows ha⁻¹, resulted in markedly asymmetrical manure distribution and mean leaching losses of 320 kg N ha⁻¹ versus 100 kg N ha⁻¹ outside the paddock area (Eriksen, 2001). Set-stocking of 10 weaned piglets in single (not rotated) 1108 m² paddocks, equal to 90 fattening pigs ha⁻¹, on a year-round basis also created significant leaching risk (Eriksen et al., 2006). This stocking rate was designed to apply manure N at a rate of 280 kg N ha⁻¹, the national guidelines for conventional, alternate-year outdoor pig production. However, owing to higher-than-anticipated N content of organic feed and greater free choice intake by pigs, net surplus was closer to 500 kg N ha⁻¹ and 86 kg P ha⁻¹. Grass cover was less than 10% during the fall and winter months, owing to rooting and overgrazing. Suggested improvements to reduce leaching risk included lower stocking rate, as noted by Williams et al. (2005), periodic redistribution of housing and troughs, and feeds with a lesser N content.

Whether organic or conventional, the results of outdoor pig rearing studies underscore the role of management in reducing N leaching from livestock. Although both outdoor feeding and grazing are outdoors, and both are on grass swards, animals dependent on imported feed constitute a greater leaching risk than those cycling nutrients from swards managed to supply much or all of livestock nutrition. Ledgard (2001) concluded that pastures wholly dependent on N fixation typically yield at low to moderately high levels, with low denitrification and leaching losses of 6 and 23 kg N ha^{-1} yr^{-1}, respectively. Rotational grazing of pigs in summer or strip grazing of grain stubble in winter, as practiced by Greg Gunthorp and others (http://www.gunthorpfarms.com/), are designed to avoid the excessive and asymmetric distribution of nutrients and sward damage reported in the Danish outdoor feeding studies. When assessing the nutrient conservation performance of grass swards, it is necessary to distinguish between swards where only feeding occurs and swards managed for grazing.

When compared to yields attainable under conventional management, organic farms often find yields limited by N (Berry et al., 2002). However, increasing N to increase yield incurs costs, such as leaching and GHG emission, which are externalized to the broader environment. Growing leguminous crops or cover crops to fix or retain N also incurs costs, but the costs are borne internally within the farm operation.

In summary, forages have traditionally been valued for livestock nutrition and health, for soil and water conservation, and for N fixation and retention. Recognition of the multiple roles of forages in whole farm management is codified in the organic standards for Canada, the United States, and elsewhere. Organic forages are typically managed not just for livestock nutrition but also to sustain livestock health and control pests and weeds. Because implied nutrient export from livestock is a small fraction of that from grain or especially forages, marketing forages via livestock products effectively minimizes nutrient export. Retaining and balancing soil nutrients supports crop health, and ultimately the health of livestock and people, as posited by Sir Albert Howard nearly 100 years ago.

For centuries, forages have been renowned for improving soils and conserving water. Yet forages have nonetheless disappeared from arable land as livestock and crop agriculture became separated, replaced to some degree by conservation tillage. The need for forages as a source of N has also been displaced to a large degree by synthetic N from the Haber-Bosch process. This process is energy intensive, now accounting for 1% of the global annual energy consumption and 30% of all energy invested in agriculture (Smith, 2002). The services provided by forages for both soil improvement and N may increase in value with awareness of the limitations of conservation tillage and with the rising cost of energy.

System Service: Weed Control

Among the many system services provided by forages, one of great interest to organic farmers is weed management. From survey results, Sooby et al. (2007) noted that organic farmers prioritized systemic pest control, not simply killing pests but enhancing overall plant vigor and resistance to pests.

Absence of synthetic herbicides may suggest that organic farmers rely primarily on mechanical tillage for weed control. However, mechanical cultivation is a tool of last resort, after exhausting a variety of "cultural" tools. Cultural methods such as crop rotation, composting to lessen weed seed density, and timely planting to produce a robust and competitive crop are intended to minimize weed issues. The integration of perennial forages and cover crops into arable crop rotations, termed grassland ley farming, is another example of preemptive weed management.

Evidence from contemporary farming supports the utility of grassland ley farming for weed control. Entz et al. (1995) surveyed 253 Manitoba and Saskatchewan farmers who were known to include forages in their crop rotations. Over 80% reported a reduction in weed pressure for one, two, or more years (11, 50, and 33%, respectively) following forages. Inclusion of forages in the rotation afforded good control of several of the most problematic weeds in western Canada, wild oat (*Avena fatua* L.), Canada thistle, wild mustard (*Sinapis arvensis* L.), and green foxtail [*Setaria viridis* (L.) P. Beauv.]. Over two-thirds of the farmers surveyed by Entz et al. (1995) also reported higher grain yields following forages, particularly in the zones with higher moisture.

The frequency of perennial forages in the rotation can materially affect weed dynamics, as demonstrated in an eight-year study on a German farm (Albrecht, 2005). The weed seed bank was monitored for two years before and six years after conversion to organic farming. In a seven-course rotation, total weed seed density increased from 4050 to 17,320 m^{-2} during the first three years, consistent with research cited from Norway, Scotland, and Slovakia, then declined to 10,020 m^{-2} by the sixth year. However, changes to the weed seedbank were crop specific, increasing by an average of 33% in years when winter cereals, sunflowers (*Helianthus annuus* L.), and lupins (*Lupinus albus* L.) were grown, but decreasing by 39% in a grass–clover mixture. Crop effects paralleled degree of crop groundcover, with sown grass–clover mixtures achieving 100% groundcover compared to groundcover levels of 55% for winter cereals, 50% for sunflowers, and 30% for lupins at harvest. Starting in Year 4, increasing the frequency of grass–clover from one in six years to one in three years apparently reversed the trend in weed seed accumulation.

Forages, including cover crops, lower the soil seedbank by diminishing weed seed delivery, by retarding germination, and by promoting seed predation and decomposition, Weed-specific differences may affect response to time under perennial forages. Mohler (1996) reviewed the literature on ecological differences between annual crops and weeds as the basis for weed control strategies. Of all weed attributes reported, seed size was most pivotal to weed suppression through increased crop density, straw mulching, and mechanical weeding within the crop row. Individual seed weight varies among weed species, with those for lambsquarters (*Chenopodium album* L.), and redroot pigweed (*Amaranthus retroflexus* L.), less than 10% that of velvetleaf (*Arbutilon theophrasti* Medik.). Because seed size limits the depth from which seedlings can successfully emerge, withholding land from cultivation under a perennial sod may be more effective in suppressing small- than large-seeded weed species.

Teasdale et al. (2004) compared the seedbank response of pigweed, lambsquarters, and annual grasses to two-, three-, and four-year organic crop rotations over a six-year period in Maryland. All crops in each rotation were grown in every year, and all rotations included live winter groundcover from a winter cereal, a perennial hay stand, and/or cover crops. Initial levels of weeds in the soil seedbank were reported to be low: 314 seeds m^{-2}, for pigweed, 987 for lambsquarters, and 566 for annual grasses. Low levels were attributed to starting the study after eight years of alfalfa followed by three years of no-till maize.

When averaged over all crops and years in each rotation, the seedbank of both pigweed and lambsquarters was favored by rotations that started with maize or especially with soybean (Teasdale et al., 2004). Rotations that started with one or two years of hay significantly reduced both pigweed and lambsquarters but increased the annual grass seed burden. The greater annual grass weed seedbank during hay years was attributed to gaps in the alfalfa stand and to the ability of some prostrate grasses to set seed despite mowing. They concluded that crop rotation, including withdrawal from cultivation under perennial forages, can be designed to reduce recruitment and encourage breakdown of the weed seedbank.

Teasdale (1996) reviewed evidence that cover crop species can suppress weeds by changing the spectral composition of light (red:far-red ratio) as well as reducing light transmission to the ground. Suppression can also occur through allelochemic effects (Liebman and Sundberg, 2006), changes to soil temperature patterns, and niche displacement. Some summer annuals, such as Johnsongrass [*Sorghum halepense* (L.) Pers.], may require exposure to a given amplitude of diurnal temperature variation to germinate. Huarte and Benech Arnold (2003) related reduced germination of curly dock (*Rumex crispus* L.) and pigweed to the lesser amplitude of temperature variation under alfalfa, as compared to bare soil. Artificial heating of the soil eliminated this effect for pigweed but not for other weed species. Factors that dampen temperature fluctuations, such as a perennial sod, retard germination of sensitive species.

Thus, both modern understanding of weed seed physiology and producer experience with grassland ley farming support the utility of reintegrating perennial forages and cover crops into arable crop rotations for weed management. Whether by competing for the same niche to reduce the seed rain, or denying requisite environmental cues for weed seed germination and growth, or creating habitat for seed predators, perennial forages and cover crops are a valuable service provider for whole farm weed control.

System Service: Greenhouse Gas Abatement

Threats from global warming have focused research effort on agriculture as both a source and a possible solution to global greenhouse gas (GHG) issues. Forages can perform important global services by mitigating GHG emissions.

Greenhouse gases, which include carbon dioxide (CO_2), methane (CH_4), and nitrous oxide (N_2O) as well as water vapor and ozone, retard the escape of terrestrial radiation from the atmosphere, resulting in global warming. The global warming potential (GWP) of each gas is affected by its reflective properties and its lifespan in the atmosphere, each of which ranges among gases over several orders of magnitude. Over a 100-year interval, the GWP of CO_2 is 1, while that for CH_4 is 23 and that for N_2O is 296 (Houghton et al., 2001). Assessing the role of forages in mitigating GHG and global warming needs to encompass processes that release or sequester not simply CO_2 but also CH_4 and especially N_2O.

Through effects on sequestration and emission, perennial forages influence atmospheric GHG both directly from the soil and through inputs or use practices that indirectly affect GHG, such as N fertilizer, ruminant methanogenesis

(Waghorn and Clark, 2006), and urination on pasture (Bhandral et al., 2007; van Groenigen et al., 2005). The sheer scale of the land base occupied by perennial forage and native range is 29 million ha in Canada (Statistics Canada, 2006) and 247 million ha in the United States (NASS, 2002a,b), suggesting the potential for quantitatively significant impacts on GHG mitigation. On a global basis, Conant et al. (2001) reported that 27 and 23% of milk and beef come from grasslands managed specifically for that purpose.

Projected GHG impacts from perennial forages and other land uses differ among studies. Sources of variation include years under cultivation, prevailing climate and management practices, and forage species under test. The scale of analysis in time as well as space, including depth in the soil (Gentile et al., 2005), also influences results. Analyses limited to on-farm phenomena obscure the GHG of synthetic inputs, such as N fertilizer, while those focusing on the crop life cycle may fail to consider plowdown and rotation effects (Kaiser et al., 1998; Ball et al., 2007). Analyses during the growing season miss freeze–thaw effects in winter (Kaiser et al., 1998), while studies focusing on CO_2 cannot detect possible countervailing effects on N_2O (Jones et al., 2006). The following review of primarily soil-based impacts of forages on CO_2 and N_2O provides a sense of the complexity of these processes.

Carbon Dioxide

Much of the early interest in agricultural mitigation of GHG derived from the known adverse effect of soil disturbance on soil organic carbon (SOC) and CO_2 release from the soil. Soil organic carbon is a net between additions and losses of soil carbon. Thus, increasing SOC to sequester atmospheric CO_2 requires increasing C input to the soil through crop and root residues and rhizodeposition, as reviewed by Johnson et al. (2006), and/or retarding C losses through erosion and degradation. Perennial forages start growing earlier and continue growing later in the season, thus accumulating above- and belowground biomass over a longer growing season. By withholding land from cultivation, perennial forages also reduce tillage-induced degradation of SOC.

Lal (2003) concluded that most agricultural soils have lost half to two-thirds of native SOC, with the magnitude loss in the order of croplands > grazing land > forest land. In a review of 126 studies, Ogle et al. (2005) concluded that long-term cultivation reduced SOC to 71 and 82% of native SOC in temperate moist and dry conditions, and to 58 and 69% of native SOC in tropical moist and dry conditions. In Canada, conversion to arable cropping has released an average of 22% of native SOC or 123 Tg of C back to the atmosphere (Gregorich et al., 2005).

Forages in crop rotations have long been known to benefit SOC, as affirmed in recent contributions (as cited, e.g., in Conant et al., 2001; Gregorich et al., 2005; Meyer-Aurich et al., 2006). Continuous alfalfa, resown at 4-year intervals, yielded significantly more SOC in the 0- to 40-cm profile than six of seven maize-based rotations over a 20-year period (Yang and Kay, 2001).

Marriott and Wander (2006) compared the effect of forage legume–based organic rotations and conventional rotations on soils sampled from nine long-term farming systems trials in the United States. Forages, which were used only in the organic rotations, included alfalfa, red clover, crimson clover (*Trifolium incarnatum* L.), hairy vetch, "hay," annual ryegrass, and timothy, while maize, soybean, and usually a small grain were grown in both systems. After an average of 10 years, the total SOC content of the top 25 cm of soil was 14% higher in forage-based organic rotations than in conventional rotations, despite limiting forages to no more than one year at a time in multiyear rotations.

In Ontario, Meyer-Aurich et al. (2006) compared C sequestration and GHG emissions over 20 years from seven maize-based rotations in two tillage regimes with that from continuous alfalfa. Rate of C sequestration for continuous alfalfa was 0.513 Mg C ha^{-1} yr^{-1}, which was significantly higher than that of all maize-based rotations apart from maize–maize–alfalfa–alfalfa. Considering only mitigation through C sequestration, continuous alfalfa achieved 1881 kg CO_2 equivalents (eq,) ha^{-1} yr^{-1}, compared with 1060 for maize–maize–alfalfa–alfalfa, zero for continuous maize, 260 for maize–maize–barley–barley, and −268 for maize–maize–soy–soy.

A series of papers by Conant and colleagues explored how management, climate, and land use history affected C sequestration in perennial swards. Conant et al. (2001) examined 115 studies from 17 countries to discern trends in how fertilization, grazing management, conversion to grassland, and other practices influenced rate of accumulation of SOC over time. Management improved SOC in 74% of the studies, with largest gains in the first 40 years and in the top 10 cm. For studies showing enhanced C sequestration, rate of C gain averaged 0.54 Mg C ha^{-1} yr^{-1}, with rate of gain averaging 0.30 for fertilization (n = 42), 0.35 for improved grazing management (n = 45), and 1.02 for conversion from cultivation to pasture (n = 23). About one-third of the sequestered C was below 50 cm. Withholding land from cultivation had the greatest effect on C sequestration. Studies that sample only the top 30 cm underestimate the C sequestration potential of grasslands, a finding corroborated by Gentile et al. (2005) in a 38-year rotation study in Uruguay and by Conant et al. (2003) in Virginia.

Conant et al. (2003) compared four pairs of farms in Virginia to assess the effect of management-intensive grazing (MIG) on C sequestration. In pastures 5, 21, and 25 years old, MIG significantly improved total SOC in the 0- to 10- and 0- to 50-cm increments, with parallel but nonsignificant effects in a 3-year-old pasture. Total SOC in the top 50 cm was increased by an average of 22% across the four pastures, with 50% of the grazing effect expressed in the 0- to 10-cm layer, 30% in the 10- to 20-cm layer, and 20% in the 20- to 50-cm layer. The difference in soil C sequestration rates between the MIG and non-MIG treatments averaged 0.41 Mg C ha^{-1} yr^{-1}. Thus, the beneficial impact of perennial forages on GHG emissions can be improved through such practices as MIG.

Practices intended to sequester CO_2 and other GHG have focused most heavily on conservation tillage, including no-till (cited in Lal, 2003 and Johnson et al., 2006). However, the utility of conservation tillage to enhance SOC varies regionally. Studies summarized by Gregorich et al. (2005) found that no-till sequestered 0.32 Mg C ha^{-1} yr^{-1} in western Canada but −0.07 Mg C ha^{-1} yr^{-1} in eastern Canada. Over a 20-year maize-based rotation trial in Ontario, Yang and Kay (2001) found that chisel plowing increased SOC by 6.4% in the 0- to 10-cm layer but decreased it by 7.8% in the 10- to 20-cm layer, with no net effect compared to moldboard plowing. The primary effect of conservation tillage in these and other trials appears to be vertical redistribution of SOC within the soil profile. Grant et al. (2004) modeled GHG emissions over 30 years in seven soil regions in Canada, in response to regimes that included no-till and converting to grassland. The range in reduced CO_2 emissions was 0.88 to 4.06 Mg C ha^{-1} yr^{-1} for converting from arable to grassland, compared with 0.22 to 0.71 Mg C ha^{-1} yr^{-1} for adopting no-till. Potential for C sequestration through conversion to grassland exceeded that from no-till in all soil regions. Thus, potential for C sequestration is greater with perennial forages than from arable crops, can be further improved with grazing management, and is greater than from adopting no-till.

Nitrous Oxide

In general, estimates of N$_2$O emissions increase with increasing N, regardless of whether the N is fixed biologically or manufactured. Because N is often yield limiting, the connection between N use and GHG emissions represents a potential conflict between yield and global warming.

Meyer-Aurich et al. (2006) calculated net GHG emissions over 20 years from seven maize-based rotations and continuous alfalfa. With alfalfa lowest and continuous maize highest, N$_2$O emissions ranged from 1379 to 2082 CO$_2$ eq. ha^{-1} yr^{-1} in direct energy use, and from 509 to 1277 CO$_2$ eq. ha^{-1} yr^{-1} for indirect energy use, such as for synthesis of N fertilizer. In the same study, net GHG emissions, after the mitigating effect of C sequestration, ranged from 7 to 3359 CO$_2$ eq. ha^{-1} yr^{-1}, respectively, with alfalfa lowest and continuous maize highest. The calculated level of soil N$_2$O emissions attributed to 160 kg N ha^{-1} yr^{-1} applied to continuous maize was almost the same as that from biologically fixed N from alfalfa: 1364 vs. 1358 CO$_2$ eq. ha^{-1} yr^{-1}. However, continuous maize caused an additional 592 CO$_2$ eq. ha^{-1} yr^{-1} or 43% more N-related N$_2$O emissions owing to fertilizer manufacture. Thus, perennial forages relying on biologically fixed N dramatically reduce net GHG emissions from N$_2$O as well as CO$_2$, and from both on- and off-farm energy use.

Studies summarized by Gregorich et al. (2005) showed that rates of N$_2$O–N emission from soils receiving N fertilizer varied with crop type. The range, measured in kg N$_2$O-N ha^{-1}, was from 0.16 to 0.62 for unfertilized and fertilized perennial grasses, and from 1.53 to 5.03 for unfertilized and fertilized grain crops. However, in the same units, emissions were greater from alfalfa (2.31) than from soybean (1.73), apparently due to frequent cutting and root and nodule dieback in alfalfa.

In a modeling study by Grant et al. (2004), converting arable land to permanent grassland reduced combined CO$_2$ and N$_2$O emissions by 2.55 Mg C ha^{-1} yr^{-1}, while shifting to no-till and eliminating fallow reduced combined emissions by 0.61 and 0.56 Mg C ha^{-1} yr^{-1}. For conversion to grassland, C sequestration accounted for 40 times more GHG reduction than that attributable to N$_2$O reduction. They make the point, however, that the potential for C sequestration reaches an upper limit over time, which would be characteristic of the particular region and management applied. Conversely, the scope for continued benefit from reduced N$_2$O emissions pertains as long as the causal management regime is applied.

Conant et al. (2005) analyzed nine studies encompassing 54 data points to monitor effects on soil N and hence N$_2$O emissions in grasslands being managed for C sequestration. The data set included four regimes: conversion from arable to grassland, conversion from native to sown grassland, fertilization, or grazing management. Soil N and C status were closely related, with rate of C sequestration accounting for 60% of the variation in rate of N sequestration. Most management treatments increased or decreased both C and N. However, because of the much greater GWP of N$_2$O, even slight changes in N$_2$O production could counterbalance changes in C sequestration. For example, N fertilization increased soil C storage by an average of 0.18 Mg C ha^{-1} yr^{-1} but also increased N$_2$O flux by 87 g CO$_2$–C eq. yr^{-1}, resulting in a net GWP of –0.16 g CO$_2$–C eq. yr^{-1}.

Conant et al. (2005) reviewed studies in which N fertilization had enhanced C sequestration. While an average of 6.1 kg C was sequestered for each kilogram of N applied, factoring in the GHG costs of making and transporting the fertilizer and assuming the loss of 1.25% of applied N as N$_2$O reduced net GWP benefit by half. Jones et al. (2006) contrasted the effects of organic and mineral fertilizer amendments to grasslands, concluding that the C sequestration benefits of poultry manure and sewage pellets were more than counterbalanced by stimulation of N$_2$O emissions, particularly in a wet year. Thus, management that sequesters C can have a net warming effect on the atmosphere if it is achieved at the expense of even modest N$_2$O emissions.

Responsiveness or manageability may also vary among specific GHGs, as noted by Jackson et al. (2007). Replicated experimental and commercial pastures in Wisconsin were subjected to four defoliation regimes: continuous grazing, management-intensive rotational grazing, haying, and set aside. Of interest was the responsiveness of GHG flux to specific grazing and haying practices. Variability in CO$_2$ flux was lowest, with variability in CH$_4$ and N$_2$O fluxes one to two orders of magnitude higher. Subsampling or local sources of variation accounted for most of the total variability in both CH$_4$ and N$_2$O, but variation among farms or blocks was greater for CH$_4$, while variation among defoliation regimes was greater for N$_2$O. Thus, varying grazing and haying management may be an effective tool for reducing N$_2$O emissions.

In summary, both historic and contemporary studies have affirmed the substantial advantage of perennial forages over arable crops in C sequestration, an advantage that may in fact have been underestimated by sampling only surface layers. The net effect of forages or any other land use on GHG emissions depends integrally on N$_2$O emissions, which in turn increase with both biologically and synthetically fixed N. This finding suggests a possible incompatibility between management intended to increase yield and management for reduced emission of GHGs. Forages have the potential to substantially reduce N$_2$O as well as CO$_2$ emissions. The net benefits of perennial forages on GHG emission will vary with climatic and managerial practices, including grazing management.

Synthesis and Conclusions

Forage crops are an essential component of ecologically based farming systems. Forages are the glue that holds together and sustains arable agriculture. Forages serve many purposes, whether for livestock feed, soil improvement, and N fixation, or for biodiversity, weed and pest management, and GHG abatement. In organic systems, forages perform functions that are otherwise served by relying on prohibited inputs, such as synthetic fertilizer, biocides, and antibiotics. Effective use of forages avoids the need for many of the inputs and practices disallowed by organic standards and can be equally valuable in conventional systems.

Diversity is central to the capacity of forages to serve and sustain agriculture. Forages are the only crop type in contemporary farming that relies intrinsically on mixtures of species to buffer against the vagaries of weather and the heterogeneity of the growing landscape. Forages may also be used in diverse ways, to sustain soil, water, and air resources and as fresh or conserved feed for livestock.

Broadly defined, forages serve agriculture in a multiplicity of forms, both above-
and belowground, as juvenile tissues and dead stubble, and in annual, biennial,
and perennial forms.

Forages are the backbone of organic systems, providing not simply the traditional services but also a vehicle for the health and welfare of livestock, a venue
for the expression of natural behaviors, and a "Swiss Army knife–like" tool for
everything from pest and weed management to internalized nutrient cycling and
environment protection. Weed management has been singled out for emphasis
because it is a priority for organic farmers and because it illustrates the principle
of problem avoidance by design. Organic farmers are able to do what they do,
without reliance on many common but prohibited inputs, specifically because of
system designs that avoid or minimize problem creation in the first place. Any
and all of these services are accessible by all farmers, but they are of particular
importance on organic farms as the framework for compliance with mandated
principles and practices.

Beyond the farm gate, forages offer additional service in GHG abatement.
While the C-sequestration advantage of forages over arable crops is unambiguous,
the potential countervailing effect of N_2O emissions has been profiled to focus attention on the inherent conflict between yield and safeguarding the environment.

In sum, forages have much to offer to farmers, especially to organic farmers
and to those charged with broader societal concerns. Capitalizing on these services requires a more holistic lens that reveals how forages not only connect the
individual farm enterprises but also join farming to the land, the rural landscape,
and the global environment.

Discussion Questions

1. Identify six services forages perform in contemporary farming, apart from
    feeding livestock. For each, discuss its relevance on organic versus conven-
    tional farms.

2. The work of Sir Albert Howard is considered to be an important foundation
    to organic farming. From both economic and ecological perspectives, how
    is his guidance still sound today?

3. The debate topic is: livestock are essential to sustainable and organic agri-
    culture. Pick your side, for or against, and present your four strongest
    positions on this important issue.

4. Define pasture *stratification* in a perennial sward, explain its causes, and
    compare its effects in land intended for haying versus for pasture.

5. Identify and discuss three reasons why organic standards mandate forage-
    based rations for livestock.

6. Identify and discuss two ways in which grazing livestock can be used to
    control insect pests in crops.

7. Identify and discuss three ways in which the use of conserved forages dif-
    fers on organic farms compared with conventional farms.

8. The debate topic is: given that conservation tillage practices are an effective
    replacement for perennial forages in contemporary agriculture. Pick your
    side, for or against, and lay out your four strongest positions on this impor-
    tant issue.

9. Nitrogen has proven to be a two-edged sword in contemporary farming. Explain the two sides of the sword (issue) and analyze how perennial forages could help to reconcile the dichotomy.

10. The debate topic is: given that the agronomic and ecological importance of the perennial forages mandated under organic standards will increase in the future. Pick your side, for or against, and lay out your four strongest positions on this important issue.

11. Explain how cultural weed management differs from cultivation, and identify three examples of cultural weed management.

12. Identify and discuss four distinct ways in which including perennial forages in an arable crop rotation reduces the weed burden in the annual crops that follow.

13. Identify and discuss the two most effective methods by which agricultural practice can mitigate against greenhouse gas emissions.

References

Abawi, G.S., and T.L. Widmer. 2000. Impact of soil health management practices on soil-borne pathogens, nematodes, and root diseases of vegetable crops. Appl. Soil Ecol. 15:37–47.

Albrecht, H. 2005. Development of arable weed seedbanks during the 6 years after the change from conventional to organic farming. Weed Res. 45:339–350.

Alroe, H.F., M. Vaarst, and E.S. Kristensen. 2001. Does organic farming face distinctive livestock welfare issues? A conceptual analysis. J. Agric. Environ. Ethics 14:275–299.

Alyokhin, A., G. Porter, E. Grodena, and F. Drummond. 2005. Colorado potato beetle response to soil amendments: A case in support of the mineral balance hypothesis? Agric. Ecosyst. Environ. 109:234–244.

Aulakh, M.S., D.A. Rennie, and E.A. Paul. 1984. Gaseous nitrogen losses from soils under zero-till as compared with conventional till management systems. J. Environ. Qual. 13:130–136.

Ball, B.C., C.A. Watson, and I. Crichton. 2007. Nitrous oxide emissions, cereal growth, N recovery, and soil nitrogen status after ploughing organically managed grass/clover swards. Soil Use Manage. 23:145–155.

Barnes, R.F., C.J. Nelson, K.J. Moore, and M. Collins (ed.) 2007. Forages: The science of grassland agriculture. 6th ed. Blackwell, Ames, IA.

Beanland, L., P.L. Phelan, and S. Salminen. 2003. Micronutrient interactions on soybean growth and the developmental performance of three insect herbivores. Environ. Entomol. 32:641–651.

Berry, P.M., R. Sylvester-Bradley, L. Philipps, D.J. Hatch, S.P. Cuttle, F.W. Rayns, and P. Goslin. 2002. Is the productivity of organic farms restricted by the supply of available nitrogen? Soil Use Manage. 18:248–255.

Bhandral, R., S. Saggar, N.S. Bolan, and M.J. Hedley. 2007. Transformation of nitrogen and nitrous oxide emission from grassland soils as affected by compaction. Soil Tillage Res. 94:482–492.

Bird, E.A., G.L. Bultena, and J.C. Gardner. 1995. Planting the future. Developing an agriculture that sustains land and community. Iowa State Univ. Press, Ames.

Clancy, K. 2006a. Greener eggs and ham: The benefits of pasture-raised swine, poultry, and egg production. Union of Concerned Scientists, Cambridge, MA.

Clancy, K. 2006b. Greener pastures: How grass-fed beef and milk contribute to healthy eating. Union of Concerned Scientists, Cambridge, MA.

Clark, E.A. 2001. Diversity and stability in humid temperate pastures. p. 103–118. In P.G. Tow and A. Lazenby (ed.) Competition and succession in pastures, CAB Int., New York.

Clark, E.A. 2004. Benefits of re-integrating livestock and forages in crop production systems. J. Crop Improv. 12:405–436.

Clark, E.A., and K. Maitland. 2004. On-farm survey of organic farm practice in Ontario 2001–2003. Univ. of Guelph, Guelph, ON, Canada.

Clark, E.A., L. Eccles, and K. Maitland. 2006a. Cover crops for late summer in organic cereal rotations. *In* Proc. of the 3rd Annu. Organic Crop Res. Symp., Guelph, ON, Canada. 27 Jan. 2006. Univ. of Guelph, Guelph, ON, Canada.

Clark, E.A., H. Karsten, B. Murphy, and B. Tracy. 2006b Ecology of plant communities in forage-livestock systems. p. 10–31. *In* E. Rayburn (ed.) Forage production in pasture-based livestock production. NRAES-172, National Resource, Agriculture, and Engineering Service, Cooperative Extension, Ithaca, NY.

Clark, E.A., and R.P. Poincelot (ed.) 1996. The contribution of managed grasslands to sustainable agriculture in the Great Lakes Basin. J. Sustain. Agric. 8:1–172.

Conant, R.T., K. Paustian, S.J. Del Grosso, and W.J. Parton. 2005. Nitrogen pools and fluxes in grassland soils sequestering carbon. Nutr. Cycling Agroecosyst. 71:239–248.

Conant, R.T., K. Paustian, and E.T. Elliott. 2001. Grassland management and conversion into grassland: Effects on soil carbon. Ecol. Appl. 11:343–355.

Conant, R.T., J. Six, and K. Paustian. 2003. Land use effects on soil carbon fractions in the southeastern United States: I. Management-intensive versus extensive grazing. Biol. Fertil. Soils 38:386–392.

Dalgaard, T., N. Halberg, and I.S. Kristensen. 1998. Can organic farming help to reduce N losses? Experiences from Denmark. Nutr. Cycling Agroecosyst. 52:277–287.

Entz, M.H., V.S. Baron, P.M. Carr, D.W. Meyer, S.R. Smith, Jr., and W.P. McCaughey. 2002. Potential of forages to diversify cropping systems in the northern Great Plains. Agron. J. 94:240–250.

Entz, M.H., J. Bullied, D.A. Forster, R. Gulden, and J.K. Vessey. 2001. Extraction of subsoil nitrogen by alfalfa, alfalfa/wheat, and perennial grass systems. Agron. J. 93:495–503.

Entz, M.H., J. Bullied, and F. Katepa-Mupondwa. 1995. Rotational benefits of forage crops in Canadian prairie farming systems. J. Prod. Agric. 8:521–529.

Eriksen, J. 2001. Implications of grazing by sows for nitrate leaching from grassland and the succeeding cereal crop. Grass Forage Sci. 56:317–322.

Eriksen, J., J.E. Hermansen, K. Strudsholm, and K. Kristensen. 2006. Potential loss of nutrients from different rearing strategies for fattening pigs on pasture. Soil Use Manage. 22:256–266.

Fales, S.L., S.A. McMurry, and W.T. McSweeny. 1993. The role of pasture in northeastern dairy farming: Historical perspective, trends, and research imperatives for the future. p. 111–132. *In* J.T. Sims (ed.) Agricultural research in the northeastern United States: Critical review and future perspectives. ASA, Madison, WI.

Forest Resources Assessment. 2001. Global ecological zoning for the global forest resources assessment 2000. Final Report. Working Paper 56. Forestry Dep., FAO, Rome.

Frame, J. 1992. Improved grassland management. Farming Press Books, Ipswich, UK.

Gentile, R.M., D.L. Martino, and M.H. Entz. 2005. Influence of perennial forages on subsoil organic carbon in a long-term rotation study in Uruguay. Agric. Ecosyst. Environ. 105:419–423.

Gerrish, J. 2004. Management-intensive grazing. The grassroots of grass farming. Green Park Press, Ridgeland, MS.

Grant, B., W.N. Smith, R. Desjardins, R. Lemke, and C. Li. 2004. Estimated N_2O and CO_2 emissions as influenced by agricultural practices in Canada. Clim. Change 65:315–332.

Gregorich, E.G., P. Rochette, A.J. VandenBygaart, and D.A. Angers. 2005. Greenhouse gas contributions of agricultural soils and potential mitigation practices in eastern Canada. Soil Tillage Res. 83:53–72.

Hamilton, C., U. Emaneulson, K. Forslund, I. Hansson, and T. Ekman. 2006. Mastitis and related management factors in certified organic dairy herds in Sweden. Acta Vet. Scand. 48:11, doi:10.1186/1751-0147-48-11.

Haring, A.M. 2003. Organic dairy farms in the EU: Production systems, economics, and future development. Livest. Prod. Sci. 80:89–97.

Hoekstra, N.J., R.P.O. Schulte, P.C. Struik, and E.A. Lantinga. 2007. Pathways to improving the N efficiency of grazing bovines. Eur. J. Agron. 26:363–374.

Houghton, J.T., Y. Ding, D.J. Griggs, M. Noguer, P.J. van der Linden, X. Dai, K. Maskell, and C.A. Johnson (eds.) 2001. Climate change 2001: The scientific basis, contribution of Working Group 1 to third assessment report of Intergovernmental Panel on Climate Change. Cambridge Univ. Press, Cambridge, UK.

Howard, A. 1943. An agricultural testament. Oxford Univ. Press, New York.

Huarte, H.R., and R.L. Benech Arnold. 2003. Understanding mechanisms of reduced annual weed emergence in alfalfa. Weed Sci. 51:876–885.

Jackson, R.D., M.M. Bell, and C. Gratton. 2007. Assessing ecosystem variance at different scales to generalize about pasture management in southern Wisconsin. Agric. Ecosyst. Environ. 122:471–478.

Johnson, J.M.-F., R.R. Allmaras, and D.C. Reicosky. 2006. Source carbon from crop residues, roots and rhizodeposits using the national grain-yield database. Agron. J. 98:622–636.

Jones, S.K., R.M. Rees, D. Kosmas, B.C. Ball, and U.M. Skiba. 2006. Carbon sequestration in a temperate grassland; management and climatic controls. Soil Use Manage. 22:132–142.

Kaiser, E.A., K. Kohrs, M. Kucke, E. Schnug, J.C. Much, and O. Heinemeyer. 1998. Nitrous oxide release from arable soil: Importance of perennial forage crops. Biol. Fertil. Soils 28:36–43.

Karsten, H.D., G.W. Roth, and L.D. Muller. 2003. Evaluation of corn hybrids at two stages of development for grazing heifers. Agron. J. 95:870–877.

Lal, R. 2003. Offsetting global CO_2 emissions by restoration of degraded soils and intensification of world agriculture and forestry. Land Deg. Dev. 14:309–322.

Ledgard, S.F. 2001. Nitrogen cycling in low input legume-based agriculture, with emphasis on legume/grass pastures. Plant Soil 228:43–59.

Liebman, M., and D.N. Sundberg. 2006. Seed mass affects the susceptibility of weed and crop species to phytotoxins extracted from red clover shoots. Weed Sci. 54:340–345.

Lund, V., and B. Algers. 2003. Research on animal health and welfare in organic farming: A literature review. Livest. Prod. Sci. 80:55–68.

Lynch, D.H., C. Roberts, and P. Voroney. 2006. Sustainability of organic dairying in Canada. *In* Proc. of the Joint Organic Congress, Odense, Denmark. 30–31 May 2006.

Maloney, T.S., E.S. Oplinger, and K.A. Albrecht. 1999. Small grains for fall and spring forage. J. Prod. Agric. 12:488–494.

Marriott, E.E., and M.M. Wander. 2006. Total and labile soil organic matter in organic and conventional farming systems. Soil Sci. Soc. Am. J. 70:950–959.

Martin, B., I. Verdier-Metz, S. Buchin, C. Hurtaud, and J.B. Coulon. 2005. How do the nature of forages and pasture diversity influence the sensory quality of dairy livestock products? Anim. Sci. 81:205–212.

Martin, D. 2005. Typical background diets for calves. Available at http://www.omafra.gov.on.ca/english/livestock/beef/facts/info_bkgrdiet.htm (verified 25 June 2009). Ontario Ministry of Agriculture, Food, and Rural Affairs, Guelph, ON, Canada.

McConkey, O.M. 1952. Conservation in Canada. Dent, Toronto, ON, Canada.

McGuirk, S.M., and S.D. Semrad. 2005. Toxicologic emergencies in cattle. Vet. Clin. North Am. Food Anim. Pract. 21:729–749.

Mellon, M., C. Benbrook, and K. Lutz Benbrook. 2001. Hogging it: Estimates of antimicrobial abuse in livestock. Union of Concerned Scientists, Washington, DC.

Meyer-Aurich, A., A. Weersink, K. Janovicek, and B. Deen. 2006. Cost efficient rotation and tillage options to sequester carbon and mitigate GHG emissions from agriculture in Eastern Canada. Agric. Ecosyst. Environ. 117:119–127.

Mohler, C.L. 1996. Ecological bases for the cultural control of annual weeds. J. Prod. Agric. 9:468–474.

Murphy, B. 1999. Greener pastures on your side of the fence. 4th ed. Arriba, Colchester, VT.

NASS. 2002a. Census of agriculture: Volume 1, Chapter 1, U.S. national level data, Table 8. Land: 2002 and 1997. Available at http://www.agcensus.usda.gov/Publications/2002/Volume_1,_Chapter_1_US/st99_1_008_008.pdf (verified 25 June 2009). USDA, National Agricultural Statistics Service, Washington, DC.

NASS. 2002b. Census of agriculture, Volume 1, Chapter 1, U.S. national level data, Table 34. Specified crops by acres harvested: 2002 and 1997. Available at http://www.agcensus.usda.gov/Publications/2002/Volume_1,_Chapter_1_US/st99_1_034_034.pdf (verified 25 June 2009). USDA, National Agricultural Statistics Service, Washington, DC.

Nation, A. 2004. Quality pasture. How to create it, manage it, and profit from it. Green Park Press, Ridgeland, MS.

Nation, A. 2008. Allan's observations. Stockman Grass Farmer 8(8):1, 9–32, 38–39.

National Standard of Canada. 2006. Organic production systems. General principles and management standards. Available at http://www.organicagcentre.ca/Docs/Cdn_Stds_Principles2006_e.pdf (verified 25 June 2009). CAN/CGSB-32.310-2006. National Standard of Canada, Toronto, ON, Canada.

Natural Resources Conservation Service. n.d. Plant nutrient content data. Available at http://www2.ftw.nrcs.usda.gov/mm/plant-nutrient-content.jsp (verified 25 June 2009). USDA, Natural Resources Conservation Service, Washington, DC.

Oehl, F., A. Oberson, H.U. Tagmann, J.M. Besson, D. Dubois, P. Mader, H.R. Roth, and E. Frossard. 2002. Phosphorus budget and phosphorus availability in soils under organic and conventional farming. Nutr. Cycling Agroecosyst. 62:25–35.

Ogle, S.M., F.J. Breidt, and K. Paustian. 2005. Agricultural management impacts on soil organic carbon storage under moist and dry climatic conditions of temperate and tropical regions. Biogeochemistry 72:87–121.

OMAFRA. 2002. Agronomy guide for field crops. Available at http://www.omafra.gov.on.ca/english/crops/pub811/p811toc.html (verified 25 June 2009). Publ. 811. Ontario Ministry of Agriculture, Food, and Rural Affairs, Guelph, ON, Canada.

OMAFRA. 2008. Vegetable production recommendations. Available at http://www.omafra.gov.on.ca/english/crops/pub363/p363toc.htm (verified 25 June 2009). Publ. 363. Ontario Ministry of Agriculture, Food, and Rural Affairs, Guelph, ON, Canada.

OMAFRA. n.d. Field crop statistics. Available at http://www.omafra.gov.on.ca/english/stats/crops/index.html (verified 25 June 2009). Ontario Ministry of Agriculture, Food, and Rural Affairs, Guelph, ON, Canada.

Padel, S., O. Schmid, and V. Lund. 2004. Organic livestock standards. p. 57–72. In M. Vaarst, S. Roderick, V. Lund, and W. Lockeretz (ed.) Animal health and welfare in organic agriculture. CABI, Wallingford, UK.

Phelan, L.P., K.H. Norris, and J.F. Mason. 1996. Soil-management history and host preference by Ostrinia nubilalis: Evidence for plant mineral balance mediating insect–plant interactions. Environ. Entomol. 25:1329–1336.

Ramírez-Restrepo, C., and T. Barry. 2005. Alternative temperate forages containing secondary compounds for improving sustainable productivity in grazing ruminants. Anim. Feed Sci. Technol. 120:179–201.

Rayburn, E. (ed.) 2006. Forage production in pasture-based livestock production. Publ. NRAES-172. National Resource, Agriculture, and Engineering Service, Cooperative Extension, Ithaca, NY.

Rayburn, E. (ed.) 2007. Forage utilization for pasture-based livestock production. Publ. NRAES-173. National Resource, Agriculture, and Engineering Service, Cooperative Extension, Ithaca, NY.

Reid, F. 2002. Integrating layer chickens into a certified organic raspberry and vegetable farm. In Cultivating Communities: Proc. 14th IFOAM Organic World Congress, Victoria, BC, Canada. 21–28 Aug. 2002. IFOAM, Bonn, Germany.

Reksen, O., A. Tverdal, and E. Ropstad. 1999. A comparative study of reproductive performance in organic and conventional dairy husbandry. J. Dairy Sci. 82:2605–2610.

Russelle, M.P., and A.S. Birr. 2004. Large-scale assessment of symbiotic dinitrogen fixation by crops: Soybean and alfalfa in the Mississippi River basin. Agron. J. 96:1754–1760.

Russelle, M.P., M.H. Entz, and A.J. Franzleubbers. 2007. Reconsidering integrated crop–livestock systems in North America. Agron. J. 99:325–334.

Russelle, M.P., J.F.S. Lamb, B.R. Montgomery, D.W. Elsenheimer, B.S. Miller, and C.P. Vance. 2001. Alfalfa rapidly remediates excess inorganic nitrogen at a fertilizer spill site. J. Environ. Qual. 30:30–36.

Samson, R., M. Sudhagar, R. Boddey, S. Sokhansanj, D. Quesada, S. Urquiaga, V. Reis, and C. Ho Lem. 2005. The potential of C_4 perennial grasses for developing a global BIO-HEAT industry. Crit. Rev. Plant Sci. 24:461–495.

Sato, K., P.C. Bartlett, R.J. Erskine, and J.B. Kaneene. 2005. A comparison of production and management between Wisconsin organic and conventional dairy herds. Livest. Prod. Sci. 93:105–115.

Sehested, J., T. Kristensen, and K. Soegaard. 2003. Effect of concentrate supplementation level on production, health and efficiency in an organic dairy herd. Livest. Prod. Sci. 80:153–165.

Smidt, N., and L. Brimer. 2005. The use of herbs in pastures: An interview survey of biodynamic and organic farmers with dairy cattle. Agric. Human Values 22:355–363.

Smith, B. 2002. Nitrogenase reveals its inner secrets. Science 297:1654–1655.

Sooby, J., J. Landeck, and M. Lipson. 2007. 2007 national organic research agenda. Outcomes from the Scientific Congress on Organic Agricultural Research. Organic Farming Research Foundation, Santa Cruz, CA.

Spedding, C.R.W., J.M. Walsingham, and A.M. Hoxey. 1981. Biological efficiency in agriculture. Academic Press, London.

Statistics Canada. 2006. Census of agriculture, farm data and farm operator data, Available at http://www.statcan.ca/english/freepub/95-629-XIE/1/1.17.htm (verified 25 June 2009). Catalogue no. 95-629-XWE. Statistics Canada, Ottawa, ON, Canada.

Steiner, R. 1929. Landwirtschaftlicher Kursus. Section for Natural Science of the Anthroposophic Society, Dornach, Switzerland.

Stonehouse, D.P., E.A. Clark, and Y.O. Ogini. 2001. Organic and conventional dairying in Ontario. Biol. Agric. Hortic. 19:115–125.

Sulc, R.M., and B.F. Tracy. 2007. Integrated crop–livestock systems in the U.S. Corn Belt. Agron. J. 99:335–345.

Teasdale, J.R. 1996. Contribution of cover crops to weed management in sustainable agricultural systems. J. Prod. Agric. 9:475–479.

Teasdale, J.R., R.W. Mangum, J. Radhakrishnan, and M.A. Cavigelli. 2004. Weed seedbank dynamics in three organic farming crop rotations. Agron. J. 96:1429–1435.

Tonitto, C., M.B. David, and L.E. Drinkwater. 2006. Replacing bare fallows with cover crops in fertilizer-intensive cropping systems: A meta-analysis of crop yields and N dynamics. Agric. Ecosyst. Environ. 112:58–72.

USDA. 2008. National Organic Program: US NOP Title 7 Part 205. http://ecfr.gpoaccess.gov/cgi/t/text/text-idx?type=simple;c=ecfr;cc=ecfr;sid=4163ddc3518c1ffdc539675a ed8efe33;region=DIV1;q1=national%20organic%20program;rgn=div5;view=text; idno=7;node=7%3A3.1.1.9.31 (accessed 7 Aug. 2008, verified 25 June 2009). USDA, Washington, DC.

Vaarst, M., S.M. Thamsborg, T.W. Bennedsgaard, H. Houe, C. Enevoldsen, F.M. Aarestrup, and A. De Snoo. 2003. Organic dairy farmers' decision making in the first 2 years after conversion in relation to mastitis treatments. Livest. Prod. Sci. 80:109–120.

van Groenigen, J.W., G.L. Velthof, F.J.E. van der Bolt, A. Vos, and P.J. Kuikman. 2005. Seasonal variation in N_2O emissions from urine patches: Effects of urine concentration, soil compaction and dung. Plant Soil 273:15–27.

Vos, J., and P.E.L. van der Putten. 2004. Nutrient cycling in a cropping system with potato, spring wheat, sugar beet, oats and nitrogen catch crops: II. Effect of catch crops on nitrate leaching in autumn and winter. Nutr. Cycling Agroecosyst. 70:23–31.

Waghorn, G.C., and D.A. Clark. 2006. Greenhouse gas mitigation opportunities with immediate application to pastoral grazing for ruminants. Int. Congr. Ser. 1293:107–110.

Williams, J.R., B.J. Chambers, A.R. Hartley, and A.G. Chalmers. 2005. Nitrate leaching and residual soil nitrogen supply following outdoor pig farming. Soil Use Manage. 21:245–252.

Yang, X.M., and B.D. Kay. 2001. Rotation and tillage effects on soil organic carbon sequestration in a Typic Hapludalf in southern Ontario. Soil Tillage Res. 59:107–114.

Zwald, A.G., P.L. Ruegg, J.B. Kaneene, L.D. Warnick, S.J. Wells, C. Fossler, and L.W. Halbert. 2004. Management practices and reported antimicrobial usage on conventional and organic dairy farms. J. Dairy Sci. 87:191–201.

6

Organic Grains, Oilseeds, and Other Specialty Crops

Kathleen Delate
Department of Agronomy and Horticulture, Iowa State University, Ames

Organic field crops and specialty vegetable and other crops are the heart of organic food production in the United States; they represent the largest contribution to the organic food sector, and they feed livestock that provide organic meat and milk. It is important to distinguish conventional commodity crops from their organic counterparts. (Marketing organic products is discussed in detail in Chapter 10, Peterson and Janke, 2009, this volume.)

Field crops such as maize (*Zea mays* L.), soybeans [*Glycine max* (L.) Merr.], wheat (*Triticum aestivum* L.), and oats (*Avena sativa* L.) are often called *commodities*, a term that should be reserved for grains and oilseeds sold in the conventional marketplace. The term *commodity* assumes large volumes of relatively homogenous quality sufficient to meet fluctuating demand and fluid replacement in the case of breach of contract or other disruptions in the supply chain. Such conditions are characteristic of the mainstream markets for major crops but are not present in organic grain and oilseed production and marketing.

In contrast, the highly regulated and fragmented nature of certified organic production, processing, and retailing has resulted in a scarce supply of heterogeneous quality that is not easily replaceable, thus moving all organic grain and oilseeds into the realm of specialty crops. Moreover, when compared to the size of the conventional agriculture market, organic production and marketing to date can only be considered diminutive, and this segment of the food system must be described in different terms.

From produce to poultry, much of the organic food matrix relies on the production of organic grains, oilseeds, and pulses. Many are used by the livestock complex as a feed; the processed foods industry uses various derivatives as ingredients; and the produce sector often relies on manure and manure-based fertilizers that are derived from livestock fed organic grains. Compared with the conventional food system, the range of organic grain and oilseeds used by the organic food matrix is more diverse, production is multisectored, prices are higher, and the marketing and utilization profiles are often more complex (Sullivan, 2003a, 2003b). Due to increasing demand for organic protein and cooking oils, for example, soybeans destined for the food or animal feed sector may have

Table 6–1. Organic grain and oilseed acreage, 2005 (USDA Economic Research Service, 2005).

Crop	Hectares	Acres
Wheat (*Triticum aestivum* L.)	109,247	277,487
Maize (*Zea mays* L.)	51,446	130,672
Soybean [*Glycine max* (L.) Merr.]	48,117	122,217
Oats (*Avena sativa* L.)	18,293	46,465
Barley (*Hordeum vulgare* L.)	15,500	39,371
Dry pulses (e.g., lentils, *Lens culinaris* Medik.; black beans, *Phaseolus vulgaris* L.)	13,243	33,636

been secured from domestic sources or from fields as far away as China and Brazil, introducing additional levels of economic risk associated with transportation and quality. For organic crops with a transgenic counterpart, such as maize, soybean, or canola (*Brassica napus* var. *napus* L.), an expensive and time-consuming testing regime is often required by the purchaser to detect and ultimately avoid contamination in the final product. Finally, since the organic grain complex is subject to the USDA National Organic Program (NOP) rules, all sectors involved in the organic value chain are subject to federal oversight (USDA Agriculture Marketing Service, 2008).

Of the many grains, oilseeds, and pulses that are produced for the organic market, only maize, soybean, wheat, oats, and barley (*Hordeum vulgare* L.) are tracked by the USDA (USDA Economic Research Service, 2005). Table 6–1 shows the areas of organic grains and oilseeds reported by certification agencies in 2005, according to the USDA Economic Research Service (ERS).

Demand for certified organic products utilizing grain, oilseeds, and pulse crops as food ingredients or animal feed, coupled with inadequate supply, has resulted in record-level prices and significantly increased imports, especially of soybean. For example, the value of the organic maize crop reached $134 million in 2005 and $200 million in 2007. The inadequate supply of organic grains is evidence of a failure of the market and agricultural policies targeted to increase the number of organic growers, although the 2008 U.S. Farm Bill begins to address these issues by providing direct support for organic certification fees.

This chapter concentrates on the more prevalent organic grains in the United States—maize, soybean, and wheat—and covers the basics of their production and marketing. A final section discusses what the USDA refers to as *specialty crops* (organic fruits and vegetables) from a production and economic perspective, using tomato (*Solanum lycopersicum* L.) and apple [*Malus sylvestris* (L.) Mill var. *domestica* (Borkh.) Mansf.] as important case studies.

Maize

A staple throughout much of the world, maize, a crop native to the Western Hemisphere, has been bred for a wide variety of uses, from feed to fuel. However, since organic maize is in limited supply, the majority of production is used as feed for ruminants, swine, and poultry or is processed into flour or other ingredients such as syrup and starch for processed foods. Although there is no physiological reason organic field maize could not be used for industrial purposes, its high value generally forecloses any economically rational possibility of such use. There are many specialty types of field maize, such as waxy and high-lysine hybrids. While those cultivars produced through classical breeding could be grown and used in an organic system, some have been bred using transgenic technology and as a result cannot be grown in a certified organic farming operation. Overall demand for organic field maize by the livestock and food sectors has limited the demand for added-trait types of maize, as buyers are struggling to find adequate supply of any organic maize. Popcorn and sweet maize comprise specialty markets in their own right.

Production

According to USDA Economic Research Service (2005) data from 2005, the total U.S. organic maize production was 53,000 ha, spanning 33 states, 10 of which accounted for 84% of the total production. The leading states were Minnesota, Iowa, and Wisconsin. This represents a 10-year increase of about 40,000 ha, or an average of 4000 ha yr^{-1} since 1995, the first year organic production was reported, when there were approximately 13,500 ha.

Maize for Feed

Feed or field maize occupies a central role in a typical organic row-crop rotation because it is a high-value food and feed crop and requires a large amount of nitrogen for optimal yields compared with other crops in the rotation. Wheat also has significant nitrogen requirements so should not precede an organic maize crop. As a result of the crop's nutrient needs, maize often drives not only the marketing but also the fertility regime of the entire farm. Organic maize production relies on hybrids, although some farmers prefer growing open-pollinated varieties despite lower yields. After fertility, weed management is of primary concern, followed by insect and disease challenges.

Fertility

The fertility regime for all organic grains and pulses depends in large part on the crop rotation. Crop rotations are required in certified organic production as part of the organic system (Delate, 2002). Maize is perhaps the most challenging, as it requires 100 to 150 kg ha^{-1} of nitrogen, depending on existing soil fertility and previous crop contributions. Since most commercial organic fertilizers are cost-prohibitive on a large scale, organic farmers must monitor nutrients in each field and take aggressive measures to achieve the desired level of fertility by using a number of sources and strategies. This requires gathering baseline information during the time of transition to determine which soil amendments will be required when the synthetic fertilizers are removed from the system. This is a continuous process involving a level of complexity and flexibility that does not exist in conventional systems.

Maize requires approximately 2.15 kg of elemental nitrogen (N), 1.03 kg of phosphate (P_2O_5), and 2.40 kg of potash (K_2O) to produce 100 kg of grain. Acceptable organic maize yields, therefore, are based on soil amendments and N contributions from leguminous cover crops to supply a minimum of 140 kg of N, 67 kg of P, and 157 kg of K per hectare. Although one of the leading goals of organic production is minimizing the use of off-farm inputs, securing adequate fertility for vigorous maize growth and acceptable production is an annual challenge for the majority of organic farmers, whether nutrients are sourced on- or off-farm (Delate et al., 2006). While one goal of a sustainable, organic farm is to achieve a relatively closed nutrient cycle, the primary reason that off-farm sources of manure are required is that most organic farms do not have sufficient livestock on-farm producing enough manure to supply sufficient N to the maize crop. As a result, farmers sequence their crop rotations with the goal of providing a bank of N that will be present when the maize crop is planted in the rotation.

In organic production systems, maize is usually planted in a field following a leguminous crop such as clover (*Trifolium* spp.), alfalfa (*Medicago sativa* L.), or field peas (*Pisum sativum* L.) for a year or more. While the legumes may provide a significant amount of N (20 to 140 kg ha^{-1}, depending on the species mixture), this contribution may not meet the complete needs of the maize crop. Before planting in the spring, most farmers will supplement the current soil nutrients with animal manure or a manure-based compost in an amount that will provide the full complement of N necessary for vigorous plant growth. Many NOP-compliant fertilizers, such as fish emulsion, humates, humic acids, surfactants, bioactivators, biodynamic preparations, and others can also be used. However, they are viewed as cost prohibitive on a large scale and, as explained later, certain types may limit marketing options. Maintaining a soil pH of 6.0 to 7.0 is also critical for optimal crop production (Widman et. al., 2001). Various agricultural liming materials can be used to neutralize the acidity of soils and to provide calcium and magnesium, but concern about soil magnesium buildup from dolomitic lime applications has led to the popularity of naturally mined calcium carbonate (limestone) in organic systems. Soil testing will help determine the need for lime and other rock mineral powders, such as rock phosphate. Hard-rock phosphate varies considerably in soil reactivity while soft-rock or colloidal phosphate has greater applicability. On many organic farms, gypsum is used to supply calcium and sulfur, especially on high-pH and sodic soils. There are several organic-compliant commercial fertilizers and soil amendments that can be used for supplemental potassium, including sulfate of potash-magnesia (e.g., Sul-Po-Mag) and naturally mined potassium sulfate, but all must be approved by a certification agency before application.

Research across the U.S. Midwest has demonstrated excellent organic maize yields in the range of 7.5 to 13 t ha^{-1} (Delate and Cambardella, 2004; Delate et al., 2003). High yields have been achieved by preceding organic maize crops with legumes, such as alfalfa, and composted manure applications. Soil quality has remained high in these systems even with multiple tillage operations.

Weed Management

In areas where soil fertility is adequate, weeds are considered the greatest constraint in organic maize production. With the focus in organic crop production on prevention of weed problems, establishment and growth of weed seeds can be reduced through crop rotations, allelopathic cover crops, and pre-plant tillage. A longer crop rotation (at least three years) can be instrumental in disrupting weed establishment. In a study in Greenfield, Iowa, the shorter two-year organic rotation of soybean–wheat had, on average, two to three times the weed population of the three- and four-year rotations. The most critical time for weed management occurs in the early stages of grain crop growth, when competition is limited. Organic farmers use several tools, including rotary hoes and harrows, for early weed management. Later, when the crop can withstand soil accumulation around the base of plants, cultivators are used to remove weeds in the row and in some cases with ridge-till equipment create ridges in the plant row. A propane flame burner may be used, especially in wet fields where tillage may cause compaction.

Insect and Disease Management

In a properly rotated organic maize field planted at a reasonable time, usually past 15 May when soil temperatures are consistently above 10°C, maize disease and insect pests do not cause economic damage. In some earlier-planted organic maize fields, damage from seed and seedling rots can occur, such as those caused by *Pythium, Fusarium, Diplodia, Rhizoctonia,* and *Penicillium* spp. and various soilborne bacteria. Classically bred (nontransgenic) plant resistance is the main avenue of protection against foliar diseases in maize, such as gray leaf spot caused by the fungus *Cercospora zeae-maydis* Tehon & E.Y. Daniels; anthracnose leaf blight caused by the fungus *Colletotrichum graminicola* (Ces.) G.W. Wilson; common maize rust caused by the fungus *Puccinia sorghi* Schwein; and Stewart's wilt caused by the bacterium *Erwinia stewartii* (Smith) Dye. Because pathogen inocula can survive on infected crop residue, tillage and crop rotation also limit continued spread of these organisms. Resistant varieties and hybrids also help manage ear rots at harvest, such as Fusarium ear rot caused by the fungus *Fusarium moniliforme* Sheldon. Harvesting at proper maturity and moisture content less than 20% will aid in preventing excessive ear rotting.

Planting later than conventional maize dates in warm soil will also help prevent seed and seedling insect pest problems. Wireworms [*Melanotus communis* (Gyllenhal)] are click beetle larvae and generally not a problem except in some cases of maize following pasture, Conservation Reserve Program ground, or fields under reduced tillage or heavy crop residue. Because wireworms can live for two to six years, rotating maize away from infested fields is a recommended practice. Seed maize maggots [*Hylemya cilicrura* (Rond.)] are legless fly larvae that attack seeds particularly in cool, wet fields. Use of quality seed to ensure quick germination also reduces the likelihood of damage.

Habitat diversification has been recommended as a strategy to enhance biological control and subsequent pest reduction in any cropping system, either through resource provisioning for natural enemies (Altieri, 1994; Andow, 1991) or through spatial interference from a mixture of crop and noncrop species (Root, 1973). Maize insect pests tend to remain below economic threshold levels when varieties with natural resistance are planted, such as those with resistance to the European corn borer [*Ostrinia nubilalis* (Hübner)]. Corn rootworms (northern and western types of *Diabrotica* spp.) are not generally problematic on organic farms where three- to four-year crop rotations are practiced. Corn earworm [*Helicoverpa zea* (Boddie)] is often observed on ear tips at harvest but is rarely economically damaging. Common stalk borer [*Papaipema nebris* (Guenée)] can be a problem along field borders in certain years. All lepidoteran pests can be treated with natural sprays of *Bacillus thuringiensis* (Bt) in organic fields, but economic thresholds vary from 15 to 50% damaged plants, depending on infestation level at a specific stage—the younger the plant, the lower the tolerance. There are many natural enemies of lepidopteran pests, however, including predators that feed on eggs and larvae, such as lady beetles (various spp.), lacewings (various spp.), bigeyed bugs (*Geocorus* spp.), damsel bugs (*Nabis* spp.), minute pirate bugs (various spp.), and others. The most significant parasitic wasps against European corn borer are *Macrocentrus grandii* Goidanich, a braconid larval parasite, and *Trichogramma ostriniae* (Peng & Chen), an egg parasite. Pathogens of corn borer include *Nosema pyrausta* (Paillot) and *Beauveria bassiana* (Balsamo) Vuillemin.

Marketing Organic Grains

In many respects, the essential structure for moving grain from producer to consumer has changed very little over time. This is because agricultural production is seasonal, consumption is constant, and grain storage and maintenance of quality are essential functions of the supply chain, regardless of epoch or production system. However, since the production volumes of organic grains are quite small compared with conventional grains, with producers scattered across a wide geographical area, there exists no overarching marketing construct. Thus, the marketing of organic grains often consumes an inordinate amount of the farmer's time and may limit expansion of the organic market. Unlike conventional outlets, there is often limited or no opportunity to market grain at a facility close to the farm. Few traditional farmer-owned organic grain cooperatives exist, and interested processors located within a reasonable distance rarely have the capital or the storage to purchase and hold large amounts of grain for future use. Similarly, no current price discovery and risk management tool on the order of the Chicago Board of Trade is available to organic framers. Instead, they rely on an ad hoc system of marketing to ensure receiving a fair price for their grain. The range of price bids is often determined by calling other farmers, brokers, grain merchants, and end users. Since instituting the bimonthly online organic grain marketing report in 2006, the USDA Agriculture Marketing Service has used this same method of price discovery, but the result is a lagging price indicator because it is a report of historical rather than current prices. However, coupled with the relatively slow adoption of domestic organic grain production, the price discovery method often means that most buyers and sellers are personally acquainted, and mutual reputations for fair dealing are often topics of industry conversation.

The determination of the actual price paid to the farmer for grain is a function of supply and demand, grain quality, distance to the delivery point, and amount of time the farmer must store the grain on-farm before the purchaser demands delivery. Of these factors, supply and demand dominates the pricing decision. If demand falls and supply remains static or increases, the farmer may find quality standards stiffen; they are asked to share the transportation and storage burden; and bid prices decrease. Indeed, since 2002, the year the organic rules were fully implemented, this latter situation was the norm and reflected, at least in part, the standard protocol of the conventional system. Grain buyers purchased grain on a delivered basis, paid only for clean grain, deducted for the amount of material other than grain, such as dirt and weed seeds, and discounted payment for the amount of damaged grain contained in the load delivered. During the 2007–2008 marketing cycle, however, the demand for organic grain increased significantly while supply remained static. Grain purchasers increased bids, lowered quality standards, obtained additional storage space, and absorbed the cost of transportation to maintain customer bases and production schedules.

As the organic supply chain has matured, the problem of storage has been addressed by some purchasers and allows for at least some of fall harvest to move directly to the buyer, but only on a limited basis. The primary driver behind the decision to purchase and store grain is the cost of storage. Many states require payment be made to in-state farmers within 30 days of change of legal possession.

In the conventional arena, a number of payment schemes exist that can avoid this requirement and could be applicable to organic production. These schemes are most often found in situations where the farmer has a vested interest in a value-added enterprise in which the production will be used or the purchaser is sufficiently capitalized and bonded to offer these variations. The 30-day-payment requirement effectively means that the buyer must have sufficient working capital to purchase the grain before being paid for the product in which the grain is utilized. Since the grain and oilseeds are very expensive, most buyers try to limit the amount of capital tied up in raw grain and can do so only by taking possession of the grain at the last possible moment.

Contracts for Organic Grain Crops

Because contracts are recommended as the most risk-averse method for marketing organic grains, an understanding of the legal and logistical aspects of contracting is an essential part of organic production (Born, 2005). The organic supply chain generally relies on a "Buyer's Call" contract in which the terms of the sale and remedies for breach are stated. As with any contract, the terms may be altered by mutual assent, but in basic form, the Buyer's Call contract allows the buyer a number of months to determine the exact date to demand the farmer make the contracted grain available for shipment. Often this means that the organic farmer must bear the costs and retain liability for maintaining grain quality for the period of the contract, which can exceed six months. Used as a tool in executing a "just-in-time" manufacturing model, purchasers prefer this type of contract because it minimizes the time any single entity in the supply chain is responsible for storing and paying for the contracted grain (Massey, 1999).

Under a Buyer's Call contract, time between contracting, shipping, and payment for the grain varies greatly and market prices can fluctuate beyond seasonal norms, such as low prices at harvest, and higher prices later in the spring and early summer. If the fluctuation results in supply sufficient to lower "spot" (current day) prices significantly, a buyer may be tempted to purchase grain from a third party and claim that the contracted grain fails to meet the required specification. If spot prices rise, the farmer may be tempted to sell contracted grain to a third party and claim low harvest yields when performance is demanded under the original contract. Moreover, the damaged party is under an obligation to limit the damages. A farmer must sell the crop, even at a lower price, and hope to recover money damages, if any, at a later date. Conversely, a buyer must attempt to purchase enough grain on a spot market to make up the loss and then seek money damages, if any, from the contracted farmer at a later date. In either case, the underlying contracts are technically breached and the damaged party may demand performance. However, it is unlikely that either party is in a position to institute legal action without damaging future relationships and likely that they would rather not incur the additional time and costs of the legal system.

Quality Standards

Organic grain and oilseed quality standards are a combination of unique end-user and universally accepted specifications. For example, "No. 2 yellow dent maize" has the same meaning regardless of method by which it was produced. End users of organic maize may also require that the presence of transgenic contamination be maintained under a maximum threshold, such as 1%. Similarly, minimum and maximum seed moisture, weight, size, relative cleanliness, and other factors that may affect the marketability of the end product will also be included in the contract (Massey, 1999).

Transgenic Contamination in Organic Production

One of the key concerns shared by all organic grain and oilseed producers and the organic industry is unintentional transgenic contamination of an organic crop. Today, maize, soybean, and canola crops are the most likely to be affected by contamination, although more transgenic crops on the horizon will likely keep this issue in the forefront of organic production. In the case of maize and canola, pollen drift is the most-feared source of contamination as well as the potential basis for legal action. Other sources of transgenic contamination include inadvertent contact with transgenic seed during the seed production-to-planting cycle and during the harvest-to-market cycle. While inadvertent contact with transgenic seed can be addressed by process precautions described below, pollen drift is not subject to reliable control measures, leaving farmers only rudimentary strategies to avoid field contamination.

Note that the organic rules only forbid the *intentional* planting of transgenic crops, require no testing before planting, and are silent as to the disposition of the crop in the event of contamination. The market regulates this issue either by requiring one or more tests for the presence of the transgenic contamination before taking title of the delivered crop or by not including a test in the contract requirements. However, since the potential consequences resulting from transgenic contamination escalate as the crop moves through the supply chain, early detection can either eliminate or mitigate financial and relational damages.

Avoiding Transgenic Contamination in the Market: Testing for Contaminants

Since the late 1990s, the organic industry has been testing for transgenic contamination, using ELISA or *strip tests* as the most widely used test because of the relative ease and low expense for rapid results. Usually performed outside of a laboratory, strip tests, however, are prone to inaccurate results due to sampling and/or operator error. The more expensive and presumably more reliable polymerase chain reaction (PCR) testing is often required, especially if the contamination can be detected in the final product, such as soymilk or maize chips (Ahmed, 2002). It is not unusual for a farmer and grain purchaser to agree to a testing regime utilizing both methods. Seed may be tested before planting, in the field, at harvest, and at delivery.

Although it may seem logical to assume that purchasing certified organic seed produced and packaged in a dedicated organic system would eliminate any transgenic contamination problem at the planting stage, this is not necessarily the case. The concentrated nature of the commodity crop breeding business and the domination of transgenic crops in the marketplace limit the options open to plant breeders to secure desirable "clean" nontransgenic traits from outside sources. As a result, breeders often rely on large seed companies for traits, which in some cases can be contaminated before arrival. While no seed company will guarantee their seed is free from contamination, organic seed companies strive to avoid contamination by carefully testing and tracking their seed production and sales system. Nevertheless, strip testing seed is a good production practice, regardless of the seed source.

Avoiding Transgenic Contamination through Field Techniques

Assuming that the organic seed is not contaminated at the time of planting, avoiding transgenic contamination in organic crops such as maize and canola during the production-to-harvest cycle involves managing systematic risks as well as possible. Organic crops should be planted with clean equipment as late in the season as is practicable to avoid pollination by wind-vectored transgenic pollen from neighboring fields. By staggering planting dates, the organic maize pollination date will in theory be past the date of pollen dispersal from the transgenic maize (Thomison, 2004). Although this may hold true in a controlled environment, the volume of transgenic maize pollen each season may limit the reliability of this strategy. Another recent strategy under investigation by the organic maize sector is a conventionally bred trait that will render the maize plant unable to utilize transgenic pollen during the reproductive stage. Known in the trade as Pura-Maize (Hoegemeyer Hybrids, Inc., Hooper, NE), this strategy has received little research attention on its efficacy or how yield performance is affected.

Once the crop is in the field, the focus shifts to avoiding contamination during harvest, storage, and delivery and is centered on using clean equipment. In the simplest case, all the equipment used during the harvest-to-market cycle is controlled by the farmer and/or is dedicated to organic production. If this is the situation, the farmer will not be burdened by extensive clean-outs of equipment that has been used during the harvest and transport of transgenic crops. Operations vary, and it is likely that some necessary equipment will not be used solely in organic production. These may include combines, augers, harvest wagons, and/or grain trucks, and the farmer will need to document the clean-out protocols of all of these to maintain organic certification. Of all the equipment used during the harvest-to-market cycle, the grain truck is probably the most likely to be owned and operated by someone other than the farmer. During harvest, the owner and operator have a financial interest in maximizing the amount of grain delivered. Since clean-out protocols are not an integral part of conventional agriculture, truck operators may be tempted to skip this step, do a less-than-adequate clean-out, and treat the paperwork required in a pro forma manner rather than a matter of necessity. To counter this tendency, farmers should inspect each truck carefully for any remaining grain in the trailer and insist that it be removed before loading the organic grain.

Remedies on Discovery of Contaminated Grain

As mentioned above, the options available to a farmer to sell a crop contaminated by transgenic material are limited only by contract and not by organic rules. Moreover, even if the farmer discovers the transgenic contamination, no legal obligation exists to disclose this discovery unless it is part of an enforceable contract. If the discovery is made in the field before harvest or before pick-up at the farm, the farmer may seek a market that does not require testing or ship the grain and hope that the buyer is unable to replicate the farmer's results, although the latter can be costly if the purchaser's tests confirm the initial results. Should the crop be rejected at the delivery point, the entity who owns the grain is then faced with the prospect of selling the load into the conventional market, returning the grain to the farmer, or finding an alternative organic market that does not test for transgenic contamination. Contamination could result in a 50% or more reduction in the selling price and a potential problem farther up the supply chain (Smyth et al., 2002). The presence of the transgenic protein marker will be detected in the eventual retail products if contamination occurs. Generally, maize producers should expect all buyers to require at least one test designed to detect the presence of the transgenic marker and implement an avoidance strategy. As an example, a transgenic marker was detected in taco shells in 2002, triggering a massive public awareness campaign. However, if the maize is sold into the livestock market, there is less chance that the transgenic contamination would be detected.

Marketing Organic Maize

In the organic arena, there are established markets for yellow, white, blue, and red field maize, popcorn, and sweet maize. In terms of acres, yields, and marketing opportunities, yellow field maize remains dominant. Most farmers are familiar with growing yellow field maize and have the necessary equipment on hand to produce and store the crop. The market value of organic maize is a function of prospective use, quality, distance to market, variety, test weight, moisture, absence or presence of toxins (mycotoxins, aflatoxin, vomatoxin), and demand. Organic field maize is often sold as livestock feed and to food processors. Contract specifications are sometimes more stringent for the food sector, although this tends to vary in relationship to supply. The largest single market for organic field maize is as a feedstock for organic poultry, the overall production of which has increased significantly over the last decade.

Other markets use organic yellow maize or a derivative as an ingredient in a wide variety of products, from chips to vodka. Accessing any given market is often determined by the volume and quality of yellow field maize to be sold. Livestock markets require large volumes of maize, can be more tolerant of contaminants and damaged grain, and often demand shipment by rail to either the East or West Coast of the United States. A standard rail grain car or hopper car holds between 73 and 113 Mg of grain and must be loaded in a timely fashion at a facility with a system and equipment certified organic under the rules. Although not without exception, organic farmers who intend to sell into this market will do so through an entity that has established facilities capable of loading rail cars.

Yellow maize along with red, blue, and white varieties are in demand as food ingredients, especially in maize chips, tortillas, and similar products. As end use moves from feeding livestock to food for human consumption, the contract specifications become more rigorous. For example, maize destined for livestock consumption may or may not be tested for transgenic contamination. In contrast, most if not all maize that is to be made into food will be tested to determine the level, if any, of transgenic contamination. Additionally, the weight, moisture, starch, oil, and protein specifications may also appear on the contract specifications because food manufacturers universally desire a consistent product that may compromise steps in production if there is sufficient variation in inputs. Although the demand for maize as a food ingredient continues to grow, it remains low in terms of overall volume compared with the livestock market. Yields also lag in red, white, and blue maize production compared with yellow maize, and additional premiums must be paid to the producer to secure production. Additionally, production of these more colorful varieties tends to be concentrated in areas that limit the distance to market.

Soybean

A boom in organic soybean sales occurred from 1990 to 2002 when sales to Japanese tofu and soy markets exceeded domestic sales. By 2007 demand had outstripped supply in the United States, and organic soybeans are now imported from China and Latin America to satisfy manufacturers' needs.

Weed Management

The most important weed preventative measure in organic soybean production is crop rotation. A cover crop of winter rye (*Secale cereale* L.), seeded at 60 kg ha^{-1} preceding the soybean crop can help provide allelopathic management of weeds (Weston, 1996). Planting at a later date than conventional soybean will allow for warmer soil temperatures, facilitating quick soybean germination and growth. Choosing soybean varieties with large canopies to shade out weeds is also recommended. Planting at high population rates (above 420,000 seeds ha^{-1}) also helps create a more competitive crop able to withstand mechanical tillage. Before planting, tilling weeds and immediately planting into a clean seedbed is also beneficial. Within four days of planting, the soybean field should be rotary hoed or harrowed when weeds are in the white-thread stage. Once the soybeans have emerged, they should be rotary hoed again, and if weed pressure is high, then again three or four days later. Two-row cultivations should be sufficient if good rotary hoeing has been accomplished. "Walking" or "roguing" the soybeans to remove large weeds, such as velvetleaf (*Abutilon theophrasti* Medik.) and giant ragweed (*Ambrosia trifida* L.) that have escaped cultivation, is important to prevent weed seed production in future crops.

Insect and Disease Management

As with organic maize crops, organic soybean plants experience few economically damaging disease and insect pests, with the exception of Asian soybean rust (*Phakopsora pachyrhizi* Syd.), which can cause significant leaf damage and yield loss in more tropical areas, and soybean aphid (*Aphis glycines* Matsumura), which appears to lower yields in years of severe infestation. A typical organic soybean field is a complex agroecosystem with more than 20 species of pest and beneficial species. Pest insect populations can vary from year to year, between sites, and between varieties, so soybeans should be scouted regularly to determine levels of infestation. Foliage-eating insects, such as cloverworm [*Plathypena scabra* (Fabricius)], looper (various spp.), and armyworm (*Spodoptera* spp.), are present at low to moderate levels in most organic soybean fields throughout the growing season, but no yield loss has been reported from these insects. Bean leaf beetle [*Cerotoma trifurcata* (Forster)] can be problematic in certain years, chewing holes in leaves and transmitting bean pod mottle virus (Krell et al., 2004). Seed-coat staining results from infection from insect-vectored bean pod mottle virus (syn. *Marmor valvolorum*), purple stain [caused by *Cercospora kikuchii* (Mastsumoto & Tomoyasu) M. W. Gardner], and *Fusarium* spp. Experiments with various organic-compliant spray treatments, however, have demonstrated few options for organic farmers (Delate et al., 2009). Varietal differences have been detected in bean leaf beetle susceptibility, but overall the best solution has come from the soybean food industry by developing a method to sort and remove the stained seed coat that results from bean pod mottle virus infection. Another beetle that is commonly reported from organic soybean fields is the spotted cucumber beetle (*Diabrotica undecimpunctata howardi* Barber), which also feeds on leaves but is rarely economically important. Green and brown stink bugs [*Acrosternum hilare* (Say), *Nezara viridula* (L.), *Euschistus servus* (Say)] can cause damage to soybean pods and seeds, and some losses are expected each year.

Beneficial insects found in organic soybean fields that help regulate pest populations include several ladybeetle species (Coccinellidae) and parasitic wasps against soybean aphid, such as *Binodoxys communis* (Gahan), a braconid wasp. Coccinellids, particularly the convergent lady beetle [*Hippodamia convergens* (Guerin-Meneville)] and the seven-spotted lady beetle [*Coccinella septempunctata* (L.)], are the most abundant predators, followed by syrphid fly larvae [Syrphidae: *Allograpta oblique* (Say) and *Syrphus* spp.] and cecidomyiids [e.g., *Aphidoletes aphidimyza* (Rondani)], but anthocorids [e.g., big-eyed bug, *Geocoris* spp.; minute pirate bug, *Orius insidiosus* (Say)] and chrysopids (lacewings, *Chrysoperla* spp.) also impact pest populations. Numerous fungal diseases also affect aphids, including *Entomophthora* spp. and *Zoophthora* spp., particularly during wet weather.

As with soybean insect pests, soybean diseases exist at low levels in organic soybean fields every year but rarely cause economic damage. Diseases affecting leaves and aboveground plant parts include bacterial blight (caused by the bacterium *Pseudomonas syringae* pv. *glycinea* Coerper), brown spot [caused by the fungus *Septoria glycines* (Hemmi)], brown stem rot [caused by the fungus *Phialophora gregata* (Allington & D. W. Chamb.) W. Gams], and pod and stem blight [caused by the fungi *Diaporthe phaseolorum* var. *sojae* (Lehman) Wehm. and *Phomopsis longicola* (Roy and Ratnayake)]. Downy mildew [caused by the fungus *Peronospora manshurica* (Naumov) Syd.] can occur in prolonged wet weather. Soybean mosaic virus and bean pod mottle virus are vectored by soybean aphids and bean leaf beetles, respectively; incidence of these diseases can affect leaf structure and reduce yields in areas of high infestation.

Similar to the management of maize diseases, resistant soybean varieties serve as the first line of defense against these pathogens, but equally important are rotating soybean with nonhost crops, such as maize, sorghum [*Sorghum bicolor* (L.) Moench], or small grains for a minimum of two years. Destruction of infected plants through tillage is also recommended for certain diseases, such as Sclerotinia stem rot [caused by the fungus *Sclerotinia sclerotiorum* (Lib.) de Bary]. Diseases affecting soybean roots that respond well to crop rotation include Phytophthora rot (caused by the fungus *Phytophthora sojae*) and Rhizoctonia stem rot (caused by the fungus *Rhizoctonia solani* J. G. Kühn). Planting in warm soil also helps alleviate soil pathogen problems. Soybean cyst nematode (*Heterodera glycines* Ichinohe) is rarely a problem in properly rotated organic soybean fields.

Marketing Organic Soybean

Organic soybean is generally marketed to the livestock feed and food ingredient markets. When used as a livestock feed, soybeans must first be heated to inactivate lipoxygenase that will inhibit digestibility. The dominant mode of heating is accomplished by extruding the soybean into meal. Organic soybeans sold into food markets are processed into tofu, soy flour, soymilk, or tempeh or used as a constituent in numerous other foods (Sullivan, 2003a). Protein requirements dominate in food markets, with minimum levels usually set at 40%. For the food market, clean seed is an imperative, and contracts often specify the minimum allowable seed size and the amount of foreign material allowed in any lot. Because of the higher-quality demands in food-grade organic soybeans, these grains garner a much higher selling price.

Wheat

Small grains, such as wheat, oats, barley, and triticale (×*Triticosecale rimpaui* Wittm.), are considered an essential part of an organic system because of their ability to mitigate weed seed germination and improve soil quality through their deep rooting growth habit and high root biomass. Generally, small grains perform better on the deep soils in far northern climates where moderate temperatures occur during the growing season. In warmer climates, disease problems, while not devastating, can lower yields and reduce kernel weight and grain quality. Good-quality seed with good germination and no weed seed present should be selected. Organic seed should be secured, according to NOP regulation §205.204 (USDA Agriculture Marketing Service, 2008). After preparing the field with a field cultivator or a disk, wheat is planted at 130 to 180 kg ha^{-1} to permit a solid stand to compete with any weeds in the field. A cultipacker or spike tooth harrow is a good implement to use to firm and smooth the seedbed and improve seed-to-soil contact. Weed growth should be curtailed by shading from the extensive tillering of a healthy wheat crop planted in narrow rows.

Pest Management

Varieties should be selected based on genetic resistance to lodging and diseases, including powdery mildew caused by the fungus *Erysiphe graminis* f. sp. *tritici* E.M. Marchal, leaf rust caused by the fungus *Puccinia recondita* f. sp. *tritici* Dietel & Holw., common bunt (stinking smut) caused by the fungi *Tilletia caries* (DC.) Tul. & C. Tul. and *T. foetida* (Wallr.) Liro, loose smut caused by the fungus *Ustilago tritici* (Pers.) C. N. Jensen, Kellerm. & Swingle, and scab (head blight) caused by the fungus *Fusarium graminearum* Schw. (Weisz, 2005). Fusarium foot rot, a seedling blight caused by the fungus *Fusarium* sp., can be managed through crop rotation, planting winter types closer to frost dates, good soil nutrition, and proper planting depth. Several viruses, including barley yellow dwarf virus, which is transmitted by aphids, can be damaging if resistant varieties are not planted.

Insect problems are less prevalent than diseases in organic wheat crops but can be significant in certain areas (Chambers et al., 1986). Mitigation strategies for Hessian fly [*Mayetiola destructor* (Say)] include planting varieties resistant to biotype L (many biotypes of Hessian fly have overcome individual genes for resistance) and planting during "fly-free periods" in late fall when peak fly emergence has passed. Crop rotation is also important, including separation from last year's wheat fields. Oats, rye, and triticale are not favorable for Hessian fly reproduction, making them preferable over wheat for cover cropping in areas where wheat for grain is also produced. Several species of aphids colonize wheat plants, and these can transmit viruses. In organic fields, encouragement of natural enemies, including the parasitic wasps *Lysiphlebus testaceipes* (Cresson), *Diaeretiella rapae* (McIntosh), and *Aphelinus varipes* (Foerster), is useful for aphid management (Schmidt et al., 2003). Frost can reduce aphid populations, and cool weather will slow down aphid feeding and activity in the newly emerged crop. The wheat stem sawfly (*Cephus cinctus* Norton) also has a natural enemy, the parasitic wasp *Collyria coxator* (Villers).

To meet certified organic rules for planting a "soil-building crop rotation," often a leguminous crop can be underseeded or frost-seeded with the wheat crop. Mammoth clover (*Trifolium pratense* L.) or medium red clover (*Trifolium medium* L.) is often planted in the Midwest (Delate et al., 2006). When planting any leguminous crop, an organic-compliant inoculant should be used to increase nitrogen fixation, making sure that the inoculant does not have any transgenic components. Clover is seeded at 11 to 13 kg ha^{-1}.

Termination of Crop

Most organic farmers combine harvest wheat for grain, but the crop can also be chopped and fed to livestock, particularly if there are "skips" and extensive weed pressure has occurred. The wheat–red clover cover crop can also be turned under with a disk or plow if used strictly as a cover crop to provide soil fertility. Rolling and crimping the cover crop could also occur if no-till organic practices are used. This would take place in June when wheat heads are just forming or after wheat harvest if turning under the red clover before a crop with a heavy nitrogen demand. When wheat is harvested for grain in mid- to late July, the crop can be windrowed first or direct combined. Again, a weedy field would be best windrowed first. The clover will grow significantly after wheat harvest when light competition with the wheat is reduced. An additional cutting of wheat regrowth, weeds and clover can be clipped before the weeds go to seed and chopped for silage. In spring, when the clover is about 25 cm tall, the cover crop of clover and wheat stubble can be turned under with a disk or plow.

Organic No-Till Wheat

Organic no-till involves growing a cover crop in the fall, followed by crushing it with a roller-crimper in the spring, and planting or transplanting maize, soybean, or other crops into the rolled cover. Following planting, no tillage is used. This differs from conventional no-till because no herbicides are used to kill the cover crop. In organic no-till, sharp disks or shovels from tillage implements do not disturb the soil, so soil structure remains more intact, ideally holding more moisture. Greater soil fertility is expected through the inclusion of organic matter from cover-crop aboveground biomass, roots, and N-fixing nodules on the legumes (Watson et al., 2002). Ideally, the cover-crop mulch provides a protective layer against transpiration, and moisture is held inside the mulch cover and soil. However, in years of low rainfall, the cash crop may not be able to compete with the mulch cover in terms of moisture, and yields will suffer as a result. Crop response has varied, depending on site and year. In years of sufficient rain, or when crops are irrigated, no-till yields have been equal (Iowa) or greater (Michigan) than the tilled control (the plots in which cover crops were tilled under before cash crop planting). In years when rainfall was lower than normal (such as in 2006 in southern Iowa), soybean yields were significantly lower than the control.

Ideally, the cover-crop mulch prevents weed seedlings from emerging. However, this can be the reverse when there are gaps in the rolled cover crop and weeds emerge and grow unrestricted by tillage (rotary hoeing and cultivation). Because less fossil fuel is used for rotary hoeing and cultivation, costs can be dramatically less in organic no-till when it works. No-till is management intensive, however, and irrigation may be needed for maximum yields in this system. If the cover crop will not crush down as well as desired and/or the cover crop continues to grow back after crushing, subsequent measures such as additional rolling, mowing, or turning under in the worst instance will be required, which adds to production costs.

Specialty Crops

According to the USDA, "specialty crops" include commonly recognized fruits, vegetables, tree nuts, dried fruits, and nursery crops. The discussion below focuses on organic vegetables and fruits, which are often cited as the "gateway" crops for organic consumers. Case studies of organic tomatoes and apples are presented.

Tomato

Production Statistics

Out of the 40,000 ha of organic vegetable production in the United States in 2005, 2700 ha were in organic tomato crops (USDA Economic Research Service, 2005). The tomato is one of the most commonly grown fresh market vegetables, but it is both high yielding and labor intensive. Organic vegetable production, and organic tomato production specifically, requires greater investments of time and labor than highly mechanized organic grain production. Conventional tomato yields range from 22 to 29 tons ha^{-1}, while organic yields are usually reduced by 10 to 40%, depending on soil fertility, weather, and disease load. High tunnels have been promoted as an effective method to increase earliness or extend the season. Production and marketing costs for intensively cultured tomatoes can be more than $10,000 ha^{-1}, with an expected gross return of $10,000 to $25,000 ha^{-1}. Efficient harvesting, handling, and marketing techniques are extremely important in the production of this highly perishable crop. The optimum temperature range for longest shelf life is between 13 and 21°C, so storage and transportation temperatures are critical.

Fertilization Practices

As with organic grain crop production, organic vegetable production requires a comprehensive systems plan to ensure adequate soil fertility and crop protection (Delate et al., 2005). Because crop rotations are required in certified organic vegetable production, the cycle of crop species usually begins with a grass–legume cover crop mixture, such as hairy vetch (*Vicia villosa* Roth) and rye, planted in the fall and tilled into the soil in the spring to build soil fertility for the following nitrogen-demanding crops. In the case of tomato, rotation to nonsolanaceous crops for three years is recommended to avoid pest problems. Rye can also serve as an allelopathic crop to help mitigate weed populations. Although the cover crop may provide 125 to 225 kg ha^{-1} of nitrogen over several years, depending on biomass accumulated and mineralization of nitrogen, the addition of composted manure may be necessary to meet the 85 to 110 kg ha^{-1} N requirements of the current organic tomato crop. Compost is the preferred method of fertilization (Delate et al., 2008a), but if raw manure is applied, fall application is recommended due to the requirement for at least a four-month interval between application and crop harvest. Fertilization with compost should take place in the spring to conserve as much of the nitrogen as possible. Compost rates range from 2.2 to 22 t ha^{-1} yr^{-1}, depending on inherent soil fertility and supplementation. High levels of nitrogen may increase herbivory by lepidopteran larvae so soil testing is recommended before any fertilization.

Pest Management

With a microbially active and fertile soil, organic tomato crops should be able to resist many diseases and insect pests. Varieties resistant or tolerant to bacterial blight are recommended. Lepidopteran larvae [e.g., tomato hornworm, *Manduca quinquemaculata* (Haworth)] can be managed with applications of natural Bt spray, such as Dipel (Valent U.S.A. Corp., Walnut Creek, CA). Straw mulch can be used to prevent weeds and retain moisture. If tomato plantings are 0.1 ha or more, some farmers plant in 70-cm rows and mechanically cultivate to manage weeds. Plastic mulch is permitted in organic rules if disposal takes place at the end of every season.

Apple

Out of the 39,000 ha of organic fruit production in the United States in 2005, 5150 ha were in organic apple crops (USDA Economic Research Service, 2005). Fruit growers located in the arid western United States have a substantial advantage in developing and servicing the nationally expanding commercial organic fruit markets, such as the large natural food grocery chains, because marketers in these corporations believe that consumers want organic apples to be cosmetically identical to conventionally produced apples. The higher humidity in the territory east of the Missouri River creates an environment that will support tree growth without irrigation but also fosters disease, weeds, insects, and mites (Delate et al., 2008b). Nonetheless, with disease-resistant cultivars and careful management, an organic apple grower can effectively produce marketable fruit for the organic consumer who prefers small-scale, locally produced, synthetic chemical-free, and third-party verified, organically raised food. Because the organic consumer is less concerned about blemishes on the fruit than knowing how the fruit was produced, the organic apple producer should also become a direct marketer, focusing on retail sales.

Weed Management

Weed management in an organic orchard consists of a combination of practices, including mowing of live cover crops and mulching. Mulches can be wood chips, bark, paper, plastic, or straw. Research has demonstrated the durability and protectiveness of bark and wood chips over the other types. Some orchardists use a Weed Badger (Weed Badger, Inc., Marion, ND) to cultivate around trees, but damage to roots and trees can occur if care is not used. Planting tree middles to a cover crop of grass with some legumes (e.g., clover) for beneficial insect attraction and mowing periodically is recommended over fallow ground (Altieri and Schmidt, 1985).

Insect Management

Organic apple production requires one of the most rigorous pest management regimes in all of organic crop production (Delate et al., 2008b). Plum curculio [*Conotrachelus nenuphar* (Herbst)], codling moth [*Cydia pomonela* (L.)], apple maggot [*Rhagoletis pomonella* (Walsh)], tarnished plant bug [*Lygus lineolaris* (Palisot de Beauvois)], San Jose scale [*Quadraspidiotus perniciosus* (Comstock)], Oriental fruit moth [*Grapholita molesta* (Busck)], rosy apple aphid [*Aphis pomi* (De Geer)], wooly apple aphid [*Eriosoma lanigerum* (Hausman)], flatheaded appletree borer [*Chrysobothris femorata* (Olivier)], apple leaf miner [*Lyonetia clerkella* L.], white apple leafhopper (*Typhlocyba pomaria* McAtee), apple rust mite [*Aculus schlechtendali* (Nalepa)], European red mite [*Panonychus ulmi* (Koch)], two-spotted spider mite (*Tetranychus urticae* Koch), apple scab [*Venturia inaequalis* (Cooke) G. Wint.], fire blight [*Erwinia amylovora* (Burrill) Winslow], rust, mildew, rots. and a host of other diseases can all be damaging to the organic orchard. The most devastating apple insect pest in the eastern and midwestern United States is the plum curculio, a weevil native to most of the apple production areas in the East (Delate et al., 2005). This beetle injures fruit in multiple ways:

- Surface feeding and egg depositing, which cause scarring
- Burrowing larvae, which cause internal damage
- Premature fruit drop
- Adults feeding in late summer and fall puncture fruit

The adult weevil overwinters in woodlots, fencerows, and hedges. Before planting new trees, examining the neighborhood or rural area can help identify overwintering sites (Vincent et al., 1999). Since maple woodlots are overwintering sites for plum curculio, it is not advisable to establish an orchard near these woods. Abandoned orchards in the surrounding area and neighboring fruit trees can be a persistent source of insect pests, since plum curculio beetles also attack crabapple (*Malus floribunda* Sieb. Ex Van Houtle), wild apple [*Malus sylvestris* (L.) Mill.], pear (*Pyrus communis* L.), plum (*Prunus domestica* L.), cherry [*Prunus avium* (L.) L.], peach [*Prunus persica* (L.) Batsch], and apricot (*Prunus armeniaca* L.). These weevils move into the orchard during bloom to feed on young flowers. After mating, the female adult beetle bores a small hole into the skin of the developing fruit, deposits a single egg, and then makes a crescent cut below the hole to protect the egg from being crushed by the rapidly expanding fruit tissue. The female lays an average of 150 to 200 eggs, which hatch 2 to 12 days later. The grubs (larvae) tunnel into the fruit's central seed cavity, where feeding commences, until development is completed in about three weeks. The larvae generate and release pectin enzymes that trigger the host fruit to drop prematurely. The grubs then chew through the fallen fruit and enter the soil to pupate. Visual observation of the adults and their egg depositing marks is the best mode of detection of beetle activity, particularly perimeter apple trees at bloom. "Trap trees" or plum trees can be used for early detection as well, since the crescent signature appears earlier on plums than on apples. Pheromone traps that attract adult beetles can be used to capture beetles as they first arrive in the orchard. Infested fruit typically drop before the larvae complete their feeding (Pinero et al., 2001). Prompt gathering and disposal of the dropped apples before the larvae exit the apple to enter the soil can reduce the number of first generation adults. Infestation may be greater in the outside two to three rows of trees than the rest of the orchard. Not all dropped apples are caused by plum curculio, as heavy fruit set and poor pollination may also be the cause.

"Tree jarring" limbs with a padded board can be used to jar adult beetles from apples to a tarp placed below the tree, specifically in the early morning when the cool temperature restricts flight and escape by beetles. Captured beetles must be destroyed immediately to prevent reinfestation. When plum curculio is in the pupal stage, mechanical disking of the top inch of soil where pupation occurs can also be an effective control. Disking should begin about three weeks after infested fruit starts to drop and continue weekly for several weeks. Encouraging beneficial insects through insectary plants is a typical practice in organic orchards (Delate and Friedrich, 2004). Parasitic wasps are likely to be attracted by a diverse array of ground vegetation with small flowers. Flowers should blossom after apple trees to avoid attracting bees away from trees. Mixing poultry feed with the soil under the trees can encourage free-ranging fowl such as chickens, ducks, and geese to scratch for larvae and adult weevils. Mobile chicken coops could be moved along the edge of the orchard as well to encourage predation.

The other main organic apple pest, the codling moth, is present throughout North America and must be managed to ensure marketable fruit production. In the warmer parts of the Midwest, the moth may pass through two to three generations per season. Several acceptable organic controls are available. *Mating disruption* is considered mandatory for codling moth management in organic apple orchards (Swezey et al. 2000). The codling moth's mating cycle can be disrupted by releasing quantities of pheromones through dispensers placed as high in the trees as possible that confuse male moths. When codling moth populations are high, an organic grower can combine mating disruption with black light traps, as both male and female moths are attracted to black lights.

Bacillus thuringiensis can be used for all lepidopteran pests. Other organic insecticides include a spinosad fungus, Entrust (Dow AgroSciences, Indianapolis, IN), and codling moth granulosis virus. Adult *Trichogramma* wasps, which parasitize codling moth eggs, feed on other insect eggs, nectar, pollen, and honeydew. Good nectar and pollen food sources, such as alfalfa, sorghum, sunflower (*Helianthus annus* L.), maize, clovers, and wildflowers, around the borders will increase wasp parasitism of codling moth eggs. Codling moth larvae can be intercepted as they descend the trunk to pupate by wrapping the tree trunks with corrugated cardboard, which will provide an artificial pupation site. The cardboard should be removed and destroyed about a month after the first larvae move down to pupate. Kaolin particle film (Surround WP, Engelhard Corp., Iselin, NJ) was introduced in 1999 for use against apple pests (Friedrich et al., 2003). Surround is reported to be an effective deterrent against plum curculio, codling moth, fruit tree leafrollers [*Archips argyrospilus* (Walker)], leafhoppers, mites, stink bugs, and apple maggot. Other reported positive effects include reduction of heat stress, fruit drop, and sunburn; improvement of color; and greater return bloom in certain cultivars. In Iowa State University trials, we lowered codling moth and plum curculio damage with the use of kaolin particle film, although other methods may be needed for full control. Woodpiles, boxes, and bins should be kept away from the orchard, since they can be a major source of reinfestation of codling moth.

Apple maggot is another major apple pest managed through red spheres covered with a sticky coating hung in the orchard in large numbers. The flies are also susceptible to pyrethrum and diatomaceous earth sprays, but organic growers who rely on frequent sprays of nonselective botanicals such as pyrethrum may be inducing minor pest problems by lowering the pest's natural enemy populations.

Most minor pests, such as mites, aphids, scale insects, and leafhoppers, primarily feed on apple stems and foliage. These pests can be tolerated in much higher numbers than can direct fruit pests, but if they occur in high enough numbers, they can seriously weaken the tree, resulting in reduced quality and quantity of fruit or even tree death. Beneficial organisms will generally keep minor pest below damage thresholds. If mites or scale insects are present, horticultural oils (vegetable-based) can be used. Oils should not be used in conjunction with sulfur or within 30 days of sulfur applications. A combination of the two can cause leaf burning. The spray program for plum curculio and first-generation codling moth should start at first petal fall and continue every five to seven days for six to eight weeks or until the infestation has passed. Although the residue is not harmful, if a full-season spraying program is used to suppress apple maggot or other late-season pests, a scrubber–washer will need to be used to remove any dust remaining on the fruit at harvest for the fresh market.

Disease Management

The most serious apple disease worldwide is apple scab (Ellis et al., 1998; Fischer, 2000). The organic system can be used on old orchards with heirloom or nonscab resistant varieties (e.g., Macintosh) varieties, but for the best results, a grower should establish an orchard with scab-resistant fruit trees. The use of these varieties is the best long-term strategy for the grower to pursue, since these trees eliminate routine fungicide applications. Jonafree, Redfree, Liberty, Freedom, Dayton, William's Pride, Gold Rush, Enterprise, Priscilla, and Nova Easygro are some of the apple varieties that show scab resistance.

Sanitation is critical as dead leaves on the orchard floor provide winter residence for this pathogen. By raking and destroying by burying, burning, or composting the fallen leaves, a grower can control and for the most part eliminate the primary scab inocula. Spores released during spring rains infect new leaves and fruits. The seriousness of infections depends on a combination of rain, longevity of leaf wetness, and temperature. Spores will germinate and cause infection when they have been wet for 48 hours at temperatures from zero to 5°C, but at 13 to 24°C only 9 hours is required for germination. If primary infections are not controlled they can erupt into secondary infections later in the season (Nicholson and Beckerman, 2008). Secondary infections can blemish apples and weaken trees. During wet periods, secondary infections develop when summer spores germinate in lesions on leaf and bud tissues and spread throughout the tree.

For the organic grower, apple scab can be controlled on susceptible varieties by timely sprays of sulfur, lime-sulfur, or Bordeaux mixture (copper sulfate plus lime). These fungicides are effective against scab spores if applied before the spores have a chance to germinate, but problems with tree damage from excessive sulfur sprays and copper toxicity have been cited (Delate et al., 2008b). Fungicide applications must occur after every rain event from the time of bud break until all the spores are discharged. If primary infections are prevented, spraying the rest of the season may be mitigated, but preventative sprays are often continued.

The bacteria *Erwinia amylovora* or fire blight is another potentially devastating disease in the organic orchard. Resistant varieties are the first line of defense and are rarely invaded beyond young wood. Warm wet conditions foster the bacteria's production (Swezey et al. 2000). Wind, rain, bees, aphids, and other insects spread the bacteria. Large numbers of new infections can occur within minutes after rain or heavy dew. Infections gain entry to the tree through blossoms or lush new growth and then spread internally through the stems working toward the roots, causing a scorched, withered, and brownish-black appearance to limbs. Once infected, there is no treatment other than cutting off infected limbs to minimize damage. Bacteria are often present in healthy tissues far ahead of visible symptoms, but high levels of reserve carbohydrate in living bark tissues compete effectively with the bacteria's water needs and limit development of symptoms. Cutting these symptomless branches breaches this natural defense and induces formation of cankers around wounds. Once under the bark, bacteria stimulate formation of a canker, where the bacteria survive to infect more trees the next year. Cankers that form around the cut can be removed during the regular dormant pruning season during the winter. After each cut, the shears should be dipped in an approved sanitizer to avoid transmitting the disease from shears to branch. Because fire blight favors young succulent tissues, cultural practices that favor moderate growth such as low fertilization and limited pruning are recommended.

Copper formulations, such as Bordeaux mixture, sprayed at green-tip stage provide some protection from infection. Streptomycin, an antibiotic produced by cultured fungi, has been used for fire blight in commercial orchards since the 1950s. Organic growers can use approved formulations of streptomycin, but the product should be considered as a last resort to avoid resistance in pathogen populations. The product is applied just before rain or heavy dew is expected during early bloom, when the average temperature is 15°C or higher. If rainy conditions persist, spraying must be repeated within four days. Streptomycin should not be use in combination with copper sprays and should never be used when burned branch tips are present.

Powdery mildew [caused by *Podosphaera leucotricha* (Ellis & Everh.) E. S. Salmon] is primarily a minor foliar disease, but if the infection is severe enough, the disease can affect the appearance of fruit. In cases where infections curl, distort, and discolor leaves, photosynthesis is reduced, affecting the health of the tree. Mildew can be controlled with the aforementioned sulfur compounds such as sulfur, lime-sulfur, or Bordeaux mixture. Cedar apple rust is caused by a fungus (*Gymnosporangium juniperi-virginianae* Schwein) that alternates between eastern red cedars (*Juniperus virginiana* L. var. *virginiana*, which are true junipers) and apple trees. By eliminating junipers within a given area, it may be possible to limit the incidence of this disease (Nicholson and Beckerman, 2008). Spores can travel up to 5 km, however, so eradication of the disease is a near impossibility. The grower must time sulfur fungicide sprays to coincide with the springtime appearance of orange gelatinous "horns" of the galls on the cedar, which is a fruiting stage containing the spores that infect the apple trees. Growers should use techniques for suppression of all disease organisms by pruning for light penetration and air circulation, pruning out diseased wood, removing fruit mummies, and avoiding poor humid sites when planting new orchards.

Timely harvests will help maximize profits from the organic orchard. Sanitation measures such as picking up and destroying all fallen or rotten apples are also necessary. Apples should be picked off trees, not off the ground, to avoid problems with *Escherichia coli* and other human diseases from apples that have had contact with animals on the orchard floor. Chickens, guinea hens, sheep, and hogs can be used to clean orchard floors of infested apples. An organic farmer has to be extremely aggressive in managing disease and insect problems. Without some form of insect and disease control, much of the organic apple crop will suffer some type of damage. To be effective, the producer must monitor constantly for insect or disease problems and develop a timely management plan. With good practices, a grower should expect to sell most of the fruit to the fresh market.

Markets

In addition to selling to large grocery store chains, on-farm sales and sales at any of the hundreds of farmers markets and small-town grocery stores across the United States should be considered. By carefully developing this market, the grower can maintain an adequate profit margin while personally connecting with consumers. A common strategy for organic growers is to integrate processed apple products into their marketing plan. By adding "value-added" products such as cider, preserves, pies, and other processed products, a grower may be able to use fruit that could not be sold fresh and thus enhance their profit margins. Securing special equipment and compliance with health regulations are needed for on-farm processing. A grower must make arrangements with other orchard owners who have processing capabilities if they do not plan to do it themselves.

Conclusions

As organic agriculture grew from a highly limited niche to a market in which organic products are found in mainstream supermarkets around the globe, there has been a natural tendency for corporations to join this emerging trend. In analyzing organic grain production and marketing, the argument that there has been a negative corporate "takeover" of organic is misplaced. In a democracy, there is no mechanism to keep new players, including corporations, from buying, processing, and/or selling organic products, unless they violate anti-trust laws. Organic grain, oilseeds, and pulse crops are grown on predominantly large acreages, compared to intensive vegetable and fruit production, because of the requirement for large equipment in highly mechanized operations. Most organic grain farmers sell their product to wholesale markets because of the convenience of truck-centered transportation and delivery, moving product from large storage bins onto trucks or rail cars for delivery to near and far markets. Organic soybeans produced in Iowa may be sold to a small-scale broker who sells them to a corporation who processes the grain into branded soymilk sold at local Iowa supermarkets. Soybeans from the same farm may be shipped as a soy flour ingredient in famine relief food to Africa. Some of the same grain may be fed directly on-farm to the farmer's livestock. Thus, organic grain growers sell to local and export markets, small-scale and corporate organic markets, signifying that there is room for all sectors to work together to meet the increasing demand for healthy food produced in a sustainable manner.

Discussion Questions

1. What are the major markets today for organic grain and pulse crops in the United States? What are the major export markets?

2. Describe the principal differences in production practices between conventional maize production and organic maize production.

3. What factors will determine which of these farming and marketing strategies will be most profitable for the farmer?

4. In what ways are the production practices and storage of organic grains on the farm more complicated than those used for conventional crop production?

5. What types of federal crop supports have been available for organic farmers growing major commodity crops, and how is this situation changing?

6. In what ways is organic crop production more energy efficient than conventional systems, and in what ways is it less efficient?

7. What are the principal sources of nutrients that are available for organic cereal production, and how do they compare in cost with conventional nutrient sources?

8. What are the major methods used to manage weeds, insects, and pathogens in organic cropping systems, and how do they differ from conventional methods?

9. What role does product quality play in the marketing of organic cereal and pulse crop grains? How can the farmer improve and ensure product quality?

10. What practices and rotations are unique to organic wheat production, compared to those used in conventional wheat?

11. What are the special challenges faced by the farmer who wants to produce wheat under a no-till or greatly reduced till system? What are the advantages and why?

12. What is unique about organic tomato production, and what practices are needed to produce a quality product?

13. What is unique about organic apple production, and what practices are needed to produce a quality product?

References

Ahmed, F.E. 2002. Detection of genetically modified organisms in foods. Trends Biotechnol. 20:215–223.

Altieri, M.A. 1994. Biodiversity and pest management in agroecosystems. Haworth Press, New York.

Altieri, M.A., and L.L. Schmidt. 1985. Cover crop manipulation in northern California orchards and vineyards: Effects on arthropod communities. Biol. Agric. Hortic. 3:1–24.

Andow, D.A. 1991. Vegetational diversity and arthropod population response. Annu. Rev. Entomol. 36:561–586.

Born, H. 2005. Marketing organic grains: Marketing, business, and risk management. Available at http://attra.ncat.org/attra-pub/marketingorganicgrains.html (verified 10 July 2009). ATTRA Publ. CT154. ATTRA National Sustainable Agriculture Information Service, Fayetteville, AR.

Chambers, R.J., K.D. Sunderland, D.L. Stacey, and I.J. Wyatt. 1986. Control of cereal aphids in winter wheat by natural enemies: Aphid-specific predators, parasitoids, and pathogenic fungi. Ann. Appl. Biol. 108:219–231.

Delate, K. 2002. Using an agroecological approach to farming systems research. HortTechnology 12:345–354.

Delate, K., and C. Cambardella. 2004. Agroecosystem performance during transition to certified organic grain production. Agron. J. 96:1288–1298.

Delate, K., C. Cambardella, and A. McKern. 2008a. Effects of organic fertilization and cover crops on an organic pepper system. HortTechnology 18:215–226.

Delate, K., C. Chase, M. Duffy, and R. Turnbull. 2006. Transitioning into organic grain production: An economic perspective. Crop Manage. doi:10.1094/CM-2006-1016-01-RS.

Delate, K., J. Dewitt, A. Mckern, D. Rosmann, D.L. Karlen, and R. Turnbull. 2009. Bean leaf beetle (Coleoptera: Chrysomelidae) response to soybean variety and organic-compliant treatments in Iowa. J. Agric. Urban Entomol. 25:145–163.

Delate, K., J. DeWitt, A. McKern, and R. Turnbull. 2005. Integrated approaches to organic pest management in the midwestern U.S.A.: Case studies of three crops. Organic Res. May, p. 8N–15N.

Delate, K., M. Duffy, and C. Chase. 2003. An economic comparison of organic and conventional grain crops in a long-term agroecological research (LTAR) site in Iowa. Am. J. Alternative Agric. 18:1–11.

Delate, K., and H. Friedrich. 2004. Organic apple and grape performance in the midwestern U.S. Acta Hortic. 638:309–320.

Delate, K., J.T.S. Walker, R. Volz, J. Johnston, A. White, V. Bus, R. Turnbull, D. Rogers, L. Cole, N. How, S. Guernsey, and A. McKern. 2008b. Organic apple systems: Constraints and opportunities for producers in local and global markets. HortScience 43:6–11.

Ellis, M.A., D.C. Ferree, R.C. Funt, and L.V. Madden. 1998. Effects of an apple scab–resistant cultivar on use patterns of inorganic and organic fungicides and economics of disease control. Plant Dis. 82:428–433.

Fischer, C. 2000. Multiple resistant apple cultivars and consequences for apple breeding in the future. Acta Hortic. 538:229–234.

Friedrich, H., K. Delate, P. Domoto, and G. Nonnecke. 2003. Effect of organic pest management techniques on apple productivity and food quality. Biol. Agric. Hortic. 21:1–14.

Krell, R.K., L.P. Pedigo, J.H. Hill, and M.E. Rice. 2004. Bean leaf beetle (Coleoptera: Chrysomelidae) management for reduction of bean pod mottle virus. J. Econ. Entomol. 97:192–202.

Massey, R. 1999. Identity preserved crops. Farm Manage. Newsl. FM 99-1. University of Missouri Extension, Columbia, MO.

Nicholson, R.L., and J. Beckerman. 2008. Towards a sustainable, integrated management of apple diseases. p. 27–42. In A. Ciancio and K.G. Mukerji (ed.) Integrated management of diseases caused by fungi, phytoplasma, and bacteria. Springer Press, Dordrecht, the Netherlands.

Peterson, H.H., and R.R. Janke. 2009. Organic marketing. p. 217–234. In C. Francis (ed.) Organic farming: The ecological system. Agron. Monogr. 54. ASA, CSSA, and SSSA, Madison, WI. (This volume.)

Pinero, J.C., S.E. Wright, and R.J. Prokopy. 2001. Response of plum curculio (Coleoptera: Curculionidae) to odor-baited traps near woods. J. Econ. Entomol. 94:1386–1397.

Root, R.B. 1973. Organization of a plant–arthropod association in simple and diverse habitats: The fauna of collards (Brassica oleracea). Ecol. Monogr. 43:95–124.

Schmidt, M.H., A. Lauer, T. Purtauf, C. Thies, M. Schaefer, and T. Tscharntke. 2003. Relative importance of predators and parasitoids for cereal aphid control. Proc. R. Soc. Lond., Ser. B 270:1905–1909.

Smyth, S., G. Khachatourians, and P. Phillips. 2002. Liabilities and economics of transgenic crops. Nat. Biotechnol. 20:537–541.

Sullivan, P. 2003a. Edible soybean production and marketing. Available at http://attra.ncat.org/attra-pub/PDF/ediblesoybean.pdf (verified 10 July 2009). ATTRA National Sustainable Agriculture Information Service, Fayetteville, AR.

Sullivan, P. 2003b. Organic small grain production. Available at http://attra.ncat.org/attra-pub/smallgrain.html (verified 10 July 2009). ATTRA National Sustainable Agriculture Information Service, Fayetteville, AR.

Swezey, S.L., P. Vossen, J. Caprile, and W. Bentley. 2000. Organic apple production manual. ANR Publications, Oakland, CA.

Thomison, P. 2004. Managing "pollen drift" to minimize contamination of non-GMO corn. The Ohio State Univ. Extension, Columbus.

USDA Agriculture Marketing Service. 2008. National Organic Program—Final rule: 7 CFR Part 205. Available at http://www.ams.usda.gov/nop (verified 10 July 2009). USDA Agriculture Marketing Service, Washington, DC.

USDA Economic Research Service. 2005. Organic production in the U.S. Available at www.ers.usda.gov/data/Organic/ (verified 10 July 2009). USDA Economic Research Service, Washington, DC.

Vincent, C., G. Chouinard, and S.B. Hill. 1999. Progress in plum curculio management: A review. Agric. Ecosyst. Environ. 73:167–175.

Watson, C.A., D. Atkinson, P. Gosling, L.R. Jackson, and F.W. Rayns. 2002. Managing soil fertility in organic farming systems. Soil Use Manage. 18:239–247.

Weisz, R. 2005. Wheat and small grain disease management. Center for Environmental Farming Systems. North Carolina State Univ., Raleigh.

Weston, L.A. 1996. Utilization of allelopathy for weed management in agroecosystems. Agron. J. 88:860–866.

Widman, N., R. Glaze, B. Miller, A. Sundermeier, and R. Reeder. 2001. No-till corn production-key management strategies for success. The Ohio State Univ. Extension, Columbus.

Production Practices

7

Practical Steps to Soil Fertility
for Organic Agriculture

Joseph R. Heckman
Department of Plant Biology and Pathology, Rutgers University, New Brunswick, New Jersey

Ray Weil
Department of Natural Resource Sciences and Landscape Architecture, University of Maryland, Collegeville

Fred Magdoff
Department of Plant and Soil Science, University of Vermont, Burlington

Soil fertility has always been a primary focus and defining character in the tradition of organic agricultural systems. From a holistic view, soil fertility is a function of the biology of the whole farm, a view that sets it apart from conventional agriculture, whereby soil fertility is primarily seen as managing mineral nutrients field by field. The conventional view grew out of a reductionist science that defined systems almost entirely in terms of chemistry. In contrast, pioneers in organic agriculture maintained a focus on the living aspects of soils and understanding fertility in relationship to diversity of organisms on and off the farm (Heckman, 2006).

The word "organic" in agriculture, not to be confused with organic chemistry, was originally described by Walter Northbourne (1940, p. 58) in the philosophical sense to mean "wholeness." He elaborated that an organic farm "must have a biological completeness: it must be a living entity" where every "branch of the work is interlocked with all others." With passage of the Federal Organic Foods Production Act of 1990, the rules for organic farming became codified in law, but the original concepts of organic farming continue to direct and define cultural practices within the community of organic farmers. Thus, it is informative to approach soil fertility management from the perspective of long held organic farming principles in combination with the USDA National Organic Program (NOP) standards.

Key cultural practices and concepts in organic farming include composting, fostering soil biological activity with organic matter amendments, using complex crop rotation cycles, integrating plants and animals on the farm, organic cycling of nutrients in the food web, linking feed and food quality to soil fertility, and increasing food quality by minimizing processing and formulations (Watson et al., 2002a,b; Magdoff, 2007). In organic farming, natural ecosystems serve as models. What are often referred to as *waste* materials are better called *organic, residue,* or *by-product* materials in this chapter since they represent a valuable resource and not really a waste. In conventional farming, soil fertility concepts have often lacked a broad ecological context, while in organic farming an ecological perspective is a prominent and defining feature. This philosophy was captured well by Albert Howard in his oft-quoted statement of the need to treat "the whole problem of health in soil, plant, animal, and man as one great subject" (Howard, 1975, p. 11)

Compost

Among the core cultural practices associated with organic farming, composting is closely tied to the law of return that encourages recycling of materials. Composting involves the collecting of natural materials from diverse "waste" streams and consolidating them to achieve conditions favorable for rapid aerobic biological decomposition. The NOP has specific guidelines that must be followed when making compost to be used for production of crops intended for human consumption (www.ams.usda.gov/nop [verified 30 July 2009]). These standards require that raw materials used for composting have C/N ratios between 25:1 and 40:1. During composting, the temperature must be maintained between 55 and 77°C (131–170°F) for 3 days for in-vessel or static aerated pile systems or for 15 days for windrow composting systems (Fig. 7–1).

Fig. 7–1. A machine, consisting of a rotating auger that is pulled by a tractor, turns a compost pile windrow. At this composting facility in New Jersey, windrows are created by combining animal manures, food waste, and sawdust. The machine is used to mix the materials and maintain well-aerated conditions. (Photo courtesy of Jami Niknam.)

Requirements for compost heating and turning are designed to encourage practices that will kill human pathogens. The destruction of plant pathogens and weed seeds is a further benefit of the process. Compost made in accordance with NOP guidelines can be used to fertilize vegetable and fruit crops during the growing season. Regulations for application of compost not meeting these standards are the same as for raw manure: Apply to soil 90 days in advance of harvest for plant portions that do not touch the soil and 120 days in advance of harvest for portions that do touch the soil.

Composting transforms soluble N into stable forms that resemble organic matter in the soil. Because compost quality and nutrient content can vary markedly depending on source materials and time of year, an analysis of compost is advisable to determine nutrient content and C/N ratio. Finished compost typically contains 25 to 35% moisture and 1 to 2% N on a dry weight basis. The C/N ratio of applied compost influences the availability of N to crops.

Appropriate application rates of compost depend on the initial fertility and organic matter content of field soil and the crops to be grown. On low-fertility soils, with low N and P availability and low organic matter content, compost applications of 60 to 75 t ha^{-1} (25 to 30 tons acre^{-1}) are appropriate. These high application rates may be especially suitable to build soil fertility during initial years of transitioning land to certified organic production. Compost may serve as the primary N source for some annual crops when applied at high rates. However, repeated heavy applications of compost as the main source of N over a period of years may cause excessive buildup of soil P.

On more fertile soils, routine compost application rates of 7 to 12 t ha^{-1} (3 to 5 tons/acre) may be appropriate. In the first year after application, 5 to 15% of the total applied N from compost may be recovered by a crop. Thus, the N from compost supplies small amounts of N over several years. Crop N uptake from soil that has had repeated compost applications will be a combination of the N becoming available from the full history of compost applications. Predicting the amount of N that will be available for crops on compost-amended soil can be difficult. Soil testing, plant analysis, and crop growth observations play important roles in monitoring nutrient availability.

A high-quality, low C/N ratio compost can be used to supply N to newly seeded crops or transplants during their initial four to five weeks. For short-cycle leafy green crops, a small compost application may be sufficient (Gaskell, 2004). Experience with crops on organic farms, however, has shown that growers should not base soil fertility programs solely on compost as the N source. If a crop has a high N requirement, supplemental N may be applied using one of several high-nitrogen-containing organic fertilizers. Compost may also be used in combination with N-fixing cover crops.

Compost applications also contribute to building soil organic matter and long-term reserves of N, P, and other nutrients. Compost is well recognized for soil quality benefits including improved soil tilth, water-holding capacity, chelation of nutrients, and disease suppression.

While local compost production can help sustain soil fertility by recycling nutrients and building organic matter, mineral-rich soils are a prerequisite for growing enough biomass on the farm to produce sufficient vegetative material to turn into compost. Transition to organic farming on soils with current high nutrient status due to previous fertilizer inputs is enabled by potential for production of more biomass, and these farms have better opportunity for producing sufficient compost.

Law of Return

The law of return is a teaching principle that Albert Howard (1943) used to encourage adoption of farming practices that follow nature's example of recycling all nonharvested natural and organic products back to the soil. To illustrate the concept, Howard described how all dead plant and animal residues in a forest are added to enrich the soil in humus. Minerals in them are also recycled by this natural process in native forests and grasslands. When humans convert land to agriculture and extract crops and livestock, mineral nutrients are removed from the soil. Our failure to effectively return the "waste" products of agriculture back to the land results in mineral depletion and a lost opportunity to build soil organic matter, a process vital to maintaining soil quality and healthy soil biological activity. Howard strongly advocated the law of return as a key principle of soil fertility management.

This highly valued practice in organic farming is widely neglected in modern agricultural management. Often practiced without an ecological foundation, most conventional agriculture separates livestock from crop production and treats manures and other natural materials as a liability, because they are bulky and expensive to transport, or simply as a waste product in need of disposal. The frequent failure of conventional agriculture, as a result of poor farming system design, to effectively recycle and utilize natural waste products for sustainable soil fertility management has increased the need to manufacture chemical fertilizers as a replacement. Through a renewable agricultural system that effectively recycles nutrients, minerals can be reused repeatedly to grow crops and livestock without exhausting this vital resource. Everyone who consumes food and fiber products from agriculture has a responsibility to participate in recycling of nutrients embedded in natural waste products back to the soil. Food wastes, such as peelings, bones, and spoiled leftovers, that are placed in landfills instead of composted and returned are lost opportunities for building and maintaining soil fertility for future generations. Even if these food wastes are composted by the consumer, they rarely find their way back to soils on the farms from which they came.

Modern societies could learn from traditional cultures in which everyone was a participant in sustaining soil fertility. One way for consumers to become active participants in sustaining soil fertility is through community supported agriculture (CSA). The members could return natural organic waste materials to the farm for composting when they visit the farm to pick up vegetables, eggs, and milk.

The law of return is a useful ecological principle that society could apply toward sustaining soil fertility (King, 1911), as well as contributing to the resolution of other environmental problems. Recycling could diminish the need for more landfill space, reduce energy demand for fertilizer manufacture, and decrease the need to strip mine for raw materials such as rock phosphate ore. Yet a few caveats must be mentioned. First, waste materials must be kept free of contamination from heavy metals or other hazardous substances. Second, the waste materials must be properly composted to destroy pathogens. Third, farmers should be aware that the recycling of the waste products of agriculture often does not in itself provide all of the minerals needed to achieve a fertile soil in a proper balance. Thus, in addition to practicing the principle of the law of return, mineral supplements or fertilizers are sometimes needed. Even a well-designed system has some extraction in the form of crop or animal products. There are nutrient losses from soil by leaching and erosion. Also, some soils have been depleted due to unsustainable farming practices, and other soils are inherently low in their natural capacity to supply nutrients.

The ban on the use of sewage sludge in organic farming makes complete nutrient cycling—as originally envisioned by organic pioneers—difficult if not impossible for wide-scale sustainable organic farming. Organic agriculture has legitimate concerns with sewage sludge biosolids, which are sometimes contaminated with heavy metals and various synthetic chemicals. Human manure and urine that are not processed by sewage treatment plants are apparently different. While human manure is not technically prohibited as a compostable waste material for use in organic farming, it is rarely used due to real concerns with pathogens and antibiotics. Once the technical, policy, and emotional issues surrounding use of human manure in organic farming can be resolved, it has great potential to improve nutrient cycling and sustainability of organic agriculture. Maintaining a positive nutrient balance in organic farming can be achieved by an ecological solution to both the human manure and nutrient management problems. For sustainability, a nonflush toilet collection system has the potential to markedly reduce water and energy consumption. These composting and recycling systems are described in Jenkins (2005).

The use of human urine is much less problematic than that of human feces since the urine is nearly sterile and rarely carries any disease hazard. Human urine is easily collected separately from feces and can be used either directly on the soil as a liquid fertilizer (diluted about 2:1 with water) or added to the compost pile to lower its C/N ratio and stimulate rapid composting and nutrient conservation. Urine is particularly effective as a source of nitrogen, phosphorus, and potassium. To avoid nitrogen loss as ammonia and to avoid the unpleasant odors, urine should be stored in sealed containers, and high pH levels (greater than 7.5) should be avoided where it is applied. It has been calculated (Brady and Weil, 2008, p. 905) that the urine from one person could provide a moderate level of highly available N, P, and K (about 50, 5, and 10 kg ha^{-1} of N–P–K) fertility for about 0.1 ha of cropland. In many Asian countries, this represents most of the cropland available per capita. Use of human urine can certainly make a major contribution to the fertility of a family vegetable garden. In Sweden technologies have been developed to collect and utilize urine for large-scale farms (Jönsson et al., 2004).

Crop Rotation Cycles to Build Soil Fertility

A well-designed crop rotation cycle that includes legumes and perennial forage crops is a key to achieving many objectives of organic farming. In addition to supplying N, crop rotations help control weed and insect pests and manage diseases in crops and livestock. Much attention is focused on biological N fixation, yet building soil organic matter, enhancing P availability, balancing nutrients, and minimizing nutrient leaching, runoff, and erosion are also important functions of crop rotations. Rules of organic certification stipulate use of rotations:

no consecutive plantings of the same crop, legumes included in the rotation, row crops rotated with solid-seeded and/or sod-building crops. Specific rules are designated by individual certification agencies and often determined by organic farmer groups that are familiar with the unique conditions and crops adapted to each ecoregion. Rotations are discussed in detail in Chapter 3 (Porter, 2009, this volume).

Organic Management of the Nitrogen Cycle

Nitrogen is an essential building block of living tissue and a component of soil organic matter. This vital nutrient is shuttled among N reservoirs in a complex cycle (Fig. 7–2). Practical knowledge of the N cycle is key to effective N management by the organic farmer. Fortunately, N is a nutrient that can be "grown" on the farm.

Although N comprises 78% of the atmosphere, this inert gas is unavailable for plant nutrition until it is chemically combined or "fixed" into a usable form. While the conventional farmer uses large amounts of N fixed by the industrial Haber–Bosh process, the organic farmer mostly relies on biological N fixation performed by *Rhizobium* bacteria in symbiotic association with legumes. The incorporation of legumes into crop rotations and the coupling of crop rotations with livestock production allows well-integrated organic farms to be self-sufficient in N. Fixed N from the atmosphere supplements N available from soil organic matter and recycled organic materials. Conversely, it may be argued that the invention and widespread use of the Haber–Bosh process effectively circumvented the need to rely on farm-based biological processes, thus leading to the uncoupling and spatial separation of crop and livestock production and resulting problems of imbalanced nutrient management.

A mixed farming system that includes livestock able to make productive use of forage legumes is in effect a kind of regenerative fertility farming. A well-designed mixed farming operation has the capacity to build and maintain soils rich in organic matter and to achieve whole-farm N self-sufficiency. The organic crop rotation cycle may include row crop grains or vegetables, but the soil fertility–building part of the rotation is primarily the forage or pasture legumes and grasses. Legumes are primary builders of soil nitrogen fertility, while their mixture with grasses builds soil organic matter and effectively captures much of the N that might otherwise be leached from the system. Chapters 4 (Entz and Thiessen Martens, 2009, this volume) and 5 (Clark, 2009, this volume) provide more details.

Maximum internal cycling of N from crop rotations and use of livestock manures can enable mixed organic farming systems to operate without the import of external sources of N (Bear et al., 1946). It may even be possible in a mixed organic livestock farming system to accumulate surplus N for export of some compost for use by other fields or nearby organic farming systems, such as fruit and vegetable production. When compost is exported, it is important to consider the balance or flow of other nutrients such as P and K among fields and farms.

Nitrogen and, to some extent, S are the only nutrients that are subject to major cycling through the atmosphere. The symbiotic association of legumes with *Rhizobium* bacteria is the primary source of N in organic farming. Although the supply of N from the atmosphere is forever renewable, numerous challenges are associated with the management of this dynamic nutrient.

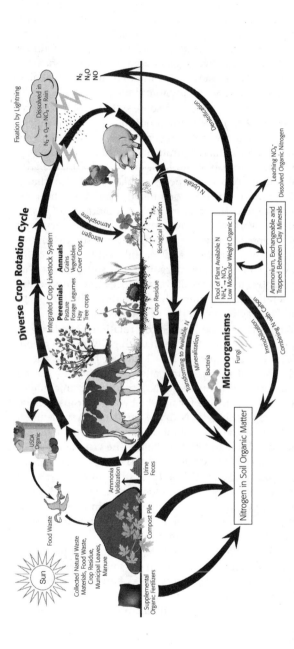

Fig. 7–2. Practical aspects of the nitrogen cycle on an organic farm. Organic farming focuses on building and maintaining a level of soil organic matter that provides a reservoir for the slow release of N and other nutrients to crops. Diversified organic farming systems are designed to use crop rotation, cover crops, perennial crops, legumes, livestock, waste recycling, mulching, and composting to build soil organic matter content and N fertility. Industrially manufactured N fertilizers and sewage sludge are not allowed on farmland certified as organic. Crop residues and manures produced on conventional farms that use either synthetic N fertilizers or sewage sludge, however, may be used on organic farms. Limited amounts of Chilean nitrate fertilizer are allowed on USDA certified organic farms. The N in organic matter is slowly converted by microbial activity into forms usable by plants at rates that vary with variations in soil temperature and moisture. Most of the N taken up by crops is in the mineral forms ammonium and nitrate, but plants can also use some low-molecular-weight organic compounds. The addition of crop residues low in N concentration can cause immobilization by which mineral forms of N are removed from the soil solution for use by microorganisms. Ammonium near the soil surface may be converted to ammonia gas and be lost to the atmosphere. Plants can take up N as ammonium ions, but it tends to quickly oxidize to nitrate, which is the major form of N uptake by most crops. Nitrate not taken up by plants or soil organisms is susceptible to loss by leaching in drainage water. Leaching can also occur as dissolved organic N. If a soil well supplied with decomposable organic matter becomes very wet, pockets of anaerobic conditions will occur in which nitrate will be converted to N-containing gases that can be lost to the atmosphere. Ammonium ions, which are attracted to exchange sites on clay minerals and humus, leach more slowly from soil than nitrate ions. In soils containing vermiculite-type clays, some ammonium ions may become entrapped between layers of these clay minerals where the N becomes unavailable for crop uptake.

A major difficulty with N management is the need to manage the many pathways of the N cycle (Fig. 7–2) through which N can be lost from the system. Although the atmosphere is a major N source via biological N fixation, appreciable amounts of N can also be lost to the atmosphere as gaseous forms of ammonia, oxides of N, and molecular nitrogen. Nitrogen is also subject to loss from the farming system when leaching or runoff carries N, primarily in the form of nitrate, beyond the reach of plant roots. The objective of good organic farming practices is to control or minimize losses of N from the system and to funnel the available N into farm products or into safe storage as soil organic matter.

Although many plants are capable of taking up some soluble organic forms of N from the soil (Watanabe et al., 2006), under the conditions of intensive nitrogen uptake typical of agricultural systems (including organic systems), most N is taken up as mineral (inorganic) ions, namely, nitrate and ammonium. The supply of mineral N to crops and its vulnerability to losses is controlled largely by mineralization and immobilization, two key processes that operate simultaneously within the N cycle. Microbial conversion of organically bound N to mineral forms is the process of mineralization. This process makes N more readily available for crop uptake, but it also converts N into forms that are more vulnerable to losses from the soil. Immobilization occurs when inorganic forms such as ammonium and nitrate are assimilated by organisms and recombined with carbon to become organically bound. This conversion of inorganic N to storage in soil as organic matter reduces its potential for loss. Cultural practices that direct a net flow of N toward either mineralization or immobilization allow the farmer to manage the rate of release and timing of availability of N to crops.

Tillage is a common practice to kill sod in the crop rotation in advance of planting row crops such as maize (*Zea mays* L.) that have high N requirements. Perennial forage crops, especially when they include legumes, have the ability to accumulate stored N in the form of soil organic matter. Tillage stimulates the microbial activity responsible for conversion of the N stored in organic matter to mineral forms, which are readily available for uptake by grain crops. Tillage should be timed to match the rate of release of N to the needs of the subsequent crop. If the sod is killed too far in advance of planting the grain crop, much of the available N may become vulnerable to leaching before the crop takes up N. Weather and soil temperatures also influence microbial activity.

Certain cultural practices may be used to direct the flow of mineral N toward immobilization. Incorporation of high C/N ratio residue such as straw helps prevent leaching of nitrate. Nonlegume cover crops, such as those in the grass and brassica families, can scavenge the soil for residual nitrate. In addition to conserving N, these cultural practices contribute to building soil organic matter.

Other factors, including soil moisture, temperature, aeration, and pH, affect the rate of mineralization and subsequent nitrification by soil microorganisms. When conditions are favorable for microbial activity, rates of mineralization and nitrification or immobilization are enhanced. Irrigating dry soil, tillage to increase aeration. and liming of acid soils may stimulate mineralization and result in an increase in supply of mineral N to crops.

High rates of microbial respiration use up the oxygen in soils that are too wet to allow its rapid resupply from the atmosphere. The anaerobic conditions that result are especially conducive to denitrification, which adds electrons to the N atom, reducing its charge from the +5 found in nitrate and causing the formation of several nitrogen-containing gases. Waterlogged conditions are especially conducive to denitrification, resulting in the loss of gaseous forms of N to the atmosphere. The mixing of easily decomposed crop residues with soil before wet, warm weather encourages nitrate losses via denitrification.

The most effective and practical way to prevent loss of nitrate from soil is to capture this very soluble and vulnerable ion through uptake by rapidly growing crops. Thus, the timing of field operations that lead to nitrate accumulation in soils should be closely followed by the planting of N-demanding crops. A crop rotation design should consider the N budgets of each crop. Ideally, high N-demanding crops should follow N-fixing crops. Incorporation of a fertility building sod crop or application of manures should be timed to allow a following crop to utilize the developing supply of mineral N.

Comparative Crop Demands and Uptake of Nitrogen

One of the primary aims of managing the N cycle in organic farming is to achieve an adequate supply of N in the soil to match the timing of demands by specific crops. In any given crop–soil combination or rotation sequence, the objective is to synchronize crop demand for nutrients with supply of N from soil. More often than any other nutrient, N needs tend to dictate soil fertility practices. Timing of cultural practices relating to P or K soil fertility is less critical because their supply in the soil tends to be more stable. Understanding variations in crop demand for N is crucial to optimizing cultural practices. Although both soil and plant testing may be used to monitor crop N status and guide soil fertility practice, interpretation of soil and leaf test results must consider each crop's unique physiology and how N demand varies with stage of growth.

The seasonal pattern of N uptake by a particular crop is often closely tied to patterns of vegetative and reproductive development. The period of most rapid N uptake corresponds with the period of most rapid vegetative growth. Leaf tissue is a major reservoir of nitrogenous compounds such as proteins. On a dry matter basis, leaf tissue N concentrations are typically in the range of 2 to 6% N. About half of the total leaf protein is present in one photosynthetic enzyme, ribulose-1,5-bis phosphate carboxylase, which may be the most abundant enzyme in nature. Nitrogen is also an essential component of the chlorophyll molecule. Thus, crop demand for N is in large part a function of leaf area development and its vital role in photosynthesis.

For N demand and recommended soil fertility practices, it is useful to classify crops into major functional categories: annuals, woody perennials, and herbaceous perennials. Leguminous crops are not considered in the discussion because when properly inoculated to carry out symbiotic N fixation, most are effectively self-sufficient with respect to N nutrition. A notable exception is green or dry bean (*Phaseolus vulgaris* L.), a crop that is a weak N fixer and often needs some additional applied N for high yields.

Annual Crops

Annual crops reach maturity in a single growing season, with a characteristic pattern of growth and N uptake. Accumulation of N by an annual crop follows a pattern similar to dry matter accumulation, especially during vegetative growth (Fig. 7–3). A maturing crop slows its N uptake rate because much of the N already

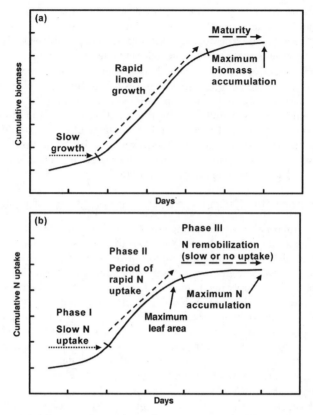

Fig. 7–3. Typical (a) biomass accumulation curve and (b) N accumulation curve for annual crops (modified from Sullivan et al., 1999).

accumulated within the plant is being redistributed from vegetative tissues to reproductive tissues. Important to soil fertility practices is N uptake patterns of annual crops that approximate their patterns of vegetative growth; these patterns suggest the appropriate times for soil nitrate testing and supplemental N fertilization if necessary.

The pattern of cumulative N uptake over the growing season follows a sigmoid curve that may be divided into three phases (Fig. 7–3b). A key time for nitrate testing is when an annual crop nears the end of the first phase and is about to enter the second phase. During the early phase, plant growth and N uptake are relatively slow (Fig. 7–3). On warm soils rich in organic matter where a recent tillage operation has stimulated microbial activity and release of N, sufficient N may be available from the soil to satisfy early demand for N. In less-favorable conditions, use of an approved organic starter N fertilizer may be necessary.

In the second growth phase (Fig. 7–3), there is a period of rapid N uptake that corresponds with rapid vegetative growth. Up to 50 to 85% of total N uptake for the growing season is during this growth phase. Farmers must become familiar with the growth pattern of each annual crop, and if supplemental N fertilizer is needed, it should be applied in advance of this growth phase to ensure that N is not limiting. In well-managed established organic farming systems, soils may have the capacity to supply sufficient N. Soils undergoing transition to organic farming are most likely to need supplemental N. With a soil nitrate test before the rapid growth phase, soil nitrate N concentration can be used to predict whether the supply of N from soil is adequate to meet the demands of the approaching rapid crop growth. If supplemental N fertilization is needed, the enlarging crop canopy may make side-dress applications of N fertilizer difficult. Under organic production, there are fewer options for side-dress applications of N fertilizer, and with use of good organic cultural practices it may not be needed. Soil nitrate testing is also useful to monitor the potential for a system to supply excess soluble N that can become an environmental hazard.

Depending on the crop, the maximum rate of N uptake may range from 2 kg to more than 11 kg N ha^{-1} d^{-1}. To achieve acceptable yields, organically managed soils need to supply N at a rate that matches maximum rate of N uptake by the crop. For crops with low maximum rates of N uptake, the N mineralized from soil organic matter or slow-release organic N sources may satisfy the crop's peak needs. Crops with high peak rates of N uptake, such as maize, are more of a challenge to match soil N supply and crop N demand. Organic farming systems with forage legumes or manure application before maize planting may satisfy peak N demands, but mineralization of N may persist after crop needs are met and may therefore leave soluble N in the soil that can be lost by nitrate leaching late in the season.

In the third growth phase (Fig. 7–3b), vegetative growth has largely ended while reproductive structures (seed, fruit, tubers) are developing. As the crop approaches maturity, N is remobilized within the plant from vegetative to reproductive tissues. Demand for N uptake from the soil has slowed. Supplying additional N beyond that already available from the soil during the final growth phase is seldom effective for increasing yields. A possible exception is indeterminate or long-season fruiting crops such as tomato (*Solanum lycopersicum* L. var. *lycopersicum*), where there may be a sustained demand for N from the soil. In that case, repeated soil nitrate testing may be useful to monitor if soil N availability remains sufficient during reproduction (Hartz et al., 2000).

Woody Perennials

The woody perennials category includes many species that are generally less well characterized and understood in terms of soil fertility management. Tree fruit crops, such as almond [*Prunus dulcis* (Mill.)] and apple [*Malus sylvestrus* (L.) Mill.], have received more research attention and are better understood than most other woody perennials (Youssefi et al., 1999). An important factor influencing soil fertility and fertilizer practice with woody perennials is the capacity to store nutrients such as N and others as well as carbohydrates in woody tissues (twigs, buds, stems, bark, and roots) from the present growing season for use in the following season. A soil fertility program for woody perennials should be developed based on observations of growth, yield, and leaf tissue analysis from the previous season along with cultural objectives of the current and subsequent growing season.

Nitrogen uptake by woody perennials may occur throughout the year, but demand for N fluctuates over the growing season depending on the strength of the various vegetative and reproductive sinks for N. In general, N uptake is lowest when leaves are absent, and the peak rate of N uptake occurs when leaves are present,. For tree fruit crops, the peak demand for N occurs during early summer when there is high demand for N in developing leaf tissue and fruit.

Amount of N uptake during a single year is generally small in relation to the total amount of N already present in the biomass of a mature tree. The capacity of trees to recycle a pool of N internally from season to season influences tree demand for N, and this has an effect on regulating N demand and uptake.

In spring before bud break, there is little uptake of N from the soil into the woody parts of the tree. There is slightly more N uptake from the soil during the first spring growth flush. The developing new leaf, shoot, and flower tissue is furnished with N primarily from reserves accumulated in bark and wood of roots, trunk, and stems during previous seasons. During the second flush of shoot growth, a tree generally has an increasing demand for external N, accompanied by increasing N uptake from the soil. In temperate zones, the soil will have warmed during this growth stage and will have stimulated N mineralization. Appropriate management of soils by organic farming practices, such as compost application or cover cropping, should match this growth stage and crop demand for N. The objective is to supply sufficient N to match the demand depending on tree size, age, fruit load, and other growth and cultural factors. The results of leaf tissue analysis from previous seasons may be used to guide cultural practices that either augment or draw down supply of available N from soil.

Woody perennials are underutilized in agriculture. They have many special attributes that hold promise for increased utilization in organic farming. *Tree Crops* by J. Russell Smith (1950) provides an excellent introduction to the valuable uses of trees as forage for feeding livestock, controlling soil erosion, and producing food. With respect to N, it is not well appreciated that woody perennials are especially conservative with nutrients. Unlike annual crops that typically have relatively short periods of high demand for N, woody perennials typically have extended periods of more moderate N demand. Perennials by nature tend to be conservative with respect to utilization of external and internal N resources. Also, the *ecto*-mycorrhiza associated with woody perennials are capable of accessing sources of N and P in soils that are largely unavailable to annual crops colonized with *vam*-mycorrhiza.

In trees such as apple, a significant portion of the N absorbed during the summer months eventually becomes stored in woody perennial tissues. Also in late summer, soon after maximum leaf area expansion, the N content of leaves begins to decrease as N is exported from leaves to perennial tree parts. This process marks the onset of senescence when amino acids or proteins are exported from leaf tissue to storage in woody perennial tissues. As much as half of the N in leaves may be remobilized to storage tissues. This reabsorption of leaf N by deciduous trees has the effect of conserving N that might otherwise be lost from the soil after leaf abscission. Stored N is used to support initial tree growth and development the following spring with minimal requirement for N from the soil resource. The high C/N ratio of fallen leaf residue also helps to immobilize and conserve end-of-season residual mineral N in the soil ecosystem.

In general, woody perennials should have a soil N supply that peaks shortly after the initial flush of spring growth. In fruit trees, if a supplemental organic approved N fertilizer is to be applied after fruit set, the amount of N to apply may be adjusted on the basis of fruit load. This is especially important if a late spring frost limits fruit set. Also in fruit trees, N management practices should reflect potential influence of N supply on fruit quality, vigor of shoot and spur growth, and flower development and fruit set in the following growing season.

Herbaceous Perennials

Nonleguminous herbaceous perennials include grasses grown for forage or turf, or crops such as strawberry (*Fragaria* spp), asparagus (*Asparagus officinalis* L.), and horseradish (*Armoracia rusticana* G. Gaertn., B. Mey. & Scherb.). A common principle that underlies this group with respect to N nutrition is the potential to accumulate some N during the growing season and carry over stored carbohydrates and N to initiate new crop growth the following spring. Herbaceous perennials primarily use root or crowns to store N and have less capacity for trans-seasonal N storage than do woody perennials. Nevertheless, established herbaceous perennials have a comparative advantage over plants from seeds by having carryover N and other stored nutrients that may be mobilized to initiate new spring growth on cold soils when microbial activity and N mineralization are slow.

The end purpose of the crop influences cultural practices and soil fertility N management. For example, perennial grasses grown for seed or for forage may require different management choices because of different patterns of demand for N. When grown for seed, N demand may be similar to annual grain crops. When managed for forage, the crop is typically kept in a perpetual vegetative state wherein the growth habit and cutting or grazing cycle dictate the demand for N from the soil.

Cool-season versus warm-season grasses have different temporal patterns of growth and N demand. In general, most of the growth and demand for N by cool-season grasses occurs in the spring and fall; in warm-season grasses, most growth and demand for N occurs in summer. Organic cultural practices or N sources should be geared to matching specific patterns of crop demand for N. If the grass is grown mixed with a legume, the legume is generally able to supply sufficient N to the grass.

When grasses are grown for turf, frequent mowing keeps the plants in an actively growing vegetative state with a continuous demand for N uptake. The standards and objectives for an organic lawn care program will likely be different than a conventional system in terms of species diversity and tolerance for "weeds." In an organic lawn, clover (*Trifolium* spp.) may be a welcome species and a significant source of N. Mowing in organic lawn care management will appropriately leave behind the clippings to be recycled. Leaving clippings on the turf can supply at least 50% of the lawn's requirement for N (Heckman et al., 2000). This internal N cycle in combination with clover and occasional compost or other approved organic N source should supply sufficient N for an organic lawn. For lawns with cool-season grasses, supplemental N applications should be applied in early fall and possibly in spring. In lawns with warm-season grasses, the supplemental N should applied in the late spring or early summer.

Soil Testing and Plant Tissue Analysis

Organic farmers have long had a keen interest in the connections among soil, plant, and animal health. Soil testing and plant tissue analysis have traditionally been useful tools in organic farming. Unfortunately, nearly all research on soil test calibration has been conducted on soils under nonorganic management. Procedures used in conventional soil test research tend to have a narrow focus on calibrating the soil test for crop yield, with limited attention to product quality or the health of the larger ecosystem. Although daily farmer observations of soils, crops, and livestock may be largely subjective, they are invaluable tools to judge soil quality and soil fertility. One challenge for the future will be to discover measurements of soil fertility that can be objectively related to productively and health of the whole organic system. Mechanistic interpretations of soil tests are not likely to completely replace the subjective observations of experienced people on the farm in concert with careful soil, crop, and animal husbandry.

Visual inspection of soils under long-term organic management immediately suggests apparent differences in soil quality as compared to the same soils under typical conventional management. This has long been recognized, and soils that are managed over time using organic techniques may have favorable biological properties that contribute to crop production in unique ways. Thus, there is need for caution in translation of soil test critical levels and optimum ranges (Stalenga, 2007) that were developed from research in conventional management systems, but the absence of soil test calibration data on soils under organic management means there is little alternative at present.

In general, soil test fertility levels may have a different management function in organic farming. In conventional farming, the approach to soil fertility testing is largely geared toward making predictions about the need for specific nutrient inputs for the current or near-term crop production cycle. In contrast, organic farming philosophically focuses on building soil organic matter and nutrient cycling for soil fertility maintenance over the long term. There are multiple challenges to the organic approach for which soil fertility tests can provide valuable guidance. Because soil fertility inputs in organic farming are typically complex, whole nutrient substances such compost or rock powders, organic management is less prescriptive and more challenging to maintain balance among individual nutrients. The buildup of some nutrients to excessive levels while others may become depleted is a practical and environmental concern of organic farming. Regular soil testing can be used to monitor the balance of soil nutrient stores against both excessive buildup and depletion. Keeping soil test records for tracking changes in fertility levels over the long term can be useful to guide nutrient management. In this context, soil test fertility categories, which may have different names depending on the soil test laboratory or region, of *below optimum*, *optimum*, and *above optimum* are meaningful for management of macronutrients in organic farming.

Soil Organic Matter Content

Organic growers tend to be especially interested how well their soil management practices promote the building of soil organic matter content. They should be aware that soil organic matter content is slow to improve and that it is useful to track changes in soil organic matter content over a long time frame, such as a decade. However, some soil test laboratories (e.g., Cornell University Soil Health program, http://www.hort.cornell.edu/soilhealth/index.htm) now can measure the microbially available, rapidly turning over fraction of the soil organic matter. This *active organic matter* accounts for only a small fraction of the total organic matter in soils but is much more sensitive to soil management practices and is closely related to the nutrient cycling and soil tilth–promoting functions of soil organic matter (Weil et al., 2003). Also, organic growers should consider the influence of climate, soil texture, and drainage class while interpreting soil organic matter levels. It is easier to build and maintain organic matter on fine-textured soils than on course-textured soils and in regions where the climate is cool rather than warm. For example, in a cool climate, an organic matter content of less than 3.0% may be considered poor for a silt loam soil but may be considered very good for a sandy loam soil. An organic matter content of 4 to 5% is generally considered good for a loam or silt loam soil.

Soil Testing for Nitrogen

Although N can be taken up from the soil as nitrate, ammonium, and some organic compounds, nitrate N is the major form taken up by most crops. An objective of any soil test is to rapidly evaluate a particular soil characteristic and then reliably predict whether the supply of N from the soil is sufficient for crop needs. Soil testing for N is usually focused on measuring nitrate N because this has a good record of success. Measurement of ammonium N has generally not improved the accuracy of soil tests for predicting N availability. The concentration of nitrate in soil, however, can change rapidly. Therefore, when soil testing for nitrate, it is important to collect samples shortly before the crop is ready for rapid growth and N uptake.

Soil testing for nitrate can be performed either at preplant or in season. Preplant soil nitrate testing is most appropriate in lower rainfall regions where nitrate is less vulnerable to leaching. In-season soil nitrate testing is commonly referred to as *pre-side-dress soil nitrate test* or PSNT (Magdoff, 1991; Heckman, 2002).

In-season soil nitrate testing is most useful with annual crops in humid regions where N is especially vulnerable to losses from leaching or denitrification. This soil test is based on sampling the soil to a depth of 25 cm during the early growing season of an annual crop. In maize soil sampling should be performed when plants are 15 to 25 cm tall. The PSNT is also useful with vegetable crops, such as sweet corn, cabbage (*Brassica oleracea* L.), squash (*Cucurbita* spp.), pumpkin (*Cucurbita pepo* L.), and peppers (*Capsicum annuum* L.) when sampling is performed at an early growth stage. Soil samples need to be handled carefully and dried quickly to prevent changes in nitrate concentration. Soil testing laboratories must report results to farmers rapidly so that they can take timely action with the growing crop.

Critical PSNT levels vary among regions and crops, but in general, when the PSNT soil test level is less than 25 mg kg^{-1} nitrate N, the soil is considered N deficient (Heckman, 2002). Side-dressed N should be applied to the crop to correct the deficit. If the PSNT test is more than 25 mg kg^{-1}, the soil is supplying sufficient N to grow the crop. But if the PSNT is more than 50 mg kg^{-1} the soil N level is more than needed for crops and there is potential for N losses.

Although organic growers do not typically apply side-dressed N, they may do so with an organically approved fertilizer. The main reason for using the PSNT in an established organic cropping system is to provide valuable feedback about the soil fertility program. After several years of soil fertility building under organic management as part of an effective crop rotation, the soil will often supply sufficient available N to annual row crops without the need for organic N fertilizer. Organic growers can use the PSNT to learn from experience how their soil-building program and crop rotation cycle are working to supply N, and how to make adjustments in future years. The PSNT can be especially useful to transitional organic growers where soil N supplying capacity is often limiting and where side-dressing may be necessary.

The options for application of rapidly available N (Table 7–1) when the PSNT calls for a side-dressing are more limited for organic farmers than for their conventional counterparts. However, USDA-NOP standards allow up to 20% of a crop's N needs to be met by the use of (Chilean) sodium nitrate. Ironically, this highly soluble, fast-acting fertilizer exemplifies the most damaging characteristic of the synthetic fertilizers eschewed by organic farming: its salt effect can burn tender plants, the sodium it contains can cause soil to harden, and the N it contains is in the very soluble nitrate form that is easily lost, encourages weed seed germination, and can lead to imbalanced nutrient uptake. Also, Chilean nitrate fertilizers may be contaminated with perchlorate, which interferes with iodide uptake into the thyroid gland. Chilean nitrate is naturally occurring, but synthetic N fertilizers are never allowed in organic crop production. Fraudulent use of synthetic N in organic farming may be detectable by analyzing the ratio of $^{15}N/^{14}N$ in the produce (Del Amor et al., 2008) since this ratio is lower in fertilizers manufactured from atmospheric N_2 by high temperature industrial reactions that form ammonia.

Table 7–1. Nitrogen content, C/N ratio, and nitrogen availability from some organic materials, after days of incubation in soil.†

	Nitrogen	Ratio	Percent converted to mineral N in days					
			14 d	20 d	28 d	35 d	40 d	56 d
	%	C/N	%					
Animal products								
Fishmeal or powder	9–14	3–4	57	59	60		63	65
Processed liquid fish residues	4							
Feather meal	12	4	57		64			64
Hoof meal	14	3		65			68	
Blood meal	12–16	3	60	60	67		66	70
Bone meal	2–4	3		7			10	
Manures								
Pellated chicken manure	2–4	36		23				36
Guano	9–14	1–3	58		60			67
Plant materials								
Alfalfa meal	3–4	21		24			32	
Soybean meal	7	5		61			65	
Cottonseed meal	6–7	5		49			54	
Castor promace	5	9		60			67	
Cocoa meal	3	15		14			22	
Peanut hull meal	1.2	54		15			15	
Yard waste								
Shade tree leaves	1	49						
Grass clippings	3.6	18				23		
Food processing wastes								
Tomato sauce waste water sludge	1.4	18				26		
Tomato skins and seeds	1.7	31				42		
Coffee grounds	1.6	32						

† Sources: Gaskell and Smith (2007); Hartz and Johnstone (2006); Heckman and Kluchinski (1996); Mikkelsen and Hartz (2008); Rogers et al. (2001); Rubins and Bear (1942).

Organic Management of the Phosphorus Cycle

A supply of phosphorus and most other nutrients cannot be procured or grown on the farm in the same way that soil N can be supplied by fixation and soil organic carbon can be accumulated from CO_2 fixed by photosynthesis. Nevertheless, P is a component of organic matter and it cycles in concert with parts of the N and C cycles. A key difference is that there is no major cycling of P through the atmosphere, as with the N and C cycles. What this means for the organic farmer is that P needs to be transported to the farm from another source to correct P deficient soils.

Natural by-product materials such as manures and many substrates used for making compost are rich sources of both N and P. Land applications of these materials return both N and P to the soil, and their nutrient cycles are in some respects are similar. Phosphorus is a constituent of organic compounds such as nucleic acids, inositol phosphates, and phospholipids. These compounds can be mineralized to inorganic P during organic matter decomposition or can be incorporated into more persistent organic forms as humus. Compost and soils rich in organic matter typically have abundant stores of organic P that is readily convertible to inorganic P. Plant uptake of P occurs primarily from the more soluble inorganic pools.

The content of P in soils varies considerably depending on the type of parent material, degree of weathering, and farm nutrient management history. Although P-deficient soils occur in agricultural regions, soils with abundant supplies of P are fairly common today as a result of many years of overapplication of manure and fertilizer. When a newly transitioned organic farm inherits a reservoir of previously added P, it is often possible to produce crops for a decade or more before enough P is exported from the farm to draw down the P supply to the critical level where additional P is needed to sustain yields. Many organic farms use imported compost or manure to secure much of their crop N needs. These materials also contain P, and their repeated application at rates needed to supply enough plant available N to crops will generally oversupply P and result in buildup of soil test P far beyond crop requirements to the point of becoming a water pollution hazard (Rosen and Allan, 2007).

There are several causes for the N source effect on P imbalance (Nelson and Janke, 2007). The ratio of N/P in crop biomass is typically 12:1 to 7:1, but the N/P ratio of manures is generally less than 4:1. This ratio may be even narrower in composted manure because composting tends to conserve P and volatize or leach some N. Furthermore, to supply the N needs of plants, manures must be applied at two to four times the rate suggested by their total N content because only 25 to 50% of the total N in manure is readily plant available. This effect is even more pronounced in composted manures, for which only about 10% of the total N is readily plant available in the first year.

The solution to this N:P imbalance problem is to increase the amount of N supplied without accompanying P by including more legumes (which add N from the air) on the farm as cash crops, forages, or cover crops. Thus, N sources and management practices influence P cycling and P availability.

Besides carbon-based P sources such as manures and compost, organic producers supplement as needed with nonprocessed mineral sources such as phosphate rock (PR) (Nelson and Janke, 2007). The raw PR is the starting material used in the manufacture of synthetic P fertilizers used in conventional agriculture. Synthetic fertilizers such as super- or triple superphosphate are made by reaction with sulfuric or phosphoric acid to increase the solubility of the P in the PR. Organic farming, which does not permit the use of such acidulated phosphate fertilizers, seeks to convert the P in PR to crop-available forms by using soil biological processes and natural soil weathering. The biological processes associated with growing legumes is one of the primary means of mobilizing recalcitrant P from PR.

The problem of poor availability of P from PR was recognized long ago. Agronomic efforts to use PR included a recommendation that it be applied to the clover in a crop rotation cycle, based on the work of Cyril G. Hopkins (1906) at the University of Illinois. Observation and experience had shown that legumes played a key role in making P from rock phosphate available to other crops. Organic farmers continue to value the synergy of growing legumes in association with PR application to enhance P availability.

From a soil genesis perspective, application of raw rock phosphate is akin to adding fresh parent material to soil. Weathering slowly transforms the apatite mineral in PR to plant available P. Depending on the source, PR may contain 12 to 16% P. Due to rock phosphate's low solubility, it is usually spread infrequently with a lime spreader at rates nearly comparable to a limestone application. A single application of PR provides slow-release P that sustains long-term soil fertility when used to supplement P that is typically recycled on the farm as compost or manure in an organic production system.

Amending soils under organic management with rock phosphate becomes necessary when initial soil P supply is below optimum levels needed for economic production. It also becomes necessary to sustain fertility when more P is exported in products harvested from the farm than is returned to the farm as compost or manure, including imported feeds for livestock. Unlike manures or non-NOP-compliant composts, there is no time restriction or waiting period required for application of PR on vegetable cropland. In organic farming, however, the focus on the use of sparingly soluble nutrient sources such as PR goes beyond providing a prescriptive immediate crop response to one of long-term building of soil fertility.

While the initial solubility of P from PR is very low (<1%) from all mine sources, there are important differences in mineralogy that influence reactivity of the raw material when applied to soil. Apatite is the P-bearing mineral in rock phosphate with the general formula of $Ca_5(PO_4)3X$, where X is one of several possible anions that affect reactivity. Of the two main sources of PR, sedimentary and igneous, sedimentary rock phosphate is generally more reactive because it has a higher level of carbonate substitution and a greater specific surface area. Although more reactive PRs are preferred sources, information on PR solubility and availability to crops is not easy to find for products on the retail market.

In the eastern United States, PR is mined from deposits in North Carolina and Florida. Generally, PRs are very finely pulverized to maximize surface area contact with soil and enhance dissolution. Increasing fineness below particle size of 150 μm generally has no further agronomic benefit. Phosphate rock from North Carolina is one of the more reactive sources even though it is typically less finely ground than other sources. Although it was once a preferred and widely used PR by organic farmers, the North Carolina raw phosphate ore is currently being used only for the production of processed phosphate concentrates. Phosphate rock from sources in Gafsa in central Tunisia is known to have relatively good P availability. Compared with other sources, the PR from the western United States has among the lowest P solubility and has higher-than-desired levels of the heavy metal cadmium.

The P from PR is most available in acid soils where the pH is 5.5 or less. Where crops and soils permit good production on strongly acid soils, PR can be an effective P fertilizer, and organic farmers can take advantage of this condition. Soils classified as Histosols or muck, which are known to have very high organic matter contents and low exchangeable aluminum, are also suitable for direct application of PR. Also, on new lands in transition to organic farming that are both acidic and low in P availability, it may be advantageous to apply PR well in advance of applying limestone to neutralize soil acidity. Limestone increases concentrations of calcium in soil, which decreases the solubility of P from PR. When possible, delaying limestone applications may allow more time for the rock phosphate to react in soil. For most crops and soils, however, a soil pH greater than 5.5 is desired to supply calcium and prevent aluminum toxicity. With appropriate cultural practices, PR can be used effectively when applied to soils with higher pH levels.

Although compost or manures are good sources of readily available P, effective use of PR requires management by the farmer to enhance P availability. Including legumes in the crop rotation helps to improve P availability, but there appears to be considerable variation among species of legumes and cover crops in their ability to mobilize P. This may be explained by the range of soil biological processes among plant species that influence P availability.

The physiology of N fixation is associated with a tendency to acidify the rhizosphere, a thin layer of soil that surrounds the roots (Nuruzzaman et al., 2005; Perez et al., 2006). Soil pH is one of the primary factors influencing the reaction that dissolves the apatite mineral in soil. Each unit decrease in soil pH is accompanied by a 100-fold increase in P solubility from PR. It is not unusual for some legumes to cause the rhizophere pH to be reduced by about two units below the bulk soil pH. This, along with the high calcium uptake of legumes, contributes to improving the efficacy of PR. Alfalfa (Medicago sativa L.), for example, has a propensity for higher levels of Ca uptake than many other crops. Calcium is a reaction product of apatite dissolution. The removal of Ca from the site of the reaction helps to shift reaction toward increased dissolution, and this may result in increased concentration of P in the soil solution.

In general, the diversity of cover crops grown in organic production systems is probably good for liberating and mobilizing P from rock phosphate and other sources (Zaharah and Bah, 1997). Excretion of low-molecular-weight organic anions from roots, especially from brassica and legume species, forms strong complexes with aluminum, iron, and calcium, metallic elements that tend to bind P in the soil. Complexing of these metals by root exudates reduces the binding and increases the availability of P in a soil

Besides providing a more readily available source of P to subsequent crops when the land-applied manure or the cover crop biomass decompose, there may be opportunities when intercropping can be used to benefit the growth of a concurrently grown intermingled crop (Li et al., 2007). The intercropping of legumes with grasses enables chemical and biological alteration of the rhizosphere that mobilizes P to enhance not only the productivity of the legume but also that of other species. This interspecific rhizosphere effect may contribute to overyielding of mixed stands of forage as well as in production of intercropped grains as with faba bean (*Vicia faba* L.) and maize.

Mobilizing P is one among the many benefits of having forage legumes or cover crops in the organic crop rotation cycle (Horst et al., 2001). The design of the crop rotation cycle is to have uptake of P from sources such as rock phosphate, which may be largely unavailable to certain crops, and then have it released to subsequent crops such as row crop grains. In forage legumes, the biomass may first pass through livestock before the mobilized P is delivered to the soil as manure or compost. In this way, animals hold an important place in the design of the organic rotation cycle because unlike plowed-down legume cover crops to feed the soil, including an animal component can produce milk or meat as cash crops. This is another example of the biodiversity benefits of integrating plant and animal systems on the organic farm.

Cover crops have different attributes, and research has demonstrated significant variation in ability to mobilize P from rock phosphate and other soil reserves. In general the rhizosphere biology associated with legumes makes them more effective in this role than nonlegume cover crops, but other factors also influence P acquisition efficiency. The slow diffusion of P to the root surface is a major limiting factor for P acquisition. Efficiency of P acquisition is enhanced by cover crops with higher root density, length, and surface area. Cover cropping with good host species tends to enhance levels of root colonization by arbuscular mycorrhizal fungi that allow the plant access to P several centimeters from the root surface.

Bones are a nutrient source with a long history of use in agriculture (Nelson and Janke, 2007). The mineral composition of bone is described as a calcium-deficient hydroxyl-apatite because one of several cations in the hydroxyapatite such as Na, Mg, K, or Sr substitute for some of the Ca in the mineral structure. It tends to be more soluble than pure hydroxyapitite because the Ca/P ratio is lower. Bone meal, made by grinding raw animal bones, is an approved P source for organic agriculture. It is more soluble than PR, but because of limited supply, bone meal tends to be expensive. As with rock phosphate, bone meal solubility decreases as soil pH increases, and it is most reactive in acid soils. Bone meal P availability also improves with increasing fineness of particle size. Commercial bone meal products are heat-treated to a temperature that ashes soft tissues and eliminates the potential to transmit diseases.

Guano is a material formed where birds or bats roost. As it ages, N and P become concentrated as a mineral called *struvite* or magnesium ammonium phosphate. Struvite is only slightly soluble, but in soils, as nitrification depresses ammonium concentrations, it dissolves more rapidly and releases N and P to crops.

When P is the limiting nutrient in organic crop production, compost is generally the preferred source because it is relatively inexpensive and its P is readily available to crops. The P from manures is also readily available, but NOP guidelines restrict the direct application of manure in many cropping situations to ensure food safety. Phosphate rock is best used to build soil fertility over the long term rather than as an immediate source of P. Supplies of bone meal are limited but renewable from the livestock industry. Supplies of guano are also limited but essentially nonrenewable in the short term. Therefore, its use, although organically approved, cannot be considered sustainable. Both of these P sources are relatively expensive and are primarily used for production of high-value organic horticul-tural crops. The goal of an organic soil fertility program is to establish a farming system in which there is maximum opportunity to recycle natural organic materi-als and thereby avoid the need to purchase nutrient inputs such as P.

Interpreting soil tests for P on soils under organic management can be chal-lenging for many reasons, but the possible presence of unreacted PR residues in soil may present an additional challenge. Some of the widely used soil test extractants are strong acids that can significantly overestimate levels of available P by solubilizing some of the unreacted PR which is not really plant-available. This can be a problem where organic farmers who use PR are required to base nutrient management plans on soil tests calibrated on conventional soils not amended with PR.

Organic Management of the Potassium Cycle

The amount of potassium (K) taken up by crops is similar to that for N and about 5 to 10 times as much for P, Ca, or Mg. Unlike N, there are no gaseous forms of K to be captured from the atmosphere. Most soils hold large reserves of K in the primary and secondary soil minerals, but only a small fraction of the total K in soil is immediately available for plant uptake. The K in the soil solution and the exchangeable K held on soil colloids are readily available for plant uptake. As the exchangeable K is depleted, it can be replenished by the reserves of nonexchangeable K, but this is a slow process that is generally not rapid enough to satisfy crop requirements.

Sustainability in agriculture requires that the nutrient status of the soil should not decline year after year by way of crop harvest. Potassium removal from the soil and the farm should ideally be balanced by inputs to create a sustainable organic farming system. It has been estimated that general agriculture in the United States replaces only 3 kg of K as fertilizer or manure for every 4 kg of K removed by crops (Mikkelsen, 2007). In some soils high in K-bearing minerals, the other 1 kg of available K may be replenished by mineral weathering and release from nonex-changeable site on soil colloids. Although the amount of K supplied to crops from nonexchangeable sources is of practical agronomic value, it may not be sufficient to provide a sustainable K balance over the long term. For example, a long-term study of four organic farms in England (Gosling and Shepherd, 2005) found that soil K levels were in decline due to export of K in harvested products.

Regional differences soil mineralogy and climatic patterns influence the long-term ability of soils to supply K. Soils in the central Great Plains and much of western North America have relatively high reserves of K-bearing parent mate-rial and least often require supplemental K fertilizer. In contrast, the soils of the southeastern United States generally have lower reserves of K and frequently need K fertilization. This is particularly true for the sandy coastal plain soils, which also lose large amounts of soluble K by leaching. An awareness of regional differences cannot be used to make site-specific K recommendations, but they do suggest dif-ferent challenges that might be faced in K management by organic farmers.

The K contents of leaves, straw, and fruits are generally much higher than that of seeds and grain. Therefore, harvests that remove whole plants or the leafy portions, such as for silage or hay, typically remove K from the soil much faster than mineral weathering can replace it. In general, when crops are fed to livestock and animal products are exported from the farm instead of forages, more K is recycled on the farm and the overall rate of K removal is less. Thus, well-diversified organic farms that integrate plant and animal agriculture have a more closed K cycle than farms that primarily produce hay and grains for sale.

Manures, compost, and crop residues are good sources of potassium that become readily available once applied to soil. Potassium remains a highly soluble cation (K^+) in living tissues, unlike N or P, which are metabolized to form complex organic compounds. Thus, there is little to no dependence on microbial decomposition to transform K present in manures or compost into plant available forms when these materials are applied to the soil. Particle size of the organic residue is probably a factor in plant access to the K. In manure slurry, an estimated 90% of K is available to crops in the year of application. In farm yard manure where there are larger particle sizes of bedding materials, only about 60% of the applied K is available in the first year.

Because K is soluble, it is critically important that manures and compost be handled carefully on organic farms to minimize potential losses of the valuable K. Most of the K is in the urine, and this fraction must be collected along with the manure solids. While K does not volatilize during composting, losses of K via leaching from the compost pile is a concern in areas of high rainfall. Importing manures and compost or animal feed to a farm can become a significant source of K that should be taken into account in the nutrient management plan for an organic farm. As was mentioned with regard to P, excessive reliance on these materials as a source of N can potentially lead to the buildup of excessive levels of K in the soil. Mulching with such materials as spoiled legume hay (which may contain 4 to 5% K in the dry matter) can unintentionally import very large amounts of K to a field. Overuse of imported high-K manures or mulches can lead to excessive levels of exchangeable K that can interfere with the uptake of Mg and Ca by crops. Excessive K in forages can likewise lead to deficiencies of Ca and Mg in livestock consuming these materials.

In organic agriculture, because of the emphasis on recycling of on-farm and off-farm natural resources, manures, composts, and crop residues are primary nutrient sources. Balancing imports and exports of K from fields and whole farms should be considered a part of the comprehensive farm nutrient management plan. The amounts of K removed from soil by harvest have been determined for many crops, and these values can be useful to determine if a net export of K is occurring from a field or the farm. When there is a net export of K from the farm and manures and compost do not supply enough to maintain soil fertility K levels, then supplementing with approved K fertilizers is necessary.

In addition to export in farm products, K is also susceptible to loss from the soil through runoff and leaching. Runoff losses can be controlled by maintaining soil surface cover and good cultural practices that prevent soil erosion. The normal electrical attraction of K to soil particles helps to prevent leaching, but soils vary in cation exchange capacity and therefore in ability to hold on to K as water flows down through the soil profile. Clay and humus are the main colloidal particles that constitute the cation exchange capacity and the ability to hold onto K. Sandy and low organic matter content soils are most susceptible to K leaching. Building soil organic matter content and proper liming and soil pH management can increase soil cation exchange capacity and reduce K leaching. Subsoil clay layers can hold considerable amounts of K that are not measured by soil tests performed on samples collected from the plow layer. Growing deep-rooting cover crops can be helpful in preventing leaching and bringing K to the soil surface from the lower soil layers and weathering bedrock.

Crops vary in ability to acquire K from soil and differ in their minimum requirements for optimum growth. In general, grasses are more effective than legumes or dicots in extracting K from soils. In a mixed stand, legumes are more vulnerable to low K fertility than grasses. The demand for K uptake by grasses can draw down the supply of exchangeable K, and this can result in the release of some K that has become fixed in interlayers of soil clays. Rock dusts are sometimes applied as sources of slow-release K and other nutrients. Grasses are among the most effective crops in mobilizing slow-release mineral sources of K and are therefore valuable plants to include in a crop rotation.

The aim of organic soil fertility management must be to supply sufficient K to meet both the crop's total seasonal K requirement and its peak rate of K uptake. The amount of K accumulated by the crop before harvest provides an estimate of the total quantity of K needed from the soil during the growing season. The peak rate of K uptake is also very important but more difficult to estimate.

Potassium accumulation rates are initially slow for young plants, but the pace of uptake increases in concert with rapid growth. Research (Mengel and Arneke, 1982) suggests that an uninterrupted K supply, which is needed to facilitate water uptake into growing plant cells, is a more sensitive physiological process than is dry matter accumulation. Thus, supplying K from the soil at a sufficient rate to be concentrated in plant cell vacuoles to support the expansion of leaf tissue needed for interception of sunlight, is an especially important soil fertility/nutritional role of K in rapidly growing plants. In addition to expansive growth of shoot and root tissues, the growth of fruit tissue, especially succulent fruits with a high water content, requires considerable amounts of K nutrition.

Although manures and composts have relatively good K solubility, powdered rocks and greensands traditionally used to supplement K in organic production are rather insoluble. These natural mineral sources of K are not generally capable of supplying K at rates sufficient to match peak crop K accumulation rates. Nevertheless, these slowly available mineral K sources may be useful in the long term. There are generally no restrictions on the use of these natural mineral K sources in organic farming, but they have the disadvantages of being bulky, heavy, and expensive to transport for a limited supply of readily available K.

The availability of K from crushed rocks, dusts, and powders varies depending on the mineralogy of the rock source, but there is little agronomic information to guide application. Over the long-term, plants are able to acquire some K from mineral sources such as biotite, muscovite, phlogopite, nepheline, and feldspar. Although biotite releases K more readily than other mineral sources, the amount of K available in the short term is limited and depends on factors that influence weathering. Soil pH, microbial activity, temperature, moisture, reactive surface area, and vegetation type influence rate of K release from these minerals. Grasses are generally more effective at acquiring K from these sources than other types of vegetation.

Greensand has long been used as a natural fertilizer and soil conditioner. It is composed largely of glauconite, a clay mineral that contains about 5% K. It occurs in natural geologic deposits on the eastern Coastal Plain of the United States. Because this olive green–colored mineral is currently only being mined in New

Jersey, it is often called New Jersey greensand. Although the material occurs as sand-size pellets, it does not behave as true sand since it has numerous micropores that increase surface area and soil water-holding capacity. Greensand also has a high cation exchange capacity that contributes to storage of exchangeable nutrients in soil. In addition to K, greensand contains small amounts of P, Ca, and trace elements. Even though greensand is not a readily available source of K for plants, as an amendment its physical and chemical properties may be beneficial to soil (Heckman and Tedrow, 2004).

Seaweed, which typically contains about 2% K, is commonly fed to organic livestock and sometimes used for crops as a biostimulant or natural fertilizer. The low K content makes it expensive as a fertilizer source but when used as an animal feed and trace mineral source, it has additional value. Whether used directly for crop production or as feed, seaweed is a source of plant available K and it can make a small contribution to maintaining a positive K balance on an organic farm.

Wood ash has been used for centuries as a fertilizer, and it is an acceptable source of soluble K. Ash derived from combustion of manures, sewage biosolids, or coal is prohibited in organic farming. Nutrient concentrations vary considerably depending on the original elemental concentrations in the wood minus any volatilized losses during combustion. The K concentration averages 5% and it also contains about 1% P and 23% Ca. Ash has strong alkaline reaction and has a neutralizing effect on soil acidity. Compared with agricultural limestone, ash may have calcium carbonate equivalent values ranging from 8 to 90%. The large stoves that are increasing being used on farms to burn wood as a renewable energy source can also provide a local source of nutrients if the ashes are land applied. Applications of wood ash should be avoided on soils when a pH increase is undesirable.

There are three commercial K fertilizers, langbeinite, potassium sulfate, and sylvinite, which may sometimes be used with certain restrictions in organic farming. All of these materials provide relatively high concentrations of soluble K.

Langbeinite (potassium magnesium sulfate, $K_2SO_4\text{-}MgSO_4$) is allowed as nutrient source if it is used as a crushed raw mineral without further refinement or purification. In North America, langbeinite is mined from underground deposits in New Mexico. It typically contains 18% K, 22% S, and 11% Mg in the form of soluble salts that provide readily available nutrients for plant uptake. Langbeinite is especially desirable for use in agronomic situations where the combination of all three major nutrients is needed. On soils especially high in Mg, another K source may be more appropriate.

Potassium sulfate (K_2SO_4) when derived from natural sources is generally allowed as a K fertilizer based on NOP standards. In some European countries, its use requires special permission. Beyond mining, crushing, and sieving, or collection by evaporation, it must not be subjected to further processing or purification. The Great Salt Lake in Utah is a major source of organically approved K_2SO_4. It typically contains about 40% K and 17% S.

Sylvinite, a natural mixture of sylvite (potassium chloride, KCl) and halite (sodium chloride, NaCl), when derived from mined sources is allowed under NOP standards with some restrictions. It must not be subjected to further processing to remove sodium salts, and its use as fertilizer must not cause a buildup of chloride in the soil. Unprocessed sylvinite typically contains 17% K and 56% Cl. The organic farming community has long held unfavorable views on the use of KCl as a fertilizer due to concerns over toxicity from its high chloride content. Chlorine, however, is well established as an essential plant nutrient that is taken up by plants as chloride.

A common characteristic of the various sources of K for organic farming discussed here is that they are unprocessed or unrefined materials that by nature contain complex mixture of nutrients. There may be some nutritional advantages to use of such raw materials as fertilizers. For example, manures, composts, seaweed, and sylvinite are materials that can be good sources of Na. Sodium has been reported to be beneficial to many crops, especially when K is deficient. In plant cells, Na can substitute in part for the role of K as an osmolite. Also, Na is essential for animals, and Na fertilization of forages improves quality and acceptability to livestock (Chiy et al., 1998).

Because crop uptake can remove large amounts of K from the soil, leading to rapid declines in soil fertility, a regular soil sampling and testing program is advisable to ensure the sustainability of organic farming.

Organic Management of the Sulfur Cycle

The soil fertility and plant nutrition aspects of sulfur (S) are similar to those of N. In the soil–plant–atmosphere system, S and N are components of soil organic matter, occur as gases in the atmosphere, and have cycles that are coordinated with parts of C cycle. In the plant, both S and N are assimilated into proteins, and a short supply of one nutrient represses the assimilation of the other.

In humid-region agricultural soils, roughly 90% of the total S is present as a component of organic matter. The C/N/S ratio of soil organic matter is typically about 100:8:1. Organic farming practices that build soil organic matter content increase the pool of S in soil, and this can help ensure an adequate supply to crops. In ways similar to the behavior of N in soil, microbial activity influences S availability by converting organic S to a mineral form easily taken up by plants. The reverse process of immobilization also occurs when inorganic forms of S are incorporated into organic matter. Adding energy-rich, low-S-content organic materials to soil can lead to immobilization of S in a way that is analogous to N immobilization. The same environmental factors—temperature, moisture, aeration, and pH—influence both N and S mineralization and immobilization. Thus, many soil management practices used to govern N availability in organic farming will generally also have a similar influence on S availability.

The atmosphere contains S gases that can be absorbed through plant foliage and can supply as much as 25 to 50% of crop S nutrition. There is wide variation in potential to capture S from the atmosphere around the globe. In heavily industrialized areas, the burning of fossil fuels releases SO_2 into the atmosphere and S deficiencies are less common. While S emissions can supply agronomically useful amounts of S in areas near industrial facilities, the amount of replenishment decreases with distance from source.

In recent decades, actions to reduce air pollution have also decreased atmospheric S depositions and increased the prevalence of S deficiencies in some areas. Regional differences in atmospheric S deposition are a consideration in replenishment of S fertility. Within the United States, the more industrialized northeastern states generally receive the highest amounts of S deposition, ranging from 9 to 27 kg S ha^{-1} yr^{-1}. Volcanic activity is also an important source of atmospheric S in some regions.

Burning of crop residues has never been a recommended organic cultural practice and for good reason. When biomass is burned, it results in loss of S, as well as N and C, to the atmosphere. This export of nutrients can lead to locally S deficient soils.

Sulfur uptake from soils is primarily in the form of sulfate. Since sulfate is a soluble anion, it is susceptible to leaching to lower soil horizons or below the root zone. Sandy soils in humid regions are especially prone to losses of S from leaching. Highly weathered soils, such as those in the southeastern United States, often have clay in the soil layers that can adsorb substantial amounts of sulfate. Crops with shallow root systems, including young plants early in the season, are most susceptible to S deficiency on these soils. Deep-rooted crops that can explore the subsoil are more effective in obtaining subsoil-adsorbed sulfate. Use of deep tillage or rotation with tap-root cover crops may help break up compacted soil layers that can restrict root access to the subsoil sulfate.

In arid and semiarid regions, soils contain less organic matter than in humid regions, and organic forms of S represent only a small fraction of the total soil S. Sulfate often accumulates in these soils as sulfate salts such as gypsum (calcium sulfate), which is sufficiently soluble to serve as a good source of sulfate to crops.

Maintaining soil surface cover is a widely used cultural practice in organic farming that may be useful for enhancing S supply to subsequent crops in several ways. Cover crops increase the potential for capture of atmospheric S in foliage. Just as with nitrate, winter cover crops can uptake and prevent leaching of residual sulfate at the end of a growing season. Deep-rooted cover crops can "pump" subsoil sulfate to the surface, where it may be more useful to other crops with shallow root systems. The channels left when the cover crop roots die and decay provide ready pathways deep into the subsoil for the root systems of subsequent crops.

When applied as part of an organic farming soil fertility program, composts and manures will generally supply enough S for most crops. Organic materials typically contain 0.2 to 1.5% S. When manure is applied as a source of N, on average 0.07 kg of S is applied for each kg of N. On soils overly enriched in P, there may be restrictions on application rates of organic N and S sources to avoid further buildup of P. Irrigation water, especially in arid regions, may provide a useful amount of S and should be analyzed for sulfate before the application of S fertilizers. Approved mineral S sources may be used as supplements if necessary. Where S is needed, applications from 10 to 40 kg S ha^{-1} are usually sufficient.

The approved K fertilizers, langbeinite and potassium sulfate are excellent sources of immediately available sulfate. Unrefined mined gypsum ($CaSO_4.2H_2O$), which contains 23% Ca and 18% S, is another good S source approved for use in organic farming. These sulfate sources are effective whether surface applied or incorporated. Sulfate salts of zinc, copper, or manganese should only be used sparingly when needed to correct known micronutrient deficiencies and not for the purpose of supplying S.

Elemental S, which is widely used as a fungicide in organic farming, is also a potential S for plant nutrition. The S in this raw fertilizer material is not immediately available to crops. It should be finely ground, broadcast, and mixed with soil two to three months before the growing season. Microbial activity, time, and favorable temperatures are required to convert elemental S to forms available to plants. Several species of bacteria are capable of carrying out the oxidation reactions that also have the effect of acidifying soil. The acidity produced may be a concern on acid soils but desirable on alkaline soils.

As with N, the complex dynamics of the S cycle make it difficult to measure and predict S availability. Soil testing for S is only rarely performed because of seasonal fluctuations in S availability and the need to sample the lower soil profile to evaluate supplies from the subsoil. An awareness of field characteristics and management histories can, however, help to evaluate the potential need for S fertilization. Sandy, highly leached, low-organic-matter soils are most likely in need of S fertilization, while soils high in organic matter or recently amended with manure are likely to supply sufficient S for most crops. Organic farmers should especially give attention to fields where harvests of large amounts of biomass may remove enough S to make them more vulnerable to S deficiency.

Crops differ widely in need for S and these differences should be considered in evaluation of need for S fertilization. Organic growers should be particularly interested in providing an adequate S supply to crops, because S nutrition is reflected in far more than crop yield. Recent observations from western Europe, where there has been a reduced contribution of atmospheric S to crop nutrition, indicate that S is a critical and previously unrecognized nutrient for inducing plant resistance to fungal diseases and conferring some resistance to insect pests (Bloem et al., 2005). In plant tissue, S is incorporated into proteins, certain vitamins, aromatics, and defensive compounds. In evaluating crop needs for S, it is often necessary to look beyond crop yield response. In wheat (*Triticum aestivum* L.), for example, adequate S nutrition is needed for synthesis of certain proteins that affect baking quality or volume of bread. Aromatic S-containing compounds in crops such as cabbage, onion (*Allium cepa* L.), and garlic (*Allium sativum* L.) impart flavor to these vegetables. An adequate supply of S is also important to vegetable quality to prevent nitrate enrichment of leafy greens. Gramineous species generally have lower tissue requirements for S than dicotyledonous crops. The crops in the *Leguminosae*, *Cruciferae*, and *Allium* plant families have higher-than-average requirements for S nutrition.

Calcium and Magnesium Management

The total Ca supply in fertile agricultural soils is generally large, and there are many good Ca sources for soil fertility maintenance. Soils in semiarid and arid regions often have an abundance of Ca present in the form of calcium carbonate, dolomite, or gypsum. In humid regions, the acidic native soils may be initially dominated by exchangeable Al^{+3}, but once these soils are converted to agriculture and the application of limestone becomes a regular farming practice, Ca becomes the major exchangeable cation in the cation exchange capacity. Calcium saturations of 60 to 70% of the cation exchange capacity are typical of fertile soils. Since plant uptake of Ca is from soil solution and the exchange complex, they have a large pool of Ca to draw on. Thus, organic farmers are not uniquely challenged for providing adequate Ca nutrition for crop production.

Although Ca deficiencies are generally uncommon in crops produced on soils with plentiful supplies of exchangeable Ca, physiological disorders related to a lack of Ca uptake into specific plant tissues, especially fruit, are a concern in several horticultural crops. Healthy fruit tissue requires a relatively high concentration of Ca in the cell walls to act as a structural component and cell wall stabilizer. Calcium also plays a role in cell membrane stability and permeability. Due to these important functions, high fruit Ca concentrations are associated with fruit firmness. Blossom-end rot, for example, is a disorder that is exhibited as a water-soaked area on the fruit of tomato, pepper, eggplant (*Solanum melongena* L.), and watermelon [*Citrullis lanatus* (Thunb.) Matsum. & Nakai var. *lanatus*]. Many of the crop production factors, including soil–plant–water relationships, are associated with this Ca translocation disorder that results in malformation of tissues. Crops with small poorly developed root systems are more likely to suffer from inadequate Ca uptake and internal transport. Improvements in soil quality that typically result from organic cultural practices could potentially alleviate soil water constraints that are conducive to these physiological disorders. It is also important to avoid excessive accumulations of cations such as K and Mg, which compete with Ca for uptake.

With tree fruit, it is a common practice to apply sprays of calcium salts to prevent bitter pit in apple and improve quality in several other types of fruit. Spraying with calcium nitrate is prohibited in organic fruit production, but certain calcium chloride products may be used

In humid region agriculture, finely ground limestone rock is the major source of calcium applied to soil. Besides providing Ca nutrition for plants and animals, limestone is applied for the purpose of neutralizing soil acidity. Recommended application rates of limestone are generally based on one of several soil test methods used to evaluate the soils lime requirement. Details of methods, which may vary depending on local soil testing services, are described elsewhere. Because limestones are not pure substances but rather mixtures of calcium carbonate or calcium magnesium carbonate with differing acid neutralizing capacities, lime requirements are typically expressed as a recommendation of tons of pure calcium carbonate equivalent required to raise the soil pH to the desired level for the crop to be produced. Burned lime, which is calcium oxide, and slaked lime, which is calcium hydroxide, cause rapid pH elevations and are prohibited soil amendments in organic agriculture.

A limestone application is usually effective for a three- to five-year period. The rate of Ca leaching and soil acidification depends on numerous factors. When ammonium-based N sources are added to soils and the ammonium subsequently nitrified to nitrate, the release hydrogen ions are a major factor contributing to soil acidification and Ca leaching. Therefore, the rate of soil acidification and the need for repeated limestone application in organic systems is related to the use of natural ammonium N sources such as manures and biological N fixation. Limestone can be applied any time of year, but traffic from heavy applicators should be limited to dry or frozen soils to prevent compaction. Because of the slowness of limestone reaction in soils, applications are best scheduled within a rotation cycle about a year in advance of crops, such as legumes, that have a high lime requirement

The amount of Ca supplied as limestone is generally more than adequate to meet the nutritional needs of crops, but Ca also has an important soil quality function. An abundance of Ca causes clay particles to form crumbs or aggregates, which improve soil tilth and drainage.

On sodic soils and other situations where additional Ca is needed but a pH elevation is not desired, mined gypsum that contains 23% Ca may be used. By-product gypsums, such as those from the manufacture of phosphoric acid, are not allowed in organic farming.

In addition to limestone, land-applied manures, compost, and natural organic materials, which may contain 2 to 5% Ca on a dry weight basis, make important contributions to soil Ca. Phosphate rock, which contains about 35% Ca, also serves as a Ca source when used as a P fertilizer.

Some organic farmers have a strong interest in the base cation ratio or percentage cation saturation concept of soil fertility management. These growers attempt to carefully select and apply liming materials and other amendments in an attempt to achieve the "ideal" percent saturation of the cation exchange capacity, said to be Ca 65%, Mg 10%, and K 5%, with acidity and other cations as the remainder. Although many researchers have failed in efforts validate these "ideal" percentages (Kopittke and Menzies, 2007; Schonbeck, 2001), there are many ardent proponents in the alternative agriculture movement who cite anecdotal observations in support of this saturation percentage approach to soil fertility management. While there is probably no harm to soils from trying to achieve these percentages in practice, and in fact many soils with good fertility are typically close to the "ideal" percentages, a potential downside of attempting to establish these saturation percentages is that farmers may sometimes incur a greater cost than needed for soil amendments such as limestone. On the other hand, for forages fed to dairy cow, high Ca content, beyond that necessary for optimal plant growth, can be of value for animal nutrition.

Crops grown on acid sandy soils are more susceptible to Mg deficiency than those grown on clay soils. Exchangeable Mg is the main source of this nutrient for crop uptake. Magnesium fertility levels are usually adequate on soils that have been properly limed and contain 10% or more exchangeable Mg. Certain types of clay and other forms of Mg-bearing minerals provide reserves of slowly available Mg.

Adequate Mg nutrition is a particular concern for grazing livestock, which can develop grass tetany (hypomagnesia). Because clovers tend to take up more Mg than grasses, growing forage mixtures can help to prevent grass tetany.

Most nutrient cations, especially K, are antagonistic to Mg uptake. Avoiding excessive applications of K and using dolomite limestone where it is appropriate are key practices for ensuring sufficient Mg nutrition. Farming practices that build soil quality and organic matter content may improve Mg availability to crops by reducing drought stress and enhancing mycorrhiza colonization of roots.

In addition to dolomite limestone, land-applied manures, compost, and natural organic materials are good sources of Mg. Manures typically contain 0.08 to 0.29% Mg. Langbeinite or Epsom salt are fertilizers approved for organic farming that can be used to supply supplemental Mg when needed. Epsom salt would be the preferred Mg source for soils already well supplied with K and when raising the soil pH is not desired.

Management of Micronutrients

Organic growers want to ensure that sufficient amounts of micronutrients are available from soil because of the many roles they play in plant and animal health. Some elements, such as Se and I, are not currently considered essential to crop production, but they are essential trace elements for animal nutrition. Crop uptake of micronutrients is important to animal nutrition. Likewise, mineral supplements fed to livestock may contribute to soil fertility through manure applications.

Micronutrient deficiencies occur on some soils, but they can be corrected when necessary for organic crop production using many of the same fertilizer materials and application practices as used in conventional agriculture. In organic agriculture, however, micronutrient fertilizer products cannot be routinely applied without prior soil or plant diagnostics to confirm the specific micronutrient deficiency.

Although micronutrient deficiencies may be more widespread in certain geographical areas, the use of common organic farming materials and practices helps to correct or prevent micronutrient deficiencies. Many of the organic materials imported onto organic farms as manures or compost to build soil organic matter also contain significant amounts of micronutrients.

Crops remove micronutrients at relatively low rates compared with amounts of these nutrients that may be applied in a typical manure application. Concerns for a negative nutrient balance on organic farms are probably less problematic for some micronutrients than macronutrients. To use broiler litter as an illustration, a single application at the rate of 5.6 Mg ha^{-1} could potentially add these amounts of nutrient (in kg ha^{-1}): N, 200; P, 100; K, 106; S, 42; Mg, 23; Ca, 115; Fe, 3.7; Zn, 1.8; B, 0.2; Mn, 1.9; and Cu, 1.3. A maize grain harvest of 11.0 Mg ha^{-1} would remove on average these amounts of nutrients (in kg ha^{-1}): N, 120.8; P, 36.7; K, 44.7; S, 9.9; Mg, 14.4; Ca, 2.6; Fe, 0.33; Zn, 0.25; B, 0.05; Mn, 0.05; and Cu, 0.03. To remove all of the manure-applied micronutrient would take from 40 harvests for Cu to about 4 harvests for B. Mineral supplementation of livestock feeds often enriches manures and soils to which they are applied, especially with Cu, and Zn. Livestock manures can be a significant source of Cl if the liquid fraction is conserved. Inorganic materials used by organic farmers, such as rock phosphate, greensand, rock powders, limestone, and seaweed, also contain trace amounts of micronutrients. While there is little information about the effectiveness of these sources, they may serve to provide an "insurance application" of a wide spectrum of micronutrients useful for both plant and animal nutrition.

Another way that organic farmers can enhance micronutrient fertility is the application of organic matter as green manures, crop residues, manures and composts—all of which decompose to produce natural chelating agents. The organic compounds are mainly produced by microbial and root processes and serve to enhance the solubility of micronutrient ions, especially Fe, Cu, Mn, and Zn, that might otherwise react in the soil to form insoluble compounds unavailable to plants.

Because soil pH strongly influences availability of most micronutrients, proper pH management is a key cultural practice. As soil pH increases, the availability of Fe, Mn, Zn, Cu, and B decreases. Limestone application rates should be selected carefully to avoid exasperating micronutrient deficiencies. Since the availability of Mo increases as soil pH increases, an application of limestone is often effective for correcting Mo deficiency.

Copper-based fungicides are widely used in organic farming for disease control in certain crops. Because Cu uptake and removal by crops is limited, there is concern of toxicity from excessive buildup of Cu in soil from repeated use of copper fungicides. Some organic certifying agencies may phase out copper fungicides for these reasons.

Silicon is now regarded as a quasi-essential nutrient with beneficial effects on disease suppression and stress tolerance in many crops. Industrial by-products, such as steel mill slag, are potential sources of plant available Si, but it is questionable if they are allowed in organic agriculture. Wollastonite is a naturally occurring mineral source of calcium silicate that may be an acceptable Si fertilizer for organic production. In many mineral soils, Si is an abundant element but mostly insoluble nutrient. Certain rotations and cultural practices, however, may mobilize Si for other crops. Straw from wheat or rice (*Oryza sativa* L.) and rice hulls can be effective sources of plant available Si for crops less efficient in Si uptake. Organic growers wanting to improve the availability of Si could use wheat or rice crop residues, either as part of a crop rotation cycle or as a composted source of Si nutrition for subsequent crops. These crop residues may have potential for benefiting organic production of cucurbits where enhanced Si nutrition can suppress powdery mildew disease. Organic growers using this approach will need to be prepared to counteract N deficiency that is likely to accompany the incorporation of the high C/N ratio residues.

Conclusions

No matter what the farming system, certain truths must be recognized and considered. Nutrient removals from a soil by harvest, leaching, volatilization, and erosion must be balanced by additions in the form of returned residues, animal or human excrement, or imported organic and mineral material, lest soils become depleted of nutrients in the long term. Given this fact, combined with the limited global supply of suitable sources for many nutrients, conservation of nutrients—the law of return—must be a central focus of organic soil management. Another kind of conservation—that of the soil itself—must also be uppermost in the minds of organic farmers. Maintaining high levels of organic matter, encouraging strong aggregation, keeping soil cover as continuous as possible, and keeping tillage to a minimum are all goals required to protect the soil from the silent ravages of erosion.

For organic farmers, management of soil fertility is not a separate activity but is part and parcel of the whole-farm system management central to the organic philosophy. Most actions undertaken to build friable, humus-rich soils also act to supply nutrients need by plants. Because of this, the organic farmer is less likely than the conventional farmer to suffer nutrient imbalances and depletion of micronutrients. On the other hand, because many simple chemical carriers for one or two specific nutrient elements are banned under organic farming, correcting specific nutrient deficiencies when and if they occur may prove to be somewhat more challenging under the organic system. Many of the practices central to organic farming, such as application of manures and composts, growing of cover crops, and avoidance of excessive levels of soluble N, should help organic farmers produce an abundance of quality plants, dense in mineral nutrients and health- and flavor-giving compounds. The methods detailed in this chapter are consistent with an ecological approach to farming, one that builds on local resources and is designed for long-term resilience and sustainability.

Discussion Questions

1. Discuss the major concepts that underlie the management of soil fertility in organic cropping systems and describe some of the specific practices farmers use to supply adequate nutrients for organic crop production.

2. What are the primary sources of materials for composting, and how are they consolidated and handled in the composting process? What is the reason for maintaining high temperature during composting?

3. In what ways does the nutrient content of compost vary, and how does a farmer make decisions about what amounts of compost to apply?

4. Describe the law of return, and discuss why this is especially important in an organic cropping system.

5. Give specific examples of how rotation cycles help to build soil fertility in the organic farming system. What are some of the recommended rotations farmers are using today?

6. What are the major components of the nitrogen cycle, and the principle flows of nutrients within this cycle? How does the cycle interact with other internal elements of the farming system and with the surrounding environment?

7. How do crops differ in their nitrogen needs, and how do organic farmers design their cropping systems to meet crop demands?

8. Describe the role and importance of soil testing and plant tissue analysis for the organic farmer and how these tests can be used to design an efficient and cost-effective nutrient management plan.

9. Why is the phosphorus cycle important in the management of an organic farming system, and what are the options available to organic farmers to assure an adequate supply of P for crop production?

10. Describe the potassium cycle in organic farming systems and the methods and materials that organic farmers can use to assure adequate K nutrition for plants.

11. Why are sulfur, calcium, magnesium, and micronutrients important for crop production, and how are they managed in organic farming systems?

12. Describe the role of livestock integration into a farming system in terms of maintaining adequate nutrient cycling and soil nutrition for crop production.

References

Bear, F.E., W.A. King, and C.B. Bender. 1946. The dairy cow as a conserver of soil fertility. Bull. 730. New Jersey Agric. Exp. Stn., Rutgers Univ., New Brunswick

Bloem, E., S. Haneklaus, and E. Schnug. 2005. Significance of sulfur compounds in the protection of plants against pests and diseases. J. Plant Nutr. 28:763–784.

Brady, N.C., and R.R. Weil. 2008. The nature and properties of soils. 14th ed. Prentice Hall, Upper Saddle River, NJ.

Clark, E.A. 2009. Forages in organic crop–livestock systems. p. 85–112. *In* C. Francis (ed.) Organic farming: The ecological system. Agron. Monogr. 54. ASA, CSSA, and SSSA, Madison, WI. (This volume.)

Chiy, P.C., A. Al-Tulihan, M.H. Hassan, C.J.C. Phillips. 1998. Effects of sodium and potassium fertilizers on the composition of herbage and its acceptability to dairy cows. J. Sci. Food Agric. 76:289–297.

Del Amor, F.M., J. Navarro, and P.M. Aparicio. 2008. Isotopic discrimination as a tool for organic farming certification in sweet pepper. J. Environ. Qual. 37:182–185.

Entz, M.H., and J. R. Thiessen Martens. 2009. Organic crop–livestock systems. p. 69–84. *In* C. Francis (ed.) Organic farming: The ecological system. Agron. Monogr. 54. ASA, CSSA, and SSSA, Madison, WI. (This volume.)

Gaskell, M. 2004. Nitrogen availability, supply, and sources in organic row crops. p. 13–20. *In* Proc. California Organic Production and Farming in the New Millennium: A Research Symp. Berkeley, CA. 15 July 2004. Univ. of California Sustainable Agric. Research and Education Program, Univ. of California, Davis.

Gaskell, M., and R. Smith. 2007. Nitrogen sources for organic vegetable crops. HortTechnology 17:431–441.

Gosling, P., and M. Shepherd. 2005. Long-term changes in soil fertility in organic arable farming systems in England, with particular reference to P and K. Agric. Ecosyst. Environ. 105:425–432.

Hartz, T.K., and P.R. Johnstone. 2006. Nitrogen availability from high-nitrogen-containing organic fertilizers. HortTechnology 16:39–42.

Hartz, T.K., W.E. Bendixen, and L. Wierdsma. 2000. The value of presidedress soil nitrate testing as a nitrogen management tool in irrigated vegetable production. HortScience 35:651–656.

Heckman, J.R. 2002. In-season soil nitrate testing as a guide to nitrogen management for annual crops. HortTechnology 12:706–710.

Heckman, J.R. 2006. A history of organic farming: Transitions from Sir Albert Howard's war in the soil to USDA National Organic Program. Renewable Agric. Food Syst. 21:143–150.

Heckman, J.R., and D. Kluchinski. 1996. Chemical composition of municipal leaf waste and hand-collected leaf litter. J. Environ. Qual. 25:355–362.

Heckman, J.R., H. Liu, W.J. Hill, M. DeMillia, and W.L. Anastasia. 2000. Kentucky bluegrass responses to mowing practice and nitrogen fertility management. J. Sustain. Agric. 15:25–33.

Heckman, J.R., and J.C.F. Tedrow. 2004. NJ greensand as a soil amendment. Better Crops 85:4–6.

Hopkins, C.G. 1906. The duty of chemistry to agriculture. Circ. 105. Univ. of Illinois Agric. Exp. Stn., Urbana, IL.

Horst, W.J., M. Kamh, J.M. Jibrin, and V.O. Chude. 2001. Agronomic measures for increasing P availability to crops. Plant Soil 237:211–223.

Howard, A. 1943. An agricultural testament. Oxford Univ. Press, London.

Howard, A. 1975. The soil and health: A study of organic agriculture. Schocken Books, New York.

Jenkins, J. 2005. The humanure handbook: A guide to composting human manure. 3rd ed. Joseph Jenkins, Grove City, PA.

Jönsson, H., A.R. Stintzing, B. Vinnerås, and E. Salomon. 2004. Guidelines on the use of urine and faeces in crop production. Available at http://www2.gtz.de/dokumente/oe44/ecosan/en-use-urine-faeces-crop-production-2004.pdf (verified 13 July 2009). Report 2004-2. EcoSanRes Programme and the Stockholm Environment Inst., Stockholm, Sweden.

King, F.H. 1911. Farmers of forty centuries. Rodale Press, Emmaus, PA.

Kopittke, P.M., and N.W. Menzies. 2007. A review of the use of the basic cation saturation ratio and the "ideal" soil. Soil Sci. Soc. Am. J. 71:259–265.

Li, L., S.M. Li, J.H. Sun, L.L. Zhou, X.G. Bao, H.G. Zhang, and F.S. Zhang. 2007. Diversity enhances agricultural productivity via rhizosphere phosphorus facilitation on phosphorus-deficient soils. Proc. Natl. Acad. Sci. USA 104:11192–11196.

Magdoff, F. 1991. Understanding the Magdoff pre-sidedress nitrate test for corn. J. Prod. Agric. 4:297–305.

Magdoff, F. 2007. Ecological agriculture: Principles, practices, and constraints. Renewable Agric. Food Syst. 22:109–117.

Mengel, K., and W.W. Arneke. 1982. Effect of K on the water potential, pressure potential, the osmotic potential and cell elongation in leaves of *Phaseolus vulgaris*. Physiol. Plant 54:402–408.

Mikkelsen, R.L. 2007. Managing potassium for organic crop production. HortTechnology 17:455–460.

Mikkellsen, R., and T.K. Hartz. 2008. Nitrogen sources for organic crop production. Better Crops 92:16–19.

Nelson, N.O., and R.R. Janke. 2007. Phosphorus sources and management in organic production systems. HortTechnology 17:422–454.

Northbourne, W.J. 1940. Look to the land. J.M. Dent, London.

Nuruzzaman, M., H. Lambers, M.D.A. Bolland, and E.J. Veneklaas. 2005. Phosphorus benefits of different legume crops to subsequent wheat grown in different soils of Western Australia. Plant Soil 271:175–187.

Perez, M.J., T.J. Smyth, and D.W. Israel. 2006. Comparative effects of two forage species on rhizosphere acidification and solubilization of phosphate rocks of different reactivity. J. Plant Nutr. 30:1421–1439.

Porter, P. 2009. Crop rotations in organic production systems. p. 51–68. *In* C. Francis (ed.) Organic farming: The ecological system. Agron. Monogr. 54. ASA, CSSA, and SSSA, Madison, WI. (This volume.)

Rogers, B.F., U. Krogmann, and L.S. Boyles. 2001. Nitrogen mineralization rates of soils amended with nontraditional organic wastes. Soil Sci. 166:353–363.

Rosen, C.J., and D.L. Allan. 2007. Exploring the benefits of organic nutrient sources for crop production and soil quality. HortTechnology 17:422–430.

Rubins, E.J., and F.E. Bear. 1942. Carbon–nitrogen ratios in organic fertilizer materials in relation to the availability of their nitrogen. Soil Sci. 54: 411–423.

Schonbeck, M. 2001. Balancing soil nutrients in organic vegetable production systems: Testing Albrecht's base saturation theory in southeastern soils. Organic Farming Res. Found. Information Bull. 10:17–21.

Smith, J.R. 1950. Tree crops: A permanent agriculture. Devin-Adair, New York.

Stalenga, J. 2007. Applicability of different indices to evaluate nutrient status of winter wheat in the organic system. J. Plant Nutr. 30:351–365.

Sullivan, D.M., J.M. Hart, and N.W. Christensen. 1999. Nitrogen uptake and utilization by Pacific Northwest crops. PNW 513. Pacific Northwest Cooperative Extension Publications, Pullman, WA.

Watanabe, T., M. Okamoto, S. Misawa, M. Urayama, and M. Osaki. 2006. Different characteristics of nitrogen utilization between lupin and soybean: Can lupin utilize organic nitrogen in soils? Can. J. Bot. 84:20–27.

Watson, C.A., D. Atkinson, P. Gosling, L.R. Jackson, and F.W. Rayns. 2002a. Managing soil fertility in organic farming systems. Soil Use Manage. 18:239–247.

Watson, C.A., H. Bengtsson, M. Ebbesvik, A.K. Loes, A. Myrbeck, E. Salomon, J. Schroder, and E.A. Stockdale. 2002b. A review of farm-scale nutrient budgets for organic farms as a tool for management of soil fertility. Soil Use Manage. 18:264–273.

Weil, R.R., K.R. Islam, M.A. Stine, J.B. Gruver, and S.E. Samson-Liebig. 2003. Estimating active carbon for soil quality assessment: A simplified method for lab and field use. Am. J. Alternative Agric. 18:3–17.

Youssefi, F., P.H. Brown, and S.A. Weinbaum. 1999. Regulation of nitrogen uptake at the whole-plant level: A study in almond trees. HortTechnology 9:598–600.

Zaharah, A.R., and A.R. Bah. 1997. Effect of green manures on P solubilization and uptake from phosphate rocks. Plant Soil 48:247–255.

8 ◐

Managing Weeds in Organic Farming Systems: An Ecological Approach

Matt Liebman
Department of Agronomy, Iowa State University, Ames

Adam S. Davis
USDA-Agricultural Research Service, Invasive Weed Management Unit, Urbana, Illinois

Weed management is an important challenge in all farming systems, but it is especially difficult in organic production without the use of chemical herbicides. Given favorable market opportunities for organic products, organic farmers would seem to have strong economic incentives to protect their crops from yield loss due to weeds and to increase the efficiency with which they suppress weed populations. Yet surveys of commercial farmers and assessments by researchers consistently find weeds to be one of the top constraints to organic production (Rasmussen and Ascard, 1995; Walz, 1999; Archer et al., 2007; Sooby et al., 2007; Cavigelli et al., 2008; Posner et al., 2008). This is perhaps not surprising, given the small amounts of money that have been invested in developing and implementing effective weed management strategies for organic farming relative to the billions of dollars invested in research and production to facilitate herbicide-based approaches. Moreover, herbicides generally have higher efficacy than cultivation, the most common direct form of weed control in organic farming (Buhler et al., 1992; Mulder and Doll, 1993).

Because organic farming systems lack the equivalent of inexpensive and nearly complete chemical weed control available for conventional systems, effective weed management for organic farming requires the concerted use of multiple physical, biological, and cultural tactics (Bàrberi, 2002; Bond and Grundy, 2001; Hatcher and Melander, 2003; Melander et al., 2005). Liebman and Gallandt (1997) characterized strategies composed of multiple weed suppression tactics that are individually weak but cumulatively strong, as the use of "many little hammers," in contrast to the single large hammer that herbicides provide.

In this chapter, we describe major components of the weed management tool kit for organic farming, highlighting areas in which important advances have been made in the last decade. We then argue that instead of approaching the development of multitactic weed management strategies as a purely empirical, trial-and-error activity, the choice and deployment of weed management tactics should instead be informed by insights from ecological theory, following the process outlined in Chapter 2 (Drinkwater, 2009, this volume). Finally, we emphasize the need for ongoing dialog between empiricists and theoreticians and between scientists and farmers, so as to better direct scarce research resources and management time to where they are likely to be most beneficial. Multitactic weed management strategies informed by theory should be useful not just to organic farmers but also to conventional farmers who seek to reduce their reliance on herbicides due to concerns over herbicide resistance in weeds, rising production costs, and environmental and human health risks associated with herbicide exposure.

The Weed Management Tool Kit for Organic Farming

Weed management has three critical concerns. The first and most immediate concern is limiting the amount of damage weeds inflict on an associated crop through competition for resources, release of allelopathic chemicals, and physical interference with maintenance and harvest operations. This concern generally is addressed by killing or suppressing weeds emerging near the time a crop is planted and for a period of weeks thereafter. The second, longer-range concern is minimizing the size of future weed populations by reducing the production and survival of new weed seeds and vegetative propagules. The final concern is preventing the introduction of new, more problematic weed species into an existing weed flora through monitoring, sanitation, and targeted eradication efforts. Comprehensive approaches to addressing all three concerns comprise both therapeutic *control* and system-level design for *prevention* (Lewis et al., 1997; Anderson, 2007).

Conventional weed management focuses almost exclusively on using herbicides to kill weeds at the seedling stage. In contrast, weed management in organic farming includes direct control tactics, such as cultivation to limit seedling survival, but also more subtle tactics that affect weed germination, reproduction, and seed and vegetative propagule survival and dispersal. The physiological and ecological processes involved in the latter set of tactics are strongly linked to major components and interactions within organic farming systems, including diversified cropping systems, soil amendment and disturbance regimes, and feeding activities of pathogens and seed predators (Liebman and Davis, 2000).

The weed management tactics we review here are widely used in organic farming systems in temperate areas. Although many of the results we report were not obtained within organic systems, the tactics used are compatible with organic production practices and certification requirements.

Crop Rotation and Sequencing

Crop rotation plays a central role in organic farming due to contributions to soil fertility, soil conservation, and suppression of certain insect pests and pathogens. Crop rotation also has long been recognized as fundamental to weed management (Leighty, 1938). For many organic growers, weed management considerations play a central role in determining rotation length and crop sequence (Walz, 1999; Bond and Grundy, 2001). Diversification of crop characteristics within a rotation helps to disrupt weed life cycles and prevent any one species from becoming too "comfortable" within the cropping system (Liebman and Staver, 2001). Nonetheless, simple alternation of crops with contrasting characteristics may be insufficient to achieve weed control benefits.

An illustration of the latter point is shown in work reported by Anderson (2003), who found that weed density increased in rotations consisting of one cool-season crop followed by one warm-season crop (e.g., winter wheat [*Triticum aestivum* L.]–chick pea [*Cicer arietinum* L.]), whereas weed density decreased in rotations consisting of two different cool-season crops followed by two different warm season crops (e.g., pea [*Pisum arvense* L.]–winter wheat–maize [*Zea mays* L.]–soybean [*Glycine max* (L.) Merr.]). Diversifying crops by including species with different planting dates within warm-season and cool-season categories enhanced the ability to kill emerged weed seedlings, thus depleting the soil seed bank while limiting the production of new seeds. Weed seed densities in soil also declined due to natural decay processes. For the warm-season weed green foxtail [*Setaria viridis* (L.) Beauv.] and the cool-season weed downy brome (*Bromus tectorum* L.), only 20% of seeds remained viable in the soil seed bank one year after seed shed due to decay, and only 5% of seeds were alive after two years (Anderson, 2003). Within the two-year rotations, enough weeds survived to replenish the soil seed bank and allow weed populations to grow. In contrast, in the four-year rotations, weed seedling survival and reproduction were suppressed to the point that seed decay was greater than seed bank replenishment, and weed populations declined.

Rotation of perennial forage crops, such as alfalfa (*Medicago sativa* L.), with annual crops such as wheat and maize, also can contribute substantially to weed suppression. In a survey of farmers in Saskatchewan and Manitoba, Canada, 83% of respondents reported fewer weeds in grain crops after alfalfa and other forages than after grain crops (Entz et al., 1995). A subsequent survey of fields on commercial farms in Manitoba found that compared with cereal crops preceding cereals, alfalfa hay crops preceding cereals lowered densities of wild oat (*Avena fatua* L.), wild mustard [*Brassica kaber* (DC.) L.C. Wheeler], and Canada thistle [*Cirsium arvense* (L.) Scop.] but had no effect on population densities of redroot pigweed (*Amaranthus retroflexus* L.), common lambsquarters (*Chenopodium album* L.), and wild buckwheat (*Polygonum convolvulus* L.) and led to increases in dandelion (*Taraxacum officinale* F.H. Wigg.) and field pennycress (*Thlaspi arvense* L.) (Ominski et al., 1999). Thus, particular crops select for and against particular weeds; a complex rotation is needed to select against a wide spectrum of weed species.

Cover Cropping

Cover cropping involves the use of actively growing nonharvested crops and their residues to increase soil productivity, suppress diseases and insect pests, and manage weeds (Clark, 1998). Depending on plant architecture, phenology, residue quality, and residue management, cover crops provide different weed management benefits (Teasdale, 1996; Gallandt et al., 1999).

Green manures, cover crops that are grown solely for incorporation into soil to improve soil quality (Pieters, 1927), can exert a strong influence on weeds through allelopathy, an effect of one plant on another mediated by chemicals emitted from living or dead plant tissue. Cereal and crucifer crops used as green manures are particularly well characterized with regard to their allelopathic effects on weeds (Gallandt and Haramoto, 2004; Boydston and Al-Khatib, 2006; Belz, 2007). Legume green manures may also have valuable allelopathic effects. In field experiments, crimson clover (*Trifolium incarnatum* L.) and red clover (*T. pratense* L.) green manures reduced common lambsquarters and wild mustard density, emergence rate, relative growth rate, biomass production, and competitive ability but enhanced sweet maize growth and yield (Dyck and Liebman, 1994; Dyck et al., 1995; Davis and Liebman, 2001). Aqueous extracts of crimson clover and red clover residues have been shown to be allelopathic under laboratory conditions (White et al., 1989; Liebman and Sundberg, 2006); for the latter species, phenolic compounds are believed to be responsible for allelopathic effects (Ohno et al., 2000).

Allelopathic responses can differ among target species, creating the possibility of selective control. Liebman and Sundberg (2006) found that red clover extracts had little or no effect on large-seeded crop species, such as maize, but strongly suppressed the germination and growth of small-seeded weeds, such as common lambsquarters and wild mustard. Phytotoxic effects of red clover green manure can result from by the combined action of phenolic acids and *Pythium* spp., which attack weeds, such as wild mustard, but not maize (Conklin et al., 2002). Advances in breeding methods that are compatible with organic production guidelines are supporting the development of cover crop cultivars with enhanced allelopathic properties (Belz, 2007).

When cover crop residues are killed and left on the soil surface as a mulch, they suppress weed germination and seedling establishment by blocking light transmittance to the soil surface and creating a physical impediment to seedling growth (Teasdale and Mohler, 2000). Thicker mulches are more suppressive of weed seedling emergence: velvetleaf (*Abutilon theophrasti* Medik.), redroot pigweed, common lambsquarters, witchgrass (*Panicum capillare* L.), curly dock (*Rumex crispus* L.), common chickweed [*Stellaria media* (L.) Vill.], and dandelion seedling emergence decreased in proportion to the amount of hairy vetch (*Vicia villosa* Roth) or cereal rye (*Secale cereale* L.) residues applied to the soil surface (Mohler and Teasdale, 1993). Chopped hairy vetch residues reduced common lambsquarters biomass within a no-till maize crop by 65%, but incomplete kill of the vetch cover crop resulted in maize yield loss (Hoffman et al., 1993). Advances in the design of tractor-pulled roller-crimpers intended to kill cover crops within no-till production systems (Kornecki et al., 2006) may offer practical options for managing weeds in organic production systems while avoiding crop yield losses to cover crop competition.

Intercropping

Intercropping combines two or more crops whose resource consumption patterns are physiologically, temporally, or morphologically complementary. Consequently, intercrops may use a greater share of available light, water, and nutrients and produce more yield per unit land area than at least one of the component crops in monoculture (Vandermeer, 1989; Willey, 1990). Greater resource use by intercrops than monocultures also can lead to improved opportunities for suppressing weeds through resource competition. For example, Baumann et al. (2000, 2001) found that shading reduced germination, growth, and seed production of common groundsel (*Senecio vulgaris* L.), an important weed that infests leek (*Allium porrum* L.) fields, and that leek–celery (*Apium graveolens* L.) intercrops intercepted more light earlier in the growing season and more effectively suppressed common groundsel than did leek monocultures. Similarly, Bulson et al. (1997) reported that when grown at the same relative density, an intercrop composed of wheat and field bean (*Vicia faba* L.) produced less weed biomass than field bean in monoculture but more weed biomass than wheat in monoculture. However, complementary patterns of resource use allowed wheat and field bean to be grown at higher densities than normal for monocultures, and when this was done, high-density mixtures contained substantially less weed biomass than normal-density monocultures of both crops.

Increasing Crop Competitive Ability

Crop cultivars vary in their ability to suppress weeds and to tolerate weed interference (Blackshaw, 1994; Lemerle et al., 1996; Mohler, 2001a). A host of crop characteristics, including leaf angle, leaf area index, crop stature, canopy duration, maximal relative growth rate, allelopathic potential, and many other attributes, contribute to cultivar effects on weeds (Callaway, 1992; Olofsdotter et al., 2002). The particular crop–weed combination may determine which attributes are most important. Jointed goatgrass (*Aegilops cylindrica* Host) seed production declined 33 and 46% in dry and wet years, respectively, within a highly competitive winter wheat cultivar compared to a less competitive cultivar (Ogg and Seefeldt, 1999). Reduced weed seed production was attributed to more rapid height growth in the competitive wheat cultivar compared with the less competitive cultivar. In dryland and irrigated sweet maize production, wild proso millet (*Panicum miliaceum* L.) fecundity was reduced by 33 and 60%, respectively, in a weed suppressive sweet maize cultivar compared to a nonsuppressive cultivar (Williams et al., 2007). Weed-suppressive ability was strongly associated with sweet maize canopy characteristics at time of anthesis, including leaf area index, interception of photosynthetically active radiation and allocation of leaf area to the top of the canopy. Variation in wild proso millet fecundity due to sweet maize cultivar characteristics propagated out beyond the first growing season, affecting wild proso millet population densities and yield of a snap bean (*Phaseolus vulgaris* L.) crop in the following year (Davis and Williams, 2007).

Organic producers often use row widths that accommodate cultivation equipment, but if row widths can be narrowed and crops sown in a more equidistant arrangement, weed suppression can be enhanced; this is especially true if crop densities can be increased concomitantly (Mohler, 2001a; Olsen et al., 2005). Crop species for which this approach may be successful include maize, pea, peanut (*Arachis hypogaea* L.), rapeseed (*Brassica napus* L. var. *napus*), safflower (*Carthamus tinctorius* L.), small grain cereals, and soybean. The use of increased crop density may be an inappropriate tactic for horticultural crops, since higher crop densities can translate into smaller size of individual harvestable units (e.g., cabbage [*Brassica oleracea* L.] heads), and crop value can be affected by unit size. The competitive ability of horticultural crops can be increased greatly, however, by transplanting rather than direct seeding (Weaver, 1984).

Soil Amendments

Managers of organic farming systems put considerable emphasis on long-term transformations of soil conditions through the accumulated impacts of organic matter amendments, such as animal manures and composts, as well as crop residues (Gallandt et al., 1999). These amendments and the manner in which they are used can affect weeds and their interactions with crops. Rasmussen (2002) found, for example, that band injection of liquid manure into soil, rather than broadcast surface application, increased barley (*Hordeum vulgare* L.) growth and competitive ability against weeds. In a study of weed and potato (*Solanum tubero-sum* L.) performance in plots amended with green manure residues, cattle manure, and compost versus barley residues and high rates of synthetic fertilizers, Gallandt et al. (1998) found that after soil management treatments had been in place four years, weed biomass production was lower and potato yields were higher in plots receiving organic amendments. Ryan et al. (2006) measured the competitive effects of mixed-species stands of weeds on maize in two contrasting systems that had been in place for 26 years: a diversified organic rotation that contained legume green manures and that received manure versus a simpler, conventionally managed rotation without legume green manures and manure. The investigators found that a given density of weeds caused more yield loss for maize in the conventional than the organic system.

It should be recognized that organic matter amendments to soil do not always work to the benefit of weed management. In a field study of interactions between maize and three weed species, compost increased seed production by common waterhemp (*Amaranthus rudis* Sauer) and velvetleaf, although not by giant foxtail (Liebman et al., 2004). Compost also increased the competitive effect of common waterhemp on soybean (Menalled et al., 2004). Thus, while soil amendments can have beneficial effects on soil fertility and crop production, effective weed control practices are needed to limit the establishment, growth, and reproduction of species that are stimulated by amendments.

Conservation Biocontrol

Conservation biological control of weeds seeks to manipulate cropping system habitats with the immediate goal of fostering natural enemies of weeds and the long-term goal of reducing population densities of target weed species (Landis et al., 2000). One approach that holds particular promise focuses on habitat management to promote weed seed consumption by seed predators (Westerman et al., 2003; Menalled et al., 2006). Weed seed shed by summer annual weed species typically takes place in temperate agroecosystems during senescence and harvest of grain crops (Forcella et al., 1996). Short-term postdispersal predation of giant foxtail seeds in maize and soybean was substantially lower (18 and 5% of seeds consumed d^{-1}, respectively) during these fall months than in a red clover cover crop (up to 58% of seeds consumed d^{-1}) (Davis and Liebman, 2003). Greater weed seed predation in red clover was at least partially attributable to higher activity density of field crickets (*Gryllus pennsylvanicus* Burmeister), which are known seed predators (Carmona et al., 1999). Including small grains, red clover, and alfalfa within maize- and soybean-based crop rotations can increase season-long seed predation rates by creating canopy cover and thus suitable habitat for insect and rodent seed predators at times when canopy cover of maize and soybean is low (Heggenstaller et al., 2006; Westerman et al., 2006).

Delaying or eliminating primary tillage can also increase overall seed losses to postdispersal predation. Three months after seed dispersal at the time of maize harvest, 40% of giant ragweed (*Ambrosia trifida* L.) seeds resting on the soil surface in no-till maize plots in central Ohio were consumed by predators (primarily small vertebrates), whereas after 12 months, 90% of seeds were lost to postdispersal predation (Harrison et al., 2003). If primary tillage had taken place immediately after maize harvest, postdispersal seed losses would have been close to zero, as the seeds would have been protected within the soil profile.

Cultivation and Other Physical Control Tactics

Cultivation is the most important direct-control tactic available to organic growers. Nonetheless, reliance on this tactic should be tempered with the recognition that its overuse may cause reductions in soil quality indices, such as soil organic matter content and aggregate stability (Grandy and Robertson, 2006). On a shorter time-scale, heavy reliance on cultivation may introduce unwanted volatility and risk into weed management if extended periods of rainfall prevent timely field operations (Gunsolus and Buhler, 1999).

A wide variety of cultivation tools and improved guidance systems are now available to the organic grower (Bowman, 1997; Pullen and Cowell, 2000; Mohler, 2001b; van der Schans et al., 2006), each suited to a particular set of management objectives and crop and environmental conditions. Interrow tools, such as shovel cultivators, work between 50 and 70% of the soil surface between crop rows, whereas in-row and near-row tools, such as spyders, spinners, and full-field implements, such as spring tine weeders and rotary hoes, work the entire field but incur some crop loss (Mohler, 2001b). Weed seedling mortality rates in maize due to cultivation with rotary hoes or tine weeders followed by two interrow cultivations with a shovel cultivator varied between 43 and 74% over two field seasons (Mohler et al., 1997). Complementing a single pass of a rotary hoe with two passes of interrow shovels supplemented by a suite of intrarow and near-row tools (including spyders, torsion weeders, spinners, and spring hoes) increased the range of weed seedling mortality to between 72 and 90% over the study period.

Various forms of tillage can be used to place weed seeds at particular locations in the soil profile, with resulting effects on seed survival and seedling emergence ability (Mohler, 2001b). In general, weed seed vulnerability to seed predators and other mortality factors is greatest on the soil surface, whereas seedling emergence ability tends to decrease with seed burial depth. In cases where production of new seeds can be prevented, zero tillage can lead to large and rapid losses of weed seeds (Anderson, 2007). Conversely, when production of new seeds does occur, deep tillage with an inversion plow can reduce weed densities due to inhibition of seedling emergence and ongoing seed decay (Mohler, 2001b). Zero-tillage systems involving direct seeding or transplanting into cover crop residues are being developed and tested for organic farming systems (Morse and Creamer, 2006).

Other physical control tactics suitable for organic production are in various stages of research, development, and implementation. These include mulches (Ozores-Hampton et al., 2001; Duppong et al., 2004), flame weeders (Ascard, 1994, 1995; van der Schans et al., 2006), in-row steam injectors (Melander and Jørgensen, 2005), and between-row mowers (Donald, 2006).

Models as Tools for Improving Weed Management

Given the growing number of tactics available for managing weeds in organic farming, and the possibility of using them in various combinations, how should researchers, farmers, and other agriculturalists proceed to develop the science and practice of weed management? One approach is to test and adapt methods empirically. Scientists taking this approach can construct ever-larger factorial experiments to examine huge numbers of individual tactics used alone and in combinations. Often, however, the experiments become unwieldy as the number of factors increases, and higher-order interactions become difficult or impossible to interpret. Alternatively, scientists and farmers can conduct "systems comparisons," in which the relative merits of suites of practices comprising different production systems are compared quantitatively. Such comparisons can approximate the reality of commercial farming but lack experimental controls that would allow mechanistic interpretations and identification of specific individual components that contribute directly to system differences. A final class of investigations involves field-scale studies in which spatially referenced information is related to overall system performance through geostatistical procedures. This approach allows for some mechanistic understanding of the impacts of biotic and abiotic factors but is very labor and information intensive and generally requires a very narrow focus within a given system (Dieleman et al., 2000).

An alternative approach to empirical experimentation that also allows for examination of whole-system properties is the construction and analysis of mathematical models (Holst et al., 2007). Models are simplified versions of reality that distill some aspect of our knowledge about a system into a formal structure that can be manipulated mathematically and tested against our observations of the world. Different models have varying degrees of realism, precision, and generality; no model has all of those attributes (Levins, 1966). Hence, multiple models of a system may be required to understand it from different perspectives. Models are more than intellectual exercises; they provide guidance for a thought-intensive, rather than a technology-intensive agriculture.

As the limits of experimental design for agroecological research are reached, models can help us to gain new insights in a variety of ways. First, they allow us to summarize a great deal of empirical data about the components of a dynamic system in an integrative manner that accounts for interactions between system components (Hanks and Ritchie, 1991). Incorporating what is known about an agricultural system into a model requires that assumptions about system organization be made explicit and therefore testable. Second, when a model adequately describes a system, it may then be used to perform thought experiments. Rather than conduct a series of experiments in which one factor after another is manipulated under a constantly changing environment, producing confounded results, one can use models to explore the consequences of environmental or management-related variation in system components. Finally, models may be used to identify gaps in our empirical knowledge of agricultural systems. Model results that are inconsistent with empirical observations, or that highlight the potential importance of a particular system component, can help focus limited funds and personnel on high-priority research areas.

Mathematical models of weed management systems generally fall into one of two groups: *demographic models*, which track changes over time in the number of individuals in a population of weeds (Cousens and Mortimer, 1995; Freckleton and Watkinson, 1998; Mertens et al., 2002), and *ecophysiological models*, which describe weed development, growth, and interference with crops (Kropff and van Laar, 1993; Grundy et al., 2000). Both types of models make use of species-level data on how dependent variables of interest respond to environmental conditions and management practices. Here, we use demographic models as a means of organizing our discussion of management effects on weed population dynamics and highlighting the importance of multi-tactic weed management in organic crop production systems.

Target Transitions: How Models Guide Weed Management

At its most basic level, demographic modeling is a form of ecological accounting: numbers of individuals in different life stages are recorded at an initial time point, and gains and losses to these groups, through reproduction, death, and dispersal, are followed over time. Because of the cyclic nature of farming system operations, with seasonal peaks and lulls in management activity and favorable growing conditions, recruitment of weed cohorts tends to be synchronized and nonoverlapping. Weed populations thus are often modeled as having discrete generations, represented with difference equations for unstructured populations and projection matrices for structured populations (Cousens and Mortimer, 1995; Caswell, 2001). In this section, we use difference equations in the MATLAB (MathWorks, Inc., Natick, MA) modeling environment to perform simulations of management effects on weed population dynamics. Numerous other excellent software packages are also available and could have been used for this purpose.

A population model's structure is dependent on the life history of the weed population to be studied. Weed species of arable systems fall into three broad life-history categories (Cousens and Mortimer, 1995): annuals, biennials, and perennials (represented by loop diagrams in Fig. 8–1). Annual weed species, such as velvetleaf or giant foxtail, complete their life cycle within a year, from seed to seed: some proportion of the seedlings that are recruited from seeds in the soil seed bank generally survive to reproductive maturity and produce new seeds to replenish the soil seed bank. Biennial weed species, such as wild carrot (*Daucus carota* L.) or common mullein (*Verbascum thapsus* L.) take two years to complete their life cycle: seedlings recruited from the soil seed bank grow to form compact rosettes (nonreproductive plants) by the end of the first year, and rosettes grow into mature plants that produce seeds and die by the end of the second growing season. Perennial weed species, such as Canada thistle and quackgrass [*Elytrigia repens* (L.) Gould], have seed banks and immature and mature plant stages like biennials, but their life cycles are not bound by strict temporal schedules and, depending on the species, they may reproduce either sexually (via seed production), vegetatively (via spread or fragmentation of perennating organs), or by both means.

Life history and environmentally driven demographic differences between weed species, or among populations of a single weed species, contain valuable information about the type of weed management tactics that will be most successful at reducing weed population density and growth. Potential differences in management impact may be explored quantitatively through *perturbation analyses*, which offer a powerful means of asking "what-if" questions about demographic

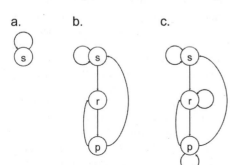

a.   b.   c.

Fig. 8–1. Life histories of arable weeds fall into three broad categories: (a) annuals, (b) biennials, and (c) perennials. Circles represent individuals at a given life stage; s = seed, r = rosette (immature plant), p = mature plant. Arrows represent transitions, following an annual time step, from stage to stage.

models. Sensitivity and elasticity analyses, the most commonly performed perturbations, quantify the partial effect on population growth rate when individual demographic transitions, such as seedling survival to reproductive maturity or seed survival in the soil seed bank, are subject to either additive or proportional changes in parameter values, respectively (Caswell, 2001).

Quantifying how changes in demographic parameters for a given species affect its population growth rate is the key to identifying *target transitions* (McEvoy and Coombs, 1999). Target transitions are those weed life stages that are most likely to produce a substantial reduction in population growth rate in response to a management intervention applied at that life stage. Target transitions can also be evaluated with regard to their relationships with various management metrics, such as production costs and crop losses to weed competition.

A broad comparison of target transitions associated with particular weed life histories highlights the importance of demographic information to guide management of a given species (Davis, 2006). For annual species, seed bank persistence is the main determinant of population growth rate, followed closely by seedling survival and fecundity. Survival of new seeds, seedlings, and rosettes is central to the demographic success of biennial species, whereas rosette survival is of prime importance to certain perennial species, with smaller contributions from survival of new seeds and seedlings.

Many Little Hammers: Theory and Application in the Management of Annual Weeds

Once target transitions are identified, weed managers must select tactics that apply pressure to these and other points of secondary importance in weed life cycles. Both empirical and theoretical evidence suggest that combining multiple tactics ("many little hammers") that may be individually weak can result in synergistic gains for the weed management system as a whole (Liebman and Gallandt, 1997; Westerman et al., 2005). In this section, we introduce a demographic model, implemented in MATLAB, for the summer annual weed giant foxtail to explore the sensitivity of crop production costs to variation in control of weed target transitions, and to project the results of single- versus multi-tactic management approaches. The model does not include tillage effects and other factors that may be of interest, but it illustrates how empirical data and models can work together to identify where weed management efforts are best invested. The demographic model is available online so that readers can experiment with it; see https://www.agronomy.org/files/publications/books/bioeconomic-model.pdf and https://www.agronomy.org/files/publications/books/bioeconomic-model-sensitivity.pdf

Our model is composed of two submodels: a demographic model that keeps track of weed population density over time and an economic model that uses weed population density as an input to calculate weed management costs and crop revenue lost due to weed competition (Fig. 8–2). The demographic submodel follows individuals, at each annual time step, belonging to four life stages: dormant seeds in soil, small seedlings, large seedlings, and reproductively mature plants. Transitions between these life stages, represented by solid arrows, are governed by demographic rates shown in lowercase letters: s_s = seed survival in soil seed bank, g = germination, s_{cult} = seedling survival of cultivation, s_{hand} = seedling survival of hand-weeding, f = fecundity (seeds plant^{-1}), and s_{pred} = seeds surviving postdispersal predation. The curved dotted line between "mature plants" and the

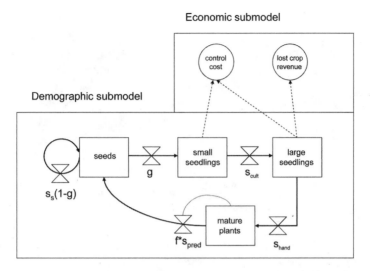

Fig. 8–2. Bioeconomic model of management effects on giant foxtail population dynamics and production costs. s_s = seed survival in soil seed bank, g = germination, s_{cult} = seedling survival of cultivation, s_{hand} = seedling survival of hand weeding, f = fecundity (seeds plant^{-1}), s_{pred} = seed survival of postdispersal seed predation.

valve representing new inputs to the seed bank indicates that seed production is density dependent, with fewer seeds produced by each individual as the population becomes crowded and more constrained by resource availability.

The demographic model intersects with the economic model through weed management costs and competitive effects of weeds on the crop (dashed arrows). Cultivation, the first weed management tactic applied to the population, is assumed to affect only the interrow area and is assumed to have constant efficacy, independent of seedling population density. A proportion of remaining weeds is then removed with hand labor. Guided by analyses conducted by Melander and Rasmussen (2001), we set time required for hand weeding as a linear function of weed population density

$$y = 4.00 + 1.022x \qquad [1]$$

where y = labor requirements in hours per hectare and x = seedlings per square meter. We calculated control costs using a fixed cost for cultivation (assumed to be $50 ha^{-1}) and a variable cost for hand weeding, obtained by entering the population density of weed escapes into Eq. [1] and then multiplying the output by a labor cost of $10 h^{-1}. Lost crop revenue was assumed to follow the rectangular hyperbolic model of density-dependent yield loss, with percentage yield loss increasing as a function of the population density of mature weed plants up to some maximum, after which yield loss reaches a plateau (Cousens, 1985). Fecundity was described using a piecewise regression to allow for density-dependent effects above a threshold of 1 plant m^{-2}.

We used the model to examine the sensitivity of production costs in the fifth year of a given management approach to changes in several mortality factors that producers can influence to some degree, including cultivation efficacy, hand weeding efficacy, seed bank decline, and seed predation (Fig. 8–3). Demographic

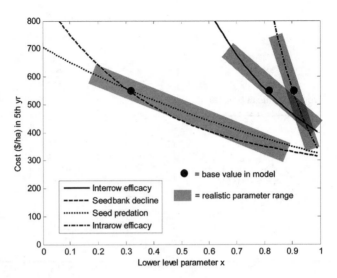

Fig. 8–3. Sensitivity analysis of the impact of variation in sources of weed mortality on total weed management costs after five years of production.

rates in the model took base values (represented by the black dot on each of the four sensitivity curves) at conservative levels, relative to published values (Davis and Liebman, 2003). The base value for cultivation efficacy of seedlings was set at 80%, near the lower end of the published range (Mohler et al., 1997), and hand weeding efficacy was assumed to be 90%. Under these assumptions, total production cost was approximately $550 ha^{-1}. Varying model parameters within realistic ranges (represented by gray boxes covering each of the sensitivity curves) resulted in overall production costs that varied from $300 ha^{-1} to $700 ha^{-1}.

The degree of sensitivity of production cost to change in a particular parameter is represented by the slope of the curve relating production cost to parameter values. Clearly, production costs are most sensitive to changes in efficacy of seedling control, with greater sensitivity to intrarow control (hand weeding of escapes) than interrow control (initial cultivation). Intrarow control was of primary importance in determining production costs since the seedlings that escaped cultivation were assumed to have the greatest impact on crop yield loss due to their size, and the population density of these seedlings drove the labor requirements for hand weeding. Although increases in hand weeding efficacy above 90% would have a marked impact on weed population densities, there are only limited data on the incremental costs associated with increasing hand weeding efficacy (Riemens et al., 2007). This is a research question that merits further study.

The high sensitivity of production costs to cultivation efficacy indicates that it is critical to hone cultivation skills, cultivate in a timely manner, and create soil conditions that support optimal cultivation efficacy. However, even at the high end of the published range for cultivation efficacy, production costs still remain above $400 ha^{-1}. To bring production costs down further, the key target transitions in this simulation are actually seed predation and seed bank decline. A conservation biocontrol approach to increasing seed mortality in this population has the potential to bring production costs as low as $325 ha^{-1}.

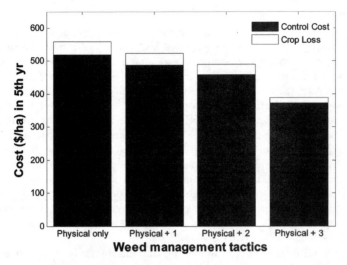

Fig. 8–4. Synergism between physical weed control and one, two, or three additional cultural control methods (Anderson 2005) reduced weed management–related production costs after five years.

Combining multiple management tactics can improve overall weed control and reduce production costs. In a study of various cultural weed management tactics, including narrower row spacing, higher crop population density, fertilizer banding, and delayed planting, Anderson (2005) found synergism between cultural tactics. A single cultural tactic reduced weed biomass in maize by 10%, two tactics combined reduced weed biomass by 25%, and three tactics reduced weed biomass by 60%. We revised our basic model to simulate moderately effective weed control (80% cultivation efficacy, 90% hand control) supplemented by one, two, or three cultural tactics. Under these assumptions, relying on cultivation and hand weeding alone resulted in production costs of approximately $550 ha^{-1}, whereas supplementing physical control with one, two, or three complementary cultural tactics resulted in declining production costs of $510 ha^{-1}, $480 ha^{-1} and $390 ha^{-1}, respectively (Fig. 8–4). A many-little-hammers approach to weed management in organic production systems that incorporates cultural control methods offers a clear path toward reducing dependence on physical weed control, improving overall weed management, and reducing production costs in organic production systems.

Ecological Management of Perennial Weeds

Perennial weeds, particularly those that spread by rhizomes, or "creeping" perennials, can present a considerable challenge to organic producers (Bond and Turner, 2006a,b). Canada thistle is a creeping perennial that spreads locally by rhizomes but also produces viable, wind-dispersed seeds that may travel long distances to colonize new fields (Donald, 1994). In this section, we discuss empirical studies of Canada thistle management and incorporate these results into a demographic model to explore the potential for a many-little-hammers approach to improve suppression of this species.

Management Tactics

Soil disturbance through tillage and cultivation, often the primary tools in an organic farmer's weed management tool kit (Walz, 1999), must be used judiciously or these measures can exacerbate a Canada thistle infestation by severing rhizomes and dispersing fragments into uninvaded areas of the field (Edwards et al., 2000). As rhizome fragment size decreases, successful establishment of new shoots from deep within the soil profile also decreases (Håkansson, 1982). One strategy based on these ecological relationships is to follow rotary tillage with full-inversion plowing, thus sending small rhizome fragments to a soil depth from which they cannot regenerate (Mohler, 2001b). To minimize shoot regeneration, such an operation should be timed to correspond with seasonal lows in root carbohydrate reserves, in mid-spring before bud formation (Gustavsson, 1997; Wilson et al., 2006). Optimizing tillage timing and depth, as described above, has the potential to reduce Canada thistle shoot regeneration within the same growing season by 70 to 85% (timing) and 70 to 95% (depth), in comparison to poorly timed and shallow tillage (Gustavsson, 1997).

A contrasting approach to managing Canada thistle is to use competition from a weed-suppressive cover crop in combination with mowing to reduce thistle growth, replenishment of root reserves, and seed production (Donald, 1990; Bond and Turner, 2006b). Several years in a perennial cover crop, such as the forage legume alfalfa, are required for eradication of Canada thistle (Patriquin et al., 1986; Donald, 1990); however the weed management benefits of long-term cover cropping may not be economically justifiable if the farming operation does not include livestock or if the primary crop is of very high value. A short-term cover crop program may also substantially reduce Canada thistle population densities in the following crop, especially when combined with a second tactic such as mowing. Compared with unsown stubble of a spring barley crop, a grass–white clover (*T. repens* L.) mixture reduced Canada thistle shoot biomass regrowth in the following year by 38% (Graglia et al., 2006). Mowing reduced Canada thistle biomass in the following crop in direct proportion to mowing frequency, with a 23 and 84% reduction in biomass with two or six mowings, respectively. The grass–white clover cover crop plus six mowings reduced Canada thistle biomass in the following crop by 91%, compared with bare stubble with no mowing.

Biological control has also been investigated as an option for Canada thistle. Inundative biological control methods, such as the use of mycoherbicides, have shown promise in field trials (Guske et al., 2004) but have not been adopted, possibly due to the high cost of the agents or lack of commercial products, or both (Hallett, 2005). Moreover, inundative biocontrol at the seed stage using exotic control agents may be ill advised due to the potential for nontarget impacts on rare thistle species (Louda et al., 1997). Conservation biocontrol may hold more promise for this species. In field studies, pre- and postdispersal seed predators reduced fecundity of Canada thistle by 10 to 30% and 55 to 88%, respectively (Heimann and Cussans, 1996). Empirical data on habitat management for increasing seed predation levels for this species are presently not available and are needed to help guide conservation biocontrol efforts.

Insights from Ecological Theory for Canada Thistle Management

A demographic model of Canada thistle (Davis, 2006) was developed based on the perennial life cycle represented in Fig. 8–1c and parameterized with demographic

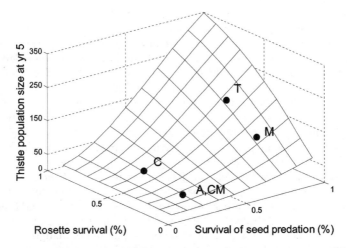

Fig. 8–5. Response surface representing the interdependence between rosette survival, seed survival of postdispersal predation, and Canada thistle population density after five years of organic production. A = continuous alfalfa for five years, C = cover crop alternating with row crop, CM = cover crop + mowing alternating with row crop, T = moldboard tillage in row crop.

rates calculated from Donald (1994). Elasticity analysis of this model indicated that management practices focusing on reducing rosette recruitment and survival, seed survival of predation, and seedling survival to the rosette stage should make the greatest contributions to reducing population growth rate of Canada thistle. For the present analysis, too few empirical data on economics and demographic impacts of management were available to run simulations of production cost per unit land area. Instead, we developed a response surface (Fig. 8–5) from the basic model for two target transitions, rosette survival to reproductive maturity and seed survival of predation, that were also likely to be affected by the aforementioned management systems. Each point on this response surface represents a projection of Canada thistle population size after five years of management (starting population density = 50 plants m^{-2}) in relation to a given combination of rosette and seed predation survival probabilities.

We placed five management systems described in the previous section, including (i) alfalfa for several years (A), (ii) a short-term legume cover crop plus mowing (CM), (iii) a short-term legume cover alone (C), (iv) mowing alone in small grain stubble (M), and (v) rotary tillage followed by moldboard plowing within a row crop sequence (T), on the response surface according to empirical results and qualitative predictions about their potential effect on rosette survival and seed predation. Both the A and CM systems were predicted to have low rosette survival and low seed survival of predation. Crop competition in both systems contributed to low rosette survival, with additional pressure from mowing in the CM system. The thick canopy offered by both systems was predicted to provide good habitat for seed predators; therefore, survival rates were reduced to the low end of the published range. The C system was predicted to have greater rosette survival than the CM system since rosettes were not mowed. Seed survival of predation in the M system was set at the upper end of the published range as bare stubble would provide little shelter for seed predators, and rosette survival was also increased due to the lack of competition from an actively grow-ing cover crop. Both rosette and seed survival were placed at the upper end of the published range for the T system since primary tillage is reported to reduce rosette biomass within the same growing season, but there is no evidence that a single primary tillage event during a cropping cycle also reduces long-term rosette survival. Repeated tillage during a bare-fallow cycle, in contrast, can erad-icate Canada thistle if continued for three years (Donald, 1990).

As the predictions of this model were based partially on speculation, this analysis is most useful for hypothesis generation. Nonetheless, we can learn several useful things about Canada thistle management from the exercise. First, quantifying the demographic context for a given cropping system can help priori-tize management tactics (Shea et al., 2005). For rosette survival and seed survival of predation, the relative impact of changes to each parameter on population size depends on the value of the other parameter. If few seeds survive seed predation, as in the A, CM, and C strategies, the sensitivity of population size to changes in rosette survival is fairly low (i.e., the slope of the plot of population size against rosette survival is low). However, if many seeds survive predation, as in the M and T systems, the sensitivity of population size to rosette survival is much greater.

This leads to a second lesson learned: Management systems that target mul-tiple life stages have a degree of buffering that single-stage tactics do not have. It can be seen in Fig. 8–5 that the slope of the response surface increases toward the top of the graph, where both survival rates are increasing toward 1. The steep slope in this region means that errors in weed management have greater nega-tive consequences than in the lower region of the surface, where it flattens out. In the A and CM systems, even a 20% variation in either parameter will result in little change to overall thistle population size. This is an illustration of many little hammers in action. When multiple tactics are applied, it reduces requirements for any one management tactic to produce successful weed management out-comes. Suppressing Canada thistle with alfalfa is an interesting case, as it could be considered a single tactic, but it influences multiple life stages, beyond those described here (including reduced fecundity, seedling recruitment, and rosette recruitment from rhizome fragments). Finally, it appears that a thick vegetative cover included at some point in a crop sequence is critically important for reduc-ing Canada thistle populations, both for its competitive effect and for the habitat it provides to seed predators.

Future Directions: Conversations, Experiments, Models, and Management

The management insights and hypotheses gained from the models presented in this chapter are a small part of a larger conversation that needs to take place between empiricists, theoreticians, farmers, and outreach specialists. Each of the parties in this conversation has something to gain through participation. By placing empirical results into a theoretical framework and putting forth test-able hypotheses, we hope we have demonstrated how models can focus research efforts, saving empiricists time and money and increasing the potential impact of their work. At the same time, models are only as good as the data used to parameterize them, and it is difficult, if not impossible, to adapt data from many agronomic experiments for modeling purposes because they have not been collected with portability in mind. Expressing outcomes of management studies in terms of survival rates or fecundity, rather than biomass alone, or providing population densities along with biomass, would allow these data to be used again and again.

Farmers contribute to this conversation as innovators, observers, hypothesis generators, fact checkers, information gatherers, and early adopters. Although the traditional model for scientific outreach placed the research scientist at the top of a hierarchy, with extension agents in the middle, and farmers at the bottom, flatter models are beginning to prevail that emphasize multidirectional information flow (Staver, 2001). Because of their immense practical experience, and their site-specific knowledge as members of a group that is dispersed across the agricultural landscape, farmers possess a wealth of information that researchers cannot afford to ignore. Extensionists can play an important role in bringing researchers and farmers together, by identifying complementary interests and personalities and by facilitating interactions.

One way in which farmers, extensionists, and research scientists can come together is through learning communities (Jordan et al., 2002, 2006), which meet on an ongoing basis to develop understanding of sophisticated topics beyond the scope of any one individual's training or experience. Some of these groups work to improve their ability to apply the many-little-hammers concept. Others identify pressing management areas with need for further scientific support. One such learning community in Michigan worked together over the course of a winter to summarize what they knew about ecological weed management, to identify gaps in scientific knowledge, and to write a guide to ecological weed management in Michigan field crops (Davis et al., 2005). The group obtained funding for a series of on-farm experiments to address the knowledge gaps, with plans to reconvene, evaluate the research findings, and update the management guide.

Information exchange between farmers, researchers, and other members of the agricultural community could lead to potentially surprising practical outcomes. Consider, for example, a survey of 10 organic farms that found the most successful farm, from the standpoint of having the lowest labor requirement for weeding, was the one on which weed seed banks had been depleted by killing and removing weeds surviving other controls, before they produced and dispersed seeds (Vereijken, 1999). At first consideration, this result would seem to lead to the conclusion that farmers should seek to completely eliminate weed reproduction, following Norris's (1999) *zero seed threshold*. Modeling analyses of weed population dynamics conducted by Westerman et al. (2005) indicated, however, that because of weed seed consumption by indigenous insects and rodents, low levels of weed survival and reproduction could be tolerated without long-term growth of weed populations. Thus, as a complement to developing better weed control machinery, emphasis could be placed on developing strategies for habitat management to increase densities and impacts of weed seed predators. By maintaining weed populations at an acceptably low level, such a strategy has the added benefit of supporting biological diversity within a field (Marshall et al., 2003).

Continued growth in the organic farming sector in the coming decades will provide new opportunities for weed scientists to serve and engage with the agricultural community. New resources will be needed to test hypotheses concerning weed population dynamics on a broad scale and over the long term, on both commercial farms and research station plots. We believe the discipline of ecology offers the most appropriate overarching framework for conducting this work and for investing time and resources most effectively. When empiricists, modelers, and farmers engage in an ongoing conversation, sharing information freely and learning from one another, each iteration of this process will make considerable progress toward economically and environmentally sustainable weed management systems.

Discussion Questions

1.   A weed can only be killed once. Why bother using multiple tactics for weed management in organic production systems?

2.   In what specific ways can mathematical models be used to guide weed management? Argue the pros and cons of a quantitative approach to ecological weed management, and discuss how this strategy can be used to help set research priorities.

3.   What are the reasons for farmers to develop distinct management practices for weeds with different life histories? Explain why and how those strategies should differ and under what circumstances, and also the conditions under which the strategies should be the same.

4.   What are three critical concerns for weed managers, and how do they relate to the development and implementation of weed management strategies?

5.   What are "target transitions" in weed life histories? How are they identified, and what is their importance for weed management?

6.   Describe how farmers, extension personnel, and research scientists might jointly develop better weed management strategies.

References

Anderson, R.L. 2003. An ecological approach to strengthen weed management in the semi-arid Great Plains. Adv. Agron. 80:33–62.

Anderson, R.L. 2005. A multi-tactic approach to manage weed population dynamics in crop rotations. Agron. J. 97:1579–1583.

Anderson, R.L. 2007. Managing weeds with a dualistic approach of prevention and control: A review. Agron. Sustain. Dev. 27:13–18.

Archer, D.W., A.A. Jaradat, J.M.-F. Johnson, S.L. Weyers, R.W. Gesch, F. Forcella, and H.K. Kludze. 2007. Crop productivity and economics during the transition to alternative cropping systems. Agron. J. 99:1538–1547.

Ascard, J. 1994. Dose–response models for flame weeding in relation to plant size and density. Weed Res. 34:377–385.

Ascard, J. 1995. Effects of flame weeding on weed species at different developmental stages. Weed Res. 35:397–411.

Bàrberi, P. 2002. Weed management in organic agriculture: Are we addressing the right issues? Weed Res. 42:177–193.

Baumann, D.T., L. Bastiaans, and M.J. Kropff. 2001. Effects of intercropping on growth and reproductive capacity of late-emerging Senecio vulgaris L., with special reference to competition for light. Ann. Bot. (Lond.) 87:209–217.

Baumann, D.T., M.J. Kropff, and L. Bastiaans. 2000. Intercropping leeks to suppress weeds. Weed Res. 40:359–374.

Belz, R.G. 2007. Allelopathy in crop/weed interactions–an update. Pest Manage. Sci. 63:308–326.

Blackshaw, R.E. 1994. Differential competitive ability of winter wheat cultivars against downy brome. Agron. J. 86:649–654.

Bond, W., and A.C. Grundy. 2001. Non-chemical weed management in organic farming systems. Weed Res. 41:383–405.

Bond, W., and R.J. Turner. 2006a. The biology and non-chemical control of common couch (*Elytrigia repens* (L.) Nevski). Available at http://www.gardenorganic.org.uk/organic-weeds/downloads/elytrigia%20repens.pdf (verified 16 July 2009). Henry Doubleday Research Association, Coventry, UK.

Bond, W., and R. Turner. 2006b. The biology and non-chemical control of creeping thistle (*Cirsium arvense*). Available at http://www.gardenorganic.org.uk/organicweeds/downloads/cirsium%20arvense.pdf (verified 16 July 2009). Henry Doubleday Research Association, Coventry, UK.

Bowman, G. 1997. Steel in the field: A farmer's guide to weed management tools. USDA Sustainable Agriculture Network, Beltsville, MD.

Boydston, R.A., and K. Al-Khatib. 2006. Utilizing Brassica cover crops for weed suppression in annual cropping systems. p. 77–94. *In* H.P. Singh, D.R. Batish, and R.K. Kohli (ed.) Handbook of sustainable weed management. Food Products Press, Binghamton, NY.

Buhler, D.D., J.L. Gunsolus, and D.F. Ralston. 1992. Integrated weed management techniques to reduce herbicide inputs in soybean. Agron. J. 84:973–978.

Bulson, H.A.J., R.W. Snaydon, and C.E. Stopes. 1997. Effects of plant density on intercropped wheat and field beans in an organic farming system. J. Agric. Sci. 128:59–71.

Callaway, M.B. 1992. A compendium of crop varietal tolerance to weeds. Am. J. Alternative Agric. 7:169–180.

Carmona, D.M., F.D. Menalled, and D.A. Landis. 1999. *Gryllus pennsylvanicus* (Orthoptera: Gryllidae) laboratory weed seed predation and within field activity-density. J. Econ. Entomol. 92:825–829.

Caswell, H. 2001. Matrix population models: Construction, analysis and interpretation. 2nd ed. Sinauer, Sunderland, MA.

Cavigelli, M.A., J.R. Teasdale, and A.E. Conklin. 2008. Long-term agronomic performance of organic and conventional field crops in the mid-Atlantic region. Agron. J. 100:785–794.

Clark, A. 1998. Managing cover crops profitably. USDA Sustainable Agriculture Network, Beltsville, MD.

Conklin, A.E., M.S. Erich, M. Liebman, D. Lambert, E.R. Gallandt, and W.A. Halteman. 2002. Effects of red clover (*Trifolium pratense*) green manure and compost soil amendments on wild mustard (*Brassica kaber*) growth and incidence of disease. Plant Soil 238:245–256.

Cousens, R. 1985. A simple model relating yield loss to weed density. Ann. Appl. Biol. 107:239–252.

Cousens, R., and M. Mortimer. 1995. Dynamics of weed populations. Cambridge Univ. Press, Cambridge, UK.

Davis, A.S. 2006. When does it make sense to target the weed seed bank? Weed Sci. 54:558–565.

Davis, A.S., and M. Liebman. 2001. Nitrogen source influences wild mustard growth and competitive effect on sweet corn. Weed Sci. 49:558–566.

Davis, A.S., and M. Liebman. 2003. Cropping system effects on giant foxtail (*Setaria faberi*) demography: I. Green manure and tillage timing. Weed Sci. 51:919–929.

Davis, A.S., K.A. Renner, C. Sprague, L. Dyer, and D. Mutch. 2005. Integrated weed management. One year's seeding. Extension Bull. E-2931. Michigan State Univ., East Lansing.

Davis, A.S., and M.M. Williams, II. 2007. Variation in wild proso millet (*Panicum miliaceum*) fecundity in sweet corn has residual effects in snap bean. Weed Sci. 55:502–507.

Dieleman, J.A., D.A. Mortensen, D.D. Buhler, C.A. Cambardella, and T.B. Moorman. 2000. Identifying association among site properties and weed species abundance: I. Multivariate analysis. Weed Sci. 48:567–575.

Donald, W.W. 1990. Management and control of Canada thistle (*Cirsium arvense*). Rev. Weed Sci. 5:193–250.

Donald, W.W. 1994. The biology of Canada thistle (*Cirsium arvense*). Rev. Weed Sci. 6:77–101.

Donald, W.W. 2006. Mowing for weed management. p. 329–372. *In* H.P. Singh, D.R. Batish, and R.K. Kohli (ed.) Handbook of sustainable weed management. Food Products Press, Binghamton, NY.

Drinkwater, L.E. 2009. Ecological knowledge: Foundation for sustainable organic agriculture. p. 19–48. *In* C. Francis (ed.) Organic farming: The ecological system. Agron. Monogr. 54. ASA, CSSA, and SSSA, Madison, WI. (This volume.)

Duppong, L.M., K. Delate, M. Liebman, R. Horton, F. Romero, G. Kraus, J. Petrich, and P.K. Chowdbury. 2004. The effect of natural mulches on crop performance, weed suppression, and biochemical constituents of catnip and St. John's wort. Crop Sci. 44:861–869.

Dyck, E., and M. Liebman. 1994. Soil fertility management as a factor in weed control: The effect of crimson clover residue, synthetic N fertilizer, and their interaction on emergence and early growth of lambsquarters and sweet corn. Plant Soil 167:227–237.

Dyck, E., M. Liebman, and M.S. Erich. 1995. Crop-weed interference as influenced by a leguminous or synthetic fertilizer nitrogen source: 1. Double-cropping experiments with crimson clover, sweet corn, and lambsquarters. Agric. Ecosyst. Environ. 56:93–108.

Edwards, G.R., G.W. Bourdot, and M.J. Crawley. 2000. Influence of herbivory, competition, and soil fertility on the abundance of *Cirsium arvense* in acid grassland. J. Appl. Ecol. 37:321–334.

Entz, M.H., W.J. Bullied, and F. Katepa-Mupondwa. 1995. Rotational benefits of forage crops in Canadian prairie cropping systems. J. Prod. Agric. 8:521–529.

Forcella, F., D.H. Peterson, and J.C. Barbour. 1996. Timing and measurement of weed seed shed in corn (*Zea mays*). Weed Technol. 10:535–543.

Freckleton, R.P., and A.R. Watkinson. 1998. Predicting the determinants of weed abundance: A model for the population dynamics of *Chenopodium album* in sugar beet. J. Appl. Ecol. 35:904–920.

Gallandt, E.R., and E.R. Haramoto. 2004. Brassica cover cropping for weed management: A review. Renewable Agric. Food Syst. 19:187–198.

Gallandt, E.R., M. Liebman, S. Corson, G.A. Porter, and S.D. Ullrich. 1998. Effects of pest and soil management systems on weed dynamics in potato. Weed Sci. 46:238–248.

Gallandt, E.R., M. Liebman, and D.R. Huggins. 1999. Improving soil quality: Implications for weed management. J. Crop Prod. 2:95–121.

Graglia, E., B. Melander, and R.K. Jensen. 2006. Mechanical and cultural strategies to control *Cirsium arvense* in organic arable cropping systems. Weed Res. 46:304–312.

Grandy, A.S., and G.P. Robertson. 2006. Aggregation and organic matter protection following tillage of a previously uncultivated soil. Soil Sci. Soc. Am. J. 70:1398–1406.

Grundy, A.C., K. Phelps, R.J. Reader, and S. Burston. 2000. Modelling the germination of *Stellaria media* using the concept of hydrothermal time. New Phytol. 148:433–444.

Gunsolus, J.L., and D.D. Buhler. 1999. A risk management perspective on integrated weed management. J. Crop Prod. 2:167–187.

Guske, S., B. Schulz, and C. Boyle. 2004. Biocontrol options for *Cirsium arvense* with indigenous fungal pathogens. Weed Res. 44:107–116.

Gustavsson, A.M.D. 1997. Growth and regenerative capacity of plants of *Cirsium arvense*. Weed Res. 37:229–236.

Håkansson, S. 1982. Multiplication, growth and persistence of perennial weeds. p. 123–135. *In* W. Holzner and M. Numata (ed.) Biology and ecology of weeds. Dr. W. Junk, The Hague, The Netherlands.

Hallett, S.G. 2005. Where are the bioherbicides? Weed Sci. 53:404–415.

Hanks, J., and J.T. Ritchie (ed.) 1991. Modeling plant and soil systems. ASA, CSSA, and SSSA, Madison, WI.

Harrison, S.K., E.E. Regnier, and J.T. Schmoll. 2003. Postdispersal predation of giant ragweed (*Ambrosia trifida*) in no-tillage corn. Weed Sci. 51:955–964.

Hatcher, P.E., and B. Melander. 2003. Combining physical, cultural and biological methods: Prospects for integrated non-chemical weed management strategies. Weed Res. 43:303–322.

Heggenstaller, A.H., F.D. Menalled, M. Liebman, and P.R. Westerman. 2006. Seasonal patterns in post-dispersal seed predation of *Abutilon theophrasti* and *Setaria faberi* in three cropping systems. J. Appl. Ecol. 43:999–1010.

Heimann, B., and G.W. Cussans. 1996. The importance of seeds and sexual reproduction in the population biology of *Cirsium arvense*- A literature review. Weed Res. 36:493–503.

Hoffman, M.L., E.E. Regnier, and J. Cardina. 1993. Weed and corn (*Zea mays*) responses to a hairy vetch (*Vicia villosa*) cover crop. Weed Technol. 7:594–599.

Holst, N., I.A. Rasmussen, and L. Bastiaans. 2007. Field weed population dynamics: A review of model approaches and applications. Weed Res. 47:1–14.

Jordan, N., J. Gunsolus, R. Becker, and S. White. 2002. Public scholarship: Linking weed science with public work. Weed Sci. 50:547–554.

Jordan, N., H. Niemi, S. Simmons, R. Becker, J. Gunsolus, and S. White. 2006. Learning groups for implementation of integrated weed management: Principles and practical guidelines. p. 825–853. *In* H.P. Singh, D.R. Batish, and R.K. Kohli (ed.) Handbook of sustainable weed management. Food Products Press, Binghamton, NY.

Kornecki, T.S., A.J. Price, and R.L. Raper. 2006. Performance of different roller designs in terminating rye cover crop and reducing vibration. Appl. Eng. Agric. 22:633–641.

Kropff, M.J., and H.H. van Laar. 1993. Modelling weed-crop interactions. CAB Int., Wallingford, UK.

Landis, D.A., S.D. Wratten, and G.M. Gurr. 2000. Habitat management to conserve natural enemies of arthropod pests. Annu. Rev. Entomol. 45:175–201.

Leighty, C.E. 1938. Crop rotation. p. 406–430. *In* Soils and men: Yearbook of agriculture 1938. USDA. U.S. Gov. Print. Office, Washington, DC.

Lemerle, D., B. Verbeek, R.D. Cousens, and N.E. Coombes. 1996. The potential for selecting wheat varieties strongly competitive against weeds. Weed Res. 36:505–513.

Levins, R. 1966. The strategy of model building in population biology. Am. Sci. 54:421–431.

Lewis, W.J., J.C. van Lenteren, S.C. Phatak, and J.H. Tumlinson III. 1997. A total system approach to sustainable pest management. Proc. Natl. Acad. Sci. USA 94:12243–12248.

Liebman, M., and A.S. Davis. 2000. Integration of soil, crop, and weed management in low-external-input farming systems. Weed Res. 40:27–47.

Liebman, M., and E.R. Gallandt. 1997. Many little hammers: Ecological approaches for management of crop–weed interactions. p. 291–343. *In* L.E. Jackson (ed.) Ecology in agriculture. Academic Press, San Diego, CA.

Liebman, M., F.D. Menalled, D.D. Buhler, T.L. Richard, D.N. Sundberg, C.A. Cambardella, and K.A. Kohler. 2004. Impacts of composted swine manure on weed and corn nutrient uptake, growth, and seed production. Weed Sci. 52:365–375.

Liebman, M., and C.P. Staver. 2001. Crop diversification for weed management. p. 322–374. *In* M. Liebman, C. L. Mohler, and C. P. Staver (ed.) Ecological management of agricultural weeds. Cambridge Univ. Press, Cambridge, UK.

Liebman, M., and D.N. Sundberg. 2006. Seed mass affects the susceptibility of weed and crop species to phytotoxins extracted from red clover shoots. Weed Sci. 54:340–345.

Louda, S.M., D. Kendall, J. Connor, and D. Simberloff. 1997. Ecological effects of an insect introduced for the biological control of weeds. Science 277:1088–1090.

Marshall, E.J.P., V.K. Brown, N.D. Boatman, P.J.W. Lutman, G.R. Squire, and L.K. Ward. 2003. The role of weeds in supporting biological diversity within crop fields. Weed Res. 43:77–89.

McEvoy, P.B., and E.M. Coombs. 1999. Biological control of plant invaders: Regional patterns, field experiments and structured population models. Ecol. Appl. 9:387–401.

Melander, B., and M.H. Jørgensen. 2005. Soil steaming to reduce intrarow weed seedling emergence. Weed Res. 45:202–211.

Melander, B., and G. Rasmussen. 2001. Effects of cultural methods and physical weed control methods on intrarow weed numbers, manual weeding and marketable yield in direct-sown leek and bulb onion. Weed Res. 41:491–508.

Melander, B., I.A. Rasmussen, and P. Bàrberi. 2005. Integrating physical and cultural methods of weed control: Example from European research. Weed Sci. 53:369–381.

Menalled, F.D., M. Liebman, and D.D. Buhler. 2004. Impact of composted swine manure and tillage on common waterhemp (*Amaranthus rudis*) competition with soybean. Weed Sci. 52:605–613.

Menalled, F.D., M. Liebman, and K. Renner. 2006. The ecology of weed seed predation in herbaceous crop systems. p. 297–327. *In* H.P. Singh, D.R. Batish, and R.K. Kohli (ed.) Handbook of sustainable weed management. Food Products Press, Binghamton, NY.

Mertens, S.K., F. van den Bosch, and J.A.P. Heesterbeek. 2002. Weed populations and crop rotations: Exploring dynamics of a structured periodic system. Ecol. Appl. 12:1125–1141.

Mohler, C.L. 2001a. Enhancing the competitive ability of crops. p. 269–321. *In* M. Liebman, C.L. Mohler, and C.P. Staver (ed.) Ecological management of agricultural weeds. Cambridge Univ. Press, Cambridge, UK.

Mohler, C.L. 2001b. Mechanical management of weeds. p. 139–209. *In* M. Liebman, C.L. Mohler, and C.P. Staver (ed.) Ecological management of agricultural weeds. Cambridge Univ. Press, Cambridge, UK.

Mohler, C.L., J.C. Frisch, and J. Mt. Pleasant. 1997. Evaluation of mechanical weed management programs for corn (*Zea mays*). Weed Technol. 11:123–131.

Mohler, C.L., and J.R. Teasdale. 1993. Response of weed emergence to rate of *Vicia villosa* Roth and *Secale cereale* L. residue. Weed Res. 33:487–499.

Morse, R., and N. Creamer. 2006. Developing no-tillage systems without chemicals: The best of both worlds? p. 83–91. *In* P. Kristiansen, A. Taji, and J. Reganold (ed.) Organic agriculture: A global perspective. Comstock, Ithaca, NY.

Mulder, T.A., and J.D. Doll. 1993. Integrating reduced herbicide use with mechanical weeding in corn (*Zea mays*). Weed Technol. 7:382–389.

Norris, R.F. 1999. Ecological implications of using thresholds for weed management. J. Crop Prod. 2:31–58.

Ogg, A.G.J., and S. Seefeldt. 1999. Characterizing traits that enhance the competitiveness of winter wheat (*Triticum aestivum*) against jointed goatgrass (*Aegilops cylindrica*). Weed Sci. 47:74–80.

Ohno, T., K. Doolan, L.M. Zibilske, M. Liebman, E.R. Gallandt, and C. Berube. 2000. Phytotoxic effects of red clover amended soils on wild mustard seedling growth. Agric. Ecosyst. Environ. 78:187–192.

Olofsdotter, M., L.B. Jensen, and B. Courtois. 2002. Improving crop competitive ability using allelopathy: An example from rice. Plant Breed. 121:1–9.

Olsen, J., L. Kristensen, J. Weiner, and H.W. Griepentrog. 2005. Increased density and spatial uniformity increase weed suppression by spring wheat. Weed Res. 45:316–321.

Ominski, P.D., M.H. Entz, and N. Kenkel. 1999. Weed suppression by *Medicago sativa* in subsequent cereal crops: A comparative survey. Weed Sci. 47:282–290.

Ozores-Hampton, M., T.A. Obreza, and P.J. Stoffella. 2001. Mulching with composted MSW for biological control of weeds in vegetable crops. Compost Sci. Util. 9:352–361.

Patriquin, D.G., N.M. Hill, D. Baines, M. Bishop, and G. Allen. 1986. Observations on a mixed farm during the transition to biological husbandry. Biol. Agric. Hortic. 3:69–154.

Pieters, A.J. 1927. Green manuring: Principles and practice. John Wiley & Sons, New York.

Posner, J.L., J.O. Baldock, and J.L. Hedtcke. 2008. Organic and conventional production systems in the Wisconsin integrated cropping systems trials: 1. Productivity 1990–2002. Agron. J. 100:253–260.

Pullen, D.W.M., and P.A. Cowell. 2000. Prediction and experimental verification of the hoe path of a rear-mounted inter-row weeder. J. Agric. Eng. Res. 77:137–153.

Rasmussen, J., and J. Ascard. 1995. Weed control in organic farming systems. p. 49–67. *In* D.M. Glen, M.P. Greaves, and H.M. Anderson (ed.) Ecology and integrated farming systems, John Wiley, Chichester, UK.

Rasmussen, K. 2002. Influence of liquid manure application method on weed control in spring cereals. Weed Res. 42:287–298.

Riemens, M.M., R.M.W. Groenveld, L.A.P. Lotz, and M.J. Kropff. 2007. Effects of three management strategies on the seedbank, emergence and the need for hand weeding in an organic arable cropping system. Weed Res. 47:442–451.

Ryan, M.R., D.A. Mortensen, and L. Bastiaans. 2006. Enhanced tolerance to weed competition: Effects of crop and soil management in a long-term cropping systems trial. *In* Proc. of the 5th Workshop of the EWRS Working Group: Crop–Weed Interactions Workshop, Rothamsted, UK. 12–15 Sept. 2006. Eur. Weed Research Society, Doorwerth, the Netherlands. Available at http://www.cost860.dk/publications/doc/2006-Rothamsted.pdf (verified 20 July 2009).

Shea, K., D. Kelly, A.W. Sheppard, and T.L. Woodburn. 2005. Context-dependent biological control of an invasive thistle. Ecology 86:3174–3181.

Sooby, J., J. Landeck, and M. Lipson. 2007. 2007 National Organic Research agenda: Soils, pests, livestock, genetics. Available at http://ofrf.org/publications/pubs/nora2007.pdf (verified 16 July 2009). Organic Farming Research Foundation, Santa Cruz, CA.

Staver, C.P. 2001. Knowledge, science and practice in ecological weed management: Farmer-extensionist-scientist interactions. p. 99–138. *In* M. Liebman, C.L. Mohler, and C.P. Staver (ed.) Ecological management of agricultural weeds. Cambridge Univ. Press, Cambridge, UK.

Teasdale, J.R. 1996. Contribution of cover crops to weed management in sustainable agricultural systems. J. Prod. Agric. 9:475–479.

Teasdale, J.R., and C.L. Mohler. 2000. The quantitative relationship between weed emergence and the physical properties of mulches. Weed Sci. 48:385–392.

Vandermeer, J. 1989. The ecology of intercropping. Cambridge Univ. Press, Cambridge, UK.

van der Schans, D., P. Bleeker, L. Molendijk, M. Plentinger, R. van der Weide, B. Lotz, R. Bauermeister, R. Total, and D.T. Baumann. 2006. Practical weed control in arable farming and outdoor vegetable cultivation without chemicals. Applied Plant Research, Wageningen UR, Lelystad, The Netherlands.

Vereijken, P. 1999. Manual for prototyping integrated and ecological arable farming systems (I/EAFS) in interaction with pilot farms. AB-DLO, Wageningen, The Netherlands.

Walz, E. 1999. Final results of the third biennial national organic farmers' survey. Available at https://ofrf.org/publications/pubs/3rdsurvey_results.pdf (verified 16 July 2009). Organic Farming Research Foundation, Santa Cruz, CA.

Weaver, S.E. 1984. Critical period of weed competition in three vegetable crops in relation to management practices. Weed Res. 24:317–325.

Westerman, P.R., M. Liebman, A.H. Heggenstaller, and F. Forcella. 2006. Integrating measurements of seed availability and removal to estimate weed seed losses due to predation. Weed Sci. 54:566–574.

Westerman, P.R., M. Liebman, F.D. Menalled, A.H. Heggenstaller, R.G. Hartzler, and P.M. Dixon. 2005. Are many little hammers effective? Velvetleaf population dynamics in two- and four-year crop rotation systems. Weed Sci. 53:382–392.

Westerman, P.R., J.S. Wes, M.J. Kropff, and W. van der Werf. 2003. Annual weed seed losses due to predation in organic cereal fields. J. Appl. Ecol. 40:824–836.

White, R.H., A.D. Worsham, and U. Blum. 1989. Allelopathic potential of legume debris and aqueous extracts. Weed Sci. 37:674–679.

Willey, R.W. 1990. Resource use in intercropping systems. Agric. Water Manage. 17:215–231.

Williams, M.M., R.A. Boydston, and A.S. Davis. 2007. Wild proso millet (*Panicum miliaceum*) suppressive ability among three sweet corn hybrids. Weed Sci. 55:245–251.

Wilson, R.G., A.R. Martin, and S.D. Kachman. 2006. Seasonal changes in carbohydrates in the root of Canada thistle (*Cirsium arvense*) and the disruption of these changes by herbicides. Weed Technol. 20:242–248.

9 🧄

Climbing Mt. Organic: An Ecosystem Approach to Pest Management

G. W. Bird and Matthew Grieshop
Department of Entomology, Michigan State University, East Lansing

Paul Hepperly and Jeff Moyer
Rodale Institute, Kutztown, Pennsylvania

All living organisms function in the context of a particular ecosystem. Every ecosystem is dependent on another ecosystem for its survival. Within this complex interdependent world of individual ecologies, agricultural systems have evolved over many millennia. Agriculture seeks to manipulate these interdependent ecosystems through the intervention of human activity to enhance the production of particular crops and animals most beneficial to our survival. Until the 1940s, these interventions were based on biological principles and use of mechanical implements to alter the natural state of the environment to suit the needs of specific crops. Since the mid-1940s, many of the primary implements of intervention have changed to chemically based strategies. The impact of these dramatic strategies is being felt throughout our ecosystems, affecting their very survival as part of the whole.

Living organisms replicate themselves, take in matter and energy from external sources, give off residuals, and respond to their environment. As humans, we share the resources of our planet with astronomical numbers of organisms classified in many different kingdoms of life; all but three of which (plants, animals and fungi) are microscopic. In addition, chemical messengers such as viruses (nucleo-proteins) and prions (small segments of protein) possess several of the properties of life and can be detrimental to food production systems. Organisms, including humans, live in ecosystems and obtain the matter and energy they require for their life processes from activities in food chains that are usually part of complex food webs. Ecosystems are always undergoing change. When they lose their natural diversity and become significantly out of balance, arthropod insects and other organisms can become pests; bacteria, fungi, and nematodes can become pathogens or disease-causing organisms, and many plants become weeds.

Conventional agriculture is based on the mechanistic worldview of biology, and rewards are dependent on neoclassical economics and globalization (Bird and Brewer, 2006; Capra, 1996). It further assumes the following

- linear system concepts (whole = sum of the parts)
- infinite system resources or replacement resources readily available
- few system feedback loops
- unlimited growth with increases throughout of matter and energy
- few components with overlapping functions
- no dependence on a vibrant ecological and human community

In contrast, organic agriculture as originally conceived is based on the ecological worldview of the science of ecology, which recognizes an interdependence among the following:

- cyclic-system concepts with emergent properties not present in their parts
- the reality that system resources are finite
- local interdependences, partnerships, and interconnected networks
- many-system feedback loops
- components with overlapping functions
- a vibrant ecological and human community

These are vastly different concepts. Learning how to become a successful organic farmer is like learning how to climb a mountain. Three stages in the process could be called exploring the foothills, mastering the slippery slopes, and maintaining prosperity at the summit. In relation to pest management, each of these stages has different challenges and options. The objectives of this chapter are (i) to provide an understanding of the concepts of ecology, (ii) to give an introduction to the interactions among the life forms associated with agricultural ecosystems, and (iii) to provide an overview of the systems approach to management options available for use in each of the three stages of Climbing Mt. Organic.

Nature of Ecology as Related to Farming

Ecology is the study of interactions among living organisms (biota) and their nonliving (abiotic) environment. Organic growers share their farms with thousands of species of organisms that can be classified into three domains and 23 kingdoms of life (Fig. 9–1). Individuals are grouped into populations of a single species, populations into communities of multiple species, and communities into ecosystems with their nonliving support components (Fig. 9–2). In ecosystems, matter is transformed and transported from one organism to another in food chains and complex food webs (Fig. 9–3).

The process of organic farming begins with the capture of solar energy by chloroplasts in cells of plants (self-feeders or autotrophs). In the process of photosynthesis, this energy is used to transform carbon dioxide from air, and water from soil, into a six-carbon sugar (glucose).

Photosynthesis (energy-demanding process)

$$6CO_2 + 12H_2O \rightarrow C_6H_{12}O_6 + 6O_2 + 6H_2O$$
$$\uparrow$$
$$\text{Solar energy}$$

Glucose serves as a source of energy, e.g., contributes the ability to do work, and provides the basic organic, carbon-based building blocks for all other parts of

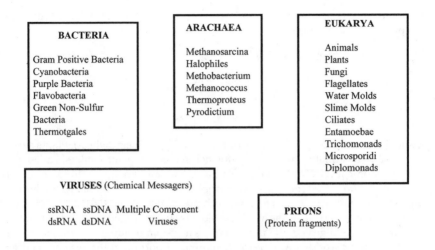

Fig. 9–1. Three domains of life (Bacteria, Arachaea, and Eukarya) and lists of 23 kingdoms of life plus reference to viruses and prions. All but three of these groups of organisms (plants, animals, and fungi) are microscopic.

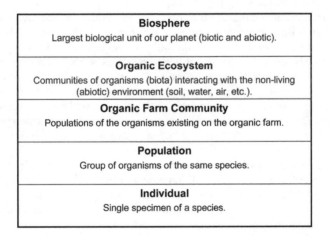

Fig. 9–2. Illustration describing the concepts of individuals, populations, communities, ecosystems, and the biosphere in relation to organic farms.

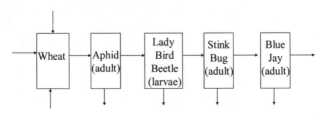

Fig. 9–3. Conceptual model of an organic farm food chain as a small part of the much larger and more complex organic farm food web, illustrating the transport and transformation of matter and energy.

plants. The energy stored in carbon-to-carbon covalent bonds is released through the process of respiration.

Respiration (energy-releasing process)

$$C_6H_{12}O_6 + 6O_2 \rightarrow 6CO_2 + 6H_2O$$
$$\downarrow$$

Energy release

Plant biomass represents the first trophic level (Fig. 9–3, e.g., wheat). Plants serve as the source of matter and energy for herbivores, or plant feeders, called the second trophic level. Plant feeders serve as matter and energy, or food, for carnivores, the animal feeders at the third trophic level. Many organisms, including humans, are omnivores, who feed on both plant and animal tissue. At each feeding level, only a portion of the available biomass is consumed. Some of the matter consumed is not digested and is given off as a system residual, referred to under the mechanistic worldview as *waste*. A significant portion of the system's energy is released into the environment as heat, a low-quality potential energy, in accordance with the second law of thermodynamics. In the absence of limiting factors, organisms have the biotic potential to increase their populations exponentially, forming a J-shaped curve (Fig. 9–4).

In both natural and managed ecosystems, the biotic reproductive potential of an organism is limited by environmental resistance, resulting in logistic increase or an S-shaped individual or population growth curve (Fig. 9–5). Environmental resistance is formed by a suite of limiting factors, such as temperature, water, space, light, food, parasites, predators, and pathogens. When any one of these parameters is below the minimum necessary to support a further individual or population growth of an organism, the biotic potential will not increase beyond a specific number, biomass, or yield. Each ecosystem has a specific carrying capacity (K). When a population increases beyond K, resources will be limited, and a population or yield decline will result (Fig. 9–6).

Note that the terms *pest* and *weed* do not exist in the language of ecology and the ecological worldview. This represents a basic paradox of organic pest management. The concepts of pests and weeds are a fundamental aspect of the mechanistic worldview. For some organic farmers, pests such as viruses, bacteria, fungi, nematodes, arthropods, and weeds are key limiting factors. They often present significant management challenges for organic farmers exploring the

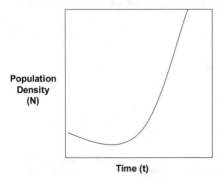

Population Density (N)

Time (t)

Fig. 9–4. Modified pest population density exponential growth curve (J-shaped curve) illustrating pest population increase in the absence of environmental resistance factors such as biological control agents, water, and other key limiting factors.

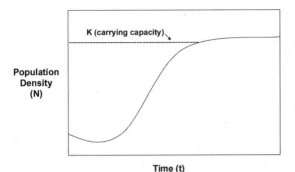

Fig. 9–5. Modified pest population density logistic growth (S-shaped curve) and ecosystem carrying capacity (*K*) in the presence of limiting factors (environmental resistance), such as lack of food, water, and appropriate temperature.

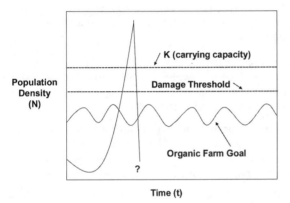

Fig. 9–6. Illustration of a population crash after exceeding *K* (ecosystem carrying capacity) in relation to the pest damage threshold and organic farm goal of maintaining potential pest population densities below pest damage thresholds.

foothills of Mt. Organic and those attempting to master the slippery slopes. For others, especially those who have mastered the slippery slopes and are farming at the summit, pests continue to present challenges. In an ecosystem approach to organic pest management, it is essential to have a solid understanding of nature and interactions among the biotic and abiotic components of the system. This knowledge of the system is necessary for the organic farmer to make proper management decisions.

In agricultural systems, plants are either healthy, injured, diseased or in some intermediate stage or combination of these three states.

Health: the state of being free of injury or disease.

Injury: a detrimental physiological process caused by the transient or momentary irritation of some causal agent, and expressed as symptoms of various kinds. Defoliation caused by a grasshopper infestation is an example of injury.

Disease: a detrimental physiological process caused by the continued irritation of an abiotic or biotic causal agent. It is exhibited through abnormal metabolic activity and expressed in characteristic pathological conditions called symptoms. Diseases may be infectious or noninfectious. Infectious diseases are caused by biotic organisms, or pathogens, and noninfectious diseases are caused by abiotic factors.

Noninfectious disease: a detrimental physiological process caused by the continued irritation by an abiotic factor. It is exhibited through abnormal activities of the impacted organism and expressed in characteristic pathological conditions called *symptoms*. Although not usually considered as such, under the above system, nitrogen deficiency is an example of a noninfectious disease.

Infectious disease: a detrimental physiological process caused by the continued irritation by a living organism. It is exhibited through abnormal activities of the impacted organism and expressed through characteristic pathological conditions called symptoms. An example is late blight of potato (*Solanum tuberosum* L.) (caused by *Phytophthora infestans*).

Symptoms of plant injury or disease can be classified as necrotic, hypoplastic, or hyperplastic. Although symptoms are usually observed visually, they may also be detected by touch, smell or taste.

Necrotic symptoms are expressions of degeneration or death of cells or disintegration of tissue. Soft rot of tomato (*Solanum lycopersicum* L.) caused by bacterial infection is an example. In this case, the matter and energy associated with the tomato has been transformed and transferred to the bacteria.

Hypoplastic symptoms are expressions of the failure or halting in differentiation, development, or growth of cells, tissues, or organs. Plant stunting associated with low fruit yield due to shading by weeds and competition for water is an example. In this case, the crop plant is prevented from growing to its normal biomass.

Hyperplastic symptoms are expressions of overdifferentiation, overdevelopment, or overgrowth of cells, tissues, or organs. Cucumber (*Cucumis sativus* L.) root galls and giant cells caused by the southern root-knot nematode (*Meloidogyne incognita*) are examples of hyperplastic symptoms. In these cases, the matter and energy that would go to normal metabolic processes associated with roots are used to feed the female nematode and produce a protective home for her young.

The Organisms

Pests are frequently studied in the separate disciplines of entomology, plant pathology, nematology, and weed science. These organisms function as parasites, predators, pathogens, vectors of pathogens, or competitors. In organic agriculture, it is essential to have an understanding of the biology of the organisms present in each ecosystem and their functional ecology, especially their multiple interactions. The nature of viruses, bacteria, fungi, nematodes and arthropods, vertebrates, and parasitic plants are introduced in this chapter. Management of weeds is covered in Chapter 8 (Liebman and Davis, 2009, this volume). In conventional agriculture, pests are referred to as "organisms that interact with humans in their quest for food, fiber, shelter or space. Other pests function as vectors of disease-causing organisms or as nuisance organisms in relation to human comfort or welfare" (Bird and Brewer, 2006).

Sir Albert Howard, one of the founders of organic agriculture, defined pests as nature's censors: "Insects and fungi are not the real cause of plant diseases but only attack unsuitable varieties or crops imperfectly grown. Their true role is that of censors for pointing out the crops that are improperly nourished and so keeping our agriculture up to the mark. In other words, the pests must be looked on as Nature's professors of agriculture: as the integral portion of any rational system of farming" (Howard, 1943, p. 161).

Viruses

Viruses are small (>20 to <2000 × 10^{-9} m) chemical messengers composed of a central core of nucleic acid, either single-stranded or double-stranded DNA or RNA, surrounded by a protein coat (Matthews, 1992). Viruses are known to cause infectious diseases of plants, bacteria, algae, fungi, and animals, including humans. Viruses have a variety of shapes, including spherical, short rods and longer flexible rods. More than 1000 types of viruses are known to be plant pathogens. Some viruses have specific parts of their nucleic acid enclosed in more than one particle. Plant viruses are introduced into host cells through mechanical cytoplasm transmission or by insect, nematode, mite, fungus, or fungus-like organism vectors. Some viruses are nonpersistent and only survive in a vector for hours to days. Others, however, are persistent and survive for days to months. In some cases, the viruses are circulative and replicate in their vector.

Upon entering an appropriate host cell, the virus sheds its protein coat and uses the metabolic structures and processes of the host cell for production of new virus particles. Viruses frequently cause diseases of leaf, flower, and fruit tissues. The hypoplastic symptoms of virus diseases of plants include stunting, dwarfing, and chlorosis; whereas the necrotic symptoms include characteristic yellowing, mosaics, mottling, ring spots, and vein banding. The fourth edition of *Matthews' Plant Virology* provides a comprehensive review of the topic (Hull, 2002).

Bacteria

Bacteria are small (1–3 × 10^{-6} m), usually single-cell organisms without a membrane around the cell nucleus (prokaryotic) and few cell organelles compared with organisms with a nuclear membrane (eukaryotic). They are classified in their own domain consisting of seven different kingdoms of life (Fig. 9–1). They may be aerobic, anaerobic, or capable of functioning in either environment. Because of differences in cell wall chemistry, bacteria stain differentially and are classified as gram positive or gram negative. Bacteria replicate rapidly through binary fission. Bacteria are basically decomposers of organic matter. Through this process, they both immobilize and mineralize essential nutrients. As part of the carbon cycle and most other cycles, the processes of nutrient mineralization and immobilization are key aspects of organic farming systems. Bacteria have resting stages, such as spores, and are designed for surviving periods of adverse conditions. Some species possess flagella for motility. The group, known as Actinomycetes, produces antibiotics and is responsible for the characteristic odor of healthy soil associated with organic agriculture

Some species of bacteria are pathogenic and cause infectious diseases of plant seed, seedling, vascular, leaf, fruit, other shoot and root tissues. They enter plant tissues through direct penetration, natural openings, stomates of hydathodes, or wounds. The symptoms may be necrotic, hypoplastic, or hyperplastic. They often appear as water-soaked tissue. Laboratory analysis is often necessary for diagnosis of bacterial diseases (Schadd et al., 2001).

Fungi and Fungal-Like Organisms

Fungi are eukaryotic organisms classified in the kingdom Mycota. Their body or somatic cells are called *hyphae* (mycelia). Their cell walls contain chitin. Fungi replicate through spores that are produced sexually or asexually in a diversity of complex life cycles. There are four classes of fungi (Ascomycetes, Basidiomycetes, Chytridiomyetes, and Zygomycetes) and several groups of closely related organisms, such as the Oomycota, Myxomycota, and Plasmodiophoromycota. In general, fungi are decomposers and essential components of organic farming systems as key parts of the carbon and other nutrient cycles. In organic agriculture, the group known as *mycorrhizal fungi* function in the transformation and transport of phosphorus to roots, improvement of soil moisture relationships, and sequestration of large amounts of soil carbon.

Some species of fungi are pathogenic and cause infectious diseases of plant seed, seedling, root, vascular, leaf, flower, fruit, or woody tissues. They enter plant tissue by direct penetration (usually enzymatic), natural openings, or wounds. Symptoms can be necrotic, such as blight or dry rot; hypoplastic, such as stunting or low fruit yield; or hyperplastic, such as hairy roots or witches broom. Some fungal species protect plants against pathogenic fungi or nematodes. Dugan's (2005) *The Identification of Fungi: An Illustrated Introduction with Keys, Glossary, and Guide to Literature* is an excellent up-to-date reference for information on the fungi that cause infectious diseases of plants.

Nematodes

Nematodes are invertebrate eukaryotic roundworms classified in the Phylum Nematoda of the animal kingdom. They are the most numerous animal on our planet, and more is known about their biology than for any other animal (Lee, 2002). They have a complete digestive system and do not have true body segments like earthworms (Phylum Annelida). Most species have males and females and reproduce sexually, while some are hermaphrodites or reproduce by parthenogenesis. Different species feed on bacteria, fungi, algae, plants, animals, or function as omnivores. The most common species feed on bacteria and release mineralized nitrogen ions on the root surface (rhizoplane) or in the area immediately surrounding the root (rhizosphere), where this nutrient is readily available for uptake by root tissue before it can infiltrate into groundwater or be released into the atmosphere as nitrogen gas. This process makes nematodes essential components of high-quality organic farming system soils. Nematode community structure is used by organic farmers as an indicator of soil quality.

Nematodes, however, can be plant pathogens. These species feed through a stylet that is similar to the piercing and sucking mouth parts of the Arthropods, discussed below. They can also vector viruses or predispose plants to infectious diseases caused by fungi or bacteria. There are three basic types of phytopathogenic nematodes: (i) ectoparasites, (ii) migratory endoparasites, and (iii) sedentary endoparasites. Although most infectious diseases of plants caused by nematodes are diseases of root tissue, a significant number of species feed on shoot tissues, resulting in infectious diseases of leaves, flowers, and seeds. The symptoms associated with these maladies may be necrotic, such as root lesions; hyperplastic, such as root galls; or hypoplastic, such as low yield and poor overall crop quality. The recent book by Perry and Moens (2006) provides an excellent overview of the biology, pathology, and management of nematode diseases of plants.

Arthropods

Arthropods are classified in the eukaryotic Phylum Arthropoda in the animal kingdom. They possess body segments, an exoskeleton, and jointed appendages. There are five classes in this phylum: (i) Chilopoda (centipedes) (ii) Diplopoda (millipedes), (iii) Arachnida (spiders, mites, and ticks), (iv) Insecta (insects, some times referred to as the class Hexapoda), and (v) Crustacea (lobster, crab, shrimp). In general, the adults of organisms classified in the Insecta have one pair of antennae, compound eyes, ocelli (eye spots), three pairs of legs, two pairs of wings, and a body divided in three parts (head, thorax, and abdomen).

There are three basic life cycles in the Insecta. These have a major impact on the behavior of various groups and their potential roles as parasites, predators, and vectors of pathogens. After the first-stage juvenile hatches from the egg, ametabolous insects look like a small version of a mature individual. They molt or shed their exoskeleton several times, grow, and eventually become an adult (subclass Apterygota). After emerging from the egg, insects with a hemimetabolous life cycle look like a small version of the adult with the exception that they lack wings (subclass Exopterygota). After several molts and growth, wing pads appear on the late instar stages. Adults with mature wings are present following the final molt. Insects with ametabolous or hemimetabolous (incomplete metamorphosis) may have biting and chewing mouthparts for consuming prey or piercing and sucking mouth parts for withdrawal of cytoplasm from their host or injection of virus particles into hosts. Insects with a holometabolous life cycle (complete metamorphosis) emerge from the egg as a larva or maggot that frequently has biting and chewing mouth parts for consuming prey (subclass Endopterygota). Following several molts the process of pupation begins with the formation of a pupa (cocoon, chrysalis). The process of pupation is completed with the emergence of the adult butterfly (Lepidoptera), moth (Lepidoptera), beetle (Coleoptera), fly (Diptera), mosquito (Culicidae), ant (Formicidae), bee (Hymenoptera), wasp (Hymenoptera), or flea (Siphonaptera). In many of these cases, the immature stages have very different feeding behaviors than the adults. Organisms such as mites and ticks classified in the other four classes of the Arthropoda can also be key or minor pests in agricultural systems.

Insects are classified into 31 different orders. Although about 13 of these contain species that are pests or considered as beneficial organisms in pest management (Table 9–1), several of the other orders contain species of significance to organic growers in the production and maintenance of high-quality soil. The symptoms associated with insect injury may be necrotic, hypoplastic, or hyperplastic. In addition, several types of insects have piercing and sucking mouthparts The sixth edition of *Entomology and Pest Management* (Pedigo and Rice, 2009) provides an excellent analysis of the Insecta in relation to agricultural pests.

Parasitic Plants

A number of species of flowering plants are parasites of other plant species. Some species like witchweed (*Striga* Lour.) and mistletoe (*Phoradendron* Nutt.) are root and stem hemiparasites, respectively. They extract water and nutrients from their plant hosts and are capable of photosynthesis. Dodder (*Cuscuta* spp.) and broomrape (*Orobranche* spp.) are root and stem holoparasites and are totally dependent on their hosts and not capable of photosynthesis. For dissemination, parasitic

Table 9–1. List of 13 orders of insects with species having potential to impact organic systems.

Order	Description
Orthoptera	Leaf and fruit pests of crops with chewing mouthparts
Phasmatodea	Plant feeders and beneficials with chewing mouthparts
Isoptera	Wood destroyers with chewing mouthparts
Blattoidea	Food contaminators with chewing mouthparts
Hemiptera	Plant and animal feeders; piercing, sucking mouthparts, insect predators
Thysanoptera	Flower, leaf, and bud pests with rasping, sucking mouthparts.
Phthiraptera	Poultry and livestock pests with modified chewing/sucking mouthparts.
Coleoptera	Plant, stored grain, and fiber pests; chewing mouthparts, insect predators.
Neuroptera	Insect predators, chewing and modified sucking mouthparts.
Hymenoptera	Plant pests, plant pollinators, honey production, insect predators
Lepidoptera	Plant pests and pollinators with siphoning and chewing mouthparts
Siphonapatera	Animal parasites and pathogen vectors; sucking and piercing mouthparts
Diptera	Plant and seed pests, animal parasites and pathogen vectors, diverse mouthparts

plants must either be attached to their host or distributed as seed. Press and Graves (1995) published a useful treatise on the topic titled *Parasitic Plants*.

Vertebrate Pests

Vertebrate pests vary greatly across different geographical regions. They may be as small as a mouse or as large as a baboon or possibly an occasional elephant. A review of the history of pest management indicates that rats were among the first vertebrate pests to mandate implementation of physical pest management tactics. Birds, raccoons, and deer are frequent pests of organic systems in the United States. The history of pest management documents that school boys were pests of major concern to the French grape (*Vitis vinifera* L.) grower Millardet (1885). In the southern maize (*Zea mays* L.) growing area of Luzon, a farmer indicated that his major pests in the crop were monkeys, crows, and wild pigs. Organic farmers face the same difficulties as conventional operators in finding strategies to manage this wide array of pest species.

Systems Approach to Organic Pest Management

Organic agriculture mandates the use of a systems approach. The system needs to take into account macro- and microecological zones as well as above- and belowground environments. The primary objective in considering all these ecosystems as part of an organic pest management plan is that the prevention of pest problems is preferable to later treating the symptoms of any problem—disease, insect, or weed. As described in relation to the metaphor of Climbing Mt. Organic, there are three distinct phases to the concept of organic pest management. The first deals with *exploring the foothills*, which relates to the process of developing an *organic system plan* based on an understanding of the entire farm system or substituting materials approved by a USDA accredited certifying agency for the synthetic pesticides used in conventional agriculture and integrated pest management. *Scaling the slippery slopes* requires development of a long-term system for minimizing the probability of pest occurrence through the use of organic practices designed to result in high-quality soil and biologically diverse ecosystems. This is key to the success of any production system. The third phase, *life at the summit*, is reserved for those organic farmers who have succeeded in mitigating

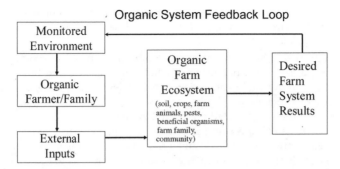

Fig. 9–7. Conceptual model of the relationships among the organic farm ecosystem, the desired system results (e.g., nutritious food, environmentally sound, high-quality family life), monitoring process, decision making, and external system inputs.

pests as a major factor in their production system. Individuals operating in the first phase often use of language of conventional agriculture and the mechanistic worldview. Those in the second phase are often in the process of increasing their eco-literacy skills for use in conversion from the mechanistic to the ecological world view. Individuals in the third phase have mastered the ecological worldview for the past and present, but are well aware that nature is dynamic and always changing. To remain successful, they must continue the task and joy of being an astute student of nature. A nematologist would say *listen to the worms*.

The first step in using a systems approach in organic farming is the development of a comprehensive long-term farm plan, defined under the USDA National Organic Program rule as an organic system plan (Electronic Code of Federal Regulations, 2009). This can be an integral part of the organic resources of the farm (Fig. 9–7). Organic farm plans are linked to the desired system responses, often quite distinct from conventional farm goals. Organic farm plans should include both short-term and long-term impacts on natural resources, quality of life for the farm family, and intergenerational equity. In a systems approach, this is linked to the process of biological (crop, pests, beneficial organisms) and environmental (soil, water, and atmospheric resources) monitoring, representing a series of feedback loops. The monitoring information is used by the farmer and farm family to determine their success or lack of success in meeting the desired system responses. The process is then used to determine what type of external system inputs are required for the next cycle of the organic farming system.

Exploring the Foothills

The philosophy, systems, and practices of integrated pest management (IPM) are often appropriate for use while exploring the foothills of organic agriculture. Goals may be to transition an existing farming system to organic or initiate an entirely new direction for the agroecosystem. The most important differences for the organic system are the certification requirements, long-term farm plan, and the use of preemptive interventions or natural or nonsynthetic pest management substances as approved by an accredited certifier or third party investigator such as the Organic Materials Review Institute (OMRI). In his environmental message to Congress on 2 Aug. 1979, President Carter defined IPM as "A systems approach to reduce pest damage to tolerable levels through a variety of techniques, including predators and parasites, genetically resistant hosts, natural environmental modifications and, when necessary and appropriate, chemical pesticides."

Although it should be the goal of the organic farmer to minimize the use of pesticides, a basic understanding of what pesticides are and how they work is necessary. The five main categories of pesticides are bactericides, fungicides, nematicides, insecticides, and herbicides. They may be synthetic (not allowed in organic agriculture unless listed on the USDA's national list), mineral, or biologically based. Ancient Chinese and Sumerian farming systems used both mineral and botanical pesticides. Pesticides may kill a target organism or alter its behavior in a way to significantly reduce the organism's potential to reduce crop yield or quality. The toxicity of pesticides is directly related to dosage. Examples of mineral pesticides include sulfur, copper, and diatomaceous earth. In the past, more toxic elements like arsenic and mercury were used. Biological pesticides are derived from plants and other natural products. Garlic juice, hot pepper sauce, soaps, pyrethrum, rotenone and neem are some of the materials that have been used successfully. Pesticides can be formulated in many ways, such as dusts, spray solution, granules, aerosols, and fumigants.

Biological and environmental monitoring and the use of damage thresholds represented the initial innovations that evolved into IPM (Fig. 9–8). When a pest or potential pest becomes a concern, the strategies consist of (i) pest exclusion or avoidance, (ii) pest containment or eradication, (iii) pest control, or (iv) doing nothing. The control tactic options include various physical, biological, genetic, cultural, regulatory, and chemical options. Details and case-study examples of

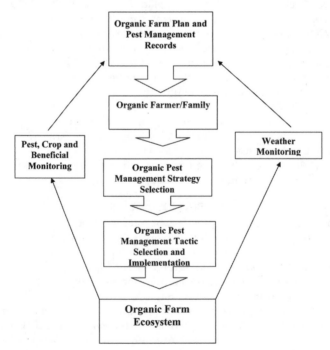

Fig. 9–8. Conceptual model of the process of organic pest management.

IPM implementation have been documented by Bird and Brewer (2006), Pedigo and Rice (2009), and Schumann and D'Arcy (2006). One of the best sources of current IPM information is *The IPM Practitioner*, published quarterly by the Bio-Integral Resource Center in Berkeley, CA. In addition to comprehensive reviews of specific IPM topics, the journal reviews in detail the highlights from the annual meetings of the Entomological Society of America, plus an annual list of the names and suppliers of the "Least Toxic Pest Management Options" (Quarles, 2009).

Although organic systems build on many IPM ideas, the organic planning strategy entails a deep understanding of the ecology of potential risks attributed to each of the pest categories as well as the control methods considered. Through this understanding, it becomes possible to design preventative measures into the system. It is also critical that the practitioner understands the basic components and concepts of soil biology. The health of soil generally translates into healthy plants. This can mitigate many of the potential risk factors in the external environment. By coupling this knowledge with the basic tenets of organic agriculture—crop rotations, cover crops, and compost to feed soil microbial life—transitioning from the foothills toward the summit becomes a manageable track.

Mastering the Slippery Slopes

High-quality biologically based soil forms the basis of organic agriculture. Soil is a medium and site where matter and energy are transformed and prepared for transport throughout the ecosystem. While significant strides have been made during the past two decades in understanding the nature of both soil biology and pest management, there have been relatively few studies linking these topics (Altieri and Nicholls, 2003). In mastering the slippery slopes of organic farming, it is imperative that the farmer focus on soil health, striving to create a soil that resists degradation, contributes resilience, and responds to management in a predictable manner. Organic soil management requires the farmer to appreciate the tremendous numbers of organisms and their activities in the soil, and viewed as a whole the soil needs to reach a dynamic and healthy state. Chapter 7 (Heckman et al., 2009, this volume) and Magdoff and van Es (2000) provide a basic understanding of these activities. Knowing the history, current state, and dynamics of the organic matter and associated biology of each production site is necessary to minimize risk potential from pests. Use of appropriate cover crops, composts, and crop rotations are part of a sound pest management strategy. The Sustainable Agriculture Research and Education program book *Managing Cover Crops Profitably* (SARE Outreach, 2007) is an excellent reference.

As with IPM, pest exclusion and avoidance should form the initial strategy of organic pest management. Use of only high-quality pest-free organic certified seed and other plant propagation stock is imperative. It is always easier to prevent a pest problem than resolve it once established. Site preparation and pest prevention crop rotation designed to break pest life cycles require a long-term systems plan designed to put it all together. This requires an understanding of the botanical relationships among the crops of interest and their seasonal adaptations. While it is neither possible nor desirable to write a prescription recommendation for organic pest management that is broader than a specific site or a farm, the book *Step by Step Organic Vegetable Gardening* (Ogden, 1992) outlines many of the management attributes to be considered for this type of system.

Merrill (1983), Oelhaf (1978), and many organic farmers work with the hypothesis that pest problems associated with organic systems are less than those associated with conventional agriculture. Possible reasons include (i) more extensive use of rotation crops, companion plantings, and preservation of beneficial organisms (Lampkin, 1990); (ii) increased plant tolerance or resistance, or reduced susceptibility (Magdoff and van Es, 2000; Phelan et al., 1995); and (iii) improved plant health as mediated through enhanced soil quality (McGuinness, 1993). Susceptibility to pests is known to be related to plant age and overall physiology (Slansky, 1990). This can be impacted by soil quality and nutrient inputs. Nutrient availability impacts not only susceptibility but also the ability of plants to recover from pest damage (Meyer, 2000). Nitrogen content in leaves has been found higher to be when plants received ammonium nitrate compared with those treated with organic fertilizers (Barker, 1975). The nutrient content and chemical composition of plants grown under conventional practices appears to differ from those grown under organic farming practices (Brodbeck et al., 2001; Eggert and Kahrmann, 1984; Lockeretz et al., 1981; Schuphan, 1974; Slansky and Rodriguez, 1987). Crops grown with organic practices have lower foliage nitrate–nitrogen content and are less susceptible to damage by some pests. Pimentel and Warneke (1989) proposed that differences in pest risk potential are due to differences in pest behavior related to variations in host nutrient content. Scriber's (1984) literature review suggested that crop plants maintained under organic farming practices would be less susceptible to pest damage. This hypothesis was supported by the plant hopper research of Kajimura (1995), European corn borer [*Ostrinia nubilalis* (Hübner)] research by Phelan et al. (1995), and research on cabbage aphids [*Brevicoryne brassicae* (L.)] and flea beetles (*Brassica oleracea* L.) associated with broccoli (*Brassica oleracea* L. var. *botrytis* L.) by Altieri et al. (1998). Although there have been studies that do not support the above hypothesis (Culliney and Pimentel, 1986; Letourneau, 1988; Letourneau et al., 1996), it must be remembered that the organic certification process takes three years and that soil-quality enhancement continues over a much longer time. In organic apple research (G.W. Bird, unpublished data, 1998–2006), soil quality did not stabilize until the seventh year after the beginning of the transition process. Future research must take as many aspects as possible into consideration concerning the dynamics of soil biology and plant chemistry.

Once a site is infested with a specific pest, it is important to contain the organism in that location. There are many tactics available, but most consist of common sense. For example, if a site is known to be infested with a key soilborne pathogen, it is always best to not work this area and then take contaminated equipment to a noninfested area. This management option includes working the noninfested site first or making sure the equipment is completely washed before moving to the high-quality site. Eradication is often not possible, and risk reduction can be a long-term and complicated process.

Although the control strategy of pest management contains physical, chemical, genetic, cultural, and regulatory options, cultural tactics are by far the most important in organic agriculture. The two cultural practices of greatest importance are soil quality–health enhancement and crop rotation. Both need to be based on the broader concept of overall ecosystem diversity. To be successful, this must be considered a multiyear process. The recommendations of Ogden (1992) for organic vegetable gardening illustrate the complexity of organic management.

In a systems approach, practices need to be integrated with variety selection, seed and seedling purchases, site selection, site preparation, timing of planting, cultivation, irrigation, mulching, composting, row covers, harvesting techniques, *example would be helpful here* storage options, and food preparation procedures. In a course taught by senior author G.W. Bird, it is always interesting to see the students' responses to a DVD showing that some of the organisms we consider as pests are successfully used as food delicacies in some societies. Finding a beneficial or value-added use for a pest is always an option.

In his environmental message to Congress on 2 Aug. 1979, president and peanut farmer Jimmy Carter indicated that pesticides should only be used in a systems approach when other practices such as biological control agents, resistant varieties, and environmental modifications are inadequate. As students of organic agriculture are aware, only those pesticides and pesticide formulations approved by a producer's certifier or an organization like OMRI are available for use without compromising a farm's organic certification. Even pesticides cleared for use in organic agriculture are designed to kill or alter the behavior of living organisms. In any ecosystem, use of an external input guarantees many matter and energy transformations among the various levels of the numerous food webs. These often lead to unintended consequences.

In both IPM associated with conventional agriculture and pest management for organic systems, it is often best to implement the fourth strategy: do nothing. If this is done in a conscientious way, it can be guaranteed that the ecosystem will respond to the right management decision. With appropriate biological and environmental monitoring information, this can often be the best short-term and long-term approach.

Sustaining Success at the Summit

There are two components to the final step of *Climbing Mt. Organic* in relation to pest management. The first relates to farmer-to-farmer education and farmer to student education. The only way to truly learn organic pest management is through firsthand experience. This can be accomplished through (i) years of personal trial and error, (ii) working closely with successful organic farmers, (iii) visiting successful organic farms and having meaningful dialog with the farmer, or (iv) more realistically, a combination of all three. Although the organic farmers that have reached the summit of Mt. Organic have done so through years of hard work and experimentation, most are willing teachers. They are interested in sharing their wealth of organic agriculture experiences. In many cases, this will be the group of individuals that when asked, "What are your pest problems"? the answer will be that they do not have any key pest issues. This is a more frequent response from agronomic grain growers than from organic vegetable and fruit producers. In these later cases, one or two key pests are still limiting or stress-creating factors in organic systems. There are organic farming operations, however, where these issues have been resolved, and farmer-to-farmer education is a big part of the solution. Students of organic agriculture should take every opportunity to visit both highly successful and less-successful organic farms. Students should also attend the organic conferences sponsored by various organic agriculture organizations. It is the overall ecosystem approach to organic agriculture that provides the appropriate strategies for overcoming pest challenges, even with the paradox of not having the words pest and weed in the language of ecology.

The second aspect of sustaining success at the summit relates to organic farmers who have reached this level of working with nature in their farming systems. These farmers fully realize that ecosystems are dynamic and constantly changing. In addition to continuing whatever practices have been used to achieve success, these growers understand that for continued success, they must also change. The fundamentals of biological and environmental monitoring must be used to continually assess the current state of their organic farming system. Although management decisions must be based on the ecosystem monitoring information, this is not enough. To remain at the summit, it is imperative to continue to engage in farmer-to-farmer education initiatives. In the words of the fifth-century BCE Greek historian, Herodotus of Halicarnassus: "Human prosperity never abides long in the same place" (Herodotus, 2004).

Discussion Questions

1.   Discuss the characteristics of organic farming systems in terms of ecological structure and function. How do these systems differ from conventional farming systems?

2.   Describe the complexity and diversity of trophic levels in organic farming systems as compared to natural ecosystems. In what specific ways do they differ in resilience and sustainability?

3.   Describe and differentiate among plant health, plant injury, and plant disease. How do you define and differentiate among different disease symptoms, and how are these used to diagnose plant diseases?

4.   Describe the general characteristics of viruses, bacteria, fungi, and nematodes. Describe and discuss the effects of arthropods, parasitic plants, and vertebrate pests.

5.   In what specific ways is a systems approach essential in managing pests in an organic farming system? How does organic pest management differ from that used in conventional farming systems?

6.   How does the organic farm plan for certification take into account pest management as one of the key components? Why is it necessary to plan ahead in organic pest management, compared with the curative approach used in conventional farming?

7.   In what ways can efficiency of pest management input use, substitution of one product or strategy for another, and redesign of systems all be used in the design of a comprehensive organic pest management strategy?

8.   What specific methods of pest exclusion and pest avoidance can be used in organic farming systems?

9.   Describe some of the physical, chemical, genetic, cultural, and regulatory methods that can be used by the organic farmer in planning a pest management strategy.

10. In what ways is pest management more difficult in organic farming systems? Once an ecological balance with pest species is achieved in the system, what are the strategies an organic farmer can use to maintain profitable yields while keep pests at an acceptable level?

11. What are the most difficult pests to manage in an organic farming system, and why are they difficult?

References

Altieri, M.A., and C.I. Nicholls. 2003. Soil fertility management and insect pests: Harmonizing soil and plant health in agroecosystems. Soil Tillage Res. 72:203–211.

Altieri, M.A., L.L. Schmidt, and R. Montalba. 1998. Assessing the effects of agroecological soil management practices on broccoli insect pest populations. Biodynamics 218:23–26.

Barker, A. 1975. Organic vs. inorganic nutrition and horticultural crop quality. HortScience 10:12–15.

Bird, G.W., and M. Brewer. 2006. Integrated pest management, eco-literacy and unexpected consequences. p. 25–50. In C.A. Francis, C.R. Poincelot, and G.W. Bird (ed.) A new social contract: Developing and extending sustainable agriculture. Haworth Press, Binghampton, NY.

Brodbeck, B., J. Stavisky, J. Funderburk, P. Andersen, and S. Olsen. 2001. Flower nitrogen status and populations of *Frankliniella occidentalis* feeding on *Lycopersicon esculentum*. Entomol. Exp. Appl. 99:165–172.

Capra, F. 1996. The web of life: A new scientific understanding of living systems. Anchor Books, Doubleday, New York.

Culliney, T., and D. Pimentel. 1986. Ecological effects of organic agricultural practices in insect populations. Agric. Ecosyst. Environ. 15:253–256.

Dugan, F.M. 2005. The identification of fungi: An illustrated introduction with keys, glossary, and guide to literature. Am. Phytopathogical Soc., St. Paul, MN.

Eggert, F.P., and L. Kahrmann. 1984. Responses of three vegetable crops to organic and inorganic nutrient sources. p. 85–94. In D. Bezdicek and J.F. Power (ed.) Organic farming: Current technology and its role in sustainable agriculture. ASA Spec. Publ. 46. ASA, Madison, WI.

Electronic Code of Federal Regulations. 2009. Title 7 (Agriculture), part 205 (National Organic Program), subpart E (Certification), section 205.400-b (Organic Farm Plan). U.S. Government, Washington, D.C.

Heckman, J., J., R. Weil, and F. Magdoff. 2009. Practical steps to soil fertility for organic agriculture. p. 139–172. In C. Francis (ed.) Organic farming: The ecological system. Agron. Monogr. 54. ASA, CSSA, and SSSA, Madison, WI. (This volume.)

Herodotus. 2004. The histories. Trans. G. Macaulay. Barnes & Noble Classics, New York.

Howard, A. 1943. An agricultural testament. Oxford Univ. Press, London.

Hull, R. 2002. Matthews' plant virology. 4th ed. Academic Press. San Diego, CA.

Kajimura, T. 1995. Effect of organic rice farming on planthoppers: Reproduction of white backed planthopper, *Sogatella furcifera* (Homoptera: Delphacidae). Res. Popul. Ecol. 37:219–224.

Lampkin, N. 1990. Organic farming. Farming Press Books. Ipswitch, UK.

Lee, D.L. 2002. The biology of nematodes. Taylor and Francis Publ., New York.

Letourneau, D.K. 1988. Soil management for pest control; a critical appraisal of the concepts. p. 581–587. In Proc. Sixth Int. Science Conf. of IFOAM: Global Perspectives on Agroecology and Sustainable Agricultural Systems, Santa Cruz, CA.

Letourneau, D.K., L.F. Drinkwater, and C. Shennon. 1996. Effects of soil management on crop nitrogen and insect damage in organic versus conventional tomato fields. Agric. Ecosyst. Environ. 57:174–187.

Liebman, M., and A.S. Davis. 2009. Managing weeds in organic farming systems: An ecological approach. p. 173–196. In C. Francis (ed.) Organic farming: The ecological system. Agron. Monogr. 54. ASA, CSSA, and SSSA, Madison, WI. (This volume.)

Lockeretz, W., G. Shearer, and D.H. Kohl. 1981. Organic farming in the corn belt. Science 211:540–546.

Magdoff, F., and H. van Es. 2000. Building soils for better crops. 2nd ed. SARE Outreach, Beltsville, MD.

Merrill, M.C. 1983. Eco-agriculture: A review of its history and philosophy. Biol. Agric. Hortic. 1:181–210.

Matthews, R.E.F. 1992. Fundamentals of plant virology. Academic Press. San Diego, CA.

McGuinness, H. 1993. Living soils: Sustainable alternatives to chemical fertilizers for developing countries. Consumers Policy Inst., New York.

Meyer, G.A. 2000. Interactive effects of soil fertility and herbivory on *Brassica nigra*. Oikos 22:433–441.

Millardet, P.M.A. 1885. The discovery of Bordeau mixture. Phytopathol. Classic 3. Am. Phytopathological Soc., St. Paul, MN.

Oelhaf, R.C. 1978. Organic agriculture. Halstead Press, New York.

Ogden, S. 1992. Step by step organic vegetable gardening. Harper-Collins, New York.

Pedigo, L.P., and M.E. Rice. 2009. Entomology and pest management. 6th ed. Pearson/Prentice Hall, Upper Saddle River, NJ.

Perry, R.N., and M. Moens. 2006. Plant nematology. CABI, Cambridge, MA.

Phelan, P.L., J.F. Mason, and B.R. Stinner. 1995. Soil fertility management and host preference by European corn borer, *Ostrinia nubilalis*, on *Zea mays*: A comparison of organic and conventional chemical farming. Agric. Ecosyst. Environ. 56:1–8.

Pimentel, D., and A. Warneke. 1989. Ecological effects of manure, sewage sludge and other organic wastes on arthropod populations. Agric. Zool. Rev. 3:1–30.

Press, M.C., and J.D. Graves. 1995. Parasitic plants. Chapman and Hall, London.

Quarles, W. 2008. 2009 Directory of least-toxic pest control products. IPM Practitioner 30 (11–12):1–40.

SARE Outreach. 2007. Managing cover crops profitably. 3rd ed. Sare Outreach, Beltsville, MD.

Schadd, N.W., J.B. Jones, and W. Chun. 2001. Laboratory guide for identification of plant pathogenic bacteria. 3rd ed. Am. Phytopathological Soc., St. Paul, MN.

Schumann, G.L., and C.J. D'Arcy. 2006. Essential plant pathology. Am. Phytopathological Soc. Press, St. Paul, MN.

Schuphan, W. 1974. Nutritional value of crops as influenced by organic and inorganic fertilizer treatments. Qual. Plant Foods Hum. Nutr. 23:333–358.

Scriber, J.M. 1984. Nitrogen nutrition of plants and insect invasion. p. 441–460. In J.D. Beaton, C.A.I. Goring, R.D. Hauck, R.G. Hoeft, G.W. Randall, and D.A. Russel (ed.) Nitrogen in crop production. ASA, CSSA, and SSSA, Madison, WI.

Slansky, F. 1990. Insect nutritional ecology as a basis for studying host plant resistance. Fla. Entomol. 73:354–378.

Slansky, F., and J.G. Rodriguez. 1987. Nutritional ecology of insects, mites, spiders and related invertebrates. John Wiley & Sons, New York.

Marketing & Food Systems

10

Organic Marketing

Hikaru H. Peterson and Rhonda R. Janke
Department of Agricultural Economics and Department of Horticulture, Forestry, and Recreation Resources, Kansas State University, Manhattan, Kansas

Organics, once a countercultural movement, is the fastest-growing segment of the global food industry today (FAO, ITC, CTA, 2001). The world market for certified organic foods was estimated at roughly $23,000 million to $25,000 million in 2003 and is growing at 19% per year (Kortbech-Olesen, 2003). The United States constitutes by far the largest national market for organic products, and the growth of its organic market has been strikingly and consistently strong since the 1990s. The average annual growth rate for organic food sales from 1997 to 2005 ranged from 15 to 21%, while the growth of total food sales ranged between 2 and 4%. The organic food industry recorded $16,700 million in sales, representing 2.8% of total U.S. food sales in 2006 (Organic Trade Association, 2007). The $938 million organic nonfood sector, including personal care and household products, supplements, pet food, fiber products, and flowers, represented 0.2% penetration. Consumer surveys show that over two-thirds of U.S. households now buy some organic items compared to less than half four to five years ago (Nutrition Business Journal, 2006).

Underlying such remarkable growth in the organic food market are drastic changes in marketing channels and market participants over the decades. During their humble early days in the 1960s, organic farm products were primarily marketed through small cooperatives and directly from small-scale farms to personalized markets (Guthman, 2004). The organic sector today has been marked with new entrants of large-scale businesses and numerous mergers and buyouts in recent years. A significant share of organic products is now sold through conventional marketing outlets.

Because the organic market, as with any market, will ultimately be determined by consumers, an understanding of their preferences is critical to gain an insight into the future evolution of the organic market. In this chapter, we first review the studies on consumer preferences and purchasing behavior. We then turn our attention to marketing channels and their evolution, followed by a discussion of markets by farm commodity. We conclude by discussing some of the emerging issues that are shaping the future organic food market to identify relevant research questions and challenges.

Consumer Demand

The force behind the remarkable growth of the organic industry is the increasing consumer interest in how the products they consume have been made. An estimated 52 million U.S. consumers (16% of the general population in 2006) are now called *LOHAS* consumers, comprising a growing segment of the economy that is interested in "lifestyles of health and sustainability" (French and Rogers, 2005). They seek out products and services that are designed to be environmentally conscious, sustainable, socially responsible, and healthier for people and the planet.

Historically, organic food production evolved as individuals took on themselves to seek an ecological balance between human health and the health of the soil. Correspondingly, the two most cited reasons for consuming organics up through the 1990s were health and environmental concerns (Dimitri and Richman, 2000). Then, several large-scale food scares involving pesticides such as daminozide (Alar, Uniroyal Chemical Company, Inc.) aroused consumer interest toward safer foods. Consumer concerns about the use of antibiotics and growth hormones in production of animal products have heightened consumer interest toward organic meat, milk, and eggs. A more recent study found that the top-three motivating factors behind organic food purchases have shifted to health and nutrition (66%), taste (38%), and food safety (30%), with the environment fourth (26%) (Hartman Group, 2002), suggesting that consumers new to organics are driven more by personal benefits than by societal benefits. Findings from one of the few studies that have attempted to decompose consumers' preferences toward organic products into disaggregated attributes confirm such a hypothesis (Onozaka, Bunch, and Larson, 2006). Regular organic buyers on average were willing to pay a premium for no pesticide residues, no genetic modification, and the use of environmentally friendly production techniques, while nonregular buyers only valued the absence of pesticide residues. As with any product, some consumers remain skeptical. In a 2006 survey, cost is the most-listed reason why people avoided organic foods (66%), followed by "have never really considered buying" (49%), and "don't believe they are safer" (38%) (Mitchell, 2007).

Many studies conducted a decade ago characterized organic consumers as high-income and well-educated Caucasians (e.g., Thompson, 1998; Richter et al., 2000; Lohr, 2001). The organic consumer segment has since expanded beyond this original base to become a diverse constituency that is not easily characterized. They can no longer be identified by specific income levels or ethnicity groups, with half of the frequent organic food consumers earning below $50,000, and African Americans, Asian Americans, and Hispanics purchasing more organic products than Caucasians (Hartman Group, 2002). Further, organic consumers are most likely in their 20s and 40s (Thompson, 1998; Lohr and Semali, 2000). Instead of demographics, some propose value-based categorization to identify organic consumers, such as the so-called cultural creatives (Ray and Anderson, 2000).

Studies have found positive values for the amounts people are willing to pay for organic products above their conventional counterparts (e.g., Govindasamy and Italia, 1999; Loureiro and Hine, 2002). The critical question is whether such organic premiums, defined as the differences between the organic product prices and the prices of otherwise similar nonorganic products, at all market levels are sufficient to ensure the profitability of the organic market system.

Several organic and conventional prices for selected products at various market levels during the recent years are shown in Table 10–1. The exercise of putting the table together illuminates the paucity of systematically collected price data in the organic markets. Until a few years ago, it was extremely challenging to obtain reliable organic market prices from anywhere, much less publicly available sources. There were intermittent trackings by the USDA, weekly reports from a privately operated Organic Business News (OBN; discontinued in October 2008), the New Farm Organic Price Index from the Rodale Institute (2009), and a few academic studies that used OBN prices in their analyses (e.g., Bertramsen and Dobbs, 2002). While the situation has considerably improved with the recent initiation of the USDA Agricultural Marketing Service reporting organic prices within their routine operations, the observations are still limited to selected items at selected market levels for short, nonconcurrent time periods. The best available data used to compile Table 10–1 lacked observations for milk and beef premiums to gauge any information about their variability over time. It also should be noted that only organic premium calculated from comparable prices at the same point in time and location can be meaningful. It is difficult to tell whether negative premiums reported, for example, for mesculin mix (a combination of specialty lettuces [*Lactuca sativa* L.] with smooth surface textures such as frisee, baby oak, red oak, and baby romaine) during January 2005 and December 2007 are due to aggregation errors.

A quick inspection of Table 10–1 reveals variability in organic premium at different times of the year and across commodities. While in general, the premiums imply the relative maturity of the produce market and demand shortages for animal products (including feed grains), discrepancies within the commodity groups are notable. Within the produce sector, the absolute and relative magnitude of premium is much lower for mesculin mix than for the other crops. Another example is within the grains, where food-grade hard red winter wheat (*Triticum aestivum* L.) commanded much lower premium than feed-grade maize (*Zea mays* L.) or soybean [*Glycine max* (L.) Merr.] in the sample. The shipment data from the Kansas Organic Producers were only available through 2005. Personal contacts and other sources suggest that organic price levels in 2007 and 2008 have been significantly higher than those in the period from 2003 to 2005. Such differences could be attributed to commodity-specific shifts in supply, as is the technical change in the case of mesculin mix, discussed below in the commodity-specific section, or commodity-specific shifts in demand. An example of the latter is the strong export demand from the United States for organic food-grade soybean in the 1980s, which disappeared when Japanese buyers began to seek them from alternative sources such as China.

Two other price or premium patterns are of interest: price behavior over time and patterns of marketing margins, which are differences between prices at different market levels (e.g., farmgate, wholesale, and retail). Due to commodity-specific market conditions, both patterns must be examined for respective commodity, and generalization of observations is most certainly misleading. Hence to date, such examination is limited by data availability. To illustrate these trends for one specific commodity, we created Fig. 10–1 and 10–2 using nominal prices for fresh carrots (*Daucus carota* subsp. *sativa*), for which farmgate and wholesale prices for organic and conventional items were collected at comparable frequencies.

Table 10–1. Recent organic prices and premiums (in U.S. dollars) for selected items.

Item	Time period†	Units	Organic price			Organic premium‡		
			Mean	Min.	Max.	Mean	Min.	Max.
Apples§	Apr. 2005–Dec. 2007	Traypack¶	$46.00	$28.50	$75.00	$17.97 (52.1%)	$3.50 (11.7%)	$55.00 (132.2%)
Strawberries#	Jul. 2005–Nov. 2007	Flat††	$22.02	$10.11	$37.90	$8.63 (65.4%)	$1.33 (15.1%)	$23.66 (166.2%)
Carrots‡‡	Jan. 2005–June 2007	21.8-kg (48-lb) sack	$20.82	$15.75	$30.15	$8.49 (78.5%)	$4.51 (33.5%)	$16.71 (124.3%)
Mesculin mix#	Jan. 2005–Dec. 2007	1.4-kg (3-lb) carton	$7.79	$6.58	$13.40	$1.17 (18.7%)	$-0.71 (-1.3%)	$1.69 (29.5)
Milk§§	Jan. 2004–Dec. 2004	1.9 L (1/2 gallon)	$4.01			$1.99 (98.0%)		
Feed-grade maize¶¶	Oct. 2003–Nov. 2005	Bushel (25.4 kg)	$4.81	$3.67	$6.30	$2.59 (119.7%)	$0.80 (25.0%)	$4.45 (241.3%)
Feed-grade soybean¶¶	Nov. 2003–July 2005	Bushel (26.2 kg)	$12.20	$11.51	$14.57	$6.11 (115.1%)	$2.08 (21.7%)	$9.11 (172.0%)
Food-grade hard red winter wheat¶¶	June 2003–Dec. 2005	Bushel (26.2 kg)	$5.97	$4.00	$6.75	$1.02 (31.4%)	$0.50 (14.6%)	$2.57 (84.6%)
Poultry##	Jan. 2005–Dec. 2007	Pound (0.45 kg)	$2.19	$2.17	$2.21	$1.49 (212.8%)	$1.39 (169.5%)	$1.62 (274.6%)
Eggs##	Jan. 2005–Dec. 2007	Dozen	$2.35	$2.34	$2.37	$1.59 (244.5%)	$0.84 (54.9%)	$1.91 (444.2%)
Beef†††	Mar. 2008–June 2008	Pound (0.45 kg)	$5.72			$2.07 (56.7%)		

† Only for months where observations were available.

‡ The organic price minus the corresponding conventional price. The numbers in parentheses are the differences as percentages of the conventional price. All prices are nominal.

§ Wholesale prices at San Francisco, CA, for Fuji, Washington extra fancy (USDA Economic Research Service, 2008b).

¶ One carton traypack contains 72 pieces.

Wholesale prices at Boston, MA (USDA Economic Research Service, 2008b).

†† One flat contains eight 0.45-kg (1-lb) containers with lids.

‡‡ U.S. farmgate prices. Organic prices obtained from Organic Business News and conventional prices from USDA Economic Research Service (2008b).

§§ National average retail price based on Nielsen Homescan data (Dimitri and Venezia, 2007, Table 4).

¶¶ Prices received by producers. Organic prices from Kansas Organic Producers shipment data (Heiman and Peterson, 2008); conventional prices from USDA Economic Research Service (2008b).

Prices received by first handler (≈ wholesale prices) (USDA Economic Research Service, 2008b).

††† National average retail price from FreshLook Marketing (Beef Retail, 2008). The organic and conventional prices reflect natural and organic beef combined and all beef, respectively.

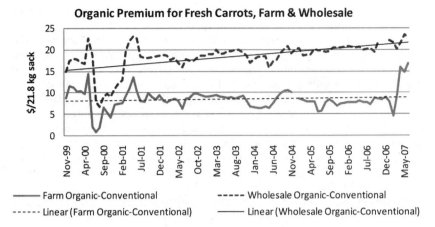

Fig. 10–1. Organic premium for fresh carrots, farm and wholesale. Information computed from USDA Economic Research Service (2008).

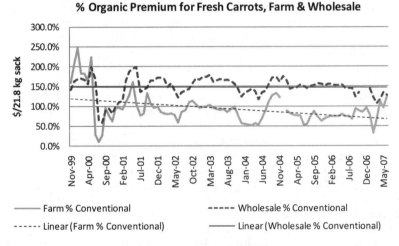

Fig. 10–2. Organic premium as percentage of conventional prices for fresh carrots, farm and wholesale. Information computed from USDA Economic Research Service (2008).

Differences between organic and conventional prices at the farmgate and wholesale over time are shown in Fig. 10–1. The wholesale premium increased, while the farmgate premium remained constant, suggesting an increase in the marketing margin that likely reflected the increase in transportation costs over the sample period. Figure 10–2 depicts the organic premium in percentages relative to conventional prices. In relative terms, the wholesale premium stayed constant, while the farmgate premium declined over time. It should be noted that while the figures suggest that the conventional prices for fresh carrots increased relatively faster than the corresponding organic prices, an opposite time trend was observed for broccoli (*Brassica oleracea* L. gp. Italica) over the same time period, again cautioning against any generalization.

Corresponding costs must be assessed appropriately to determine whether these price premiums are sufficient to ensure profitability of the organic food system at every level. Several existing studies focused on the farm level and reported that organic cropping systems are at least as profitable as conventional cropping systems (Welsh, 1999; Mahoney et al., 2001; see Greene and Kremen, 2003, for reviews of other studies). However, it is challenging to enumerate all possible costs specific to organic operations. For example, the potential difficulty of marketing certain crops used in the cropping rotation should be accounted for. Grain growers must pay for and/or manage the on-farm storage of the grain before sale and manage the risk of contamination on and off the farm (Born, 2005). For poultry farmers, costs may differ from conventional counterparts due to smaller flocks, higher mortality, longer production cycles for broilers, and shorter production cycles for laying hens.

Other key pieces of information regarding consumer demand are elasticities of demand, which measure how demand responds to changes in the price of the good or of related goods or in how much the consumers spend on food overall. These elasticities are critical in predicting sales and policy implications. For example, if the demand for a specific organic item is own-price elastic—that is, when the price of an item decreases, quantity demanded increases proportionally more than the price decrease—the overall sales will grow by lowering the price. Yet, data availability has led to the paucity of the estimated demand elasticities for organic foods.

The recently available scanner sale and household data permit econometric demand analysis for organic foods. However, these data are rather expensive and are not available for most bulk products such as fresh fruit and vegetables, which constitute the largest category of organic foods. Currently available studies have found demand for frozen organic vegetables (broccoli, green beans [*Phaseolus vulgaris* L.], green peas [*Pisum sativum* L.], and sweet corn), organic milk, organic baby food, fresh fruit (apple [*Malus domestica* Borkh], banana [*Musa* L.], grape [*Vitis* L.], orange [*Citrus* × *sinensis* (L.) Osbeck], and strawberry [*Fragaria* × *ananassa* Duchesne]), and fresh vegetables (potato [*Solanum tuberosum* L.] and tomato [*Solanum lycopersicum* L.]) to be highly elastic to their own prices, much more so than their conventional counterparts (Glaser and Thompson, 1998; 2000; Thompson and Glaser, 2001; Zhang et al., 2006; Lin et al., 2008); demand for fresh organic onions (*Allium cepa* L.) and lettuce was less own-price elastic than their conventional counterparts (Zhang et al., 2006). The limited available data illustrate both the complexity and the dynamic nature of organic markets.

Distribution Channels

Traditional Outlets

Traditionally, marketing of organic farm products has been direct to consumers and small scale. Direct marketing is an attractive option for small- to medium-scale farms, allowing them to receive retail-level prices with relatively low marketing costs. A recent survey of growers in the Kansas River Valley (corresponding roughly to a 10-county region in northeastern Kansas) who reported earning an average gross farm receipts less than $25,000, found that larger percentages of these growers used direct outlets, including farmers' markets (66.7%), roadside stands, and farm stores (26.0%), and restaurants (26.0%), than those using cooperatives (3.6%) and wholesale buyers, brokers, or packers (8.3%). The survey was administered in November 2007, with 15% growers responding (Peterson et al., 2008). The mailing list was constructed to focus on growers who were likely to participate in direct market outlets due to their membership in local farmers' market associations. The list also included members of Kansas and Missouri fruit and vegetable associations, and multiple responses were allowed in the particular question regarding marketing outlets. According to the National Organic Standards Board, farms with less than $5,000 gross sales of organic production may market their products as organic under the small-farm exclusion rule, as long as they are following the guidelines that certified organic farms follow. Farms with more than $5,000 in gross sales must be certified to use the word *organic*.

It was less than three decades ago that the concept of open-air trading areas became popularized in the United States as farmers' markets. As of 2008, there were 4685 farmers markets operated in the United States, averaging over 7% annual growth since 1994 (USDA Agricultural Marketing Service, 2008). They started largely as places for people with large gardens to sell their excess produce, sometimes at bargain rates, and have evolved into sophisticated multimillion-dollar sales opportunities for communities of producers to sell not only vegetables and fruit but also frozen or smoked meats, cheeses, honey, eggs, and other value-added food products, and in some markets, crafts and other items. State and local health regulations must be followed, but local markets often form their own organizations with memberships, dues, and bylaws and are self-regulating in terms of space allotment and hours of operation, among other issues. The degree of regulation varies; highly regulated markets with waiting lists of vendors may insist on only locally grown items and perform routine inspections of member farms.

Farmers' markets provide immediate customer feedback, allowing growers to test the market with minimal investment. Some market organizations help cover the cost of liability insurance for the market location. They may also handle sales tax receipts and reporting, saving each grower from registering with the state. Some issues include the variability of customer base and frequency of the market, which may not be sufficient for growers expanding the scale of their production, and pricing. Some small-scale growers only intending to sell excess products may unknowingly undercut the price for other vendors. Some vendors sell locally grown products only, while others may bring in items purchased at wholesale from outside the area, which could similarly undercut the price for others.

Another common direct outlet is community-supported agriculture (CSA), which began as the Japanese *teikei* movement in 1971, aimed to provide "food with the farmer's face on it" to consumers. In the United States, farms in New England first adopted the model in 1986. By 1996 there were about 600 CSA projects involving at least 100,000 consumers, and in 2007, there were an estimated 1700 CSAs (Henderson and Van En, 2007).

The original CSA model involved a pool of consumers paying for their "shares" at the beginning of the growing season, sharing in the work and the yield risk. In return, they received a weekly allotment, or share of the harvest from the farm, divided among the members. Payment methods may still include an upfront payment, but more CSAs are opting for weekly or monthly payments, either at a flat rate or based on the produce in the bag that week or month. The connection to the farm remains the big draw, and a farm newsletter, recipes for new or unusual vegetables, and farm visits or picnics are part of most CSAs. Some grocery stores offer pseudo-CSAs, where items from local sources are bagged to be picked up once a week (e.g., Balls Food Store, http://www.henhouse. com/cnt/BFBL_GrowersAllianceCSA.html [verified 22 July 2009]).

Advantages of the CSA model for the grower include receiving all or part of the payment up front and having the weekly sales volume guaranteed. The CSA model also partners growers with consumers who are committed to sharing risk and often willing to play an active role in organizing the logistics and payments. At the same time, having a ready market for a known quantity could be a burden for growers. In case of a crop failure, growers may feel obligated to buy produce from other growers to fill their orders. To guarantee sufficient supply, they may overplant or salvage crops that would be better plowed in and replanted (see interview with Jon Cherniss in Janke, 2008). To have a continuous supply, they may make successive plantings that extend beyond the optimal growing conditions, thus increasing their risk exposure.

In addition to farmers markets and CSAs, other direct outlets include selling directly to restaurants, food-buying clubs, food cooperatives, and grocery stores. In some cases, schools and other institutions such as senior centers and hospitals have explored buying foods directly from nearby farmers. These direct methods entail time to develop relationship and to communicate specific quality requirements with volume variability.

These traditional outlets continue to thrive and provide critical outlets for many small growers in today's organic market, although the share of organic products marketed through them has declined continuously. Farmers' markets accounted for 3.5%, while food service purchases of organic food accounted for 3.3% of sales in 2005. The Organic Trade Association (2006) publication (citing 2005 data) did not categorize CSAs as a distinct outlet but likely included them as part of the "other" category called "boutique/specialty," which made up 0.4% of sales. Direct-market outlets such as the Internet and mail order only accounted for 0.2% of sales each (Organic Trade Association, 2006).

Recent Developments

Notable changes have appeared in the structures of the U.S. organic food system over the past decade. Throughout the system, the participants have grown in size through acquisitions and mergers, and larger shares of organic products are handled by the conventional firms that have newly extended their operations into the organic sector (see Howard, 2008, for a graphic illustration of the changes in the organic industry structure).

At the producer level, for instance, Aurora Organic Dairy (Boulder, CO) and Dean Foods (Horizon Organics, Dallas, TX) operate as factory dairy farms with as many as 10,000 cows, in contrast to family-scale farms that typically milk 50 to 70 cows (Kastel, 2006). Large-scale, agrofood corporations such as Heinz (Pittsburgh, PA), Gerber (Florham Park, NJ), and General Mills (Minneapolis, MN) have become major players in the organic food supply network (Krissoff, 1998; Rowan, 2000). While wholesaling of organic produce remains highly fragmented and competitive—the largest player being Albert's Organics (Bridgeport, NJ) with approximately 12% share of the market—the overall natural foods sector is practically dominated by a single firm; United Natural Foods (Dayville, CT) boasts about 95% share of the nonperishable organic food market (T. Green, personal communication, 2008).

The most notable changes are occurring at the retail level. Before the late 1990s, organic food was sold almost exclusively in natural product stores. This has been changing over the greater part of the last decade, with the entry of conventional and mainstream retailers. Only 24% of organic food sales were through independent natural food stores and cooperatives in 2007, a shift from earlier years—it was 68% in 1991 (Dimitri and Venezia, 2007)—when these stores were the dominant source of organic foods. Other natural food retail outlets accounted for an additional 24% of organic food sales in 2005 (Organic Trade Association, 2006) and have been subjected to the forces of consolidation. What were more than 13 natural food retail companies in the 1990s has now consolidated into 3, as Whole Foods (Austin, TX) completed the purchase of Wild Oats in 2008. Mainstream distributors such as Safeway (Pleasanton, CA) and Kroger (Cincinnati, OH) have dramatically extended the availability of organic products. In 2005 roughly 46% of total organic food dollar volume was sold through the mass-market channel, including supermarkets, conventional grocery stores, mass merchandisers, and club stores (Organic Trade Association, 2006).

Commodity-Specific Markets

Produce

Fruits and vegetables make up the largest category of the organic foods purchased, representing 40% of organic food sales in 2006 (Organic Trade Association, 2007). Along with dairy, nondairy beverages, and baby food products, produce is referred to as the *gateway* product that introduces many consumers to organic foods (Dimitri and Oberholtzer, 2006). Correspondingly, the organic penetration rate throughout the marketing chain is the highest among those farm products. For example, as of 2005, organic acreage of fruits and vegetables comprised 3.4% of total acreage of fruits and vegetables in the United States, compared with the overall rate of organic cropland and pasture at 0.5% (USDA Economic Research Service, 2008a).

A major development in the organic produce sector during the mid-1990s was the "salad mix boom." Due to mechanization, competition, consolidation, and new technology in packaging, bagged salad mixes fell from about $7 lb^{-1} ($15.40 kg^{-1}) in the 1980s to about $2 lb^{-1} ($4.40 kg^{-1}) in the mid-1990s (Fromartz, 2006). The scale of large organic salad mix companies such as Natural Selection Foods (San Juan Bautista, CA), with brands such as Earthbound Farm, favors contracting with large-scale growers at prices that can undercut the prices of smaller-scale competitors while making organic salads accessible to more consumers. Consolidation can also lead to large-scale food safety nightmares, even in organic foods, as exemplified by the 2006 outbreak of *Escherichia coli* O157:H7 in spinach (*Spinacia oleracea* L.), which sickened individuals in 26 U.S. states and was eventually traced to the south processing plant of Natural Selection Foods.

Dairy

Dairy represented 16% of organic food sales in 2006 (Organic Trade Association, 2007). Since the mid-1990s, organic milk sales have increased to exceed $1,000 million in 2005 or an estimated 6% of total milk and cream sales (Dimitri and Venezia

2007). In 2006 overall sales of dairy products were $2600 million (Organic Trade Association, 2007). Despite a 575% increase from 1997, organic dairy cows in 2005 comprised only 0.96% of the U.S. herd (USDA Economic Research Service, 2008a).

As of May 2007, two main suppliers provide approximately 75% of the country's branded organic milk: Horizon and Organic Valley (LaFarge, WI), the latter an independent cooperative, primarily farmer–producer owned, founded in 1988. Horizon has produced organic dairy products since 1992 and was acquired by Dean Foods Company in 2004. A third firm, Aurora Organic Dairy, began processing private-label organic milk in 2003. Private-label organic milk made up 10% of organic milk purchases in 2004 (Dimitri and Venezia, 2007). This is in contrast to conventional milk, with more than 100 brands and no individual brand capturing more than 1% of the market. It is anticipated that the presence of private label organic milk will increase in the future.

Another trend that is capturing consumer interest is local milk, often in glass bottles and sometimes with home delivery services. Many of these dairies face difficulties obtaining sufficient organic feed, or have other reasons for not taking the step to organic certification, but attract customers through word of mouth, articles about the farm in local newspapers, and name recognition. Given that production-enhancing hormones are naturally found in milk, it is difficult to market milk under "hormone-free" or "produced without rBGH (bovine growth hormone)" labels, which are considered to be illegal claims in some states.

Grains

Breads and grains represented 10% of all organic sales in 2005 and 2006 but experienced growth in those years of 19 and 23%, respectively, above the growth for organic foods in general, which was 16 and 21% (Organic Trade Association, 2007). Consumer groups in the 1970s focused on this sector of the market, with local buying clubs, the precursors to many of today's independent food co-ops, seeking out sources of natural "brown" foods as an alternative to processed "white" foods (Belasco, 1993). Reflecting an industrial pursuit of economies of scale in grain production during the last century, organic grains and beans represent a low penetration rate of 0.35 and 0.2% of the respective acreage in the nation (USDA Economic Research Service, 2008a). The rates vary across crops, ranging from 0.09% of sorghum [*Sorghum bicolor* (L.) Moench] to 3.11% of dry pea and lentil (*Lens culinaris* Medikus) acreage.

Given the challenge of accessing market information for grains, many growers have opted to join marketing cooperatives. In a nationwide survey of organic grain producers, 72.5% of the respondents identified cooperatives as sources of price information, in contrast to 23.9% indicating that they marketed though cooperatives, either through contract before harvest or after harvest (Peterson and Kastens, 2006). Marketing cooperatives for grains could be in several shapes. Some are "non–brick and mortar," providing strictly marketing services. At the beginning of a crop year, members contract their production to the cooperative to be marketed. The cooperative may or may not obtain possession of the grain. The cooperative maintains inventory of planted acres between planting and harvest and of stored grain after harvest and receives sale offers. If members have retained the ownership of the grain, they decide whether to accept the offer; otherwise, the cooperative decides on the offer. The cooperative handles payment and delivery for agreed transactions and collects a fixed percentage of sales revenue as marketing fees. Other marketing cooperatives own cleaning and processing facilities.

Even the marketing cooperatives that handle negotiations and seek buyers on behalf of their members have limited market information. To improve the transparency of the market in the United States, several cooperatives have formed an alliance to exchange market information. Organic Farmers' Agency for Relationship Marketing (OFARM) was established in 2002 by seven marketing cooperatives to coordinate the efforts of producer marketing groups to benefit and sustain organic producers. Now representing growers from 19 states, member cooperatives meet bimonthly to exchange market information and to establish target price levels to prevent undercutting. This organization also allows members to pool contracts to meet large orders (http://ofarm.org/ [verified 22 July 2009]).

Poultry and Eggs

Meats had the smallest market share among organic food sales in the United States (2%), behind snack foods (5%) and sauces (2.4%), but enjoyed the fastest growth rates of sale of 55% in 2005 and 29% in 2006 (Organic Trade Association, 2007). One reason for this delayed growth of the organic meat sector relative to the others is because there was no legal label for organic meat until 1999, which was followed by a more detailed label in 2002 when the USDA's National Organic Program was enacted. Hence, a large segment of the meat industry has developed under various versions of a "natural" label, which continues today in competition with the organic label.

Within the U.S. organic meat sector, poultry accounted for nearly two-thirds of sales in 2005, or $161 million (Oberholtzer et al., 2006). Sales of broilers account for the majority of the organic poultry sales. Organic egg sales were $161 million in 2005, or 1.2% of organic food sales, up from $140 million in 2004, with an average annual growth rate of 19% between 2000 and 2005. As of 2005, 2.4 million organic layer hens and 10.4 million broilers comprise 0.7% and 0.12% of total flock size in the United States, respectively (USDA Economic Research Service, 2008a).

In contrast to the conventional poultry sector, where about 90% of broilers and eggs are produced under contracts, there is still room for small and medium independent producers in organic broilers and egg production. Data for organic eggs from 2003 shows that the top 5 companies held approximately 55% of the market share, with the top 10 companies being organic and specialty companies (Nutrition Business Journal, 2004).

Organic poultry and egg products compete with other labels both regulated by the USDA and unregulated with no third-party inspection requirement. "Free-range" or "natural" labels are regulated by the USDA. Producers must demonstrate that poultry has been allowed access to the outside for "free-range" or "free-roaming" claims, with no specific requirement for amount of time or stocking density. Products with the "natural" claim must not contain any artificial ingredient or added color and only minimal processing. The phrases "no antibiotics" and "no hormones" may be added to the label if there is sufficient documentation demonstrating that the animals were raised without antibiotics or hormones, respectively. Labels not regulated by the USDA include "cage free," suggesting that poultry (generally layers) were not raised in cages, but not necessarily with access to the outdoors. "Pasture poultry" implies a modified free-range system in which the birds are raised in moveable pens on grass.

Other Meats

Organic beef cows comprised 0.11% of all beef cows in the United States in 2005 (USDA Economic Research Service, 2008a). Combined with natural beef, it represented a small share of total beef retail sales: about 2% of total beef volume and 3% of total sales during the year ending on 29 June 2008 (Beef Retail, 2008).

Although there is a large difference between organic and natural beef in terms of regulations on feed, processing plant, and audit trail, both consumers and some within the beef industry seem to regard these products as nearly identical; the National Cattlemen's Beef Association tracks the sales of these two products combined (Enis, 2007). Like poultry and eggs, the claim "natural" has no firm definition for meat, unless it is accompanied by other terms such as "grass fed" or "antibiotic free."

Organic hogs were 0.02% of the total U.S. herd; organic sheep and lambs were 0.07% of the total U.S. herd in 2005 (USDA Economic Research Service, 2008a). Both of these products, along with beef and poultry, are experiencing growth, but dissaggregated statistics are more difficult to find for these and other minor meats. A search on the LocalHarvest Website (www.localharvest.org) in October 2008 found that quite a few farms are direct marketing beef (1921 farms, 41% are organic), pork (1219 farms, 43% organic), lamb (1145 farms, 35% organic), bison (119 farms, 31% organic), and ostrich (15 farms, 40% organic).

Emerging Issues

The sustainability concept underlying the organic movement maintains profitability for farmers, along with the preservation of the environment and social justice (Gold, 1999). The recent changes in the market structure that are marked primarily by entries of large-scale businesses imply direct economic consequences in the U.S organic food system. A tension that has emerged over the past decade between established organic industry members and new entrants, most notably conventional firms (Dimitri and Oberholtzer, 2006), involves not only philosophical differences but also concerns regarding how economic benefits within the organic sector are distributed among its participants. A nationwide survey of organic grain producers found that one of their major concerns is the entry of large-scale producers and entities into the organic market, compromising the traditional definition of the organics or the sustainability goals (Peterson and Kastens, 2006). Some observers have noted that price premiums for organics have become less stable and decreased in some cases (Dimitri and Oberholtzer, 2006). If so, the share received by smaller players of the growing pie may be shrinking with time.

The issue of social justice regarding whether the farmer or the farm workers receive a living wage was not addressed in the development of organic standards. In Europe, the International Federation of Organic Movements (IFOAM) has been revising their certification guidelines. The USDA National Organic Program has not taken up this issue, but private nonprofit organizations such as Rural Advancement Foundation International (RAFI) have, and farmers can apply for a "local" and a "fair trade" label through their program (http://www.rafiusa.org/programs/justfoods.html [verified 22 July 2009]). Also, the concept of "value-based food supply chain" businesses, which emphasizes transparency and the need for each player at each point in the chain to make a profit, is receiving more attention. Relative to the non–value-chain models, these businesses seem to formulate longer-term contractual relationships with partner organizations at other levels of the value chain (Hoshide, 2007). Opportunities and barriers for advancement on this aspect of organic businesses should be explored further.

Another marked trend in the organic market has been an increase in imports, suggesting that domestic producers need to be cognizant of the competition and opportunities they face in today's globalized market. Corresponding to the growth in U.S. organic food market, the production of organic foods elsewhere has been on the rise. In agriculture, the overall certified organic acreage in the United States increased nearly 3.5-fold from 1995 to 2005 to represent 0.5% of total farmland acreage in 2005, while the number of certified organic farms increased 75% over the same decade to reach nearly 8500 in 2005 (USDA Economic Research Service, 2008a). Such rapid expansion of the organic production, however, has failed to keep pace with the growth of the demand for organic products, necessitating outsourcing. While the export markets for U.S. organic commodities have been expanding in Canada, Japan, and the European Union, the United States is now a net importer of organic products. The value of U.S. imports of organic commodities was estimated to be $1000 million to $1500 million in 2002 and exceeded exports by a ratio of approximately 8 to 1 (USDA Foreign Agricultural Service, 2005).

Many organic manufacturers are reported to be facing shortages in dairy ingredients, cocoa, grains, and nuts among others (Nutrition Business Journal, 2006). For example, Whole Foods peanut butter is made from organic peanuts (*Arachis hypogaea* L.) from China due to lack of domestic supply (T. Green, personal communication, 2008). When the demand for conventional commodities is strong, it is challenging to offer sufficient economic incentives for conventional growers to switch to organics. The origin of ingredients is typically not labeled for consumers, and an unknown question is which consumers, if any, would care enough to pay for such information and to distinguish domestic organics from imported counterparts.

Tropical products and counter-seasonal fresh produce from the Southern Hemisphere are also the top items imported by the United States. In conventional retail outlets, consumers expect year-round offering of fresh produce staples; such expectations drive these outlets and their competing large-scale natural outlets to supplement domestic supply with imported supply to meet the expectations. Counter-seasonal fresh produce has arguably helped sales of U.S. organic produce by providing such continuity. To date, no evidence suggests that imports have cannibalized the domestic sales (T. Green, personal communication, 2008), but the extent of overlapping market season observed in the conventional sector is likely expected.

Organic is a credence attribute, which is not visibly apparent, and consumers must be informed of its presence. Thus, it will always compete with other labeling schemes and identity preserved systems. Certification systems, ranging from "the farmers' pledge" (no third-party inspection) to other labels of sustainability claims have been developed as alternatives to the more expensive and rigid organic label. Information sources exist to sort out the verifiability of these labels, such as the Consumers Union Website on greener choices (http://www. greenerchoices.org/eco-labels/eco-home.cfm [verified 22 July 2009]). Unless one has online access while shopping, however, the meaning of the various labels encountered at the market may be obscure.

A recent growing interest among consumers is for so-called local foods. The definition of local is not standardized, either among consumers or among retailers and distributors. Some define *local* by a specific distance, either in mileage or driving time, whereas others define it by political boundaries ranging from within the residing counties to a region encompassing neighboring states or to even the entire United States (e.g., Guptill and Wilkins, 2002; Zepeda and Leviten-Reid, 2004; Selfa and Qazi, 2005; Whole Foods Market, 2008; Hartman Group, 2008). Numerous studies seem to indicate consumer demand for locally grown foods (Schneider and Francis, 2005). There is also a branch of literature related to people's preferences toward country of origin labeling (e.g., Peterson and Yoshida, 2004). Local claims could naturally complement organic claims, but when they compete, evidence is too scarce to determine how different consumers value the trade-offs between the two claims.

Impacts of changes affecting overall agriculture on the organic markets cannot be ignored. A major policy initiative in the 2000s was the promotion of biofuels. In response to subsidies for biofuel production, conventional maize and soybean acreage expanded and cannibalized wheat acreage. As more of the harvested grains were diverted away from traditional feed use and toward the biofuels sector, food prices rose to historic highs, raising questions about the sustainability of these policies. The direct impact on the organic sector has been upward pressure on already-high prices for organic grains, which had been rising due to the new demand for organic feed for livestock and poultry. A casual check in April 2008 revealed that organic premiums for these grains were being maintained (Moore, 2008). It remains to be seen how the emphasis on biofuels will evolve under the Obama administration and in light of the global food shortage.

These emerging issues offer ample research opportunities in the area of organic marketing. Other issues will surely arise as the organic market continues to expand, both in the United States and in the world, requiring rigorous explorations to further our knowledge and support the growing industry. Even though the organic sector currently consists of less than 1% of the entire U.S. agriculture, organics have impacted awareness and behavior of more than half of the general population. The foremost limitation to future research is the availability of quality data, and we conclude this chapter with a plea for enriching the organic-related market data.

Good-quality data for relevant economic analysis of an industry or a marketing system consists of systematically collected observations on agricultural production, price, and trade for all major commodities, in addition to information on the makeup of marketing channel constituents. The deficiencies in price and trade data were discussed earlier. Publicly available, current prices promote efficiency in the market by enhancing transparency. Public and private entities can contribute by coordinating to organize the data they collect into informational exchanges. The USDA only began to collect general statistics on the number of organic farms with the 2002 Census (USDA National Agricultural Statistics Service, 2008). Thus, we remain dependent on industry studies and surveys for production data. Complete and current production data, coupled with up-to-date crop enterprise budgets, provide valuable information regarding welfare implications of agricultural-related policies on the organic farming sector. Crop enterprise budgets are also extremely valuable references for current and future organic producers to evaluate their profitability performance relative to their peers.

Marketing in the organic food sector of the total U.S. food system involves a series of complex issues, only some of which are under control of the individual farmer. The organic portion of the entire U.S. food supply remains small but is expanding rapidly, with no signs of its growth slowing. There is still a lack of understanding of what *organic* means in the minds of many consumers, as well as a high level of confusion over the labeling terms used to identify organic products in the marketplace. Challenges to the organic labeling rules by corporations will probably continue, as large industrial model operations attempt to bring their economies of scale and cost-cutting decisions into the organic marketplace. The emergence of interest in local foods, concerns about social dimensions of the production process, and distribution of benefits from the system are issues that will need to be addressed by U.S. society in the near future. The organic segment of the food sector will continue to be a dynamic and complex area for further study, and it is essential that more refined data be collected and made available so that we can better understand the trends and impacts of organic marketing.

Discussion Questions

1. In what specific ways would the organic sector have been better off if it had stayed a small niche market, avoiding the issues associated with growth and industrial model processing and marketing?

2. Of the major trends and issues described in the "emerging issues" section, which do you think are the most important, and why?

3. Discuss the similarities and differences between organic and nonorganic foods and marketing channels. Why are the larger supermarkets important sources of organic foods, and in what ways does this increase accessibility to a greater portion of the population?

4. Discuss the major differences among the various types of organic products in terms of marketing; for example, grains versus processed foods versus meats.

5. Discuss how the small organic market segment of about 1 to 2% could have a wide impact on consumer perception and behavior in the overall food marketplace. Can you provide any other examples of market phenomena in which a small producer movement has had a relatively large impact on consumer behavior or perception?

6. What specific impacts does the industrial and global marketplace for organic foods have on smaller-scale local producers, processors, and retail vendors of organic foods?

References

Beef Retail. 2008. Fresh data shows trend in natural/organic beef category. Available at http://www.beefretail.org/reseNaturalOrganicNicheContinuestoGrow.aspx (verified 17 Aug. 2009). Beef Retail, Centennial, CO.

Belasco, W.J. 1993. Appetite for change: How the counterculture took on the food industry. Cornell Univ. Press, Ithaca, NY.

Bertramsen, S.K., and T.L. Dobbs. 2002. An update on prices of organic crops in comparison to conventional crops. Economic Commentator 426. South Dakota State Univ. Brookings.

Born, H. 2005. Marketing organic grains. ATTRA Publ. CT154. Available at http://attra.ncat.org/attra-pub/PDF/marketingorganicgrains.pdf (verified 22 July 2009). ATTRA National Sustainable Agriculture Information Service, Fayetteville, AR.

Dimitri, C., and L. Oberholtzer. 2006. A brief retrospective on the U.S. organic sector: 1997 and 2003. Crop Manage. doi:10.1094/CM-2006-0921-07-PS.

Dimitri, C., and N. Richman. 2000. Organic food markets in transition. Policy Studies Report 14. Available at http://www.winrock.org/wallace/wallacecenter/documents/pspr14.pdf (verified 22 July 2009). Henry A. Wallace Center for Agricultural and Environmental Policy, Greenbelt, MD.

Dimitri, C., and K.M. Venezia. 2007. Retail and consumer aspects of the organic milk market. Available at http://www.ers.usda.gov/Publications/LDP/2007/05May/LDPM15501/ (verified 22 July 2009). USDA Economic Research Service, Washington, DC.

Enis, M. 2007. Sales up for natural, organic and conventional beef. Supermarket News 55:36.

FAO, ITC, CTA. 2001. World markets for organic fruit and vegetables: Opportunities for developing countries in the production and export of organic horticultural products. Food and Agriculture Organization, International Trade Centre, Technical Centre for Agricultural and Rural Development, Rome.

French, S., and G. Rogers. 2005. LOHAS market research review: Marketplace opportunities abound. Available online at http://www.lohas.com/journal/trends.html (verified 22 July 2009). LOHAS Journal, Louisville, CO.

Fromartz, S. 2006. Organic Inc.: Natural foods and how they grew. Harcourt, New York.

Glaser, L.K., and G.D. Thompson. 1998. Demand for organic and conventional frozen vegetables. In Am. Agricultural Economics Assoc. Annu. Meeting, Nashville, TN. 8–11 Aug. 1998. Am. Agricultural Economics Assoc., Milwaukee, WI.

Glaser, L.K., and G.D. Thompson. 2000. Demand for organic and conventional beverage milk. In Western Agricultural Economics Assoc. Annu. Meeting, Vancouver, BC. 29 June–1 July 2000.

Gold, M.V. 1999. Sustainable agriculture: Definitions and terms. Available at http://www.nal.usda.gov/afsic/AFSIC_pubs/srb9902.htm (verified 22 July 2009). USDA National Agricultural Library, Washington, DC.

Govindasamy, R., and J. Italia. 1999. Predicting willingness to pay a premium for organically grown fresh produce. J. Food Distribution Res. 30:44–53.

Greene, C., and A. Kremen. 2003. U.S. organic farming in 2000–2001: Adoption of certified systems. Agric. Inf. Bull. 780. USDA Economic Research Service, Washington, DC.

Guptill, A., and J.L. Wilkins. 2002. Buying into the food system: Trends in food retailing in the US and implications for local foods. Agric. Human Values 19:39–51.

Guthman, J. 2004. Agrarian dreams: The paradox of organic farming in California. Univ. of California Press, Berkeley.

Hartman Group. 2002. Hartman organic research review: A complication of national organic research conducted by the Hartman Group. Hartman Group, Bellevue, WA.

Hartman Group. 2008. Consumer understanding of buying local. HartBeat, 27 February. Available at http://www.hartman-group.com/hartbeat/2008-02-27 (verified 22 July 2009). Hartman Group, Bellevue, WA.

Heiman, R.D., and H.H. Peterson. 2008. Determinants of premiums received by organic field crop producers. Rev. Agric. Econ. 30(4):729–749.

Henderson, E., and R. Van En. 2007. Sharing the harvest: A citizen's guide to community supported agriculture. Chelsea Green, White River Junction, VT.

Hoshide, A.K. 2007. Values-based and value-added value chains in the Northeast, Upper Midwest, and Pacific Northwest. Draft Report. Available at http://www.agofthemiddle.org/papers/value_chains.pdf (verified 22 July 2009). Ag of the Middle, np.

Howard, P. 2008. Information graphics: Organic industry structure. Available at https://www.msu.edu/~howardp/organicindustry.html (verified 22 July 2009). Michigan State Univ., East Lansing.

Janke, R.R. 2008. Farming in the dark: A discussion about the future of sustainable agriculture. University Readers, San Diego, CA.

Kastel, M.A. 2006. Wal-Mart: The nation's largest grocer rolls-out organic products—Market expansion or market delusion? White Paper. Cornucopia Institute, Cornucopia, WI.

Kortbech-Olesen, R. 2003. Market. In M. Yussefi and H. Willer (ed.) The world of organic agriculture. International Federation of Organic Movements, Tholey-Theley, Germany.

Krissoff, B. 1998. Emergence of U.S. organic agriculture: Can we compete? Discussion. Am. J. Agric. Econ. 80:1130–1133.

Lin, B.-H., S.T. Yen, and C.L. Huang. 2008. Demand for organic and conventional fresh fruits. In Am. Agricultural Economics Assoc. Annu. Meetings, Orlando, FL. 27–29 July 2008. Am. Agricultural Economics Assoc., Milwaukee, WI.

Lohr, L. 2001. Factors affecting international demand and trade in organic food products. p. 67–79. In Anita Regmi (ed.) Changing structure of global food consumption and trade. WRS01-1. USDA Economic Research Service, Washington, DC.

Lohr, L., and A. Semali. 2000. Retailer decision making in organic produce marketing. p. 201–208. In W.J. Florkowski, S.E. Prussia, and R.L. Shewfelt (ed.) Integrated view of fruit and vegetable quality. Technomic, Lancaster, PA.

Loureiro, M., and S. Hine. 2002. Discovering niche market: A comparison of consumer willingness to pay for local (Colorado grown), organic, and GMO-free products. J. Agric. Appl. Econ. 34:477–487.

Mahoney, P.R., K.D. Olson, P.M. Porter, D.R. Huggins, C.A. Perrilo, and K. Crookston. 2001. Risk analysis of organic cropping systems in Minnesota. In Am. Agricultural Economics Assoc. Meeting, Chicago, IL. 5–8 Aug. 2001. Am. Agricultural Economics Assoc., Milwaukee, WI.

Mitchell, R. 2007. Chugging forward. Meat Deli Retainer, Oct.–Nov., p. 24–29.

Moore, R.T. 2008. Organic transition schemes for a Morris County, Kansas grain farm. Master's thesis. Kansas State University, Manhattan.

Nutrition Business Journal. 2004. NBJ's organic food report 2004. Penton Media, San Diego, CA.

Nutrition Business Journal. 2006. NBJ's organic foods report 2006. Penton Media, San Diego, CA.

Oberholtzer, L., C. Greene, and E. Lopez. 2006. Organic poultry and eggs capture high price premiums and growing share of specialty markets. Amberwaves. USDA Economic Research Service, Washington, DC.

Onozaka, Y., D. Bunch, and D. Larson. 2006. What exactly are they paying for? Decomposing the price premium for organic fresh produce of heterogeneous consumers. Working Paper. Univ. of California, Davis, Dep. Agric. Resource Econ, Davis, CA.

Organic Trade Association. 2006. U.S. organic industry overview. Available at http://www.ota.com/pics/documents/short%20overview%20MMS.pdf (verified 22 July 2009). Organic Trade Assoc., Greenfield, MA.

Organic Trade Association. 2007. Executive summary: Organic Trade Association's 2007 manufacturer survey conducted by Packaged Facts. Available at http://www.ota.com/pics/documents/2007ExecutiveSummary.pdf (verified 22 July 2009). Organic Trade Assoc., Greenfield, MA.

Peterson, H.H., R.R. Janke, T. Selfa, and P. Garfinkel. 2008. Understanding growers' needs to supply locally in the Kansas River Valley. In Local Ag Research Meeting, Kansas City, MO. 14 July 2008.

Peterson, H.H., and T.L. Kastens. 2006. Organic grain farming in the United States: Report of the findings from a nationwide survey: Part I. Summary of survey responses. In Proc. of the 2006 Risk and Profit Conf., Manhattan, KS. 17–18 Aug. 2006. Dep. of Agricultural Economics, Kansas State Univ., Manhattan.

Peterson, H.H., and K. Yoshida. 2004. Quality perceptions and willingness to pay for imported rice in Japan. J. Agric. Appl. Econ. 36:123–141.

Ray, P.H., and S.R. Anderson. 2000. The cultural creatives: How 50 million people are changing the world. Harmony Books, New York.

Richter, T., O. Schmid, B. Freyer, D. Halpin, and R. Vetter. 2000. Organic consumer in supermarkets: New consumer group with different buying behavior and demands. p. 542–545. In T. Alfödi, W. Lockeretz, and U. Niggli (ed.) Proc. of the 13th IFOAM Scientific Conf., Zurich. vdf Hochschulverlag, Zurich.

Rowan, C. 2000. Sourcing organic and non-GM ingredients. Food Eng. Int. 25:28–31.

Schneider, M.L., and C.A. Francis. 2005. Marketing locally produced foods: Consumer and farmer opinions in Washington County, Nebraska. Renewable Agric. Food Syst. 20:252–260.

Selfa, T., and J. Qazi. 2005. Place, taste or face-to-face? Understanding producer-consumer metworks in "local" food systems in Washington State. Agric. Human Values 22:451–464.

Thompson, G. 1998. Consumer demand for organic foods. Am. J. Agric. Econ. 80:1113–1118.

Thompson, G.D., and L. Glaser. 2001. National demand for organic and conventional baby food. In Western Agricultural Economics Assoc. Annu. Meetings, Logan UT. 9–11 July 2001.

USDA Agricultural Marketing Service. 2008. Farmers market growth: 1994–2008. Available at http://www.ams.usda.gov/AMSv1.0/ams.fetchTemplateData.do?template=TemplateS&navID=WholesaleandFarmersMarkets&leftNav=WholesaleandFarmersMarkets&page=WFMFarmersMarketGrowth&description=Farmers%20Market%20Growth&acct=frmrdirmkt (verified 22 July 2009). USDA Agricultural Marketing Service, Washington, DC.

USDA Economic Research Service. 2008a. Organic production. Available at http://www.ers.usda.gov/Data/Organic/ (verified 22 July 2009). USDA Economic Research Service, Washington, DC.

USDA Economic Research Service. 2008b. Organic prices. Available at http://www.ers.usda.gov/data/OrganicPrices/ (verified 22 July 2009). USDA Economic Research Service, Washington, DC.

USDA Foreign Agricultural Service. 2005. U.S. market profile for organic food products, February 22. Commodity and Marketing Programs—Processed products Division, International Strategic Marketing Group, USDA Foreign Agricultural Service, Washington, DC.

USDA National Agricultural Statistics Service. 2008. 2002 census publications. Available at http://www.agcensus.usda.gov/Publications/2002/index.asp (verified 22 July 2009). USDA National Agricultural Statistics Service, Washington, DC.

Welsh, R. 1999. The economics of organic grain and soybean production in the midwestern United States. Policy Studies Rep.. 13. Henry A. Wallace Inst. for Alternative Agriculture, Washington, DC.

Whole Foods Market. 2008. Locally grown: The Whole Foods Market promise. Available at http://www.wholefoodsmarket.com/products/locallygrown/index.html (verified 22 July 2009). Whole Foods Market, Austin, TX.

Zepeda, L., and C. Leviten-Reid. 2004. Consumers' views on local food. J. Food Distribution Res. 35:1–6.

Zhang, F., C.L. Huang, B.H. Lin, and J.E. Epperson. 2006. National demand for fresh organic and conventional vegetables: Scanner data evidence. In Am. Agricultural Economics Assoc. Annu. Meetings, Long Beach, CA. 23–26 July 2006. Am. Agricultural Economics Assoc., Milwaukee, WI.

11

Organic Agriculture and Food Security: Saving the Environment, Feeding the World?

Patricia Allen and Hilary Melcarek

Center for Agroecology and Sustainable Food Systems, University of California, Santa Cruz

Food security is humanity's most basic and universal need after air and water. Yet this security, by which we mean sustained access to nutritious food, is beyond the reach of large segments of our global population. More people go hungry today than at any point in human history, and skyrocketing food prices do not portend an improvement in this situation. The future food security of even larger numbers of people is in question, as the natural resources required for food production are being degraded and depleted through industrialized food-production practices. Both of these conditions—food insecurity now and in the future—are unacceptable and unnecessary. What needs to change to ensure that all people have food without compromising the environmental conditions of production and their attendant ecosystem services?

Organic agriculture has been proposed as an effective solution to this crucial problem. In the early 1900s, the connection between food security and environmental conservation was made by Sir Albert Howard, whose advocacy for organic production methods was inspired by his concerns about hunger and long-term food security (see Chapter 7, Heckman et al., 2009, this volume). Based on his observation of the relationship between healthy soil and healthy crops, he eschewed the use of agrichemicals in farming in his volume *An Agricultural Testament* (Howard, 1943). The advice of Howard and those who came after him, including J. I. Rodale, has influenced a small segment of innovative growers but has not been heeded by mainstream agriculture or the international development community.

One exception to this is the Food and Agriculture Organization of the United Nations (FAO), an international development agency that works to eliminate hunger worldwide. This institution has advocated organic agriculture since 1999, when the Committee on Agriculture recommended the development of a cross-sectoral program on this farming strategy (FAO, 2003).

Today the situation is even more dire than it was in Howard's time, as we are witnessing accelerations in both hunger and environmental destruction. What do we see as the role for organic agriculture in facilitating both immediate and longer-term food security? Answering this requires first understanding the reasons for food insecurity and then analyzing the role organic agriculture can play in improving food security. In this chapter, we set the context of the contemporary food situation, focusing on environment and hunger. We then discuss the ways in which organic agriculture contributes to food security. Next, we look at the ways in which organic agriculture is currently unable to contribute to food security and explore mechanisms for improving access to organic food. Our conclusion is that organic agriculture is essential for long-term food security and that it can feature in immediate food security, but this will require changes in distribution practices that are outside the purview of agricultural production methods and regular market mechanisms.

An Agrifood System in Crisis

The current world agrifood system is in crisis, a situation that presents us with the dual problem of environmental collapse and widespread and increasing food insecurity. In this section, we provide a brief overview of this crisis. It is instructive to explore this crisis as related to the environment, to hunger, and to food security

Environment and Long-Term Food Security

Industrial agricultural practices have long ignored "nature's economy," attempting to maximize agricultural production through the intensive use of resources and agrichemicals. The result has been the depletion of the very resources on which agricultural production depends. Contemporary agricultural practices have led to the worldwide degradation of agricultural land by topsoil erosion, waterlogging, and soil salinization, which are causing an irretrievable loss of an estimated 6 million arable hectares per year (Pimentel, 1993). The use of fertilizers has compromised beneficial soil microbial activity, and much pesticide application has been counterproductive; crop losses to insect pests have been increasing since the advent of pesticides, partly due to pests developing genetic resistance to these biocides.

Without significant changes in agricultural production systems, these kinds of problems are predicted to increase over time, reducing our ability to produce food in the long term. Worldwide, environmental problems have the potential to wreak havoc on our global food system, resulting in large-scale collapse and a severe reduction in our ability to produce food. For example, loss of fresh water due to overuse, pollution, and salinization of our aquifers will likely lead to lack of irrigation in some agricultural fields, with those located in ecological deserts such as the U.S. Midwest bread basket and the agriculturally productive Central Valley of California perhaps becoming especially vulnerable. More systemic environmental problems will have equally dire effects. Global warming could cause agricultural zones to shift, increase extreme weather conditions, and decrease weather and climate predictability—all of which would make planning farm operations difficult, if not impossible (Bazzaz and Sombroek, 1996). The decline of domesticated honey bees (*Apis mellifera* L.) and their contributions as pollinators may cause the disappearance of some fruits and vegetables from our food supply. Soaring fuel prices and the exhaustion of economically "harvestable" oil will likely exacerbate trends of widespread hunger and environmental degradation.

Hunger and Immediate Food Security

The possibility of an increase in worldwide hunger is frightening, given the already unconscionable numbers of people who go hungry day after day. According to

FAO statistics, there were 923 million chronically hungry people worldwide in 2007 (FAO, 2008). An estimated 24,000 people die every day as a result of hunger and undernutrition (United Nations World Food Programme, 2007). This means that approximately every three-and-a-half seconds, someone dies of hunger. That someone is most often a child. Every year that hunger continues at current levels, there are five million children who lose their lives (FAO, 2006). Even when people are able to consume adequate calories and protein, those with long-standing undernutrition and micronutrient deficiencies are so weakened that they are still at risk to die of diseases easily treated in wealthy nations, such as measles or dysentery (United Nations World Food Programme, 2008). In fact, 53% of childhood deaths worldwide have undernutrition as a synergistic cause (United Nations World Food Programme, 2007).

Despite the spread of technologies for increasing food production, food security is not improving. Hunger figures for 2007 show a 75 million person increase from FAO's estimates for 2003 to 2005 (FAO, 2008). Much of this increase is related to the rise in the cost of food. In 2008, global food prices rose an average of 52% (FAO, 2008). This drastic increase was due to extreme weather conditions, rising fuel prices, higher shipping costs, market speculation, and rising demand worldwide. Prices of some staple crops rose even more: the price of rice (*Oryza sativa* L.) rose about 75% globally in 2008, while the price of wheat (*Triticum aestivum* L.) increased 120%, causing the price of a loaf of bread to more than double in poor countries (CNN.com, 2008). Those hardest hit include the rural landless, pastoralists, small-scale farmers, and the urban poor in impoverished nations. Rises in food costs caused food riots across Asia and Africa and were perhaps most pronounced in Haiti, the poorest country in the Western Hemisphere, where 66% of the population subsists on less than $1 a day and 47% are undernourished. In a country where people eat cookies made of mud, oil, and salt just to fill their stomachs, protests against food price hikes in April 2008 turned violent, resulting in the deaths of at least six people (Guyler Delva, 2008).

This is not to say that some are not profiting from food price increases. While hundreds of millions of people face severe hunger, the world's richest multinational agrifood corporations made record profits. During the first months of 2008, Monsanto's (St. Louis, MO) net income was more than double what it was over the same period in 2007—from $543 million to $1120 million. Cargill's (Minneapolis, MN) net earnings jumped by 86% from $553 million to $1030 million over the same three months. Archer Daniels Midland (Decatur, IL), one of the world's largest agricultural processors of soy [*Glycine max* (L.) Merr.], maize (*Zea mays* L.), and wheat, increased its net earnings by 42% from $363 million to $517 million (Lean, 2008).

Although those at greatest risk of hunger are women and children living in rural areas of Asia, Africa, and Latin America, many people in relatively affluent countries also go hungry. In the United States, the world's largest producer of food, some 36 million people—or 11% of the population—were food insecure in 2007, meaning that at times they did not have enough money for food. The prevalence of hunger is not equally distributed—it is disproportionately experienced in single-mother households and by low-income people, children, and people of color (Nord et al., 2008). Food-insecure households with children often need to rely on diets and meals that lack nutritional variety and adequacy (Nord, 2003), so undernutrition is present even when absolute hunger is not.

In the United States, food insecurity has been exacerbated in recent years due to the increased cost of food and fuel, inadequate food stamp benefits, unemployment, the recent spike in foreclosures and rent or mortgage costs, and the increased cost of living in general. A May 2008 national survey by Feeding America, previously known as America's Second Harvest—the nation's largest charitable hunger-relief organization, found that an average of 15 to 20% more people were forced to resort to emergency food aid in 2008 than in 2007. Intensifying these trends, emergency food centers are unable to meet the demands of hungry people. Nearly all surveyed food banks reported an increase in the number of people seeking food assistance, and most have been forced to cut back on food distribution (Reuters, 2008). More than 80% of surveyed food banks indicated they were unable to meet demands without reducing the amount of food distributed (Reuters, 2008). Across cities surveyed by the U.S. Conference of Mayors (2007), 17% of food-insecure people and 15% of food-insecure households with children did not receive food assistance in 2007. Compounding the issue, USDA bonus foods have declined by $200 million, and local food donations were down nationally about 9% over the same period (Reuters, 2008).

While the very poor living in impoverished countries suffered the most during the 2008 food crisis, the global food price crisis was made apparent in the United States with rice shortages. In late April 2008, big-box warehouse stores Costco (Issaquah, WA) and Sam's Club (Bentonville, AR) limited rice purchases by customers (Flynn, 2008; Jagger and Charter, 2008; Raine, 2008). For the first time in recent memory, food shortages affected many middle-income families.

Sometimes it is useful to put numbers into terms we can better apprehend. Put into a spatial perspective, for example, when every three-and-a-half seconds someone dies of hunger, that is equivalent to the entire population of San Francisco, CA killed by hunger every month. The number of children who die of hunger on an annual basis can be pictured as 10,000 jumbo jet crashes every year, each crash with 100% fatalities. These situations would be considered catastrophes. They would likely result in continuous news feeds, and all available resources would be brought to bear on the problem, particularly if we had the solutions.

In the case of today's food insecurity problems, we do have the solutions, and organic agriculture can play a key role. In the case of tomorrow's food security problems, organic agriculture may be the only solution, given the commitment of organic farmers to environmental soundness and the concern of many for food equity.

Contributions of Organic Agriculture to Food Security

Organic agriculture offers our best chance for producing food over the long term without degrading the natural resource conditions on which food production depends. In other words, organic agriculture offers a sustainable approach to feeding the world's population. The FAO has proposed organic production as a way to increase farmer incomes, relieve poverty, and improve food security, especially in impoverished nations.

Can Organic Agriculture Provide Long-Term Food Security?

Organic agriculture may well be essential for ameliorating the environmental degradation that threatens our ability to produce food in the future. Most agree that organic agriculture is more environmentally sound than conventional agriculture, primarily because it does not use synthetic pesticides and fertilizers. According to Cassman (2007), however, one cannot assume that organic systems are more environmentally sound than conventional systems simply because they do not use these inputs. Nonetheless, much research comparing organic and conventional farming systems has found that organic systems are more environmentally sound, largely due to this fact (e.g., Altieri, 1995; Gliessman, 2007).

Compared with conventional agricultural practices, organic farming improves biodiversity and soil health and reduces erosion and pollution. Studies comparing organic and conventional farming systems have shown that external costs of organic farming, such as soil erosion, death of wildlife, and polluted drinking water, are one-third those of conventional farming and that organic farms host more wildlife species than conventional farms (Halweil, 2006). In an evaluation of organic, integrated, and conventional farming systems in Tuscany, Pacini et al. (2003) found that organic farming systems had less nitrogen losses and pesticide risks and higher plant biodiversity than integrated and conventional farming systems. Organic agriculture by nature has a lower energy footprint because it prohibits synthetic nitrogen fertilizers. Wood et al. (2006) found that organic farms in Australia used more local and on-site energy sources than conventional farms, which tend to use a very high proportion of energy embodied in the off-site production of synthetic fertilizers.

Organic systems often maximize resource use efficiency through nutrient cycling by primarily utilizing compost, cover crops, animal manures, and other nutrient sources produced on site. Further, organic systems tend to restore functional biodiversity through the incorporation of crop rotations and natural insect predators (FAO, 2007). In addition, research using models and estimates shows that nitrogen-fixing legumes used as green manure can provide enough biologically fixed nitrogen to replace the entire amount of synthetic nitrogen fertilizer currently in use, without clearing additional land for agriculture (Badgley et al., 2007; Badgley and Perfecto, 2007). Thus, organic agriculture is designed to conserve the long-term environmental conditions of production on which global food security ultimately depends. However, with the present state of technical knowledge, are yields from organic farming sufficiently high to feed the hungry today?

Can Organic Agriculture Produce Enough Food?

According to current predominant opinions, the conventional agribusiness perspective has been that organic agriculture cannot produce sufficient amounts of food to feed everyone. The oft-quoted statement from former Secretary of Agriculture Earl Butz is emblematic of this perspective: "Before we go back to organic agriculture somebody is going to have to decide what 50 million people we are going to let starve" (Goldstein, 2008). Can organic agriculture "feed the world"? In looking solely at yields and calories produced, the answer to this question is a resounding yes. Despite the long-standing argument that organic farming would produce one-third to one-half of the yields of conventional farming, research shows that a shift worldwide from conventional to organic food production will provide equivalent, if not higher, yields, as well as more than sufficient calories to support the world's population (Badgley et al., 2007; Badgley and Perfecto, 2007). According to FAO, conversion of global agriculture to organic would result in a global supply of 2640 to 4380 calories per person per day, and in countries in the global south, sustainable intensification through organic practices could increase production by 56% (FAO, 2007). Thus, organic agriculture can produce ample calories per day for the current population and has promise for enabling us to produce long into the future without degrading the environment.

The green revolution, which began in 1945, boosted agricultural yields through the use of synthetic pesticides and fertilizers, large-scale monocropping, plant breeding, and development of irrigation systems. However, it has not ended hunger. In addition, the agricultural practices developed during the green revolution have degraded the environmental conditions of production. Many of the crop failures that led up to the food crisis of 2008 were caused by decades of unsustainable agricultural practices of the green revolution. For example, these practices have led to massive soil erosion, loss of soil fertility, loss of agricultural land through salinization, depletion of water tables, and increased pest resistance. Other environmental costs of the green revolution include surface and groundwater contamination, release of greenhouse gases—especially through deforestation and conversion into agricultural land—and loss of biodiversity.

A "second green revolution" has been proposed by some agronomists who endorse the use of genetically engineered organisms (GMOs) to provide crops that are herbicide resistant or contain vital nutrients to "feed the world." Most knowledgeable scientists agree that GMOs are useful for reducing some insect problems in crops, and for simplifying weed management, yet conclude that they will not make a major impact on such complex traits as drought tolerance or crop yields. In addition, there is no reason to believe that a second green revolution would be any less degrading to the environment on which food production depends. Nor is there any evidence or experience that such a revolution would improve food security for impoverished people, given the inequities in access to food that have persisted despite technological advances in the past several decades. In fact, the use of genetically engineered crops has been shown to increase the amount of pounds of pesticides applied (Lopez Villar and Freese, 2008).

Can Organic Agriculture Eliminate the Economic Barriers to Food Security?

In a market economy in which plenty of food is produced, the primary obstacle to food security is poverty. Within the current market framework, organic agriculture could contribute to food security by improving conditions for the poor in two ways. One is to provide higher incomes to impoverished food producers. The other is to produce food at lower prices than conventional food so it is affordable to low-income consumers.

For farmers who are so poor that they are themselves at risk of food insecurity, organic farming can improve their economic situation. Organic farming has been found to be as profitable as or more profitable than conventional farming and can therefore lead to poverty reduction, especially in impoverished nations (FAO, 2007). Conversion to organic agriculture has the potential to improve food security by increasing productivity and diversity, conserving natural resources, and reducing risks for farmers, benefits which could in turn lead to poverty reduction and a reversal of rural to urban migration (FAO, 2007).

Although organic cash crops cannot be grown as frequently over time due to their dependence on crop rotations to supply nutrients and control pests, overall economic returns of organic and conventional farming systems have been found to be similar. This is due in part to price premiums received for organic produce. For example, prices for organic maize and soybean in the marketplace often range from 20 to 140% higher than for conventional maize, soybean, and other grains (Pimentel et al., 2005). Similarly, in studying the outcomes of conversion to low cost, locally available, and environmentally sensitive practices and technologies by 89 agricultural projects in Africa, Asia, and Latin America, Pretty et al. (2003) found an average per project increase in yields per hectare of 93%. According to the authors, this shows that transition to sustainable agriculture can provide substantial benefits to rural poor populations (Pretty et al., 2003). Thus, organic agriculture has the potential to increase the economic situation of farmers by capturing price premiums, increasing farmer incomes, and improving yields, especially in impoverished nations.

Organic agriculture contributes to food security both for the present and for the future. By preserving rather than consuming environmental resources used in production and working in harmony with "nature's services," organic agriculture can enable long-term food security. In the present time, organic agriculture can produce the kinds of yields necessary to provide enough food for every man, woman, and child. Beyond this, organic agriculture can help increase the incomes of farmers so that they will have the "effective demand" to buy the food they need to provide complete and nourishing diets for their families. However, there are other obstacles to meeting food security needs that are not achieved through organic agriculture, either because they are outside the purview of organic agriculture or because they are not yet incorporated into the practice of organic agriculture.

Food Security Needs Not Met by Organic Agriculture

While organic agriculture may improve farmer incomes, it does not necessarily improve incomes for everyone who works on the farm, nor does it increase food security for consumers. In this section, we focus on the situation of farmworkers and low-income consumers in the United States.

Food Security for Worker–Producers on Organic Farms

While there is high potential for organic agriculture to increase incomes of farmer–producers, it is not clear that this income increase would be extended to the landless laborers who work directly in the fields, growing organic fruits and vegetables that they may well not be able to purchase themselves. Throughout the world, these landless laborers are some of the poorest, most vulnerable workers in society. Even in a wealthy agricultural country such as the United States, the economic challenges facing farmworkers are many. For the past two decades, the wages of farmworkers have declined; average wages paid to workers on crop farms declined 10% (from $6.89 to $6.18) between 1989 and 1998. The average salary a farmworker can expect to earn lies between $7,500 and $10,000 per year—poverty-level wages. Lack of overtime pay and seasonal employment exacerbate economic challenges. During peak harvest seasons, farmworkers in some states may still work 80 hours per week without overtime pay. However, during the off-season, the majority of farmworkers are unemployed or underemployed (Shreck et al., 2005).

While farmworkers on organic farms in some ways may be better off economically than those on nonorganic farms, this is not always the case. One economic advantage to working on an organic farm is that there is less seasonal unemployment. Organic farmers generally plant several types of vegetables to diversify their fields; multicropping patterns tend to demand year-round, permanent labor, which allows farmworkers to work on the same farm for the entire year (Mello, 2006). However, wages on organic farms are not necessarily higher than those on conventional farms. For example, a 1999 study of 150 California organic farmers found that more than half paid their workers the minimum wage and less than 10% paid more than $7.50 per hour (Mello, 2006). Even if they work on organic farms, farmworkers may not be able to afford to buy organic food for themselves and their families.

Organic Agriculture and Low-Income Consumers

Issues of price and location often bar low-income people, especially those living in poor, inner-city neighborhoods, from being able to purchase organic food. Although prices are often the consequence of the higher cost of organic production, the price premiums on organic food can make it unobtainable to those who struggle to put food on the table. Price premiums, a result of higher production and distribution costs—as well as consumers' willingness to pay more for organic food—have remained high as demand for organic foods has risen. For example, from 2000 to 2004, price premiums for organic broccoli (*Brassica oleracea* L. var. *botrytis* L.) and carrots (*Daucus carota* subsp. *sativus*) rose to almost twice those of conventional produce (Dimitri and Oberholtzer, 2005). Although organic food has become widespread in the United States in recent years, this increased availability does not provide equal access for all. According to the Hartman Group (2001), 30% of surveyed consumers do not purchase organic food because it is too expensive, and 13% do not because it is not available where they shop.

While organic food is now available in large chain supermarkets and big-box warehouse stores, such as Wal-Mart (Bentonville, AR), Safeway (Pleasanton, CA), and Costco, many poor urban residents do not have access to supermarkets, let alone organic food. Recently, many urban neighborhoods have become "food deserts" due to migration of middle-class families to the suburbs and subsequent abandonment of inner-city neighborhoods by supermarket chains (Short et al., 2007). Several researchers have documented both the paucity of supermarkets and the higher prices of food in poor urban areas compared with suburban areas and wealthier neighborhoods (Chung and Myers, 1999; Hendrickson et al., 2006). Given that supermarkets are where the majority of organic food purchases take place, the combined absence of supermarkets and the high price of organic food renders these products beyond the reach of many low-income people who are at risk of food insecurity. In addition, while organic agriculture has been growing in impoverished countries, most of this food is exported for consumption by people in other nations. For example, at least 85% of the organic food grown in Mexico is exported to other nations, including the United States, some European Union members, and Japan (Adams, 2004). While no one would argue that it is the job of organic agriculture to provide low-priced food to low-income consumers, a number of institutional alternatives have developed in recent years that can make organic food more accessible to those at risk of food insecurity.

Increasing the Accessibility of Organic Food

The regular market has not provided access to organic food to all who want to purchase and consume this special type of product. While many low-income consumers would prefer to eat organic food, prices are high and sometimes it is not available at all to those at risk of food security. What roles can alternative market mechanisms such as "beyond organic" labels, farmers' markets, and community-supported agriculture (CSA) operations play in increasing access to organic food? What about forms of self-provisioning such as urban agriculture?

Alternative Market Mechanisms

A number of efforts are under way within the market system that could increase access to organic food. These include beyond organic labels and standards that improve farmworker wages and alternative markets such as CSAs and farmers' markets.

Labor Standards and Labels

Movements are underway to improve wages and working conditions for farmworkers on organic farms. The basic standards of a major international organic certifying body, the International Federation of Organic Agriculture Movements (IFOAM), has included social justice in its list of principle aims since 1996. Its goal is to "progress toward an entire production, processing, and distribution chain which is both socially just and environmentally responsible," and this includes a focus on labor conditions. According to IFOAM's basic standards for social justice and social rights in organic agriculture and processing, farm laborers should have access to health insurance, maternity and retirement benefits, potable water, fair wages, and protection from exposure to toxic chemicals, among other protections (IFOAM, 2005). The latest IFOAM statement of principles includes health, ecology, fairness, and care, which were articulated after a two-year process of negotiation among the member groups (IFOAM, 2009).

In the United States, there are efforts to develop beyond organic labels that could offer certification for farms in which farmworkers receive overtime pay, vacation time, health benefits, and a livable wage. The Comite de Apoyo a las Trabajadores Agricolicas (Farmworker Support Committee) is working to develop standards that will ensure farmworkers' rights to negotiate fair contracts and the right to unionize, protect the rights of undocumented workers, and reduce and address safety issues in the workplace (Comite de Apoyo a los Trabajadores Agricolas, 2005).

CSAs and Farmers' Markets

Both CSAs and farmers' markets have grown rapidly over the past two decades, alongside the increase in demand for organic food. In 1994 the USDA reported 1755 farmers' markets nationwide; in 2008 this number increased to 4685 (an 167% increase in 14 years) (USDA Agricultural Marketing Service, 2008). In 1990 the number of CSA programs in the United States was estimated at 50 and has since grown to over 1500 (Local Harvest, http://www.localharvest.org [verified 23 July 2009]). Both of these market mechanisms often feature organic produce. Indeed, the vast majority of CSAs are managed by farmers who use organic farming practices even if they are not organically certified. Unlike supermarkets that are concerned primarily with providing good returns for shareholders, CSAs and farmers' markets may be able to develop targeted ways of increasing access to organic food by low-income consumers.

Two market-based alternatives for providing organic food are promising and are gaining popularity: CSAs with flexible payment options and farmers' markets located in low-income communities. A typical subscription to a CSA costs $350 to $500 for the entire season, with payment due before the beginning of the spring harvest. This provides the customer with a weekly box of seasonal vegetables and the farmer with a secure customer base, security in case of crop failures, and an upfront investment. To alleviate the challenge of such a large payment, some CSA programs offer the option of weekly payments of $15 to $20. Others offer subsidized share prices for low-income customers, with elevated share prices for higher-income customers. Still others accept payments via food stamps or Electronic Benefit Transfer (EBT).

Several examples of CSAs that offer creative payment options exist. People's Grocery, a food justice organization located in a low-income, predominantly African-American neighborhood of Oakland, CA, offers a weekly subsidized "grub box," which "allows neighborhood residents to subscribe to a seasonal, culturally appropriate bag of organic fruits and vegetables" harvested from the farm and gardens operated by the organization for only $12 per week, payable by EBT. To subsidize these shares, the organization offers a "sponsorship box" for twice this price (People's Grocery, http://www.peoplesgrocery.org/article.php/grubbox [verified 23 July 2009]).

Another example is the Food Bank Farm in Hatfield, MA, which donates half of its produce grown on 24 ha (60 acres) of farmland to 400 local food pantries, while the other half goes to its 600 CSA members (Food Bank of Western Massachusetts, n.d.). The Holcomb Farm CSA in Hartford, CT, another CSA with social justice goals, sells market-rate shares to its 300 members and deeply discounted shares to 11 community organizations that work with low-income earners. In this way, the CSA distributes 30 to 40% of its produce to Hartford's 1200 low-income residents through the community organizations (Holcomb Farm, http://www.holcombfarmcsa.org/ [verified 23 July 2009]). In addition, Just Food's Fresh Food For All program coordinates 50 CSAs in New York City, the majority of which have flexible payment options and accept food stamps. At the same time, the nonprofit trains community groups to set up CSA programs located within low-income New York City neighborhoods (Lyons, 2008).

There is a long history of setting up farmers' markets to provide fresh, affordable produce to low-income consumers. One example is the Mo' Betta Foods Farmers' Market in West Oakland, CA. Although small—the market currently draws about 100 customers each week—the market works to create demand for organic produce within an African-American community whose agricultural background is dominated by a history of slavery (Alkon, 2007). To do this, the market offers predominantly culturally appropriate produce such as collards, sweet potatoes, and okra and by associating food justice with racial empowerment. There is also a history of public-policy efforts to make farmers' market produce affordable to low-income consumers, and many farmers' markets in the United States are set up to receive payments via EBT. Still, for many low-income consumers, organic produce remains beyond their reach. One alternative is circumventing the market by growing one's own food.

Self-Provisioning of Organic Food

Self-provisioning of organic food through urban agriculture offers an outside-of-the-market approach to improving food security. Urban agriculture is any agricultural venture that produces a diversity of food, fuel, and livestock in response to the daily demands of consumers within a town, city, or metropolis, primarily using and recycling local natural resources and urban wastes (Smit et al., 1996). Urban agriculture can occur on either an individual (e.g., in a private garden in one's own yard) or collective (e.g., in a community garden or other collective gardening venture) basis. According to the U.N. Development Program, urban agriculture contributes to about one-third of agricultural production of vegetables, eggs, meat, and fish worldwide. Similarly, 30% of U.S. agricultural products are produced within metropolitan areas (Smit et al., 1996), as defined by the USDA.

In impoverished countries throughout Africa, Asia, and Latin America, urban agriculture is an important strategy for improving food security. Poor families are able to sell produce and livestock raised near their homes—thus decreasing poverty and raising money to purchase other staples—and at the same time grow food to feed their own families. Some international urban garden programs improve food security for those most in need. For example, Gardens for Health, a community garden organization in Rwanda, develops easily replicable gardens throughout the country to simultaneously target malnutrition and HIV–AIDS (http://www.gardensforhealth.org/ [verified 28 July 2009]). The urban production of vegetables, fruits, and small animals is well known in Havana and other Cuban cities (Funes et al., 2002), where the government has put priority on encouraging use of vacant land and local resources to produce food in neighborhoods.

In the United States, urban agriculture takes many forms. Community gardens are perhaps the most familiar type of urban garden and consist of lots divided into smaller plots tended by individuals or households. Community gardens often exist in poor, inner-city neighborhoods with high proportions of apartment dwellers and other residents without space to grow their own food. In addition, there are also numerous school gardens, entrepreneurial gardens, and healing and therapy gardens located in every region throughout the United States. For the most part, urban garden programs in the United States have the primary goal of communal food production. However, they are also a way to mitigate poverty, improve neighborhood aesthetics, provide space for the study of nature and ecology, and develop a sense of pride and public citizenship (Bassett, 1976).

Throughout history, food production in urban areas has increased as a response to times of social and economic crisis. From the early 1890s through the present, vacant lot gardens in the United States have arisen out of food insecurity and unemployment brought about by economic depression, war, and social unrest created by population, industrial, or institutional changes (Bassett, 1976; Lawson, 2000). During World War II, urban agriculture in the United States produced over 40% of fresh produce that was consumed; almost all available city land was cultivated—including rights of ways, city parks, school yards, vacant lots, and people's yards. In the 1980s, urban agricultural production accelerated dramatically worldwide. For example, surveys in Moscow in 1970 and 1991 show a shift from 20 to 65% of families engaged in urban agriculture (Smit et al., 1996).

In the 1990s, gardening became (and remains) the number one reported hobby in the United States. The current era of food crisis is no exception; in a time of soaring food and fuel prices and with the majority of the world's population living in urban areas—over 50% worldwide, almost 80% in the United States—it is crucial to improve food security and access to organic food.

The reasons urban agriculture is such an ideal strategy for food security are twofold. First, it is a viable form of self-provisioning of organic produce; thus, the chains of reliance on the current market structure to provide access to organic produce are broken. Through urban gardening programs, poor, disenfranchised people are empowered to grow their own organic food, either in their own yards or as part of a community garden. Second, urban gardens of all types often utilize land that has been vacant or unused because it is otherwise unattractive for urban development (Brown and Jameton, 2000). Urban agriculture uses available land in people's backyards, on rights-of-ways, and in vacant lots.

The following garden programs illustrate how urban agriculture makes use of people's yards as a secure, stable way to improve food security and self-provisioning of organic produce. City Slicker Farms, located in a low-income, racially diverse neighborhood in Oakland, CA, helps low-income residents set up gardens in their yards through their Backyard Garden program. The organization provides soil, planter boxes, seeds, and starts, builds planter boxes, and offers advice free of charge on how to keep up the garden. In addition, a garden mentor makes quarterly check-ins with the garden recipient to answer any questions and provide any supplies needed (http://www.cityslickerfarms.org [verified 30 July 2009]). My Farm, in San Francisco, CA, is a decentralized urban farm–CSA that grows organic vegetables in backyards throughout the San Francisco Bay Area. My Farm crews set up gardens in members' backyards, and members receive produce from their own and neighboring yards (http://myfarmsf.com [verified 30 July 2009]). These programs show how urban residents, especially those who do not already know how to garden, can be empowered to grow their own food and could prioritize working with low-income people.

Increasing Food Security beyond the Market

All three of these ventures—CSAs, farmers' markets with alternative payment options, and urban agriculture—are viable strategies to improve access to organic produce and food security. However, they are also idiosyncratic; no standard practice is in place that will ensure access to organic food or sustain the production of organic food itself. For this, changes to public policies and economic reward systems are required (Allen and Kovach, 2000). Several examples illustrate this situation.

As previously noted, the average income of American farmworkers, even on organic farms, is at poverty level. One within-the-market mechanism that is being developed to change this is the "beyond organic" labels, discussed above, which incorporate labor standards. According to Brown and Getz (2008), voluntary certifications and labels that work to incorporate social accountability into California agricultural production do not alter power relations between labor, capital, and the state like traditional forms of social justice organizing have. Instead, they embrace key neoliberal principles, such as the role of the market as a mechanism for addressing environmental and social ills, the privatization of regulatory functions, and the assertion of the rights and responsibilities of citizen-consumers.

Many organic farmers who employ farmworkers do not support social certification that would improve farmworker conditions (Shreck et al., 2006). One argument organic farmers make for not paying better wages to farmworkers is that it would put the farmers at an economic disadvantage relative to conventional farmers, who are already subsidized by not having to pay the public costs of the damage done by agrichemicals. This means that the entire political framework of cost accounting in agriculture would need to change in order for organic farmers to be able to pay nonpoverty wages.

So far, the regular market has failed in terms of providing access to organic food for low-income people. Alternative markets, such as CSAs and farmers' markets, have done a marginally better job in this respect, but they confront the same structural situations of the market. Their primary purpose is to earn money, and therefore they tend to be located in areas where they would be best situated to do so. Subsidization of CSA shares and EBT payment options at farmers' markets increase the accessibility of low-income consumers to organic food. However, these alternatives are small, few, and idiosyncratic and encounter many of the same challenges as their market-driven counter parts. As long as organic food is available only via the realm of the market, it will remain mostly inaccessible to low-income people, and it will not become a viable option for increasing food security.

While CSAs and farmers' markets are perhaps in good positions to provide organic food and improve food security for low-income people, they also present barriers. These include economic and cultural obstacles (see Allen 1999, 2004). In one instance, even a CSA program that was explicitly set up for low-income people tended to attract primarily affluent, educated, European-American people (Hinrichs and Kremer, 2002). This is in keeping with the findings of Guthman et al. (2006), who found that while farmers' market and CSA managers in California feel that it is important that their products are accessible to low-income consumers and had engaged strategies to increase their participation in the markets, actual attendance and purchasing nonetheless remained low. As with the regular market, the goals of income security for farmers and food security for low-income consumers in these alternative markets will be at odds without significant market intervention from the public and private sectors. This is not to say that organic food cannot be a part of successful strategies that improve food security. Alternative strategies for food security that are both socially just and environmentally sound exist both within and outside of the market. In other words, there are alternative alternatives that can help provide organic food to low-income consumers.

The case of urban agriculture also highlights the need for public support of alternative strategies. In the United States, urban agriculture has historically increased during times of public sponsorship. When funding and support has been taken away, programs have disappeared. In 1976 the federal government sponsored the Urban Gardening Program, in which the USDA's Agriculture Extension Service established offices in urban areas to promote and support gardening efforts first in 6, then in 16, and finally in 23 U.S. cities (Lawson, 2000). By 1980 the Urban Garden Program served 200,000 urban residents. Then, reductions in public funding led to their decline. When the budget was capped at $3.6 million, even as the number of cities served increased, funded organizations responded by reducing staff and cutting programs. In 1993 the Urban Gardening Program was removed as a line item from USDA's budget due to lack of support within Congress, USDA, and Cooperative Extension (Brown and Jameton, 2000). As a result, many urban garden programs ended while others downsized (Malakoff, 1994; Lawson, 2000). Increasing access to organic food will require a social commitment and public support, both domestically and internationally.

The FAO recognizes that public intervention is necessary to improve food security through increasing support for organic agriculture. To do this, it provides recommendations pertaining to advocacy and training, information and assessment, and strategy and coordination. For advocacy and training, the FAO recommends investment in agricultural and environmental education: building organic knowledge in university and research institutions and providing organic training to extension officers and farmers field schools. In terms of information and assessment, the agency recommends mapping vulnerable groups and local food needs and facilitating small-scale farmers' entry to organic agriculture. Their strategy and coordination recommendations include integrating national agricultural development and poverty reduction strategies, restoring quality financial incentives in agricultural and rural programs, protecting organic lands from contamination (e.g., GMO-free zones), developing coherent policy—including removal of subsidies on synthetic inputs, and discouraging imports of organic foods produced locally (FAO, 2007). Government policies and support that promote organic agriculture and food security are crucial.

Conclusions

In this chapter, we have addressed the question of the role of organic agriculture in achieving food security. Certainly, a new approach is needed, as both hunger and environmental degradation due to agriculture are increasing. Our conclusion is that organic agriculture is essential for long-term food security because it can conserve the environmental conditions of production on which our ability to grow food ultimately depends. In addition, because organic produce commands higher prices, organic agriculture may be a strategy to increase the incomes, and therefore food security, of impoverished farmers. It is precisely these prices, however, that limit the value of organic agriculture for improving food security for low-income consumers, including the farmworkers who earn poverty-level wages. Outside the regular market, a number of alternative market mechanisms exist that can increase access to organic food, but these do not fully serve the needs of low-income consumers. In the long term, the ability of organic agriculture to play a significant role in increasing food security will depend on far-reaching public policies and programs. Organic agriculture and organic food are social goods that require social support.

Discussion Questions

1. How does environmental degradation caused by industrial agricultural practices affect both present and future food security?
2. Describe a number of social and economic causes of food insecurity, and discuss why they are important.

3. What were the root causes of the 2008 worldwide food crisis, and in what countries and regions was this felt most strongly? Why?

4. Who is at greatest risk for food insecurity in most countries of the world? What are the principal causes for this insecurity?

5. How can organic agriculture contribute to current and long-term food security? How does this relate to local and national food sovereignty?

6. What are some of the reasons certain segments of the population do not have access to organic food?

7. What are some alternative market mechanisms that could increase access to organic food? What are the reasons they work or do not work?

8. What are potential outside-of-the-market approaches to improving access to organic food and to food security? Why will organic food remain mostly inaccessible to low-income people if it is only available via the realm of the conventional marketplace?

9. Why is urban agriculture an ideal strategy for improving food security?

10. What is the danger of public sponsorship of urban agriculture primarily during times of economic and social crises?

11. What changes could be made to current distribution practices, food policies, and economic reward systems to enhance the ability of organic agriculture to improve food security worldwide?

References

Adams, L.J. 2004. Mexico spreading organic eating at home. Associated Press, 30 Sept.

Alkon, A. 2007. Growing resistance: Food, culture, and the Mo'Better Foods Farmers Market. Gastronomica 7:93–99.

Allen, P. 1999. Reweaving the food security net: Mediating entitlement and entrepreneurship. Agric. Human Values 16:117–129.

Allen, P. 2004. Together at the table: Sustainability and sustenance in the American agrifood system. Pennsylvania State Univ. Press, University Park.

Allen, P., and M. Kovach. 2000. The capitalist composition of organics: The potential of markets in fulfilling the promise of organic agriculture. Agric. Human Values 17:221–232.

Altieri, M. 1995. Agroecology: The science of sustainable agriculture. Westview Press, Boulder, CO.

Badgley, C., J. Moghtader, E. Quintero, E. Zakem, M.J. Chappell, K. Aviles-Vazquez, A. Samulon, and I. Perfecto. 2007. Organic agriculture and the global food supply. Renewable Agric. Food Syst. 22:86–108.

Badgley, C., and I. Perfecto. 2007. Can organic agriculture feed the world? Renewable Agric. Food Syst. 22:80–82.

Bassett, T.J. 1976. Vacant lot cultivation: Community gardening in America, 1893–1978. Master's thesis. Univ. of California, Berkeley.

Bazzaz, F., and W. Sombroek. 1996. Global climate change and agricultural production: Direct and indirect effects of changing hydrological, pedological and plant physiological processes. Available at http://www.fao.org/docrep/W5183E/W5183E00.htm (verified 30 July 2009). FAO, Rome; John Wiley & Sons, Chichester, UK.

Brown, K.H., and A.L. Jameton. 2000. Public health implications of urban agriculture. J. Public Health Policy 21:20–39.

Brown, S., and C. Getz. 2008. Privatizing farm worker justice: Regulating labor through voluntary certification and labeling. Geoforum 39:1184–1196.

Cassman, K. 2007. Editorial response by Kenneth Cassman: Can organic agriculture feed the world - science to the rescue? Renewable Agric. Food Syst. 22(2):83–84.

Chung, C.J., and S.L. Myers. 1999. Do the poor pay more for food? An analysis of grocery store availability and food price disparities. J. Consum. Aff. 33:276–296.

CNN.com. 2008. Riots, instability spread as food prices skyrocket. Available at http://www. cnn.com/2008/WORLD/americas/04/14/world.food.crisis/ (verified 28 July 2009)). Cable News Network, Atlanta, GA.

Comite de Apoyo a los Trabajadores Agricolas. 2005. Farmworker perspective on standards and pilot process: Toward social justice and economic equity in the food system. Comite de Apoyo a los Trabajadores Agricolas, Glassboro, NJ.

Dimitri, C., and L. Oberholtzer. 2005. Organic price premiums remain high. Amber Waves 3(4):2.

Flynn, R. 2008. Rice shortage roils San Francisco stores, markets, food banks. http://www. freedom4um.com/cgi-bin/readart.cgi?ArtNum=79029&Disp=0 (verified 28 July 2009). Bloomberg, 25 April.

Food and Agriculture Organization. 2003. Action taken by FAO on organic agriculture: 1997 to 2003. FAO, Rome.

Food and Agriculture Organization. 2006. The state of food insecurity in the world 2006: Eradicating world hunger—Taking stock ten years after the World Food Summit. FAO, Rome.

Food and Agriculture Organization. 2007. International Conference on Organic Agriculture and Food Security: Report. FAO, Rome.

Food and Agriculture Organization. 2008. Hunger on the rise: Soaring prices add 75 million people to global hunger rolls. FAO, Rome.

Food Bank of Western Massachusetts. n.d. The Food Bank Farm: A 60-acre community-supported farm. Available at http://www.foodbankwma.org/farm/ (verified 23 July 2009). Food Bank of Western Massachusetts, Hatfield, MA.

Funes, F., L. Garcia, M. Burque, N. Perez, and P. Rossett. 2002, Sustainable agriculture and resistance: Transforming food production in Cuba, Institute for Food and Development Policy, International Research Development Centre, Ottawa, Canada.

Gliessman, S.R. 2007. Agroecology: The ecology of sustainable food systems. Taylor & Francis Group, Boca Raton, FL.

Goldstein, R. 2008. Earl L. Butz, secretary felled by racial remark, is dead at 98. Available at http://www.nytimes.com/2008/02/04/washington/04butz.html. New York Times, 4 Feb.

Guthman, J., A. Morris, and P. Allen. 2006. Squaring farm security and food security in two types of alternative food institutions. Rural Sociol. 71:662–684.

Guyler Delva, J. 2008. World Food Program sees 'major crisis' in Haiti. Available at http://www.reuters.com/article/worldNews/idUSN3055799520080501?virtualBrandChannel=10005 (verified 28 July 2009). Reuters, 30 April 2008.

Halweil, B. 2006. Can organic farming feed us all? World Watch 19:18–24.

Hartman Group. 2001. Healthy living: Organic and natural products. Hartman Group, Bellevue, WA.

Heckman, J., J., R. Weil, and F. Magdoff. 2009. Practical steps to soil fertility for organic agriculture. p. 139–172. In C. Francis (ed.) Organic farming: The ecological system. Agron. Monogr. 54. ASA, CSSA, and SSSA, Madison, WI. (This volume.)

Hendrickson, D., C. Smith, and N. Eikenberry. 2006. Fruit and vegetable access in four low-income food deserts communities in Minnesota. Agric. Human Values 23:371–383.

Hinrichs, C., and K.S. Kremer. 2002. Social inclusion in a Midwest local food system project. J. Poverty 6(1):65–90.

Howard, A. 1943. An agricultural testament. Oxford Univ. Press, London.

International Federation of Organic Agriculture Movements (IFOAM). 2005. Excerpt of the IFOAM Basic Standards Version 2005. Available at http://www.ifoam.org/organic_facts/justice/pdfs/IBS_Ch_8_2005_Norms_Version_060621.pdf (verified 28 July 2009). IFOAM, Bonn, Germany.

International Federation of Organic Agriculture Movements (IFOAM). 2009. The principles of organic agriculture. Available at http://www.ifoam.org/about_ifoam/principles/index.html (verified 28 July 2009). IFOAM, Bonn, Germany.

Jagger, S., and D. Charter. 2008. Food crisis: Rationing introduced in bid to protect rice supplies. Times (Lond.), 24 April.

Lawson, L. 2000. Urban-garden programs in the United States: Values, resources, and role in community development. Ph.D thesis. Univ. of California, Berkeley.

Lean, G. 2008. Multinationals make billions in profit out of growing global food crisis. Global Research, 8 May. The Independent, London.

Lopez Villar, J., and B. Freese. 2008. Who benefits from GM crops? The rise in pesticide use. Available at http://www.centerforfoodsafety.org/pubs/FoE%20I%20Who%20Benefits%202008%20-%20Full%20Report%20FINAL%202-6-08.pdf (verified 27 July 2009). Friends of the Earth, Washington, DC.

Lyons, Z.D. 2008. Food Stamp-CSA opens access to the freshest food. Available at http://www.rodaleinstitute.org/20080317/nf1 (verified 28 July 2009). Rodale Institute, Kutztown, PA.

Malakoff, D. 1994. Final harvest? How the federal government's Urban Gardening Program, which served 23 of America's poorest inner-cities, flourished—then faltered. Community Greening Rev. 1:4–12.

Mello, F. 2006. Organic farms: Hard labor. Nation 283:21–28.

Nord, M. 2003. Food insecurity in households with children: Food assistance research brief. USDA, Washington, DC.

Nord, M., M. Andrews, and S. Carlson. 2008. Household food security in the United States, 2007. Econ. Res. Rep. ERR-66. USDA, Washington, DC.

Pacini, C., A. Wossink, G. Giesen, C. Vazzana, and R. Huirne. 2003. Evaluation of sustainability of organic, integrated and conventional farming systems: A farm and field-scale analysis. Agric. Ecosyst. Environ. 95:273–288.

Pimentel, D. (ed.) 1993. World soil erosion and conservation. Cambridge Univ. Press, New York.

Pimentel, D., P. Hepperly, J. Hanson, D. Douds, and R. Seidel. 2005. Environmental, energetic, and economic comparisons of organic and conventional farming systems. Bioscience 55:573–582.

Pretty, J.N., J.I.L. Morison, and R.E. Hine. 2003. Reducing food poverty by increasing agricultural sustainability in developing countries. Agric. Ecosyst. Environ. 95:217–234.

Raine, G. 2008. Global rice squeeze hitting U.S. consumers. Available at http://www.sfgate.com/cgi-bin/article.cgi?f=/c/a/2008/04/25/BUUR10AOLH.DTL (verified 28 July 2009). San Francisco Chronicle, 25 April.

Reuters. 2008. New survey underscores urgent need for Farm Bill as demands are up, food down. Available at http://www.reuters.com/article/pressRelease/idUS197219+12-May-2008+PRN20080512. Reuters, 12 May 2008.

Short, A., J. Guthman, and S. Raskin. 2007. Food deserts, oases, or mirages? Small markets and community food security in the San Francisco bay area. J. Plann. Educ. Res. 26:352–364.

Shreck, A., C. Getz, and G. Feenstra. 2005. Farmworkers in organic agriculture: Toward a broader notion of sustainability. Sustain. Agric. Newsl 17(1):1–3.

Shreck, A., C. Getz, and G. Feenstra. 2006. Social sustainability, farm labor, and organic agriculture: Findings from an exploratory analysis. Agric. Human Values 23:439–449.

Smit, J., A. Ratta, and J. Nasr. 1996. Urban agriculture: Food, jobs, and sustainable cities. United Nations Development Programme, New York.

United Nations World Food Programme. 2007. World Hunger Series 2007: Hunger and health. World Food Programme, Rome; Earthscan, London.

United Nations World Food Programme. 2008. Who are the hungry? Available at http://wfp.org/aboutwfp/introduction/hunger_who.asp?section=1&sub_section=1 (verified 30 July 2009). World Food Programme, Rome.

U.S. Conference of Mayors. 2007. A status report on hunger and homelessness in America's cities: A 23-city survey. Sodexho, Gaithersburg, ND; United States Conference of Mayors, Washington, DC.

USDA Agricultural Marketing Service. 2008. Farmers' market growth 1994–2008. Available at http://www.ams.usda.gov/AMSv1.0/ams.fetchTemplateData.do?template=Temp lateS&navID=WholesaleandFarmersMarkets&leftNav=WholesaleandFarmersM arkets&page=WFMFarmersMarketGrowth&description=Farmers%20Market%20 Growth&acct=frmrdirmkt (verified 30 July 2009). USDA Agricultural Marketing Service, Washington, DC.

Wood, R., M. Lenzen, C. Dey, and S. Lundie. 2006. A comparative study of some environmental impacts of conventional and organic farming in Australia. Agric. Syst. 89:324–348.

Implementation & Outreach

12 🧄

Center for Environmental Farming Systems: Designing and Institutionalizing an Integrated Sustainable and Organic Agriculture Program

Nancy G. Creamer, J. Paul Mueller, Chris Reberg-Horton, Michelle Schroeder-Moreno, and Steve Washburn
Center for Environmental Farming Systems, North Carolina State University, Raleigh

John O'Sullivan
Center for Environmental Farming Systems, North Carolina Agricultural and Technical State University, Greensboro

The Center for Environmental Farming Systems (CEFS) is a partnership among North Carolina State University (NCSU), North Carolina Agricultural & Technical State University (NC A&T SU), North Carolina Department of Agriculture and Consumer Services (NCDA & CS), and many nonprofit organizations and farmer groups. While the work at CEFS is not only about organic agriculture, many of its current programs and its history, implementation, maturation, lessons learned, and future directions can be instructive to other land-grant universities as they develop integrated organic programs at their institutions.

In 1990, the North Carolina Cooperative Extension Service (NCCES) selected sustainable agriculture as one of several national issues for special focus. In early 1991, Dean Durwood Bateman of The College of Agriculture and Life Sciences (CALS) at NCSU, Dean Burleigh Webb at the School of Agriculture at NC A&T SU, and Commissioner Jim Graham at the NCDA formed a task force composed of research and extension faculty and a diverse group of advisory personnel. The early 1990s was a period when the organic agriculture community and many of the nongovernmental organizations (NGOs) supporting it were very critical of the university's lack of programming on organic and sustainable agriculture. Farmers were forging ahead with virtually no institutional support to find solutions for the many challenges they faced in organic production in the southeastern United States.

The strategy of the Sustainable Agriculture Task Force was to meet this criticism directly by including these groups in its process. This strategy resulted in the development of many collaborative relationships between the universities and their former critics; these relationships have grown over the years. Carolina Farm Stewardship Association and Rural Advancement Foundation International (RAFI-USA) were early partners followed by Landloss Prevention Project, Operation Spring Plant, and other groups across the state. During the first two years, program support and faculty interest grew steadily, and The North Carolina Agricultural Research Service (NCARS) became a collaborative partner in the Task Force.

A survey of CALS faculty with sustainable agriculture interests at that time revealed a relatively high success rate in obtaining competitive grant funding through the early USDA Low Input Sustainable Agriculture (LISA) and later the Sustainable Agriculture Research and Education (SARE) programs. Furthermore, it was obvious that significant research and extension activity existed that was not directly in support of organics but involved components of sustainable agricultural systems. Dr. Larry King in Crop Science and Dr. Mike Linker in the Integrated Pest Management (IPM) program were early leaders whose work opened the path for integrated systems thinking in research. Nevertheless, there appeared to be a pressing need to address the complex, multidisciplinary issues involved in the concept of sustainable and organic agriculture. The ability to focus on holistic, long-term, interdisciplinary work not driven by single commodity interests was seen to be very important.

The integration of a sustainable agriculture program through all aspects of the land-grant mission—academic, extension, and research—was a goal. The acquisition of a field research and education center (now the Center for Environmental Farming Systems) dedicated to sustainable agriculture and including a focus on organic farming was thought to be highly desirable and could serve as a focal point for program support. In all phases of the work of the Sustainable Agriculture Task Force, a high priority was given to seeking participation by farmers and other nonuniversity advisors.

Specific recommendations made by the sustainable agriculture task force in December 1992 to enhance sustainable and organic agriculture programs at the universities and in North Carolina are listed below, together with actions that were taken as a result of each recommendation.

Sustainable Agriculture Task Force Recommendations in 1992

1. While in transition to a formal program status, continue to build the sustainable agriculture program through the work of the Task Force. *The Task Force evolved into an advisory group for the Center for Environmental Farming Systems (CEFS).*

2. When formal program status is achieved, retain the Advisory Council structure as an integral part of the program. *Today advisory councils exist for CEFS and for the North Carolina Sustainable Agriculture Research and Education Program.*

3. Seek ways to formally link IPM and Sustainable Agriculture programs. *During the past 15 years, IPM and sustainable agriculture programs worked closely on a variety of projects. Unfortunately at the time of this writing (August 2009), due to budget short-fall, the FTE assigned to the CALS IPM position was eliminated and IPM duties reassigned internally.*

4. Establish a North Carolina Research and Education Center that is a cooperative effort representing a broad coalition of groups and organizations

with a stake in the future of North Carolina agriculture. *As a result of the Task Force recommendations, the 800-ha (~2000-acre) CEFS facility was dedicated in 1994 at the Cherry Research Farm located near Goldsboro, NC.*

5.   Build strong cooperative and interdisciplinary teams including farmers, farm advisors, and researchers to plan, conduct, and review sustainable agriculture research and demonstration projects. *Such teams exist today and are focused on work at several of the CEFS units.*

6.   Promote the usefulness of a full range of farming options for North Carolina producers from small-scale organic to large-scale commercial operations, provided they embrace the basic tenets of the sustainable agriculture concept. *Sustainable agriculture principles and practices have been developed for a full range of farming systems.*

7.   Integrate sustainable agriculture concepts into academic curricula of the Colleges. *Four new courses and a new Agroecology Minor program have been developed and taught, including introductory and advanced agroecology courses, an online agroecology course, and a graduate level course in sustainable agriculture at NCSU.*

8.   Reassign research and extension personnel to concentrate on sustainable agriculture programs. *A part-time sustainable agriculture coordinator and three new faculty positions have been added.*

9.   Build regional leadership by offering to host the Southern Regional SARE Program if the opportunity arises. *Although NCSU did not compete for the Regional SARE Research and Education Management entity, together NCSU and NCA&T were awarded the assignment as the first management consortium for the Regional SARE Professional Development Program.*

10.   Provide training for agricultural extension agents that assists them to implement sustainable agriculture programming in their respective counties. *Agricultural Extension has offered sustainable agriculture training annually for the past 15 yr. This year all agents will be required to complete an online training module created by the national office.*

In the ensuing 15 years since the Task Force published its report, the focus on organic agriculture and agricultural sustainability in the colleges of agriculture at both land-grant universities has continued to increase. This is evidenced in part by the success of NCSU faculty, NC A&TSU faculty, farmers, and NGOs in the USDA Southern Region SARE competitive grants program. North Carolina ranked number one in four of the six grant categories and number one overall in funds awarded. Nevertheless, perhaps the most obvious reflection of the Task Force recommendations has been the development and growth of the Center for Environmental Farming Systems.

Center Development and Implementation

In 1994, the three partner institutions and several participating NGOs came together to dedicate the 800-ha (~2000-acre) site near Goldsboro, NC, which was formerly a state farm associated with Cherry Hospital state mental facility. Teams of faculty and stakeholders were formed to determine what research and demonstration "units" would be included, where they would be sited, how they would be managed and developed, and how they would be funded. Already at Cherry Farm, there was a confinement dairy, confinement swine facility, and beef production unit. The teams determined that the initial research and outreach units to develop at CEFS would be a farming systems research unit designed to compare diverse farming systems over the long term, an organic unit designed to compare organic farming systems over the long term, dairy and beef units redesigned to be pasture based and demonstrate sustainable production systems, and a conservation tillage unit. These are descriptions of the individual CEFS Research and Demonstration Units:

Conservation Tillage Unit

This was one of the first long-term experiments to be initiated at CEFS under the leadership of Dr. George Naderman, NCSU Soil Scientist. This no-till comparative experiment ran from 1996 to 2001 and included typical North Carolina crops in the rotation: maize (*Zea mays* L.), soybean [*Glycine max* (L.) Merr.], cotton (*Gossypium hirsutum* L.), peanut (*Arachis hypogaea* L.), and wheat (*Triticum aestivum* L.). Scientists monitored yield and economics, soil quality, nutrients, and pesticides in groundwater and runoff, and the effects on wildlife. A report on this research is available online (Naderman et al., 2006). Although the Conservation Tillage Unit does not currently have an active research program, conservation tillage remains an important research topic at CEFS, a component of research on the Farming Systems Research Unit (FSRU), and the subject of several recent graduate student projects at CEFS. In addition, researchers from NC A&T SU have recently initiated a conservation tillage study on the CEFS Small Farm Unit.

Farming Systems and Organic Research Units

Although the initial concept was to develop two long-term systems trials, the discussions resulted in considerable overlap. The farming systems research group began meeting in 1994 to identify and design an experiment to assess short- and long-term biological, environmental, and economic impacts of different agricultural systems. This group included research and extension faculty representing both land-grant universities; conventional, transitional, and organic farmers; and representatives from many of North Carolina's agriculture-based, nonprofit organizations. This 3-yr group process consisted of regular meetings in which various models and concepts of systems research were presented and discussed. The project actually began as two separate studies. The first experiment was being developed for implementation on the Organic Unit at CEFS. That trial was to compare several different long-term organic farming management strategies (e.g., with or without the integration of animals). At the same time, the FSRU experiment was also being developed, but without an organic component. In March of 1997, a workshop facilitated by Dr. Bill Liebhart and the late Dr. Benjamin Stinner was held to address the key issues involved in system design and implementation. As a result, faculty arrived at a consensus on the significant benefits in combining the two experiments and working together in this effort. That decision increased the breadth and depth of the experiment and resulted in the drafting of a research proposal. The proposal was submitted in 1997 to USDA Southern Region SARE and was awarded funding in 1998 to initiate the study.

The long-term organic comparative systems research was integrated within the FSRU with four organic subplots each replicated three times, allowing comparisons within different types of organic management in addition to comparisons with other management systems. Nevertheless, the need for a dedicated organic unit for research, demonstration, and outreach was still evident. Subsequently a 40-ha (~100-acre) site was located for the organic unit, and organic crop production began in 1997 after a 3-yr transition period. The site was certified in 1997, and three organic crops were produced: soybean, maize, and wheat. After severe flooding from hurricanes Fran (1996) and Floyd (1999) the organic unit was moved to an upland site in 2000.

On the FSRU, 81 ha were divided, on the basis of intensive soil mapping, into three replications of five systems (Mueller et al., 2002):

- conventional cash cropping system (i.e., best management practices, short-rotation cash-crop)
- integrated crop–animal system
- organic production system
- plantation forestry/woodlot (commercially valuable forest species)
- successional ecosystem (i.e., old field succession)

Each system was further divided into subplots allowing internal systems comparisons. Soils on the FSRU were intensively mapped in 1996 on the basis of soil type and drainage. Blocks were designated based on similar "diagnostic" soil types assigned within each block of five systems. All intensive sampling and measurements were made within these diagnostic soil units. Five permanent, georeferenced sampling points were designated within the diagnostic soil of each subplot in each block and system (Fig. 12–1).

Finally, it was understood from the beginning that the long-term experiment must have the capability to "nest" short-term studies within the overall structure of the experiment without compromising the long-term goals. Even the most avid supporters of the concept are uncomfortable with the idea of having to wait 10 or 15 yr or longer to obtain results. Furthermore, it was deemed important that the systems under study be fundamentally quite different to be able to withstand periodic changes in rotations and other details without compromising the long-term objectives of the experiment. A summary of the experiment and early experimental findings can be found in Mueller et al. (2006).

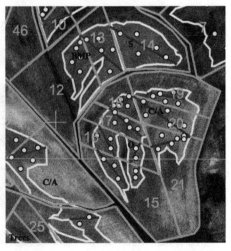

Fig. 12–1. Soil mapping in 1996 of the 81-ha Farming Systems Research Unit.

Dairy Unit

Eastern North Carolina and other rural areas in the South have potential advantages for pasture-based and organic dairy production systems. Such advantages include productive land, long growing seasons, potential for diversification, and less urban pressure than areas near growing cities. Lower-investment pasture systems may provide a competitive advantage for new or relocating dairy farm businesses. North Carolina and other states in the south-eastern United States are deficient in fluid milk products; pasture-based and/or organic dairying may be one way to help stabilize local milk supplies. Local milk supply for both conventional and organic milk has become even more important as transportation costs have escalated for moving milk long distances.

The pasture-based dairy unit at CEFS was established to examine practical strategies and herd management techniques applicable to dairy grazing systems in the South. Pasture-based dairy farms in the South represent a relatively small percentage of dairy production, similar to other areas of the country. Organic milk represents only a small proportion of total production. However, beginning in 2007, some dairy producers in North Carolina transitioned to certified organic milk production, looking to CEFS for ideas and practices that could be implemented on their farms.

The CEFS dairy differs from most other U.S. dairy research farms for several reasons. The dairy is designed to conduct studies examining performance efficiencies of differing systems across multiple years. Short-term component studies can also be included within the primary systems. Approximately 180 cows and associated young stock do most forage harvesting via grazing, although supplemental concentrates and stored forages are available if needed. The pasture-based system also means that there is minimal manure storage because cattle recycle a high percentage of nutrients from urine and feces directly back to pastures. Milking facilities are "swing-type" with 14 units that allow for cows to be milked efficiently within 2 to 3 h each milking. Cows are seasonally calved so that calves, heifers, and cows can be managed efficiently in groups. Crossbreeding is studied in comparison with pure Jerseys and pure Holsteins. Newborn calves are started on pasture in small groups by 2 wk of age and fed milk once daily (Fig. 12–2).

Fig. 12–2. Jersey, Holstein, and crossbred calves with access to pasture at an early age illustrate the novel aproaches used at the CEFS dairy unit.

Cows are not housed, but shade paddocks are used in summer, and supplemental forage is provided in designated winter lounging areas.

The CEFS dairy has worked on a number of practices applicable to organic dairy systems. One of the biggest challenges to organic production has been control of horn flies [*Haematobia irritans* (L.)], which are implicated in spreading mastitis from infected cows to other cows and heifers. Several promising alternative strategies to control horn flies without use of commercial insecticides have been studied. Populations of dung beetles have been monitored under various management systems for effects on nutrient recycling. Successfully rearing young dairy stock without use of anthelmintics has been demonstrated. Various combinations of pasture species and use of legumes to reduce nutrient inputs are being examined. Also, varying stocking rates and types and amounts of forage and grain supplementation have been investigated. Differences in fatty acid, flavor characteristics, and consumer acceptability of milk from pastured cows have also been studied. Because of the organic requirement for using pasture, the assurance that milk from pastured cows is readily acceptable across seasons is very important.

Work done during the first several years at CEFS is having an impact in the region and beyond. A Missouri dairy producer indicated that CEFS was one of the few places in the United States doing relevant pasture-based dairy research. There have been several opportunities for dairy producers and other dairy professionals to get ideas from CEFS, either from educational meetings on site or from other educational events that included research results or updates about ongoing research. A few dairy producers have started anew in pasture-based dairying in the past several years and New Zealand dairy producers are investing in pasture-based dairying in the South. There have also been several existing dairy producers who have increased use of pasture and crossbreeding on their dairy farms. We expect to have a similar impact with our organic dairy clientele as we proceed.

With cooperation and incentives from Organic Valley, the few current organic producers in North Carolina and neighboring states are looking for research support of these systems. Other producers with potential interest in organic production are hesitant to transition their herds without seeing documentation via research or from successful organic producers. SARE-funded Research initiated in 2009 at CEFS will further examine strategies applicable to organic dairy production systems in the South. This will include managing a portion of the herd organically and testing various organic production techniques and concepts within that system.

Both station research and summaries of commercial dairy farm business records have documented that pasture-based dairy production systems can be economically competitive with confinement feeding systems. Well-managed dairy systems that use pasture often have lower milk production per cow than other management systems, but also lower feed costs, lower labor costs, improved animal health, and lower capital investment for housing and manure systems that generally more than offset lower milk income. Pasture-based dairy producers often participate in formal and informal networks with other dairy graziers to share ideas and solve problems. The same principles apply to organic dairy production. SARE Professional Development funding has been obtained to facilitate information exchange among organic producers across different areas of the

South. We are also working to raise awareness of opportunities and issues associated with organic dairy production, so veterinarians, extension faculty, and others working with the dairy industry will have greater understanding of the growing organic dairy industry.

Beef Unit

The beef unit at CEFS is managed primarily as a demonstration using best management practices appropriate for eastern North Carolina and other coastal areas in the South. Typical of other beef cow–calf herds in the area, the approximately 120-cow beef cow herd is assigned to some of the less productive land at CEFS. Much of the work to date has examined appropriate cattle genetics and pasture species for local conditions. Starting with an Angus base, we have incorporated Senepol, a hybrid breed developed in the Caribbean with heat tolerance and resistance to insects, including horn flies. In addition, Braunvieh, as a terminal sire breed, has been introduced to increase weaning weight potential of the calves.

The beef herd calves from January through March and is managed mainly on pasture using combinations of cool season and warm season species. Supplemental forage, primarily as grass hay, is fed during winter or during droughts. Limited amounts of grain are fed to newly weaned calves during the first fall and winter. In recent years, there has been more interest in pasture-finishing beef animals, and such work will likely increase in the future. Trials using dairy cross steers have compared pasture-finishing with grain finishing; this work looks promising for certain markets and likely is applicable to more traditional beef breeds as well. In North Carolina, local, pasture-finished, and "natural" seem to be of more interest than certified organic in beef production and marketing at this point.

Swine Unit

At the time CEFS was dedicated, there was a conventional swine operation on the site that was later closed down because of an outdated lagoon found to be leaking. State money had been designated to rebuild the conventional swine facility at CEFS, but a grant from the W.K. Kellogg Foundation leveraged the NCDA&CS to apply that funding toward building an alternative facility at the site instead. The CEFS Swine Unit was developed in 2006 and consists of five approximately 12 by 27 m (40 by 90 feet) deep-bedded hoop houses (Fig. 12–3). While deep-bedded hoop houses are common in Iowa and other parts of the Midwest, the industry

Fig. 12–3. Hoop house facility established at CEFS in 2006.

in North Carolina had been built around slatted floor confinement facilities that rely on lagoons to handle waste. A complementary outdoor unit has also been developed, and funds have been received to evaluate conservation practices for outdoor swine production. These new initiatives will fit well with an organic swine program. There is interest in the production of organic swine among producers, but currently other alternative markets exist and are driving the market. These include antibiotic-free and pasture-raised swine. At this time there are no slaughter facilities in North Carolina that carry organic certification, so growers must take advantage of other niche markets. Constraints to organic production are few as long as availability of organically certified land and feed are available. Currently, the work in the hoop houses is focused on antibiotic resistance, using a unique herd that has been antibiotic free for more than 30 yr.

Small Farm Unit

The SFU provides research and demonstrations of organic and sustainable production and marketing practices to diverse audiences. The SFU consists of approximately 12 ha (~30 acres) with a wide range of soil types, equipment, buildings, and educational focal points. The function of the SFU is to provide stakeholders a place where a systems approach demonstrates a whole farm model in which research is embedded that is relevant to successful sustainable small farm operation. Research topics are nested into the whole farm unit design. A certified organic integrated crop and animal farm of approximately 3 ha (7.5 acres) is at the core of the SFU. The SFU began as a student intern farm (1998–2005) where organic production concepts and practices served as its base. In addition, because of the growth of organic markets and opportunities, organic research and demonstrations are important to meet customer needs in local food markets. The organic focus demonstrates production steps to producers and local extension agents, who need to see actual functioning organic production in their region of the state.

Interns are involved for a short-term experience (~8 wk), and apprentices work in the small farm unit for extended period of time. Both groups are very much part of the vitality of the small farm unit in terms of labor and decision making. The interns develop skills and understanding of organic farming, sustainable agriculture, and community food systems that will serve them in graduate school. Apprentices learn the skills of managing a functioning demonstration and research farm with the collaborations of all the stakeholders. They are thus prepared for jobs and careers in sustainable school farm programs or farming across the country.

Currently the SFU is engaged in the following research efforts: organic systems work (utilizing animals, soil building, and high value crops such as organic vegetables), season extension (high tunnels), organic transplant production, small fruit (blueberries [*Vaccinium angustifolium* Aiton]), pastured meat (goats and poultry), grafted tomatoes (*Solanum lycopersicum* L.), cover crop/no-till system (organic and conventional), as well as agroecology biosystems. Education outreach programs include agriculture in the classroom (Discover Ag, which serves third-grade students in the surrounding county), a variety of workshops (i.e., high tunnel, organic certification short course), and a Farm Festival reaching out to the community.

During the past two years, nearly 3000 people visited the Small Farm Unit for educational reasons. More than 800 third-graders and their teachers from Wayne County schools learned about farming and agriculture. More than 650 farmers learned new production practices in workshops and demonstrations on cover crops and rotations, small farm equipment selection and use, greenhouse management, and alternative enterprises. More than 50 Cooperative Extension Agents from North Carolina, South Carolina, and Virginia learned from research and demonstrations on the Small Farm Unit and brought that information back to share with farmers and growers in their counties. Approximately 150 under-graduate and graduate students at NCSU participated in field education classes in IPM, insect identification, and other practical education. In 2007, 1000 people were hosted for the CEFS Farm Festival and observed the various education and demonstration sites across the Small Farm Unit.

New Organic Research Unit

The Center for Environmental Farming Systems is surrounded on all sides by either the Neuse River or the Little River. In 1996 and 1999, shortly after initiation of CEFS, hurricanes Fran and Floyd left most of the facility under water, as Eastern North Carolina experienced a 100-yr flood, followed 3 yr later by a 500-yr flood. The original Organic Unit was particularly flood prone, and a decision was made to move the unit to another site on higher ground before money was invested in physical infrastructure. Beginning in 2000 at the site of what is now the Small Farm Unit, the Organic Unit was developed as an integrated organic working farm with land available for research as well. As interest in organic grains has grown in the state, the Organic Research Unit was moved for a third and hope-fully final time to accommodate a much larger area and large-scale agronomic research in addition to smaller scale horticultural research. The new Organic Unit is now 32 ha (~80 acres) and is undergoing certification.

As funding for organic research has steadily increased, the number of researchers and the diversity of disciplines involved have also increased. This growth is placing new demands on experiment stations to determine what changes in their operating procedures are needed to cater to this new audience. Organic farmers have argued that research on organic systems must be con-ducted in an appropriate setting. Experiments for short periods of time on land that is otherwise managed conventionally or on small plots of land sandwiched between conventionally managed land may not result in relevant conclusions. Their arguments have been bolstered by studies of the changes in insect com-munities, weed populations, diseases, and soil quality that occur over long time periods and large spatial scales under organic management.

The CEFS was in a position to address many of the concerns that organic farmers had voiced, in addition to the growing interest in organic grain produc-tion in the state. With a large land base and adequate staffing, and a new organic farming systems specialist at NCSU, we could once again develop and manage a large-scale organic research unit as we had in its early years before the hurricane flooding. The mission of the new Organic Research Unit is to supply a research environment that approximates as much as possible a working organic farm. To guide CEFS in this effort, a panel of organic farmers and agricultural profession-als was convened to decide how this unit would be managed, including the types of practices and crop rotations to be used. A 4-yr rotation of maize, soybeans,

Fig. 12–4. Using a high residue cultivator in a rolled rye cover crop organic system.

wheat, hay, and various cover crops was decided on by the farmer panel (Fig. 12–4). Farmers evaluated multiple criteria in developing the rotation. The rotation needed to break up pest cycles, be economically viable, and match production realities for the region in which CEFS is located. While the unit is designed to host research on any type of food or fiber crop, we also realized that horticultural crops would be too difficult to maintain as a base part of the rotation.

The realities of a research station were also considered when designing the Organic Research Unit. Planting and cultivation of crops has to be done in a timely manner to be effective. With multiple research projects occurring at any one time, labor can easily become a limiting factor. The inclusion of hay in the rotation was a partial answer to this dilemma because it requires less attention than organic row crops. The other answer was to purchase a separate set of equipment for the unit. This relieved some scheduling conflicts with other units at the center; also, concern about contaminating the organic plots with conventional seeds or pesticides is reduced. A separate storage facility for equipment and working area for organic researchers was also constructed.

To ensure that the new unit serves a diverse group of researchers, a system of managing information was developed so that researchers could easily acquire past data on a field's history, soil type, and production potential. Each field was divided into sections (0.2 ha, 0.5 acres) for record keeping, and an online database was established so researchers could both record their activities and search past activities on every parcel. This database will also serve to keep stakeholders informed of what research is being conducted on the unit.

Future directions for the Organic Research Unit involve replicating this model at other stations around North Carolina. Multiple stations have approached CEFS to create their own organic units in response to local farmer needs. The 18 stations in North Carolina represent a diversity of cropping systems, soil types, and plant hardiness zones. New rotations, crop management strategies, and equipment needs will have to be developed in conjunction with local organic farmers. In many ways, this process is reminiscent of how many of these stations were started in the first place—farmers asking for information that applies to their locality and cropping systems.

Complementary to the development of the Organic Research Unit is a newly funded Cooperative State Research, Education, and Extension Service (CSREES) Integrated Organic Program grant. The grant will establish and conduct whole farm-level evaluations of field border vegetation effects on organic management of insect pests and weed seed banks, and on farmland wildlife. The researchers will examine the effects of different types of border habitat plantings on the beneficial insect communities they harbor, and the effects of these communities on insect as well as weed management in adjacent crops. They will assess the value of the border habitats as cover and a food resource for quail. In addition, they will examine the arthropod diets of songbirds that move between the borders and crop fields to assess the value of these habitats, and the potential contribution of early successional songbirds to insect management in adjacent crops. A 2009 USDA Organic Agriculture Research and Extension Initiative grant will fund a project on breeding for several organic crops and on-farm testing.

Organic Extension Programming

From the beginning, CEFS had a focus on extension training and outreach, and integrated these activities with the research whenever possible. Annually, we offered comprehensive field days that showcased research on the comprehensive facility, or discipline-oriented extension training sessions that highlighted specific topics.

Before 1998, extension agents in North Carolina had little formal training in organic agriculture, and yet interest among consumers and farmers was on the rise. There had been piece-meal training on components over the years, but no comprehensive training that immersed agents in the subject matter. It was our hypothesis that extension agents were reluctant to work with organic farmers in part because they were uncomfortable with their own knowledge base and had limited experience with biologically based systems. Reluctance was based on other factors as well, including lack of an adequate research database and discomfort in assessing the validity of anecdotal information, plus attitudinal barriers about who organic growers are and what they believe.

A comprehensive training for agents in the form of a four-credit graduate level course at NCSU was proposed. Funding from Southern Region SARE made the training possible. In North Carolina, agents are required to take one graduate level course every 5 yr to fulfill their professional development requirement. We offered the in-service training as an "off-model" course, which consisted of six intensive 2-d sessions spanning a year. This fulfilled agents' continuing education requirements and was more desirable to them than attending classes in Raleigh three times per week for an entire semester, especially since some agents drive 4 h each way to campus. In addition, we wanted to provide an experience that spanned an entire production year, cover crop to cover crop. These 2-d training sessions consisted of lectures, hands-on demonstrations, group discussions, field trips, class exercises, and homework. Two unique features of the workshops were the interdisciplinary, team teaching approach and the emphasis on integration of information about interactions among production practices. Interdisciplinary teaching teams allowed for a fully integrated treatment of subject matter and presented a "whole systems" perspective. Topics included engaging organic farmers, marketing, information delivery, organic fertility management, composting, organic greenhouse management, soil quality, cover cropping, tillage systems, crop rotation and intercropping, livestock systems, and organic insect, weed, and disease management.

Agents reported that the training was very successful. The course met a professional development requirement but was offered in a unique way that made it convenient for them. Because of this, many agents took the course because they were interested in the professional development opportunity, even though some were skeptical about organic farming. This made for a diverse audience, with varying interest levels—we were definitely not "preaching to the choir." Agents brought diverse ideas, opinions, biases, and philosophies to the training program. This diversity of opinion and thought greatly enhanced the training by facilitating open dialog and honest intellectual examination of the principles and practices expounded.

Evaluations indicated that because of the basic focus on biological systems the information learned would not only be useful in much of their future educational programming, but also in day-to-day problem-solving with all types of farmers and farming enterprises. Written and oral comments from agents indicated appreciation for the in-depth focus on topics, the hands-on nature of the training, and the interaction with organic farmers and NGO participants. Cooperating with growers in their counties, three of the agents in the class were awarded SARE producer grants after writing the proposals as their final assignments in 1999. Many have initiated organic training sessions in their counties and are still very actively facilitating the growth of organics in the state. A full description of the training was reported by Creamer et al. (2000).

Academic Programming: The CEFS Internship Program

In addition to establishing a strong research and extension program at CEFS, there was a concerted effort to develop diverse educational activities in sustainable and organic agriculture and agroecology at NCSU (Schroeder et al., 2006). Within the CEFS facility, a 3-ha student farm was originally developed, primarily for agroecology and sustainable agriculture education. This farm was designed specifically to provide an area for students to explore sustainable and organic agriculture practices, and a Sustainable Agriculture Summer Internship program was developed in 1999 and has been offered annually since (Fig. 12–5). The principal goal of the Sustainable Agriculture Summer Internship program was to provide hands-on experiences in organic farm management linked with an

Fig. 12–5. The CEFS Residential Internship Program provides hands-on experience.

interdisciplinary education in sustainable agriculture principles. During the program, students are exposed to various sustainable agriculture topics and activities through a diversity of inquiry-based learning methods, including classroom instruction and discussions, field-based activities, local farm field trips, faculty-mentored research projects, organic farm production practices, and marketing experience. Each week, members from an interdisciplinary faculty teaching team engage students in a variety of topics, such as integrated pest management, soil ecology and management, socioeconomics and marketing, and sustainable animal production through in-class lectures and field activities.

The Sustainable Agriculture Summer Internship program continues to attract up to 20 students per year with varied interests, many from outside North Carolina (63%) and some international (11%). More than one-half of the students (56%) have not had any agriculture or related training. At the end of each internship program, students are individually interviewed to assess course content, activities, and organization. The faculty teaching team uses these qualitative student evaluations to improve and continually enrich the sustainable agriculture internship curriculum. Many students consider the research experience and interactions with faculty to be an important part of the internship program that they wouldn't have obtained from their general undergraduate curriculum. Several students have gone on to graduate programs in sustainable agriculture at NCSU with their faculty mentors. From the accumulation of student evaluations, an evaluation of sustainable and organic agriculture internship programs offered nationally, and administrative changes, the student farm was transitioned into a Small Farm Unit focus at CEFS. The Sustainable Agriculture Summer Internship program has also evolved to emphasize more of a sustainable agriculture research focus. Students continue to participate in weekly discussions and field activities related to the diversity of sustainable agriculture topics, but now are much more involved with faculty research projects related to a specific area of sustainable and organic agriculture. In response to the increasing demand of individuals desiring more of an experience focused on hands-on farming, a Sustainable Agriculture Apprenticeship program was initiated in 2006. This apprentice program was designed for one to three individuals per season to work closely with the farm manager on the Small Farm at CEFS for a longer period of 2 to 12 mo. The apprentices are involved in all aspects of sustainable and organic crop production and animal management on the farm. The apprenticeship program, with less academic focus than the internship program, provides needed education to individuals interested in beginning to farm organically.

Maturation of CEFS

As CEFS has evolved, our research has become more diverse and sophisticated. Rather than measuring just a set of parameters associated with various farming systems we can begin to look at what the parameters mean with regard to sustainability. Our extension and outreach programming has become much more expansive, and now we reach out to a much broader audience. While in the early years we hosted field days targeted to producers and extension agents, we now include educational sessions aimed at consumers, youth, health professionals, city planners, and more. Our academic programming has evolved from a summer internship for undergraduate students and a site and platform for graduate research to a formal academic program in agroecology. New strategic initiatives have been added that aren't necessarily based on one of the previously described units at the 2000-acre facility, as programming has become more statewide. New strategic initiatives include organic animal production, energy conservation in agriculture, and community-based food systems.

Research

During the first 10 yr at CEFS a rich diversity of research has been published spanning some 23 different peer-reviewed scientific journals. Research at the FSRU has continued to expand and broaden from the initial focus (Mueller et al., 2006) to include new dimensions, such as the influence of natural areas on weed populations in adjacent crop fields and assessing the performance of agricultural production systems based on environmental indicators. As the systems are entering a more mature state after 10 yr, focus is shifting to carbon flux, and changes in soil quality. For example, one of the most recent studies involves an indicator system that provides an estimate of which production system would result in the best environmental performance in the conditions similar to small-farm environments in North Carolina. The analysis concentrates on environmental impact of the various production systems and looks at possible differences in yield estimates only to provide some insight into economic performance of these systems.

Extension and Outreach

From the inception of CEFS until 2006, most of the extension and outreach programming was geared toward producers and agricultural extension personnel. We would generally host five or six targeted extension training programs on specific topics, such as pasture management, organic disease management, cover cropping, or soil quality (Fig. 12–6). We would also host one field day per year that included a comprehensive tour of the site. While we were careful to highlight

Fig. 12–6. Extension field training on the role of cover crops in organic systems.

new research initiatives taking place on the tours, because much of our work is long-term, some felt the tours became redundant over time.

As our thinking matured, we recognized the need to reach out to a much broader audience with our message about organic production and local sustainable food systems. At the same time, especially over the last 3 yr, the interest in these issues has exploded. Now, it's difficult to keep up with the diverse groups that are becoming interested in the local foods movement, not always organic. These include groups and individuals focused on public health and nutrition, youth, food justice, consumer issues, policy, city and county governments, environmental groups, and more. To meet the growing interest, we have greatly expanded our extension and outreach programming to go well beyond a focus on narrow production issues geared only toward farmers and extension agents.

"Seasons of Sustainable Agriculture" is a workshop series initiated in 2006 to celebrate the first 10 yr of programming at CEFS. The workshop series has now become a permanent part of CEFS, and the offerings are advertised together in a brochure that is distributed widely and also appears on the CEFS website. In 2008 the series included 36 workshops including a range of topics reaching a broad audience including: small fruit production; maintaining breeding flocks of standard breed chickens; why buy local?; organic grain production; techniques, husbandry, and evaluation for outdoor hog production; gardening with kids; bread wheat and organic production; managing energy risks, reducing energy costs and exploring alternative energy sources; pasture-based dairy management; bugs in the garden, making use of beneficial insects for crop pest management and pollination; organic certification; and developing community-based food systems.

In 2007, we initiated an annual "Sustainable Agriculture Lecture," meant to reach a broad audience, stimulate thought, and initiate dialog about a broad range of sustainable agriculture topics among the general public, faculty and students from area universities, and members of the agricultural community. This first inaugural lecture was given by Carlo Petrini, founder of the International Slow Food Movement. Approximately 800 attended his lecture, and another 400 attended a farm-to-fork picnic featuring pairings of the area's top chefs and farmers. Several articles in area press broadened the impact of the visit. The 2008 lecture was offered by Judy Wicks, connecting the local foods movement to the local business movement.

In 2007, again associated with our 10 yr programming anniversary, we initiated an annual "Farm Festival." This open house takes place at the Small Farm Unit, the most picturesque unit at CEFS, but includes tours to the rest of the facility. The open house is designed to be informative, with educational displays and activities, but to also celebrate sustainable agriculture and local food, targeting families and the general public. Approximately 1000 visitors attended each of the two years since inception. In 2007 the Festival included more than 35 educational booths, eight workshops, tours of both the entire farm and the Small Farm Unit, kids activities (including a crop maze, scavenger hunt, seed art, hat making, maize grinding, and a farm olympics), farmers market booths, local food, and six live musical acts. Through this event, our goals were to share the work of CEFS, introduce visitors to a broad range of organizations, programs, and concepts in sustainable and organic agriculture and community-based food systems, and highlight the diversity and importance of sustainable and local agriculture in North Carolina.

Academic Programming

From the growing student interest in sustainable and organic agriculture generated from the internship program, members of the interdisciplinary faculty team at CEFS led the development in 2004 of an interdisciplinary undergraduate Agroecology Minor program in the Department of Crop Science at NCSU. With an additional USDA grant and a commitment from the College of Agriculture and Life Sciences, a new agroecology curriculum and new courses were developed. Agroecology, which connects agriculture and ecology into a science of sustainable agriculture, uses holistic, problem-solving approaches to critically examine production practices and food systems from an ecological, economic, and social perspective (Schroeder et al., 2006). The very nature of agroecology as a field of study is multidisciplinary, drawing on knowledge from many disciplines, including ecology, plant, soil, animal, and related sciences (Altieri and Francis, 1992). Essential to the success and sustainability of this program was a new faculty position dedicated to the course and curriculum development, student recruiting, and advising. Although the curriculum for this interdisciplinary agroecology program involves courses from 12 different departments, the agroecology program coordinator advises students, seeks curriculum changes, coordinates associated faculty, oversees the program Web site, and informs and advises students from the Department of Crop Science at NCSU, which has proved to be a successful approach.

The primary goal of the Agroecology Minor is to provide students from all disciplines a fundamental understanding of agricultural systems from an ecological, economic, and sociological perspective. We believe an interdisciplinary agroecology program that emphasizes a systems-level approach, critical thinking, and opportunities for research and international experiences will increase student understanding of sustainable and organic agriculture and expand future career options. Two new agroecology core courses, Introduction to Agroecology and Advanced Agroecology, were developed specifically for this minor program (Fig. 12–7). A distance education online section of Introduction to Agroecology was subsequently developed to reach additional people who would otherwise be

Fig. 12–7. Michelle Schroeder-Moreno presents biocontrol principles to Advanced Agroecology students.

limited by time or geography. Whether in a classroom or online, the agroecology courses and program at NCSU emphasize developing students' oral and written communication skills, critical thinking skills, working in collaborative learning groups, and experiential learning though a variety of teaching strategies using guest lectures, student-led discussion papers, peer review of student topic papers, and field trips to local farms (there is a virtual tour of a local organic farm for the online course). The Advanced Agroecology course additionally has a laboratory section, allowing for more hands-on experiences and examination of sustainable and organic agriculture practices.

To increase students' global awareness of the challenges to organic and sustainable agriculture internationally, a study-abroad course, Sustainability of Tropical Agroecosystems, was developed in a partnership with the University of Georgia (UGA) and NCSU in 2005. Students spend 3 wk traveling to diverse biomes within Costa Rica examining different agricultural production systems and neighboring natural systems, interacting with local producers, and meeting an international team of researchers and students at two different agricultural universities, EARTH University and the Tropical Agricultural Research and Higher Education Center (CATIE). This international agroecology course is open to students from all disciplines, and students in the agroecology courses and program are highly encouraged to participate.

Interest in agroecology and sustainable agriculture education continues to increase at NCSU and nationally, drawing in many new students and groups that have been traditionally underrepresented in agricultural sciences. Both the Sustainable Agriculture Internship Program and agroecology courses have been successful in attracting a diversity of students, including those from majors in agriculture education and extension, agronomy, horticultural science, soil science and animal science, but also from botany, ecology, environmental sciences, environmental engineering, forestry, and political science. The agroecology program has also been a vehicle to attract more women to agriculture. From 2004 to 2006, 45% of students enrolled in the Introduction to Agroecology course were female, compared to a 7% female enrollment in the degree programs in the Crop Science Department. From this growing demand, a new Agroecology Concentration within a new Plant and Soil Sciences degree program was developed for the fall semester of 2008. This new Agroecology concentration program is similar in focus to the Agroecology Minor, but the curriculum is expanded to serve as a building block for a new Agroecology degree program to be developed at NCSU in the near future. A degree program in agroecology that emphasizes a whole-system approach to agricultural science education is needed to prepare students to meet the increasingly complex challenges in our food and natural resource systems globally. The sustainability of our food systems depends on a new set of agricultural science leaders that can understand these complex environmental, social, and economic issues and integrate knowledge across disciplines. Land-grant universities need to be prepared to provide students the skills and knowledge in the areas of agroecology and sustainable and organic agriculture.

New Initiatives

In 2007 a strategic planning process was initiated through a committee made up of CEFS faculty, staff, and board members. Through that process, three new strategic initiatives were added to complement the activities already in place. These new initiatives are not attached to any physical unit at CEFS as programming has been in the past, but are statewide and cross-cutting across several of the units. These new initiatives include organic animal agriculture, energy, and community-based food systems.

Organic Animal Agriculture

Consumer demand for organic meat, dairy, and poultry products is rising. North Carolina leads the nation in organic laying hens, with more than 800,000 reported in 2005. Organic Valley, the largest cooperative of organic dairy farmers in the country, is helping North Carolina dairy farmers to convert to organic and is working with one existing milk processor to bottle organic milk in our state. A growing number of farmers in North Carolina are raising animals (e.g., pork, beef, chicken, and lamb) using sustainable and organic production practices and selling directly to consumers through farmers markets and community-supported agriculture (CSA) agreements to consumers interested in "pasture-raised," "grass-fed," and "free-range" meat and poultry products.

Key missing pieces in organic animal production systems include the local production of organic grains, reliable production of organic pasture, and access to organic slaughter facilities. To date, the organic industry in North Carolina has been primarily small-scale vegetable producers, and there has been little interest among grain commodity growers. As such, the overwhelming majority of the grain being fed to these animals is purchased from other states. In 2006, the department of Crop Science hired a new faculty member to work specifically on the development of an organic grains industry to meet these growing needs. An Organic Farm Panel was initiated to develop a research and education program on organic grain production. The panel is comprised of farmers, county agents, nonprofit partners, and researchers and meets twice annually. The Center for Environmental Farming Systems farm-to-fork Organic Animal initiative will have four major components: research, education and extension, processing, and marketing.

Research. Key topics of interest include:
- Organic grain production—weed management strategies in organic grain production, no-till production of organic grains, cover cropping, beneficial insect habitat
- Conservation practices in outdoor hog production—appropriate stocking densities to maintain ground cover, rotation patterns, appropriate pasture species, and pasture, woodlot, and wallow management
- Grass-fed, grass-finished and organic beef—achieving appropriate weight gain on summer forages and the relationship to meat quality, fly control in organic beef production, weed control in organic forages without the use of herbicides, and organic transition strategies for existing, weed-infested pastures.
- Organic dairy management

Education and Extension. Support for organic animal production will require activities that train extension agents and help cultivate the interest of new farmers willing and able to implement sustainable and organic practices. This includes outreach, education, professional networking, and mentoring opportunities for farmers, as well as technical services and training.

Processing. Supporting transitioning farmers to new markets will require expanded capacity to harvest and process sustainably and organically raised animals and develop value-added products from beef, poultry, and dairy. Limited infrastructure is available or accessible to local, independent producers. For example, there are only two processors with the equipment to smoke and cure pork products for independent producers, and no processing facility in North Carolina that is certified organic. Despite unprecedented demand, there are a variety of challenges within the current animal processing and meat distribution system in North Carolina that make it difficult to expand the market for organic meat and dairy. These include:

- A limited number of meat processing facilities that operate on a small-scale and that are accessible to independent producers and provide quality packaging
- Almost no value-added processing facilities that enable farmers to create products such as smoked bacon, cured hams, or hot dogs, all of which use "trim" or "end" meats and enhance farmers' profits
- Few trained butchers, the result being inconsistent meat cutting quality and packaging
- Lack of business enterprises (e.g., grower cooperatives, brokers, distributors) that operate at the local level and supply retail and restaurant venues with the volume of meat and the type of cuts they need to be competitive.

Marketing. A transition will also require increased awareness among consumers and committed buyers willing to rethink current systems of distribution, transportation, marketing, and consumption. Buyers need information, support, and strategic alliances to participate in rebuilding local food systems. Specific needs that CEFS can fulfill include:

- Becoming an information clearinghouse for consumers that explains the value of sustainable and organic animal production and meat consumption both to personal health, our environment, and our communities
- Developing strategic market alliances and a business model for delivering local, sustainable, and organic meat to retail markets
- Developing innovative direct market models—farmers who direct market meats have the highest net returns and cultivate a loyal, stable consumer base. Direct marketing requires a host of skills not all farmers are equipped with, and direct marketing meats requires dealing with meat processing, introducing an added expense and host of complex issues. We believe it is important to enable all farmers to diversify their market portfolio and include direct marketing whenever possible.

Energy and Sustainable Agriculture

Addressing energy needs and conservation emerged from the strategic planning process as an important new initiative for CEFS. The focus of our programs is on-farm energy conservation, on-farm energy production and use, reducing energy use in agricultural systems, and reducing greenhouse gas emissions. While we are also supporting some innovations around biofuels as they are incorporated into on-farm energy use, or waste oil use, we are not currently promoting biofuels as a viable solution in meeting our future energy needs and believe important sustainability evaluations and assessments are required in this arena first to help determine appropriate production practices and use of biofuels.

The CEFS energy focus to date has primarily been in partnership with the National Center of Appropriate Technology that is now staffing an energy specialist in North Carolina. Through two Risk Management Agency grants they received, we have undergone a complete assessment of the energy use and energy systems at CEFS. A report was generated to suggest ways to improve energy savings and efficiencies, and we have begun to implement its findings. We have hosted workshops for farmers to review findings and suggested solutions, and to demonstrate alternatives when appropriate as many of the findings are also relevant to other North Carolina farms.

In cooperation with North Carolina Farm Bureau, Rural Advancement Foundation International, and Carolina Farm Stewardship Association we hosted an energy forum in 2006 to bring together agriculture leadership of conventional and sustainable agriculture groups to discuss energy issues and solutions where we have common ground. Approximately 80 agriculture leaders attended, and a listserve facilitates ongoing communication.

Since 2006, again in cooperation with the National Center for Appropriate Technology and with funding from Risk Management Agency we hosted two "Fueling the Farm" workshops that focused on managing energy risks, reducing energy costs, and exploring alternative energy sources. We have new funding from the SARE PDP to train south-eastern extension personnel as certified energy advisors as they seek to meet the needs of producers suffering from rising energy costs.

There is also capacity at CEFS with the long-term farming systems experiment to evaluate carbon sequestration and greenhouse gas emissions across a range of production systems, particularly representing south-eastern agriculture. We are seeking funding to implement an in-depth research initiative around this topic.

Community-Based Food Systems

In 2002, CEFS received a grant from the W.K. Kellogg Foundation to develop direct markets for sustainable pork producers. The North Carolina Choices project involved providing technical support for producers and developing new direct markets through engagement with new partners. In particular, we partnered with the major environmental groups in the state who agreed to be the "market" for sustainable pork. The Sierra Club for example, could reach all 17,000 North Carolina members via email, and were committed to providing this "pull" to allow producers to raise pork in a way that agreed with their environmental ethic. Through this 4-yr project, several lessons were learned that has broadened the CEFS work to include a farm-to-fork approach to rebuilding North Carolina's local food economy.

While there were ample producers eager to produce for this market and join the North Carolina Choices network, *and* ample market for their products, the critical missing link, as in most states, was the infrastructure in the middle that would allow for local production, processing, distribution, and marketing. When we started the project, there was no place for independent pork producers to make value-added products like bacon or smoked hams, even though North Carolina is one of the nation's top pork-producing states. Sale of these value-added products can make the difference between a profitable enterprise and an unprofitable one. While the lack of infrastructure is especially true for meat, it is true for other products as well.

At CEFS, we believe there are important reasons to build a local sustainable food economy in North Carolina, including economic development, job creation within farming and food sectors, preservation of open space, decreased use of fossil fuel and associated carbon emissions in some cases, enhanced consumer access to fresh nutritious foods, and improved food security. These issues have become even more important in today's economy. We have launched a new focus of CEFS to go beyond developing sustainable and organic production systems, to include work toward rebuilding a local food economy and community-based food systems.

A community-based food system is one in which sustainable food production, processing, distribution, and consumption are integrated to enhance the economic, environmental, social, and nutritional health of a particular place (Garrett and Feenstra, 1999). Locally supported, small-scale, diverse, and sustainable enterprises improve the ecological environment and also enhance the quality of life in local communities by positively impacting economic and social capital.

Our approach includes both statewide and county- or region-based farm-to-fork initiatives that include developing new markets, consumer education, supporting new businesses, incubating new farmers, implementing new policies, and educating the next generation of farmers and leadership. Currently there are many different organizations, including CEFS, operating a variety of projects on food systems piecemeal across the state of North Carolina. This shotgun approach with a new market here and a farm incubator there has had many successes, but lacks the synergy of a coordinated effort in one location, and the ability to build the momentum necessary to effect systemic change. One of our roles will be to develop county-based comprehensive initiatives with broad-based representative planning teams that can do work specific to the needs of the area and make significant progress toward building a sustainable local food economy.

We received grant funding in 2008 to provide leadership in developing a statewide action plan for developing a local food economy in North Carolina. Through the project, we systematically gathered counsel from leaders in all sectors of the food system, crafted priority actions and programs, explored policy options through working groups and regional meetings, and hosted a Sustainable Local Food Systems Summit to create the state action plan. The action plan will provide recommendations to decision makers, including policy makers, regulators, funders, and citizens and will guide collaborative initiatives led by statewide working groups formed at the Summit and created through this project. Through this project, we are reaching out to a much broader coalition than in the past, and these new players are self-motivated in their interest around the food system issue. In addition to CEFS partners, there are key leaders in the North Carolina food system—producers (new and existing), suppliers, processors (meat and produce value-added), small business development organizations, distributors (e.g., Eastern Carolina Organics), farm organizations, direct marketers (buying clubs, CSAs, farmers markets) banks, retailers, consumers and consumer groups, farm workers, granting agencies, government officials, including state and county, county planners, health and wellness organizations (e.g., the UNC Center for Health Promotion and Disease Prevention), nonprofit organizations, youth, and more. One key outcome already has been legislation establishing a sustainable local food advisory council.

We have also recently received endowment funding (NCSU and NC A&T SU) from the W.K. Kellogg Foundation to initiate a comprehensive effort on community-based food systems that will include endowed chairs at each institution. We have funding from SARE PDP to train agents in working within their counties to facilitate these activities as well.

Sustainability of Programs

One of the most significant challenges for land-grant university programs is securing ongoing funding for innovative programs initiated though grant funds and for long-term research. Many foundations and governmental agencies are reluctant to give grants to ongoing projects, so it's important to develop alternative funding streams. Fortunately, NCSU and NC A&T SU administrations have been generous in providing ongoing support for programs and have provided key matching resources to obtain grant funding when necessary. To develop ongoing funding streams, in 2006 CEFS initiated a Board of Advisors, a Friends of CEFS organization, and a sponsorship program for its special events and workshop series.

Board of Advisors

The CEFS Board of Advisors was established to provide recommendations on strategic directions and long-range goals, develop and provide stewardship of financial resources, serve as ambassadors to endorse and raise awareness of CEFS in the greater community, and advise in the development of policies that support the mission of CEFS. We have board members who are influential in North Carolina and nationally on these issues, who represent both our traditional grower or constituent base or are connected to new groups of constituents with whom we seek to engage. They also may be recruited if they have special expertise, such as in communications, fundraising, organizational development, or energy, that CEFS is seeking as it grows and develops. The board has been established with 10 members, with expectations to expand it to 25 members over time.

Friends of CEFS

As CEFS began more programming to reach out to the broader community, we anticipated that individuals would be interested in becoming "members" as a way to learn more about our programming, support our activities financially and through volunteering, and receive membership benefits such as reserved seating at our annual lecture and discounts to attend workshops. In the first year, approximately 100 individuals or families joined the organization, many of them at generous membership levels. We also provide an opportunity to make a higher level donation that targets funding in support of a CEFS apprentice or Intern.

Sponsorship Program

With the new public events that needed funding, we have sought corporate, business, and organizational support from those with interest in incorporating sustainability into their business or operating principals. This has allowed CEFS to generate funding for our special events, developed important relationships in the business community, and allowed like-minded business and organizations to receiving advertising benefits at very public events.

Fee-Based Educational Programs

To date, most of the CEFS workshops have been offered either free of charge or for a nominal fee. Registration fees up to $45 have been charged for full-day workshops that include lunch. With interest growing among diverse groups for intensive sustainable agriculture and community-based food systems training, we see an opportunity to develop targeted curriculum and host longer trainings, perhaps 1 or 2 wk depending on the group or needs, that can be developed in a fee-for-service self-supporting model. We have conducted one international training program with an NGO from Turkey (HASNA) using this model. Targeted groups may include health professionals, peace-corps trainees, environmental educators, policymakers, city and county governments, and international groups.

Endowment Funding

In April, 2006 CEFS was approached by the W.K. Kellogg Foundation and invited to submit a proposal for an endowment to support the community-based food systems work. In July 2008 both NCSU and NC A&T SU received Kellogg endowments that will be matched significantly by each institution in support of endowed professorships at each institution and ongoing programmatic funding for the work. This significant achievement will institutionalize the CEFS program at both institutions and allow CEFS to apply for official "Center" status within the UNC system, which will carry with it institutional benefits and status. Centers have increased authority to manage space, budget, and personnel, thereby facilitating more interdisciplinary and interagency efforts. The endowment funding will facilitate increased programming in the area of community-based food systems.

Lessons Learned

Changing a Mindset

The early years of program development (1992–1998) can be characterized as controversial and in some instances combative. There seemed to be no clear understanding or agreement by those engaged in the discussion of the value of or the need for organic and sustainable agriculture programs. Meetings were often contentious, and polarization based on different agricultural paradigms was obvious. Nevertheless, views gradually began to shift as mounting evidence pointed a finger at a myriad of problems related to agriculture, the environment, and declining rural communities. Clearly, the USDA SARE Program had a large and important impact on organic and sustainable agriculture programs in North Carolina and in the southern region. SARE funds have helped to launch and maintain many of our research initiatives, and grant funds available from many other SARE programs have aided extension agent training, graduate student projects, and on-farm research. Having these funds available has been crucial to accumulating a "critical mass" of interested faculty to form an interdisciplinary group engaged at CEFS. The SARE program has also been instrumental in fostering networking among scientists at land-grant universities and NGOs working in organic and sustainable agriculture organizations. Certainly the growing demand for organic vegetables, dairy products, and meat products has brought a measure of legitimacy to organic research and education programs that continues to gather momentum for further program refinements. There have been many other granting programs and foundations that have also played a key role in the development of CEFS. Being able to respond with research or programming to the critical issues of the days, and to successfully achieve the objectives by relying on a broad base of expertise is important to ongoing success.

Institutional Change

As we move toward this new programming area, we recognize that it goes beyond the traditional role of land-grant universities and extension, so it is important to think about the types of institutional change that will be required. At NCSU there is a commitment among university administrators for community engagement and in extension specifically for community-based food systems and a broader farm-to-fork approach. However, there are several barriers as well. With regard to faculty, as tenure and promotion decisions are primarily made at the departmental level through peer review, it is important that the understanding of peer faculty and departmental administrative policies evolve to appreciate this type of engagement, and reflect that appreciation in the review and reward process. Otherwise, the current situation will prevail, in which administrators and department heads (and funding agencies) promote interdisciplinary research and engagement, but those making the initial tenure decisions sometimes do not.

We believe that a mentoring program is critical because often young faculty reluctantly avoid participation in interdisciplinary activities, engagement, or sustainable agriculture in favor of more traditional scholarly pursuits that focus on a specific narrow research concept to ensure promotion and tenure. By the time these faculty achieve tenure, they are often entrenched in their disciplinary research and have lost their initial spark for community engagement or sustainable agriculture work. A mentoring program would provide support and a sense of community for these faculty, while providing practical advice and assistance for them to achieve tenure and promotion.

Institutional change among extension will also be important to support community-based food systems. In North Carolina, community-based food systems has recently been adopted as a major initiative in the new North Carolina extension strategic plan, but this type of programming activity will be new for extension and is broader than the traditional role of bringing research-based disciplinary information to producers. Extension administration will be required to facilitate and allow for a broader approach. In addition, this approach will require broad collaboration of extension personnel across disciplines, including agriculture agents, 4-H agents, family and consumer sciences agents, and marketing and business planning specialists. This has been less common in the past and will require new working models. These changes generally bring us back to the original intention and purpose of land-grant universities and programming in the interest of the public good. These are important concepts to maintain as pressure mounts for industry partnerships as mechanisms to fund research at universities in general.

Involving New Students and Youth

Increasing student interest in organic and sustainable agriculture and agroecology has been observed not only in our programs, but nationwide. Many agricultural universities recognize the importance of incorporating sustainable agriculture into agriculture curricula (Borsari and Vidrine, 2005), and the number of peer agricultural universities also offering undergraduate and graduate programs addressing organic and sustainable agriculture and agroecology is growing (e.g., Iowa State University, Michigan State University, Ohio State University, Penn State University, University of California–Davis, University of Florida, University of Illinois, University of Maine, University of Nebraska, University of Wyoming, and Washington State University). We recognize that the agroecology and sustainable agriculture educational programs at NCSU are a means to attract new students to agriculture and connect urban individuals with individuals from farming backgrounds. We have observed that students from very diverse backgrounds are attracted to our Sustainable Agriculture Internship program and new Agroecology Minor program, including those from majors in agriculture education and extension, agronomy, animal science, botany, ecology, environmental sciences, environmental engineering, forestry, horticultural science, political science, and soil science. For many of the students in the introductory agroecology course, this was their first agriculture-related course ever. Given their education training and experiences, many of these students would generally not enroll in an agricultural curriculum at the university. We also know from direct experience that students in biological sciences are interested in system approaches to agriculture and in its relationship to natural systems. We feel that learning about sustainable agriculture and agroecology is important for students from all disciplines and have successfully incorporated the introductory agroecology course into the curriculum General Education Requirements for all majors at NCSU.

We also recognize that a multidisciplinary sustainable agriculture or agroecology program is a vehicle to attract more women and other traditionally underrepresented groups to agricultural sciences at both the undergraduate and graduate level. From 2001 to 2006 there have been a total of 29 graduate students that have completed their M.S. or Ph.D. work in sustainable agriculture at CEFS, and more than 72% of the graduate students were women. This is a considerable difference from the traditional agronomy programs in the Crop Science Department at NCSU, where less than 33% of those receiving graduate degrees during this same time were women. Other similar programs have noted this increased participation of women and underrepresented minority individuals in sustainable agriculture fields. Research suggests that female students are more attracted to courses and programs that emphasize a broad social and economic connection to the content and that involve participatory, active-learning opportunities (Mayberry, 1999). Sustainable and organic agriculture programs that integrate the environmental, social, and economic perspectives of agriculture together with global context will no doubt continue to attract more underrepresented individuals to agricultural sciences.

There is no question that today's students need a multidisciplinary education with a strong foundation in sustainability, and they need to be equipped with various skills, research experiences, and global perspectives that will enable them to develop workable solutions to the challenge of providing safe, affordable, and secure supplies of food and fiber in a sustainable way.

International Collaborations and Global Perspectives

Living in a world that is becoming increasingly interconnected, it is important to direct our educational programs toward the broad perspective of global citizenship. The way our food and fiber is produced and the route it takes from the farm to our table have major environmental, economic, and social implications crossing many boarders. Universities truly dedicated to developing successful, high quality programs in sustainable and organic agriculture and agroecology must incorporate strategic means to create this sense of global citizenship in students and faculty. Students need to be exposed to global perspectives in their classrooms and encouraged to step beyond the classroom and participate in international study-abroad or internship opportunities related to sustainable and organic agriculture. Faculty need to be supported to develop international engagement in sustainable agriculture research and collaborative projects. Increased study-abroad and service learning opportunities related to sustainable agriculture, increased international student enrollment and scholar exchange, and an emphasis on language proficiency are necessary to prepare a new cadre of graduates with the requisite global perspectives, multidisciplinary knowledge, societal and human dimensional considerations, communication skills, and professional networks to assume leadership positions in the national and international sustainable agriculture arenas.

Discussion Questions

1. What was the value of combining the two original long-term experiments at CEFS, the Farming Systems Experiment and an Organic Systems Comparison study? What are other options for doing combined analyses across locations and/or experiments?

2. What factors contribute to the success of extension intensive organic training courses? How can these be instituted in different states, and what are the advantages of multistate training?

3. What is the advantage of broadening an outreach program targeted to extension agents and producers to a broader range of constituents? What can be accomplished through this wider range of clients?

4. What might a new degree program in agroecology offer students that is not available in the current programs focused on single agricultural disciplines?

5. Why is it important to broaden research and outreach initiatives in the university to embrace community-based food systems?

6. What are the key challenges to maintaining and financing long-term research and education programs? What are some potential solutions to these challenges?

References

Altieri, M.A., and C.A. Francis. 1992. Incorporating agroecology into the conventional agricultural curriculum. Am. J. Altern. Agric. 7:89–93.

Borsari, B., and M.F. Vidrine. 2005. Undergraduate agriculture curricula in sustainability: An evaluation across borders. J. Sustain. Agric. 25:93–112.

Creamer, N.G., K.R. Baldwin, and F.J. Louws. 2000. A training series for Cooperative Extension Agents in Organic Farming Systems. Horttechnology 10:675–681.

Garrett, S., and G. Feenstra. 1999. Growing a community food system. Community Ventures: Partnerships in Education and Research Circular Series Topics. A Western Regional Extension Publication WREP0135. Washington State Univ. Ext., Pullman.

Mayberry, M. 1999. Reproductive and resistant pedadagogies: The comparative roles of collaborative learning and feminist pedagogy in science education. p. 1–22. In M.

Mayberry and E.C. Rose (ed.) Meeting the challenge: Innovative feminist pedagogies in action. Routledge Press, New York.

Mueller, J.P., M.E. Barbercheck, M. Bell, C. Brownie, N.G. Creamer, S. Hu, L. King, H.M. Linker, F.J. Louws, M. Marra, C.W. Raczkowski, D.J. Susko, and M.G. Wagger. 2002. Development and implementation of a long-term agricultural systems study: Challenges and opportunities. Horttechnology 12:362–368.

Mueller, J.P., N.G. Creamer, M. Barbercheck, C. Raczkowski, M. Bell, C. Brownie, A. Collins, K. Fager, S. Hu, L. Jackson, S. Koenning, N. Kuminoff, M. Linker, F. Louws, S. Mellage, D. Monks, D. Orr, J. Seem, C. Tu, M. Wagger, R. Walters, A. Wossink, and W. Zhang. 2006. Long-term, large-scale systems research directed toward agricultural sustainability. *In* J. Raupp et al. (ed.) Long-term field experiments in organic farming. ISOFAR Scientific Ser. 1. Verlag Dr. Köster, Berlin.

Naderman, G., B.G. Brock, G.B. Reddy, and C.W. Raczkowski. 2006. Long term no-tillage: Effects on soil carbon and soil density within the prime crop root zone. Project Report 2006. Available at http://www.cefs.ncsu.edu/PDFs/naderman%202006%20number.pdf (verified 28 July 2009). CEFS, Cary, NC.

Schroeder, M.S., N.G. Creamer, H.M. Linker, J.P. Mueller, and P. Rzewnicki. 2006. Interdisciplinary and multi-level approach to organic and sustainable agriculture education at North Carolina State University. Horttechnology 16:418–426.

13

Education in Organic Farming and Food Systems

Charles Francis

Department of Agronomy and Horticulture, University of Nebraska, Lincoln

While the area in organic production continues to expand, and we see a grow-ing selection of organic products in the U.S. marketplace, the *"Why organic?"* debate continues. Many proponents of organic production methods claim this is the only viable strategy for cleaning up the environment and creating a sus-tainable food system based on contemporary energy and other resources. Critics contend that higher yields can only be achieved with chemical fertilizer and pes-ticide use, and that this strategy is essential for maintaining our food supply in a future with growing human populations and competition for scarce farmland, water, and fossil energy. There is a near religious faith in the health and safety benefits of organic foods among those consumers who increasingly seek out these products for their families. Proponents of industrial agriculture argue with equal fervor that the U.S. food system is the safest in the world and that there are no proven differences between organic food products and those produced with chemical fertilizers and pesticides. In this chapter, a perspective is advanced that the debate is due to lack of education and is not based on the merits of one type of farming or food versus another, but on our inability to ask the right questions about our food system.

The kinds of questions we ask in the research process, and those that we explore in education, depend in large part on a world view of what constitutes success in agriculture. With a narrow focus on production and short-term eco-nomics, we ask narrowly based questions. Many of us in agriculture could be accused of taking a myopic view of the food system and minimizing the impor-tance of environmental and social issues. When we become proponents of a single-component-at-a-time approach to finding technologies to solve each prob-lem as it arises, it is easy to ignore the impacts of the whole system. For efficiency reasons as well as concern for finding universal truths about agriculture and food systems, we have asked these questions and looked for solutions that are appli-cable across the widest area possible—new crop hybrids and varieties, fertilizer recommendations, and pest management strategies. Most research is designed to seek specific answers for specific questions, rather than questions that recognize and embrace the complexity and dynamic nature of the production system.

Conventional thinking has been that most serious research questions in agriculture should be addressed by university and USDA scientists and explored under the controlled conditions of the experiment station. It is important to examine our assumptions about efficiency, and to see if the research and education system built on them truly leads to a sustainable agriculture production and food system. Increasingly, we are placing the research and education agenda in an ecological framework, as described by Laurie Drinkwater in Chapter 2 (2009, this volume), and building on science plus farmer experiences. What questions should we ask in education?

To begin to understand the roots of this dilemma, it is useful to explore the origins of education in farming and food systems. It is essential to understand the overwhelming impact of the industrial revolution on agriculture and, even more importantly, its impact on our awareness of the power of science and technology in food and other sectors. The reductionist approach to understanding natural phenomena as well as agroecosystems, one factor at a time, has permeated our research planning and is highly apparent in the discipline of agriculture. This topic is discussed in more detail by Fred Kirschenmann in Chapter 15 (2009, this volume). He provides a thoughtful look at where we are and how we arrived here, including how education in the sciences has brought us to depend on ever more complex technologies to solve problems in production. There is danger in simplification, in looking at small pieces of a puzzle, only one segment at a time, because we soon lose sight of the large picture and the myriad interactions that run the systems and create their emergent properties. When our world views follow a mechanistic model, we assume that the sum of the parts is equal to the whole, and we often forget to ask the right questions about interactions, context, and multiple impacts of each system on a host of players in the landscape.

Improving agricultural systems could be achieved in three ways according to MacRae et al. (1989) and Hill and MacRae (1995): (i) improved efficiency, (ii) input substitution, and (iii) system redesign. For example, in organic systems, the first approach (improved efficiency) involves making better use of applied compost for soil fertility or finding the least expensive cultivation strategy to manage weeds. Most research is done using this strategy, with focus on system components and tracking the system. The second (input substitution) would be to substitute a less expensive input for one we are using now to achieve the same results, or to change from one crop to another, the second most popular approach. The least utilized strategy is to redesign the system to make it more efficient or to eliminate the need for external inputs. Research and most teaching in organic farming have been parallel to the conventional system, with focus on improvements in the order: efficiency > substitution > redesign.

One could argue that the best approach to achieve long-term sustainability would be to consider the whole farm and farming system, and to take a systemic approach to designing a future system that would achieve the farmer's goals while minimizing expensive inputs and adding as much value as possible to crops and livestock before they leave the farm gate. This approach would be possible only by incorporating all three methods with much greater emphasis on system redesign—in both research and education. This is part of asking the right questions.

In this chapter, the importance of systems education is framed in the context of an educational philosophy that promotes experiential or action learning. It is well established that adult learning is based on experience. The importance of questions uncovered by personal experiences and integrating these with theoretical as well as hands-on training is central to all learning, not only in learning about organic farming. How our students become life-long learners, able to sort out information and evaluate its sources, and apply this to a complex and uncertain future is crucial to our thinking about design of learning. Specific examples of education programs, both in universities and in Extension, are provided as case studies, or models of what can be done in unique situations. Since innovative programs for learning about organic farming abound in the nonprofit sector, we can examine how these fit into the educational arena and how they complement formal teaching in charting a potential route for students through the learning landscape.

A strategy for learning in research and in the classroom is described that considers the following five challenges to the conventional research and education agenda:

- How do we integrate biophysical and social science methods in research-based education to study complex issues?
- Why do we focus on whole system analysis and evaluation? Why do we search for alternative future systems?
- How can we emphasize site-specific systems and solutions consistent with ecological principles?
- Why is it important to foster a culture of raising questions rather than fine-tuning current answers?
- How do we include farmers as part of the research and education team in a mutually beneficial strategy for learning?

We need to explore ways to apply these principles in education, both in the classroom and with clients in the food system. Beyond organic farming, we can ask whether these principles should be applied in all teaching programs. Above all, educators need to raise questions and develop in our students and clients the capacity and courage to challenge our current agricultural systems and find innovative ways to improve them. One of our highest priorities should be to encourage autonomous learners who understand education and embrace change as a life-long process.

History of Experiential Education...and Organic Farming

Just as organic farming was the foundation for development of human food systems, the education of farmers was for millennia a process of internship to older practitioners. Young people learned from elders in their families or were apprenticed to other farmers to increase family income and in the process learned how to efficiently raise crops and animals. This was the predominant form of agricultural education until the last two centuries. The tradition continues today, for example on the biodynamic farm of Trigve Sund about 3 km from Stange, Norway, where more than 200 young people have been apprentices during the past three decades. There is an international network of organic farmers who offer experiences to aspiring farmers. The WWOOF (World Wide Opportunities on Organic Farms), described in more detail later, provides a chance for beginners to work in exchange for food and lodging while learning the details of organic production and often marketing. Similar experiences have been gained by aspiring organic farmers, many of whom today do not come from farm backgrounds, who have joined one of the non-profit or college organic farms dedicated to practical training. This informal education could appear to have little relevance to the challenge today of moving the message to large audiences, yet the internship approach exemplifies what has been known as an important strategy in adult learning for more than a century. Hands-on learning leads to relevant questions that are specific to goals and context and provides an awareness of the need for more information.

The foundation for experiential learning is based on long-term experience as shown in the literature on adult education. Students often view their transition to the university as a new dimension of learning, connected to prior schooling but not especially linked to their own practical experience. In 1916, well-known educator John Dewey insisted in *Democracy and Education* (Dewey, 1942) that people need to integrate new information and learning with their prior experience. He was an early proponent in academia of experiential learning. Decades ahead of his time, Dewey was not at all in step with the hierarchical methods of teaching passed down from the era of the reformation, with lectures in the church and in universities. He argued that learning should not be done in an authoritarian environment, but should celebrate, validate, and build on the experiences of each individual. In essence, what Dewey describes is creating a culture of questioning, just as he himself challenged the dominant theories and experts in education over a century ago.

Among those who seriously questioned the emerging paradigm of chemical agriculture were many skeptical farmers, plus a few people in academics: William Albrecht (1996), Rudolf Steiner (1958), Walter Northbourne (1940), and Efraim Hernandez Xolocotzi (1987), already mentioned in Chapter 1 (Francis and Van Wart, 2009, this volume). Authors frequently cited for their detailed research or careful observation of organic methods are Albert Howard, Evelyn Balfour, and Louis Bromfield, whose ideas formed the foundation for much of our practical education in organic farming in the United States.

Organic research was publicized in the United States through the extensive efforts of author and publisher J.I. Rodale (1946), a strong advocate of chemical-free farming. Along with some technical articles and several popular books, an information base was built for English-speaking peoples, as described in the first chapter. Yet most scientists and educators in the mainstream remained unaware of or uninterested in this research, embracing a rapid conversion after World War II to a chemical-intensive agriculture. Starting from the assumptions of inexpensive fossil fuels, an environment that could absorb just about anything that we applied to the soil, and confidence in technological solutions to all problems, we moved away from the study of ecological processes in agriculture. Many forgot to ask logical questions about whole systems and their impacts, including the assumptions behind our present—often monoculture—production paradigm.

Many of us who are researchers and educators in agriculture are unfamiliar with the theoretical landmark concepts in adult learning. David Kolb's (1984) *Cycle of Learning* concept describes the sequence of:

- *Concrete experience* where we learn to identify problems,
- *Reflective observation* and thinking about solutions,
- *Abstract conceptualization* that helps us evaluate consequences and select a priori the most useful solutions, and
- *Active experimentation* that includes trying out the solutions.

Comparing the results with reality and seeing if the desired goals are achieved is a concrete experience, and the cycle of learning continues. Important to acquisition, processing, and application of knowledge is placing that information into context. We have found this concept highly useful in our education in the holistic and trans-disciplinary area of agroecology. At each step in the process students learn to ask questions. The cyclical process has been expanded into the concept of learning spirals, each of which builds on the experience of the one before (Wilson and Morren, 1990; Sriskandarajah et al., 1991). Each of the ascending cycles shown by these authors rep-resents a new series of higher order questions generated by students. This approach to education has guided our students to learn how to ask questions about production and economics, while not ignoring the crucial environmental issues that arise from different technologies nor the social implications for families and communities. One of the key assumptions in our agroecology teaching programs is that learning needs to lead to responsible action (Lieblein and Francis, 2007).

The application of agroecology through action must be context specific in agriculture. Echoing the work of Dewey from a century before, Jack Mezirow (2000) described how we build our individual understanding around the con-texts that we know, and what we know is a reflection of our previous experiences. His transformation theory helps us grasp how important it is for both teachers and learners to first explore their personal expectations and assumptions, and especially for teachers to understand those of the audience or clients. Thomas Kuhn (1962) in his landmark book *The Structure of Scientific Revolutions* says sim-ply that we see what we know. He argues that we build on more than experiences, and that our basic paradigms or ways that we see the world strongly influence what we see and what we learn. In a recent paper we described how "our practi-cal experience in an agricultural science dominated by disciplinary research and teaching leads to the situation where a soil scientist will see nutrient deficiencies, a weed scientist will see the understory of undesirable plants, and an economist will think of the inputs and potential outputs when all three professionals walk through the same field of maize, on the same farm, in the same landscape talking to the same farmer, who are all connected to the same society (Francis et al., 2008). We see what we know, and what our experience has led us to observe. If students or farmer clients have only known a chemically based agriculture during their entire experience, it is difficult to introduce alternatives that will be considered seriously. Another complication is definition of terms and confusion about what is organic farming, how it relates to other systems, and at times deliberate manip-ulation of language and resistance to change by those with vested interests in the current system.

Organic Farming, Sustainable Agriculture, Agroecology

Organic farming is often associated with other terms found in the literature and in education. Courses in sustainable agriculture and agroecology often use organic farming examples to illustrate the potential for long-term viability and an ecological approach to agriculture. For those already critical of organic farming as a viable option it is tempting to seize on this confusion. For effective discussion in education it is important to define and make clear what these terms mean. For education that leads to probing questions about our current systems and how to improve them, common definitions are essential for effective communication.

The term *organic farming* was probably first used by Walter Northbourne (1940), and popularized in the United States by J.I. Rodale (1946) and by his son and successor in publishing, Robert Rodale, at their Rodale Press in Emmaus, Pennsylvania. As used in the previous chapters organic farming means production of crops and livestock without synthetic chemical fertilizers and pesticides, no use of GMOs, and humane treatment of animals. Although there have been different criteria for certification used by various public, nonprofit, and private agencies, there are now uniform standards that are set forth by the U.S. Department of Agriculture in the National Organic Program in 2002 and by the E.U. for their member countries. The rules are similar but vary in details, and the International Federation of Organic Agriculture Movements (IFOAM) international standards provide a set of guidelines for rules around the world. The IFOAM rules are described in the opening chapter, with the goals of achieving health, ecology, fairness, and care. Farmers must work with their chosen certification agency or company to be sure they satisfy the rules of the countries where they intend to market.

Sustainable agriculture has been variously defined by many authors over the past two decades, but in general refers to a philosophy, a direction, or a set of goals that will achieve adequate production and economic return, while at the same time including attention to the environmental and social impacts of agricultural production systems. Sustainable agriculture is not prescriptive, nor does it promote a specific rotation or set of production practices. It is a confusing term, as no one would advocate a "nonsustainable" agriculture. Yet it has been useful as a term to help focus on those practices, systems, and structural adjustments in policy and supports to production that will lead to more durable systems for the long term. Sustainability is often associated with organic agriculture because many of the same people have been involved in courses and writing about the two topics. They are not synonymous terms for most people in agriculture. Sustainable agriculture could be considered a journey or a philosophy toward higher or better quality production, economic feasibility, environmental soundness, and social acceptability of future systems.

Recently the term *agroecology* has come to represent an academic approach to the holistic study of agricultural systems. Originally used to describe the combining or complementarity of agriculture and ecology (Gliessman, 1997), it may now be used more broadly by many to encompass the ecology of food systems (Francis et al., 2003). Similar to sustainable agriculture, the term suggests looking at whole systems and looking at the interactions of production, economics, environment, and social dimensions of the system with use of both biophysical and social science methods. To suggest that agroecology is only the study of organic or mixed farming systems would be to narrow the interpretation of this term. We use the term in education to include study of all agricultural systems, and to use a broad ecological platform to do comparisons of their efficiency, potential for providing ecosystem services, and contributions to long-term sustainability of food production and other outputs or services. There is continuing confusion about the use of these terms, and whether agroecology, for example, should best be called a science, a movement, or a practice (Wezel, 2009). The same could be said about organic farming.

To summarize this discussion, we could conclude that organic farming is a specific set of certified practices, and sustainable agriculture is a long-term goal.

Agroecology is the term best suited for serious study of the many interacting components in the complex structure and function of agricultural systems, and a palatable way to introduce practical systems research into academia. Some of the confusion and overlap in use of these terms is the confounding of ideas and language used to describe systems with courses in the university that challenge the long-term viability of current systems. Often the same folks who challenge the status quo are those who promote organic farming. What is essential is that we use this platform to challenge ourselves and our understandings of agricultural and food systems, and to raise questions that will lead to research and further education on alternatives that are more likely to sustain us and preserve the environment on which we depend.

University and College Programs in Organic Agriculture

A chapter on educational programs should provide examples of available locations and the types of curricula and practice they offer. Several examples are given of curricula and internships that have become available over recent decades as a component of formal education. This is not exhaustive, but represents the current range of opportunities. There is easy access to information on current programs online, especially through the ATTRA site at the National Center for Appropriate Technology in Fayetteville (available at: http://attra.ncat.org/education.html, verified 22 July 2009). For example, there is a comprehensive listing of universities and colleges in the up-to-date online publication *Educational and Training Opportunities in Sustainable Agriculture*, available on the ATTRA site at http://www.nal. usda.gov/afsic/pubs/edtr/EDTR2006.shtml (verified 22 July 2009).

One of the oldest and best known programs in an academic setting is the University of California at Santa Cruz apprenticeship program in agroecology and organic farming and gardening (http://casfs.ucsc.edu/, verified 22 July 2009). Begun in 1967, the Chadwick Garden was just over 1 ha (3 ac) and has now expanded to include more than 10 ha (28 ac), with 40 apprenticeship positions available each year. Practical training includes all steps in organic production as well as local marketing. Their comprehensive manual *Teaching Organic Farming and Gardening* (University of California–Santa Cruz, 2003; also available on line) is an excellent 600-page collection of background materials, exercises, study questions, and references on the practical details of production and marketing. Each year several apprentices are invited to stay for a second year to assist in the instruction of new people, to guarantee continuity of learning and to provide an opportunity to learn about how to teach practical skills. The program cost is $4,000 for an experience that lasts through the growing season, typically from March to November in their agroecozone.

The organic farm at University of California at Davis (http://studentfarm. ucdavis.edu/, verified 22 July 2009) began in 1977 as a learning and demonstration site, and since 1980 has provided market garden internships for students on campus. The nearby ecological garden includes a demonstration of how to mimic natural ecosystems while producing plants for our needs. There is a focus on vegetables and fruits, medicinal and culinary herbs, how to save seeds, and what plants are useful for attracting butterflies as well as beneficial insects to control plant pests. A large composting facility takes advantage of the animal science project manure on campus to produce high quality organic matter and useful nutrients that maintain fertility on the organic farm (University of California–Davis, 2007).

Another opportunity is found at Evergreen State College in Washington (http://www.evergreen.edu/cell/organicfarm.htm, verified 22 July 2009), where the organic farm was established in 1972, a year after the founding of the college. The goals are to study ecological agriculture, to examine the food system from the farm to the table, and to look at specific practices to achieve a sustainable agriculture. Students can access practical courses on campus as well as one complete quarter of study that is dedicated to teaching the fundamentals of an organic, sustainable agriculture and the implications of such a system at the local, regional, and global levels.

Dartmouth College in New Hampshire established an organic farm in 1994, which now serves as an education resource for courses in six different departments. There are studies on organic soil practices, intercropping, permaculture and aquaculture, and design of organic farming and gardening systems. It is administratively under the Outdoor Programs Office of the college (http://www.dartmouth.edu/~doc/organicfarm/, verified 22 July 2009).

One unique opportunity for immersion in the growing and marketing of organic products is offered at Michigan State University in their year-round Student Organic Farm (http://www.msuorganicfarm.org/home.php/, verified 22 July 2009) that includes a community supported agriculture dimension (Biernbaum et al., 2006). The authors cite declining enrollment in traditional agricultural programs, with one reason the lack of opportunity for early involvement in sustainable agriculture courses and practical aspects of farming. In addition to the mainstream courses available for students, there is also under development an organic farming certificate program based on 40 credits with a full year on campus plus a 16 wk internship. The Student Organic Farm at Michigan State University has proven to be a place where research, teaching, and outreach are integrated into experiential learning and communication.

Another comprehensive educational program is being developed in conjunction with the research and outreach program at North Carolina State University (http://www.cefs.ncsu.edu/commfoodsys.htm, verified 22 July 2009). A description of this program is found in Chapter 12 (Creamer et al., 2009, this volume). Likewise, an undergraduate and a graduate degree program in sustainable agriculture are now offered at Iowa State University (http://extension.agron.iastate.edu/organicag/, verified 22 July 2009). There is also an organic farm run by students, and more information is provided in several of the chapters about programs at Iowa State University. These are but a few examples of what is available within the academic community.

Courses in universities and colleges on organic farming, gardening, and food systems are spreading rapidly. Imbedded in the ATTRA Website are lists of institutions by state, and a short description of both educational and research projects in the relevant departments. In addition to courses in organic farming, there are many titles such as sustainable agriculture, agroecology, renewable resources, alternative farming and energy systems, conservation and environment, integrated pest management, and grass-based livestock systems, among others. There are some agriculture and food systems courses designed for nonscience majors to help them focus on food education and awareness of agriculture. These are only examples of programs available today, and a quick online search for "organic farming education" will reveal many more programs across the United States and elsewhere.

Private and NGO Opportunities

In addition to formal course offerings or complementary to them, much of the education in organic farming has taken place in the internship programs and outreach from non-profit research and learning centers. Rodale Institute in Pennsylvania was founded by J.I. Rodale as the Soil and Health Association in 1947, and has a continuous record of field research and training interns for several decades. Paid internships run for 6 to 9 mo, and most learning is on the 135-ha (333-ac) certified organic farm near Kutztown in southeast Pennsylvania. More information can be found online at http://www.rodaleinstitute.org/work_with_us (verified 22 July 2009). Michael Fields Agricultural Institute (http://www.michaelfieldsaginst.org/programs/garden/index.html, verified 22 July 2009) in Wisconsin has two programs, the Foundation Year, which is a 9-mo experience in organic and biodynamic agriculture, and a Short-Term Foundation Study, a 2- to 4-mo long experience in the Garden Student Program. These fee-based programs are designed to provide both theoretical and experiential education to develop skills in the field and give students a good start on literacy in sustainable agriculture and agroecology.

These are some examples of private, nonprofit programs, of which there are many more. The overall situation is changing rapidly, as universities and colleges are embracing organic farming and food systems as one important niche for their student clients. The holistic planning and systems management used in organics are also revealing strategies that are useful for what is called conventional farming, although this impact is difficult to measure.

Learning opportunities on farms are also important to those seeking farmer perspectives and hands-on practice in organic farming and food systems. Learning to ask the right questions is valuable to those who want to farm, to those who return to a formal course or curriculum as described above, and to university teachers and researchers concerned about the relevance of their programs. On-farm opportunities offer a chance for growth in independent learning, communication skills, and management of organic farms. The World-Wide Opportunities on Organic farms (WWOOF) organization Website (http://www.wwoof.org/home.asp, verified 22 July 2009) provides a quick overview of many opportunities across a number of countries. The aims of WWOOF are:

- to enable people to learn first-hand about organic growing techniques
- to enable town-dwellers to experience living and helping on a farm
- to help farmers make organic production a viable alternative
- to improve communications within the organic movement

Volunteers, so-called WWOOFers, make their own arrangements with the host families, provide their own travel and insurance, and donate their labor to the farm in exchange for meals and a place to sleep. A number of students in the Norwegian agroecology course have experienced farm work through this organization and report the activity to be highly valuable. There are currently organizations in 31 countries.

Internships available in the Canada and the United States are announced on the ATTRA Website (http://www.attrainternships.ncat.org/, verified 22 July 2009), where an up-to-date roster of educational opportunities is provided. This list is open access, and each person interested in being a volunteer or worker on an organic, biodynamic, or other sustainable farm must make their own arrangements with the host farmer.

Outreach to Farmers: Cooperative Extension and NGOs

Cooperative Extension in the land-grant universities has been especially slow to move into the organic farming arena. This is *not* to say that there have been no proponents and a complete absence of information available from Extension. The program in integrated pest management (IPM) at University of California–Davis, the organic agriculture research and outreach program at Iowa State University (see Chapter 6, Delate, 2009, this volume), and the Agroecology and Farm and Garden Project of the non-land-grant University of California–Santa Cruz are noteworthy. The new comprehensive program shared by North Carolina State University and North Carolina Agriculture and Technical University has an impressive array of workshops and field tours for farmers as part of the Center for Environmental Farming Systems (CEFS), with additional support from the state department of agriculture and nonprofit groups in North Carolina (see Chapter 12, Creamer et al., 2009, this volume). These are only some of the programs that have emerged in the last decade; there is not space to describe them all.

One major national program that has stirred interest and resulted in a number of on-farm outreach experiments, cooperative work on farmer grants, and numerous projects on organic farming is the Sustainable Agriculture Research and Education (SARE) Program of the USDA. Initiated in 1987 as the Low-Input, Sustainable Agriculture (LISA) Program, this federal grant program celebrated its 20th anniversary in March 2008 in Kansas City. This has become one of the prime sources of support for alternative agricultural education and research in the United States, including organic farming. While other federal programs have experienced level funding and often reductions over the past two decades, the SARE program has actually had an increase in funding in most years. The programs are headed by an office in USDA, but major responsibilities for decisions on priorities and grants to researchers, educators, farmers, and students are decentralized and assigned to four regional administrative councils. Among the many publications available online from SARE is *Transitioning to Organic Production* (Friedman, 2001), with clear outline of the steps to certification and profiles of individual farmers who have made the change. The highly successful programs of the North Central Region have been described and summarized in the recent book *Developing and Extending a Sustainable Agriculture: A New Social Contract* (Francis et al., 2006).

One of the most comprehensive programs in the Midwest is the organic agriculture research, demonstration, and Extension work at Iowa State University. The first full-time organic agriculture specialist in Extension, Dr. Kathleen Delate (see Chapter 6, Delate, 2009, this volume) was hired in 1997 in the Departments of Horticulture and Agronomy, and has developed a widely publicized series of field projects and organized many demonstrations and meetings for farmers (Sayre, 2007). In one comparison, recent results show that over 9 yr, the yields of corn (*Zea mays* L.) and soybean [*Glycine max* (L.) Merr.] were the same in organic and conventional systems, even in the 3-yr conversion period. The Iowa State

University Website (http://extension.agron.iastate.edu/organicag/, verified 22 July 2009) is an especially rich trove of practical information for organic farmers. A series of full-color bulletins available online are full of information and examples for conversion to organic and specific practices. The first overview bulletin is *Fundamentals of Organic Agriculture* (Delate, 2003). Collaboration with the Practical Farmers of Iowa (PFI) has been central to success of this program, as well as the support of the Leopold Center for Sustainable Agriculture.

Another noteworthy programs in organic agriculture at the land-grant universities is the cooperative researcher–farmer program at Cornell University in New York (http://www.organic.cornell.edu/ocs/index.html, verified 22 July 2009). With experiments on vegetable production, grain crops, compost, green manure crops, and tillage, this project looks both at practices and the conversion process. There are initiatives on organic dairying and on marketing. University of California–Davis has identified a number of experts on the statewide and county levels who are prepared to answer questions on organic farming, including practices and regulations (see http://www.news.ucdavis.edu/sources/organic_issues_regs. lasso, verified 22 July 2009). Washington State University began studies in the 1970s comparing energy use in organic cereal production versus conventional systems. Today their Center for Sustaining Agriculture and Natural Resources has surveyed the people and resources within the university that are dedicated to organic farming, and there are programs on local nutrient sources, cover crops, farming systems, soil quality, and a number of other projects (http://csanr.wsu. edu/Organic/index.htm, verified 22 July 2009). University of Nebraska has a Website on organic farming at their Center for Applied Rural Innovation (CARI, http:// cari.unl.edu/, verified 22 July 2009), and a project with SARE grant support for organizing workshops on organic farming in North and South Dakota, Nebraska, and Kansas. The cooperative North Carolina State and North Carolina A&T outreach program described in Chapter 12 (Creamer et al., 2009, this volume) has blossomed in the last few years. These are examples of current efforts in organic farming Extension in the mainstream universities.

The New Agriculture Network (http://www.new-ag.msu.edu, verified 22 July 2009) that links researchers and Extension specialists' activities in Michigan State University, Purdue University, and University of Illinois is looking at specific farms as sites for collecting data on organic farming systems. They are cooperating with farmers in the three states to run field research, hold farmer workshops and tours, and look at common challenges in this Midwest agroecoregion.

State Conservationists, such as Dr. Steve Chick in Nebraska of the NRCS, are promoting education for their specialists across the state to become more familiar with the practices used in organic farming, as well as regulations and certification procedures. Farmers applying for a number of their federal entitlement programs to promote better conservation practices, such as the EQIP and WHIP, can more easily qualify if they meet organic production standards. NRCS is a key organization that annually reaches a high proportion of the nation's farmers, and efforts to promote education for their field staff is a high priority to get information to more farmers.

As the land-grant and NRCS programs build momentum for practical and dynamic programs in a number of states, they are building on a strong foundation already in place in the nonprofit sector, where a number of farmer-initiated groups have been working for some time. Private research centers and farmer organizations have field days, publications, workshops, or other outreach activities. Among the many organizations across the United States are the Rodale Research Center, Michael Fields Institute, Kansas Organic Producers, Practical Farmer of Iowa, Northern Plains Sustainable Agriculture Society, Nebraska Sustainable Agriculture Society, and active local chapters of the Organic Crop Improvement Association. Often they work in collaboration with state programs in the land-grant universities.

Should Organic Farming Education Be Different?

As suggested in the introduction, current education in organic farming is parallel in many ways to education in conventional, industrial farming (Fig. 13–1). Most research and outreach has focused on improving efficiency of components of the system and on substitution of nonchemical methods of fertility and pest management for the chemicals used in conventional systems. This is not surprising because most researchers and teachers have moved from the conventional agriculture arena and continue using the same methods and designs they have learned from prior experience. To suggest that a conventional-type research and education agenda will contribute to more than minimal success in improving

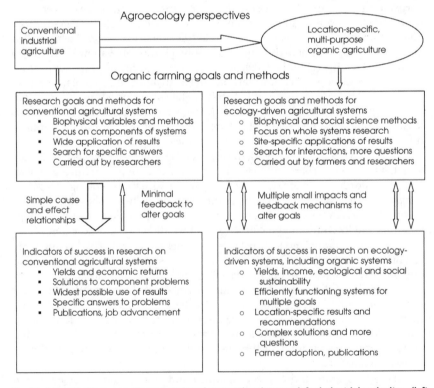

Fig. 13–1. Contrast between characteristics of conventional research for industrial agriculture (left-hand side) and research needed for ecology-driven agricultural systems such as organic farming (right-hand side), with bridge provided by agroecological perspectives and methods (with credit to Geir Lieblein and Edvin Østergaard, personal communication, November 2007).

organic systems requires an examination of the five questions that were posed in the introduction to this chapter.

Are yields and income the major goals of organic farmers? Although these are both essential to the success of organic systems, the literature on philosophy and goals of long-time organic farmers suggests that they are motivated in addition by a strong environmental ethic, a desire to treat labor well, a consideration for animal welfare, and the goal of contributing to their local communities. It is not possible to address all these issues with a standard set of tools from the biological sciences, and this is why we find the addition of methods from social sciences to be so important. The goals written into the IFOAM organization include a broad set of principles to achieve an agriculture that promotes health, ecology, fairness, and care. The strategy to follow these principles in designing systems is complex, so much of the agenda falls outside the biophysical realm and requires a more comprehensive look at systems, including using some methods from social sciences. Among the methods used in our experiential courses in the Nordic Region are mind maps, activity calendars, force field analysis, rich pictures of farms and community food systems, and exercises that examine the learning process for individuals and groups (Francis et al., 2005; Seppänen and Francis, 2006; Lieblein and Francis, 2007).

Will component research solve production problems in organic farming? If there is a single limiting factor that is constraining production, it is obvious that finding a solution to that constraint may improve yields and income. Yet the complexity of organic systems, their dependence on natural methods and system design for managing soil fertility and pests, and the importance of interactions among elements for success drive us to examine whole systems. The importance of multiple outcomes, including environmental and social goals, means that emergent properties of systems must be considered. For long-term sustainability, it is essential to design systems that depend on contemporary resources and do not externalize costs, either in space or time. For these reasons, a systemic approach is more appropriate for both research and extension in organic systems than the component focus often found today in most research and teaching.

Are we seeking wide application of results of research for organic systems, and should we teach menus for practices that are useful for organic farming? Study of ecology tells us that every niche on each farm is unique in some ways. Conventional, industrial model farming uses large quantities of production inputs to make production conditions similar or uniform across fields and over many farms, while recognizing that this may be difficult and costly. A plant breeder is successful if a new corn hybrid or soybean variety can be sold across a wide region of adaptation. A herbicide used across thousands of acres can more easily return the costs of research and generate profits than one for a minor crop or with limited application. A generalizable response curve to nitrogen or another major nutrient that can be applied in as many areas as possible simplifies the building of fertilizer recommendations. In organic systems, it is important to fit the practices and systems to each niche, meaning that recommendations must be based on fully understanding the local soil and pest conditions and planning for each field accordingly. It does not mean that research needs to be done on every field and farm, but it does mean that each situation requires careful thought and planning to fit the crop rotation and practices to the unique conditions of each field. Moreover, the system must be designed to meet the multiple goals of the farmer and family.

Are there specific answers to identified questions and problems in organic farming? In research and teaching, we often think about seeking the answers to specific production constraints, and applying a chemical fertilizer or pesticide to solve that problem. In organic farming, it is more common to focus on a problematic situation and look for multiple alternative ways to improve that situation. This means surveying a number of possible design options and ways to change the system, evaluating a priori their potentials for success, and implementing the most indicated solution. The process is similar to the IPM strategy of looking at pest populations, considering potentials for economic damage, evaluating options for control or management, and then choosing the least expensive and environmentally disruptive option. In this way, the many interactions in a system and potential consequences of interventions are considered. This is a more complex process than finding a specific answer that will automatically solve a problem. In agroecology we use open-ended cases to explore complexity on the farm, delving into situations where the answers and at times even the right questions are not yet known (Francis et al., 2009). This learning strategy is in stark contrast to using decision cases where the answers are known to the instructor and the student's task is to find out what the teacher is thinking.

Who is most likely to be involved in research and education? In the standard approach to research in conventional farming situations it is the university faculty member who is responsible for these activities. Faculty members as well as Extension specialists are responsible for teaching. For all of the reasons discussed above—location specificity of practices and rotations, complexity of systems with multiple goals and outputs, the need for social science methods, a focus on asking the right questions rather than seeking fixed answers—it is essential to examine the research process needed to address challenges in organic systems. Education in organic farming needs to follow the same process. In the science-based organic farming course at University of Nebraska we invite farmers into the class sessions to share their philosophy and goals, farm planning and design, and marketing strategies. In Extension meetings we also team with farmer organizations such as the OCIA to hold tours and workshops where farmers are featured as presenters. These events are not merely lectures in the field or in the classroom by a farmer; instead they are structured learning activities with clear learning objectives and a plan for evaluating the outcomes. We have found that including farmers as instructors highlights their unique perspectives as integrators of practices and implementers of systems, and their involvement brings a realism and specific context to learning.

Conclusions

The examples presented in this chapter indicate that we currently have a rich variety of initiatives in classroom teaching, outreach, and research underway to support the learning environment in organic farming. The overall impact of these programs is difficult to assess, since there is undoubtedly a strong influence of organic agriculture education and systems strategies for learning on a wide range of farming systems, beyond those farms certified organic. Although much of the framework for learning organic practices and systems is parallel to the study of agriculture for other systems, there are several ways in which the nature of organic whole-system planning must be more complex and inclusive, and organic farming requires the integration of biological and social science methods. There is a greater emphasis on seeking out and asking the right questions for each ecological niche, rather than looking at fixed answers that lead to monoculture thinking and practice across a wide area. Based on experience, we have found that involving farmers in the teaching as well as research adds a rich dimension of reality and helps to put work into context, make it relevant, and make results easier to adopt.

We need to develop the capacity through education to look at complete systems. In agriculture, this means expanding to more than a singular focus on the production potential from a given piece of land and management system, and the short-term economic gain that can be realized. We need to examine the environmental impacts and social context in which technology is applied. Education needs to prepare a new generation of farmers, food systems experts, and consumers to deal with a complex food system in an uncertain and rapidly changing world. We have a role in both university education and in Extension to help people begin to ask the right questions.

Study Questions

1. Why are there major differences between academic education in conventional and in organic farming? What are these differences, and how do they influence the research and education agenda?

2. What cooperative programs in research and education in public, private, and NGO organizations are currently active in organic farming, and why are the linkages among them important?

3. What is the current role of nonprofit environmental groups in education in agriculture? In what ways could we establish better linkages between universities and these organizations?

4. Why are site-specific practices and systems more important in organic farming than in conventional operations?

5. Why is experiential learning important for those planning to pursue certified organic farming as a practitioner or an instructor?

6. In what ways are questions more important than answers in the educational process, especially in organic farming systems?

References

Albrecht, W.A. 1996. The Albrecht papers volume I: Foundation concepts. C. Walters, Jr. (ed.) Acres International, Metairie, LA.

Biernbaum, J.A., L. Thorp, and M. Ngouajio. 2006. Development of a year-round student organic farm and organic farming curriculum at Michigan State University. Horttechnology 16:432–436.

Creamer, N.G., J.P. Mueller, J. O'Sullivan, C. Reberg-Horton, M. Schroeder-Moreno, and S. Washburn. 2009. Center for Environmental Farming Systems: Designing and institutionalizing an integrated sustainable and organic agriculture program. p. 255–282. In C. Francis (ed.) Organic farming: The ecological system. Agron. Monogr. 54. ASA, CSSA, and SSSA, Madison, WI. (This volume.)

Delate, K. 2003. Fundamentals of organic agriculture. PM 1880. Iowa State Univ. Ext., Ames.

Delate, K. 2009. Organic grains, oilseeds, and other specialty crops. p. 113–136. In C. Francis (ed.) Organic farming: The ecological system. Agron. Monogr. 54. ASA, CSSA, and SSSA, Madison, WI. (This volume.)

Dewey, J. 1942. Democracy and education. Macmillan Publ., New York.

Drinkwater, L.E. 2009. Ecological knowledge: Foundation for sustainable organic agriculture. p. 19–48. In C. Francis (ed.) Organic farming: The ecological system. Agron. Monogr. 54. ASA, CSSA, and SSSA, Madison, WI. (This volume.)

Francis, C., J. King, G. Lieblein, T.A. Breland, L. Salomonsson, N. Sriskandarajah, P. Porter, and M. Wiedenhoeft. 2009. Open-ended cases in agroecology: Farming and food systems in the Nordic Region and the U.S. Midwest. J. Agric. Educ. Extension (Wageningen). (In press.)

Francis, C.A., G. Lieblein, T.A. Breland, L. Salomonsson, U. Geber, N. Sriskandarajah, and V. Langer. 2008. Transdisciplinary research for a sustainable agriculture and food sector. Agron. J. 100:771–776.

Francis, C., G. Lieblein, S. Gliessman, T.A. Breland, N. Creamer, R. Harwood, L. Salomonsson, J. Helenius, D. Rickerl, R. Salvador, M. Wiedenhoeft, S. Simmons, P. Allen, M. Altieri, C. Flora, and R. Poincelot. 2003. Agroecology: The ecology of food systems. J. Sustain. Agric. 22:99–118.

Francis, C., G. Lieblein, H. Steinsholt, T.A. Breland, J. Helenius, N. Sriskandarajah, and L. Salomonsson. 2005. Food systems and environment: Building positive rural–urban linkages. Hum. Ecol. Rev. 12:60–71.

Francis, C., R. Poincelot, and G. Bird (ed.) 2006. Developing and extending a sustainable agriculture: A new social contract. Haworth Press, Binghampton, New York.

Friedman, D. 2001. Transitioning to organic production. SARE, USDA, Washington, DC.

Gliessman, S.R. 1997. Agroecology: Ecological processes in sustainable agriculture. Lewis Publ., CRC Press, Boca Raton, FL.

Hernandez Xolocotzi, E. 1987. Xolocotzia: Obras De Efraim Hernandez Xolocotzi. 1st ed. University of Chapingo, Mexico.

Hill, S.B., and R.J. MacRae. 1995. Conceptual framework for the transition from conventional to sustainable agriculture. J. Sustain. Agric. 7:81–87.

Kirschenmann, F. 2009. Farming in the middle: An ethical imperative. p. 325–342. In C. Francis (ed.) Organic farming: The ecological system. Agron. Monogr. 54. ASA, CSSA, and SSSA, Madison, WI. (This volume.)

Kolb, D. 1984. Experiential learning: Experience as the source of learning and development. Prentice Hall Publ., Upper Saddle River, NJ.

Kuhn, T. 1962. The structure of scientific revolutions. 3rd ed. Univ. Chicago Press, Chicago, IL.

Lieblein, G., and C. Francis. 2007. Towards responsible action through agroecological education. Ital. J. Agron. Riv. Agron. 2:79–86.

MacRae, R.J., S.B. Hill, J. Henning, and G.R. Mehuys. 1989. Agricultural science and sustainable agriculture: A review of the existing scientific barriers to sustainable food production and potential solutions. Biol. Agric. Hortic. 6:173–219.

Mezirow, J. (ed.) 2000. Learning as transformation: Critical perspectives on a theory in progress. Jossey-Bass Publ., San Francisco, CA.

Northbourne, W. 1940. Look to the land. J.M. Dent, London.

Rodale, J.I. 1946. Pay dirt. Rodale Press, Emmaus, PA.

Sayre, L. 2007. Leading the way in organic ag research and extension. Available at http://newfarm.rodaleinstitute.org/features/1004/delate/index.shtml (verified 22 July 2009).

Seppänen, L., and C. Francis. 2006. Design of farmer education and training in organic agriculture. p. 407–419. In P. Kristiansen et al. (ed.) Organic agriculture: A global perspective. CSIRO, Australia.

Sriskandarajah, N., R.J. Bawden, and R.G. Packham. 1991. Systems agriculture: A paradigm for sustainability. AFSRE Newsl., Univ. Arkansas, Fayetteville 2(3):1–5.

Steiner, R. 1958. Agriculture: A course of eight lectures. Biodynamic Agric. Assoc., London.

University of California–Davis. 2007. The student farm, College of Agricultural and Environmental Sciences, Davis, California. Available at http://studentfarm.ucdavis.edu/ (verified 22 July 2009).

University of California–Santa Cruz. 2003. Teaching organic farming and gardening. Center for Agroecology and Sustainable Food Systems, Univ. of California, Santa Cruz.

Wezel, A., S. Bellon, T. Dore, C. Francis, D. Vallod, and C. David. 2009. Agroecology as a science, a movement or a practice. Agron. Sustain. Devel. doi:10.1051/agro/2009004.

Wilson, K., and G.E.B. Morren. 1990. Systems approaches for improvement in agriculture and resource management. Macmillan Publ. Co., New York.

14

Human Ecology in Future Organic Farming and Food Systems

Charles Francis and Laurie Hodges
Department of Agronomy and Horticulture, University of Nebraska, Lincoln

The acceleration of growth in global population, as described in Chapter 3 (Porter, 2009, this volume) and illustrated in Fig. 3–1, appears to have slowed in many parts of the world. Likely causes are aging populations, especially in Europe and in other mature industrialized societies; near-pandemics such as AIDS in Africa; increased education of women in many countries; and some appreciation of the limits that a finite nonrenewable resource base imposes on growth. From an ecology point of view, this last factor is perhaps the most important.

Unfortunately, this growing awareness of resource limitations and the consequences for potential future food sustainability has limited relevance to more than one billion hungry people who currently subsist on less than US$1 per day (World Vision, 2009). The previous chapters presented a rationale for an expansion of organic farming, with most examples and applications from the United States. This book's authors firmly believe that organic farming methods and systems hold promise to fulfill many of the food needs of the global population; indeed, some would argue that in a world of scarce resources and overwhelming pollution we have no choice in the long term but to convert to a largely organic food system.

A recent publication by Alex Wezel and colleagues (2009) explores the origins of agroecology, and by implication organic farming, in terms of agricultural *practices*, the *science* behind these human activity systems, and the recognition of agroecology and organics as a social *movement*. They distinguish different stages of activity as well as distinct differences between countries in how, in general, they have embraced these ecologically sound farming and food systems. In France, for example, the trends toward agroecology and organic farming have been seen as practices and to some degree a movement, with the science relegated to agronomy departments in research institutes and universities. Germany, in contrast, has traditionally focused on the science of these and other facets of farming, with the distinct exception of the biodynamic movement identified with Rudolph Steiner (1958). In the United States and Brazil, as well as throughout Latin America, various groups embraced organic field practices, the science of alternative systems, and the movement of organic farming.

The confusion of terms and interpretations of what organic farming means and how this is related to agroecology and to sustainable agriculture further clouds the discussions of these agricultural innovations. The situation is clarified and simplified if we accept the definition of organic farming and foods as stated in the legislation forming the U.S. National Organic Program (USDA-NOP, 2002). However, to adhere too closely to this definition may limit open discussion of key issues in organic agriculture, possibly excluding creative opportunities for the future.

In this chapter we go beyond current thinking and practical decisions about implementation of organic practices for fertility and weed management, designing efficient crop and animal systems, and farmers accessing the growing markets and meeting demands for organic food. Here we shed the conceptual and practical limitations imposed by those who wear the blinders of what is realistic and possible within current thinking and constraints to agriculture. We take seriously the third option presented by MacRae et al. (1990) and go beyond better efficiency and substitution of inputs to embrace the need to redesign agriculture and food systems. Most importantly, we follow the admonition of the late René Dubos (quoted in Hawken et al., 1999) that *trend is not destiny*. This is the perspective needed to reach food sufficiency for all—a goal that is essential along with rebuilding a livable environment for ourselves and most other species. This goal is only possible through the implementation of both an ecologically sustainable and socially viable agriculture and food system. One of the key solutions is to interject *ecology* into the design of organic farming systems.

Human Ecology and Awareness of Current Challenges

As a relatively self-aware species, *Homo sapiens* is collectively beginning to realize that in many ways we are *not* different from other species in terms of resource needs and space requirements. Over the past two centuries and until recently, our numbers have expanded nearly exponentially in response to new technologies, using nonrenewable fossil fuels to increase labor efficiency and scarce fresh water to irrigate crops. As described by Kirschenmann in Chapter 15 (2009, this volume) we have also enjoyed a relatively benign and constant climate during this time. It is not surprising that many have been lulled into a sense of complacency in enjoying the creature comforts and adequate food supply brought about by science and technology, and one consequence is a vast increase in human population. However, much of this largesse has not reached a large number of people on the planet. Despite the ability of medical science to avert many disease problems that once limited human population, we still cannot sustainably produce enough food and make it available to all. Economic and political factors interact with food production and allocation priorities to reduce equity and prevent access to sufficient food by many who are poor.

As we have used up ancient and nonrenewable fossil fuels and appropriated most available fresh water for agriculture and other needs, we have recently started to identify and appreciate the negative emergent properties of some technologies. We are also becoming ever more aware of the degree to which we can foul our nest with chemical pollutants that may reduce quality and length of life. However, although many have taken seriously the admonitions of Rachel Carson (1962) in *Silent Spring*, there is still a high level of trust in the system of regulation and control of pesticides and in the government oversight of food safety. Recent highly publicized food quality problems, to be discussed later, have challenged this complacency. Debate continues about the safety of transgenic crops, to the point that some countries in dire need of food assistance have rejected imports of donated grains that come from genetically modified organism (GMO) hybrids or varieties. Further, our growing incidence of diabetes, cancer, and other seemingly preventable diseases is likely caused by ignorance about correct diets as well as exposure to certain new chemicals and antibiotics we are introducing into our environment and to which we have no historical exposure or genetic selection experience.

Potential negative consequences of the chemical revolution in agriculture and the food system include chemicals and antibiotics that permeate the water and air we ingest, and sometimes the food we consume. Decisions made at the level of federal policy and statute have a tremendous impact on the practices used in agriculture. The rejection of scientific data regarding environmental contaminants by recent U.S. administrations in favor of environmental decisions that will benefit industry by relaxing or omitting regulations has made a mockery of the precautionary principle. The accepted economic paradigm has been economic growth at any cost, and the consequences of such national policies are just coming to our attention.

Concern about the safety and security of the U.S. food system, and growing interest by individuals about where their families' food comes from and how it is produced have combined to ensure a growth in the organic food sector of about 20% per year over the past two decades, as described and referenced in the first chapter (Francis and Van Wart, 2009, this volume) and throughout the book. Food alarms related to several highly publicized food-related problems and environmental issues have sounded:

- DDT [1,1,1-trichloro-2,2-bis(4-chlorophenyl)ethane] accumulation and impacts on the food chain and bird reproduction
- ALAR [daminozide, N-(dimethylamino)succinamic acid] used as a chemical growth regulator on fruits, but now withdrawn from the market due to proven carcinogenic properties
- BSE (Bovine Spongiform Encephalopathy) or "mad cow disease" that caused massive preventive destruction of herds in the U.K.
- Bovine Growth Hormone (rBGH) used to increase feed consumption and milk production in industrial dairy herds
- Foot and Mouth Disease, a viral disease in cattle and other livestock that rarely attacks humans but can devastate a country's livestock industry and cancel exports
- Melamine in baby foods from China that has taken dozens of young lives, as well as contaminated pet food
- Peanut butter and other products recalled by plants in Georgia and Texas due to *Salmonella* contamination, and both these plants had certified organic production lines

Although the conventional U.S. wisdom is that we have the safest food system in the world, the Center for Disease Control in Atlanta reports that each year 76 million people in this country get sick, 300,000 are hospitalized, and 5000 die from foodborne illnesses (Center for Disease Control, 2009). Perhaps we are complacent about our personal food safety habits because of this wide belief that food is safe? Or perhaps it is because we have put our trust in an expedient global trade system with enough oversight that has supposedly served us well enough for decades?

We have a system today that lacks any local connection with farmers, one that destroys our identity with food that seems to come from everywhere, but also from a global nowhere (Kloppenburg et al., 1996). The alarming concerns of Carson (1962) in *Silent Spring* that created more awareness in the 1960s and led to the formation of the Environmental Protection Agency, regulation of pesticides, air and water quality standards, and more careful testing and regulation in the agricultural environment may have now given way to complacency.

The EPA rules in agriculture have also eroded due to industrial agriculture and food system pressures, as well as political expediency. People are most concerned about food price rather than quality or even safety. We now depend on a preponderance of processed and packaged food in our diets, and still trust that the government will enforce safety standards and protect us. In fact, less than 1% of imported fresh foods are actually inspected or tested, and the ability of government agencies charged with this responsibility have been severely understaffed and underfunded over the past decade. Our inspection rate on imports is only a small fraction of what is enforced in the European Union (Suppan, 2008).

In this chapter the growth of organic agriculture and the popularity of organic foods for consumers are explored, along with current challenges and opportunities related to the future of organic food systems. There are innovative agricultural practices and systems used by organic farmers that hold promise for more efficient food production. A small cadre of scientists and farmers are uncovering ecological principles that could help transform the entire food system, including many practices in conventional agriculture. Creative local production and marketing opportunities offer strategies that can raise public awareness about food production, quality, marketing, and distribution and connect consumers with farmers. We focus on the human awareness and attitudes about the organic farming and food opportunities because farmers and consumers will make the ultimate decisions on the future of this food sector, along with the support of government through incentives and regulations. All these interacting components form the complex human activities that result in farming and food systems, and the focus of this book is how concepts of ecology can help us understand and resolve future challenges.

Innovative Practices and Systems

The preceding chapters provide excellent examples of how organic farmers practice efficiency in crop and animal management, by understanding their production and climatic environments and reducing off-farm inputs and cycling nutrients whenever possible. Because much of the relevant research has been conducted by farmers, there is a strong pragmatic element in what has emerged, and less concern about the details of experimental design, statistical probabilities, publication, or broad recommendations that characterize most typical experiment station research. Although on-farm research and experiences often lack the statistical rigor and repeatability of what is done by university and federal research scientists, the successful experiences of organic farmers often spread to others in the community and become ingrained in the organic farming knowledge base. There is growing appreciation among both farmers and researchers, especially among those interested in organic farming, that on-farm research has high value in promoting creative thinking and change in agriculture. In fact, many of the ideas that researchers pursue in both conventional and organic investigation originate with farmers, and scientists lend credence to farmers' conclusions and intuition by putting these ideas to rigorous statistical testing. Laurie Drinkwater describes in Chapter 2 (2009, this volume) the value of cooperative farmer–researcher studies and how to approach research using ecological principles and site-specific goals.

Improved efficiency is the first principle described by MacRae et al. (1990). Efficient provision of adequate plant nutrients is accomplished through use of cover crops, rotations of cereals with legumes, and other practices that promote an internal cycling of nutrients on the farm. In Chapter 3, Paul Porter (2009, this volume) describes the importance of cover crops for future contributions of fertility to the system, as well as their efficient moisture use, nutrient capture, and storage for subsequent crops. What has not been explored adequately are mixtures of cover crop species and sequences of different cover crops that would be most appropriate for the crop or crops that follow. Following the ecological principle of diversity would lead us to testing the resilience of survival and nutrient contributions of a biodiverse cover crop mixture, a strategy that has not often been tried. Likewise, our adherence to a single species of cover crop that grows well and appears to fit the system is similar to the continuous crop monoculture mentality that drives us to embrace a maize (*Zea mays* L.)–soybean [*Glycine max* (L.) Merr.] rotation or even continuous maize. We tend to not think enough about biodiversity; cover crop mixtures or sequences could be one excellent strategy for organic farmers to initiate.

Efficient internal nutrient cycling within the farm can be promoted through integration of crops and animals into the system (Chapters 4 [Entz and Thiessen Martens, 2009] and 5 [Clark, 2009], this volume), based on an understanding of the dynamics of the nitrogen cycle (see Fig. 7–1 in Chapter 7, Heckman et al., 2009, this volume). Weed management in organic systems involves understanding the ecology of weed life cycles, their physiology and ecology; developing an appreciation of the importance of competition at different stages in crop growth and development; and using economic plus other threshold criteria for making management decisions. As described in Chapter 8 (Liebman and Davis, 2009, this volume), organic farmers often delay planting to accomplish at least one preplant cultivation to destroy or suppress weeds, allowing the crop to be planted into warm soil where it will develop quickly to out-compete unwanted species in the field. Organic farmers understand which weeds are prevalent in high or low nitrogen situations, and in low phosphorus or low pH conditions. They use allelopathic cover crops such as mustards, turnips, or rye to suppress weed populations. These methods can all improve the efficiency of nutrient and weed management, using current equipment and known methods, while integrating an understanding of the whole agroecological system.

The second principle from MacRae et al. (1990) is substitution. Organic farmers as well as researchers in this arena are highly motivated to seek products and methods that will substitute for those currently effective in conventional systems. The concept of pulling a product off the shelf has been ingrained in farmers and researchers since the value of new chemical fertilizer and pesticide technologies became known and accepted. We also live in a culture that expects immediate results, and thus we are attracted to a starter fertilizer that turns the crop green or an insecticide that knocks the critters off the crop plants. In response to this mindset, companies have developed a wide selection of organic products that are now available and accepted in the certification process, including those authorized by the Organic Materials Review Institute (2009).

An intriguing study of accepted organic plant nutrient products that challenged this way of thinking was conducted by the Rodale Institute in Pennsylvania in the early 1980s. In a replicated field evaluation of 20 such products, some were observed to have positive visual effects on the maize crop, and none was found to be harmful to the crop. However, not one of the products was recommended as an economically viable choice for organic farmers (McAllister, 1983). Thus, in spite of the advertising and testimonials and availability of a wide range of available products, and the appeal of simply replacing one easily applied product by another, most organic farmers today opt for thoughtful use of crop rotations, animal manures, compost, and green manure crops to provide sufficient nutrients for crop growth.

By far the most important potential change in organic systems to promote resource-efficient and environmentally sound management is the redesign of systems (MacRae et al., 1990). This is more difficult than improving efficiency or substituting an organic product for a conventional chemical product but has the possibility to initiate systemic and lasting change in farming practices. The redesign process requires a thorough understanding of system structure and function, an appreciation of what is achievable through ecological design, and likely a change in the paradigm of what constitutes success.

To understand system structure and function implies knowing intimately the component crops and animals in the system, their seasonal needs and behaviors, their growth cycles and nutrient requirements, and their actual and potential interactions. This knowledge can go into the design of a long-term crop rotation, an introduction of new crops into the sequence, and an optimum crop–animal mix for specific conditions and system goals. Knowing growth cycles of crops can help in design of weed, insect, and nutrient management strategies, protecting the crop when it is vulnerable and providing nutrients when they are used most efficiently in the crop cycle. Understanding the synergy of cereals and legumes that are intercropped and the dynamics of nutrient cycling in a rotation of crops and pastures can lead to integration efficiencies that are not possible in monoculture crop or feedlot animal production systems. These aspects of crop–animal systems are discussed in Chapters 4 (Entz and Thiessen Martens, 2009, this volume) and 5 (Clark, 2009, this volume).

Ecological design of cropping and farming systems was explored in Chapter 2 (Drinkwater, 2009, this volume), and the observation of natural ecosystems provides some clues to design of agroecosystems. The principles of biodiversity, competition and complementation, system resilience and response to rapidly changing conditions, and cycling of nutrients are all integral to nonmanaged, natural ecosystems. Although agroecosystems differ greatly because of the goal to extract products from the production environment, the principles of conservation of water, nutrients, energy, and organic matter within the system, and promoting cycling of these elements, can reduce production costs, increase profits, and preserve the natural resource base on which long-term stability depends.

A change in farming system goals may be the most important adjustment that a farmer or researcher can make to successfully redesign systems. Accepting a certain level of weeds in the field may be anathema to those who grew up thinking that clean fields were close to parenthood and apple pie, but economic research shows that weeds up to a threshold level do not damage the crop and in fact may provide some nutrient trapping and cycling. The social acceptance of growing the same crops as other farmers in the community and using similar cultural practices and markets can be a strong social deterrent to change, yet successful organic farmers often go against the grain in many ways and can establish a special market niche for crops or animal products that are in high demand by society. Avoiding high-volume dry matter crops that are sold off the farm, such as hay or maize silage, provides a resource-conserving philosophy that is followed by most organic farmers. Integration of crops and livestock, especially through multi-species grazing systems, is a strategy used to conserve nutrients and add value to the local natural resource base on the organic farm.

One method of increasing resource use through redesign of cropping systems lies in planting of multiple species in the same area. Long used by farmers with a limited land base, especially in the complex systems of East Asia (King, 1948), multiple cropping systems have allowed farmers to use intensive systems to provide family subsistence and products for barter or sale (Francis, 1986). Often highly dependent on hand labor, such systems are hardly practical for large-scale, industrial or extensive commercial application. Yet most multiple species systems over the centuries have been de facto organic, with no outside inputs of chemical pesticides or fertilizers, and their inherent biodiversity has provided an impressive degree of protection against pests and built a capacity for internal nutrient cycling and resilience in system yields. The land equivalent ratio (LER) is a measure of the efficiency of multiple crop systems compared with monocrops:

$$\text{LER} = \Sigma Y_{ai}/Y_{am}$$

where Y_{ai} is the intercrop yield of ath crop and Y_{am} is the monocrop yield of the ath crop; the index is the sum over all crops in the mixture, a measure of land area use efficiency.

In well-designed intercrop system, this LER is frequently well above 1.0, indicating that the land use is more efficient when two or more crops are planted together. Notable examples are the multiple-species vegetable systems of southern China, where as many as 15 crops may be planted both mixed and in sequence in the same field each year (King, 1948), or the humid forest zone systems of Nigeria, where at least 20 different species or varieties may occupy the land at the same time (Smith and Francis, 1986). Current applications of these intensive cropping principles in mechanized U.S. farming include alternating strip cropping of maize–soybean–wheat (*Triticum aestivum* L.) and relay cropping of winter wheat–soybean. When enough water is available from rainfall or irrigation, both of these crop combinations often "over-yield", that is, have LER > 1.0. Multiple cropping systems have also reduced economic risk through multiple marketing opportunities and marketable products that spread income through more of the year.

Thinking of farming and food systems as one highly integrated series of activities and looking for ways to add value on the farm can make a smaller farming operation financially successful, even in the U.S. Midwest. In this region the conventional wisdom supported by USDA data (USDA-ERS, 2009) is that a minimum of 400 ha (1000 acres) of owned land or 800 ha (2000 acres) of leased land is essential to produce enough maize and soybean to support a family. There is no question that adopting new technologies can be just as important to the organic farmer as in conventional agriculture, but the choice of these new advances needs to be within the criteria of organic certification and must make economic sense in the long term.

Quandary of Transgenics in Organic Systems

Transgenic crop and animal strains are not allowed in certified organic production systems. The term *genetically modified organism* is misleading, since all of our major crops have undergone "genetic modification" during the selection process. As described in Chapter 1 (Francis and Van Wart, 2009, this volume), the certification process only applies to production and processing, and does not guarantee that the final product is free of pesticide residues, transgenic genetic material, or other prohibited substances. These disallowed substances can enter the production or processing of organic products at any number of stages, from contamination by pollen from neighbors' GMO crops, to accidental spray drift onto organic fields, to mixtures of component crops during processing and packaging for distribution. Certification of the production process does minimize, although not eliminate, the entry of these substances into the organic food chain. One element of particular concern is pollen drift and contamination from nearby fields of GMO crops of the same species, i.e., those developed using a transgenic mechanism to incorporate genetic material.

The ubiquitous presence of GMO pollen from cross pollinating species is illustrated by the U.S. maize crop, where today there is a market penetration of over 50% with hybrids developed using transgenic technologies. Maize pollen can travel with the wind up to 10 km from the source if conditions are favorable. Although soybean is a self-pollinated crop, and thus does not have the same potential for pollen spread as maize, the fact that more than 90% of the U.S. soybean area is now planted to GMO varieties greatly increases the opportunity for contamination of an organic seed supply with seed from a conventional source. These two examples illustrate the magnitude of the challenge for keeping organic crops free from GMO contamination.

Why are plants produced by transgenic breeding methods not allowed in organic certification? The California Certified Organic Farmers (2005) provide a summary of concerns:

- GMO crops impact on beneficial insects and other nontarget species
- Pests resistant to chemicals or pesticides are likely to develop with widespread applications of single GMO products, just as they do with similar strategies using chemical pesticides
- Genetic pollution is already affecting organic and nonorganic growers
- GMO crops and their effects on human health—there is concern that not enough testing has been done to determine the long-term effects of these new genetic combinations on human health, whether from the transgenes themselves or from markers (often antibiotics) used in the transfer and selection process
- Increased costs and liability to organic and nonorganic farmers due to contamination of organic crops

The California Certified Organic Farmers further discussed the inconsistencies in federal regulations and the inability to detect contamination of the food supply by experimental or nonapproved GMO products, some of which have already caused high-profile food recalls with large losses to the food industry. This organization supports a general moratorium on field testing of GMO crops until adequate understanding is gained through research on the long-term side effects of this new technology.

There is currently a high level of debate within agriculture about the costs and benefits of this technology. The European Union currently prohibits importation of grain products or foods that contain over a minute level of contamination with GMO-derived crop ingredients. U.S. seed and chemical companies as well as farmers interested in export of commodities are opposed to this ban by the E.U. The argument in favor of GMOs is that any advances in genetic resistance to pests that can reduce broad applications of chemical pesticides ultimately may be better for the environment, as well as potentially provide more profitable production strategies for all farmers. Although all GMOs are prohibited from current use in organic production systems, it would seem wise for the organic community to keep an open mind about a technology that in the future may prove to be safe and may help the organic farmer produce crops and livestock in an environmentally friendly and chemical-free way. Today, this is not even an issue for serious debate in the organic farming and food system sectors.

Innovations in Marketing

The marketing of organic grains, oilseeds, and some specialty crops is described by Kathleen Delate in Chapter 6 (2009, this volume). The channels available to organic farmers for these specialty commodities are similar in most respects to those for conventional grains, although the numbers of buyers and locations that will accept an organic product generally are more limited in the case of major grain crops. Early in the development of organic grains and oilseeds, there was some difficulty for farmers to find buyers and there were some players in the market who turned out to be less than trustworthy. As with any business sector, these operators were rather quickly weeded out. It appears today that the market for organic grains is one of high demand, with a high degree of confidence between most producers and buyers. The spike in maize, other cereal grains, and oilseed prices in mid 2008 apparently lured some farmers to abandon their organic certification to pursue high prices for conventional grains. With the subsequent and equally rapid decline in commodity prices a few months later, it is likely that those same farmers regret their decision to forego the long-term opportunity value of staying in organic production.

A number of alternative marketing opportunities for organic produce and specialty crops are presented and discussed by Hikaru Peterson and Rhonda Janke in Chapter 10 (2009, this volume). The authors discuss farmers markets, community-supported agriculture (CSAs) with direct delivery of products to customers or to a pick-up point, U-pick operations, sales from farm shops, local restaurants and markets, and sales to individuals with or without need for advertising. One of the beauties of these local markets is the direct communication between farmer and consumer, and the mutual respect and trust that can grow from such a collaboration. In some CSAs, for example, there is an option for members or consumers to work on the farm to defray part of the cost of their weekly market box or basket. Such involvement increases their appreciation of the production process, the challenges and risks inherent in agriculture, and their relationship with the farmer. In fact, some farmers using organic practices have decided that with this level of trust and consumer knowledge about their operations, it is not necessary to certify organic, with all of the expense and paperwork that this entails. Others depend on local markets, but will certify their farms to support the movement in principle. Many farmers who sell in local markets write newsletters and blogs to further a personal connection with their customers. Extending this concept to reach consumers in wholesale and retail marketing of organic products could be one step toward improved agricultural literacy in the general public, a group of people largely ignorant about all aspects of the U.S. food supply, from production through its arrival at the supermarket.

While most CSAs have been initiated by individual farmers or a small group of cooperating farmers, the Farm to Folk cooperative in Ames, IA (Farm to Folk, 2009) actually was started by consumers. Recognizing a need for ready access to local produce, a group of people in Ames decided to seek out farmers willing to produce and deliver food to meet their needs. They recruited eight farmers to produce a range of crops and animal products. The consumers took responsibility for assembly and delivery of the products to their group. This is an innovative variation on the CSA model, and one that could be replicated wherever there is a critical mass of consumers with like interests in local food and farmers willing to cooperate in production.

The opportunity for self-production or "self-provisioning" of organic foods was described by Patricia Allen and Hilary Melcarek in Chapter 11 (2009, this volume). This concept is based on tradition going back to the origins of agriculture, but is one that has been virtually abandoned in the current commercial and global economy. Careful observation while driving through communities and the countryside today reveals that few people plant a vegetable garden, fruit trees, or berry plants for their own use. Some exceptions to this trend are notable. During the Second World War, partly due to the well-publicized support of Eleanor Roosevelt at the White House in 1943, there were "victory gardens" across the United States. The goal was to self-provision as many families and food needs as possible so that food could be released for shipment to troops in other countries and to places where food was in deficit due to the war. As a result, about 40% of produce needed by domestic families in the U.S. was produced for a time on their own sites (Victory Garden, 2009).

Another well-known exception is the wide array of individual garden and farming plots, legally called "household plots" in Russia and the former Soviet Socialist Republic states in eastern Europe. The quantity of food produced in these small areas has been highly successful in helping the population avert hunger during times of political and economic turmoil. Indeed, the production per unit area apparently has exceeded that of the large, state-owned, collectively managed farms (Lerman et al., 2004). Food production on an individual scale is obviously still very much a way of life for millions of subsistence farmers throughout the developing world. There are lessons in self-provisioning that could be useful for everyone in the future. A *New York Times* article (Burros, 2009) announced that First Lady Michelle Obama was planting a vegetable garden on the White House grounds, creating a highly visible model that people can take responsibility for some of their own food.

An emerging marketing opportunity for organic produce is found in local markets, restaurants, and institutional food preparation sites. Although seeking out these markets is a time-consuming chore for busy farmers, this local approach can add value to products and capture much of the food dollar that currently goes into the wholesale sector, including all that is spent on advertising. According to Stuart Smith at University of Maine, the proportion of the money spent on conventionally produced and marketed food in the United States that actually reaches the farmer has decreased from about 24% in 1900 to less than 10% today. The livestock farmer enjoys more of an advantage, perhaps 16 to 18% of the food dollar from animal products that are less processed. The proportion is as low as 1 to 2% for cereals, where most of the money is invested in processing, packaging, transportation, and advertising.

Local foods have been a large draw for customers at locally owned markets and restaurants. A program called Good, Fresh, Local that brings local ingredients to University of Nebraska– Lincoln dormitory cafeterias has proven to be popular with students and others in the community (University of Nebraska, 2009). The myth that buyers in large institutional food establishments such as universities, city schools, state offices, hospitals, and prisons are closely tied by contract to one or a few wholesale dealers turns out not to be the case. Most institutional food buyers will survey several wholesale sources for availability and price, but are not restricted from considering local farmers, especially when produce is in season. An interesting hybrid model is the current affiliation of the large wholesaler Sysco with local groups, where they use the corporation's wide-scale distribution system to provide locally sourced foods to local customers (see http://www.freshpoint.com/services/environment.html, verified 2009).

In surveying this range of alternative marketing and local food production options, one has the impression that we have yet to tap into the growing concern of the consumer about where and how food is produced. There is widespread publicity about specific problems that have arisen in food safety, but most people see no clear alternatives to what they presently do. For the farmer, there is accountability to consumers as well as the liability involved in marketing food directly. Most farmers markets require the individual farmer to have a product liability policy. For the typical consumer, long hours on the job and a busy life style plus lack of knowledge or concern about food issues seem to work against growing one's own food. Economic concern about the comparative price for any item precludes the search for locally grown produce, concerns about where things are produced, or the wider implications of how important food may be to the local and national economy.

The potential effects of natural disasters on the food production and distribution system and, consequently, on the availability of food to meet immediate needs are largely ignored. For many people, the term *food security* is now considered only in relation to bioterrorism rather than to the accessibility of food for daily meals as it was during the 20th century. There are many situations that can disrupt the food supply, as England experienced in 2000 when fuel prices increased dramatically and the oil supply was threatened, resulting in temporary rationing (Guardian Staff, 2000).

To prepare for any emergency or situation that affects the food supply and distribution system, some experts have recommended that each community and city should produce or supply one-third of its food, although the current estimate is that only 5% is provided in close proximity (Community Food Security Coalition's North American Urban Agriculture Committee, 2003). Although it is doubtful that peri-urban agriculture can supply 30% of the food for the multi-million population of a metropolis, there is certainly an opportunity for more production and diversity of production in urban settings, and, for many reasons, much of this may be most appropriately produced organically. Such production could provide economic opportunities for numerous entrepreneurs, public awareness of food production, educational opportunities addressing environmental and ecological aspects of organic food production, links with local restaurants, corporate food service facilities, and numerous other community benefits. Examples of successful commercial gardens operating within U.S. cities and worldwide are available (e.g., www.foodsecurity.org, http://rooftopgarden.com/, verified 23 July 2009). This is a fertile area for education and expansion of organic foods.

Emergence of "Big O" and Globalization

One major change in the organic food production and marketing sector over the past two decades has been the emergence of an industrial organic sector, often called "Big O" by those who are small-scale and have been in organics for a longer time. In some ways this is a part of a larger and longer-term trend toward the industrialization and globalization of agriculture and the food system. Farm size in the United States and other industrialized countries has increased as farms consolidated to take advantage of efficiencies of scale, larger equipment, and labor-saving technologies such as pesticides and chemical fertilizers, as well as federal farm support programs that focus on a small number of commodities. Although the environmental benefits and labor and management details in organic food production apparently were unattractive to larger producers at the outset, they now recognize that this is the only real growth area in the food sector. Market growth combined with the substantial price premiums received for organic products have attracted the interest of industrial producers and marketers, both individuals and transnational corporations. There is mixed reaction in the organic farming community to this change.

On the positive side, there may be efficiencies of scale for some produce grown on a very large scale, assuming that industrial-model farms meet the same organic standards of production for which they are certified and maintain the absence of pesticide residues and quality of product throughout the production and marketing chain. Such large-scale production could result in greater access to organic food by those with lower income levels who could not afford the prices at specialty organic supermarkets or the generally higher (10–50%) premium that characterizes organic food. Since more than 50% of organic food is now sold through large supermarket chains, one could expect some of the efficiencies of scale in mass marketing to reduce consumer prices and make organic food more accessible. The exclusive nature of organic food for only "well-to-do" customers was discussed in Chapter 11 (Allen and Melcarek, 2009, this volume).

The negative side of the industrialization of organic food systems within the United States includes a further separation of consumers from where their food is produced, the increased costs of transportation of food from distant sources, the erosion of the philosophical and social justice foundations of organic agriculture found among local-scale organic farmers, and the potentials for widespread distribution of unsafe products and difficulties in locating the sources. When both organic and conventional products are grown, branded, and sold by transnational corporations, questions are raised regarding corporate motivation and dedication to organic principles as well as regulations. There has been a movement among smaller, traditional organic farmers and their certifiers to establish some type of higher order certification that would include more stringent social concerns as well as a local production stipulation. So far this initiative has not borne fruit, although there are calls from many in the "small o" organic food sector for more local growing and purchasing of organic and pesticide-free foods.

The challenges of certifying organic crop production and enforcing regulations are complicated by the globalization of the food system. Just as with imported conventional foods, there is concern among U.S. consumers that regulations may not be enforced or that substances prohibited in this country may still be used elsewhere to control pests. Although the organic certification rules are similar in all groups that are under the IFOAM umbrella, the anonymity of distance hangs over the system. With certification only of the production process and not the food itself, there is no guarantee that the food meets expected standards. Because of the large numbers of small farmers who produce certain organic crops, for example coffee, there are large logistical difficulties and high costs to using the normal inspector system of certifying each farm. Instead, a culturally and economically appropriate method of certifying large groups of farmers is being used, with certain farmers designated as inspectors to visit the rest of the farms in the group. The decentralized decision making in such a system could lead to abuses.

These are among the issues related to scale that are yet to be resolved in organic production and marketing. They swirl around the large versus small farm debate, marketing in small shops versus large supermarkets owned by national or international corporations, some promoting local organic producers while purchasing relatively little. Also important are the treatment of labor and distribution of benefits to those who produce the crops and livestock and work in the food sector, and the potentials for abuse of the system, especially when decisions are made far from the local level by people not known to the consumer.

Food Safety and Quality Issues

Another area of continuing debate about the organic food system revolves around issues of food safety and the nutritional quality of organic foods. There is little doubt about the lower levels of pesticide residue carried on organic products, but there are many conflicting opinions and research results on the nutritional quality of organic produce and other products made from organic ingredients. This is confusing for consumers who are concerned but have a hard time understanding and interpreting the evidence.

The clearest information is available about the presence of pesticide residues. There are multiple ways that pesticides or other contaminants can come in contact with organic products, including pesticide drift from neighboring conventional production fields, mixtures of product on the farm or in storage, and comingling or contamination further down the line in processing, packing, transport, or marketing the final product. The certification system is designed to prevent this from happening, but such systems are always less than perfect, and the certification process only takes into account the production and processing of food. There is limited further testing for residues in the organic food chain. New methods of detection of minute amounts of pesticide residues also make it possible to find traces of chemical materials that formerly escaped detection. With these caveats, we can objectively assess the differences between organic and conventional foods in terms of pesticide residues.

Analysis of three independent studies that examined pesticide residues in conventional and organic produce found that organically grown samples consistently had far smaller percentages with pesticide residues: 6.5–27% of organic samples vs. 71–90% of conventional produce. Possible sources of the pesticide residues found in organic produce were attributed to environmental contamination from pesticide carryover due to use in the past, pesticide drift from adjacent non-organic farms, and the possibility of mislabeled organic produce. Incorrect labels could either be because of fraud or because of lapses in maintaining the identity of organic foods through the distribution chain (Baker et al., 2002).

Food quality is a more complex issue. A growing body of literature shows a nutritional advantage of food products produced under organic conditions, especially due to increased content of antioxidants, minerals, protein, flavonoids, and other components (Cooper et al., 2007; Dangour et al., 2009; Organic Center, 2008; Worthington, 2001). There is a lesser but substantial number of publications that suggest no differences in quality between organic and conventional foods (e.g., Ordóñez-Santos et al., 2009). It is certain that the methods used in most comparisons of these two sources of food are often less than controlled, especially if the foods are chosen from the shelf in a retail market (Harker, 2003). Unless grown under near-identical environmental and cultural conditions and from the same genetic seed source (at a minimum the cultivar level) it is unlikely that plants labeled as organic and conventional will test for quality parameters in an unbiased and scientific way. For example, crop yield greatly influences the protein and thus the nitrogen content of foods, and if yields in one system are greatly different from those in the other for whatever reason, this yield difference will be confounded with the system differences one is attempting to measure. Also, vitamin content is often expressed on a fresh weight basis, which in turn varies widely with environmental conditions during production through the time of sample analysis.

Without additional controlled testing over a range of organic and conventional food products, it is difficult to draw conclusions about product quality. For now, we conclude that organic food does indeed carry lower levels of pesticide residue, although these organic products are not completely free of residues. The question of quality is not yet resolved, in spite of the voluminous popular literature and some scientific studies showing a superiority of organic food. There are many other defensible reasons for purchase and consumption of organic food— especially if it is produced by local farmers under environmentally sound and socially acceptable conditions—but buying for increased quality in general or for a specific quality attribute such as nutritional composition is still questionable.

An interesting example of the role of quality claims in the market is the quandary of organic milk sales in Norway by TINE, the dairy monopoly owned by farmers. This same corporation markets mostly milk from conventional dairies. They need to advertise organic milk as having certain qualities that are attractive to the consumer without any implication that the rest of their product line is inferior or dangerous to the consumer in any way. On their organic milk cartons, there is a simple statement that the milk is produced by dairies that are certified organic and that the cows are raised according to those standards (C. Francis, 2008, personal experience). The issue of quality, particularly in relation to human health, is likely to receive added attention in the future, and will continue to encounter controversy within and outside the organic food sector.

Structure of U.S. Agriculture and National Food Policy

During the past 70 yr, many decisions by farmers and others in the U.S. food system have been driven by various farm program incentives and regulations, representing a strong intervention of federal government in farming. According to esteemed agricultural economist Willard Cochran, emeritus professor at University of Minnesota and advisor to several U.S. presidents, we have been attempting to apply well-meaning farm programs to stabilize production and adequately reward farmers for more than half a century, and we have yet to get it right (Cochran, 2003; Levins, 2000). Surely with the amount of money spent on support programs over this time there should be some lessons learned?

It appears that the United States does not have a national food policy, but rather a strong posture of supporting an industrial agriculture production model and indirectly the agribusiness sector and grain trade monopoly. This is food policy by default. Unlike a number of other countries, we have addressed this issue in a piecemeal manner and mostly in response to lobby groups from national farm organizations, input suppliers, manufacturers, and grain export giants. The results have accelerated a move toward consolidation of farms and businesses, and a concentration of wealth and decision making in a few hands in the food sector. This topic is articulately described by Fred Kirschenmann in the book's concluding Chapter 15 (Kirschenmann, 2009, this volume). He contends that we need a system that preserves and strengthens an "agriculture of the middle," which is to say, the family farms on which this industry was originally built.

In a recent review entitled "The Future of Food," author Whitney Sanford (2009) summarizes the findings in six recent books about the agricultural production and food system in the U.S. and around the globe. In his words, "Until recently, cheap food and overflowing supermarkets have made food and agriculture a non-issue to most North Americans, who tend to assume that scientific and technological ingenuity will solve problems of hunger and scarcity." He cites the spike in food prices during 2008, the several food safety scares that quickly became international issues, and the debate about biofuels taking food away from people as symptoms of a failed system, one that cannot be left entirely to the vagaries of the free market when hunger is prevalent and people's lives are at stake. Sanford goes on to describe how agricultural experts and thoughtful social scientists are now challenging the dominant "productionist paradigm" as inadequate to address the challenges of food supply and food equity in a globalized food industry.

Other countries put higher priority on food. For example, national governments in Denmark, United Kingdom, Iceland, Netherlands, and Kyrgyzstan have "food" in the title of one of the ministries, often together with environment and/ or agriculture. Provincial governments in Ontario and Bavaria have put emphasis on food at the regional level. Japan has placed a high priority on domestic rice production since World War II, with strict controls on area and price, resulting in the country depending on domestic production for 96% of the total needs (Japan Times, 2000), with a goal of 100% (Mogi, 2009), in spite of high land and production costs and population pressures. Rice was formerly imported for decades at a lower price, especially from Thailand and Southeast Asian neighbors. Perhaps the food shortages during WWII still influence the national priorities on production, even in a globalized food economy?

According to Organic Eprints (2009), there are specific goals in many European countries to reach a certain level of organic food production and products on the market by a specified year; for example, Norway has a goal of 15% by 2015, and Sweden 20% by the same year. Although these are national goals set by parliaments, there are generally no corresponding increases in research and extension funds to help the agricultural sector meet the goals. What is impressive, however, is that public awareness and concern about food quality and security in Europe has spurred the passage of this legislation, and such priorities represent national policies that are not known in the United States.

Coordination among Universities, NGOs, and Farmers

As described in relation to the cooperative North Carolina research and education program in Chapter 12 (Creamer et al., 2009, this publication) and in the overview on education in Chapter 13 (Francis, 2009, this publication), much of the progress in organic farming has been a result of technology design, testing and demonstration by farmers, and often in collaboration with land-grant university extension programs. In addition, the research and education programs in nonprofit organizations, such as the Rodale Institute and Michael Fields Institute, have been invaluable in outreach and the testing of practices and systems in organic farming. Farmer–researcher cooperation has combined the practical experience and farming credibility of people on the land making key decisions in their production systems with efforts of scientists who bring rigor in statistical design and analysis as well as precise studies of system components and functional mechanisms. The participation of scientists in a project increases the potential to design for testing the repeatability of results, to assess the statistical significance of differences, and to understand the biological principles and mechanisms that drive results in the field.

Nancy Creamer and colleagues (Creamer et al., 2009, this publication) from two colleges of agriculture worked closely with a farmer advisory group and with cooperative extension to establish and build a high profile research center that is today closely linked with outreach and education in North Carolina. Prompted in part by some spectacular natural disasters and contamination from agriculture, this program has moved aggressively to provide biodiverse and economically sound alternatives to the conventional specialized cropping and confined livestock industrial style operations in the state.

Similar cooperation is found in the programs of the Practical Farmers of Iowa, the Leopold Center for Sustainable Agriculture, and the researchers and extension specialists at Iowa State University. Iowa State University is one of the few land-grant universities to employ a scientist with full-time emphasis on organic farming. Kathleen Delate, author of Chapter 6 (2009, this publication) on organic grains, oilseeds, and specialty crops, has provided a focal point for both experiment station and on-farm research in organic farming components and systems in the Midwest. Some of the experiment designs that are appropriate for on-farm comparisons of fertility options, weed management, and cultivars were developed and tested on Iowa and Nebraska farms (Rzewnicki et al., 1988).

Organic pest management strategies were developed and tested with success in the cooperative on-station and on-farm studies at University of California at Santa Cruz and the nearby Salinas Valley (Center for Sustainable Agriculture and Food Systems, 2009). One of the major applied research programs of the University of California–Santa Cruz Department of Environmental Studies and the Agroecology Program (now named the Center for Agroecology and Sustainable Food Systems) has been directed at biological control of pests in perennial crops such as asparagus (*Asparagus officinalis* L.) and artichoke (*Cynara cardunculus* L.), as well as in diverse plantings of perennial fruit and annual vegetable crops. What distinguishes all these mentioned programs is the high degree of participation by farmers as full members of the research teams, helping design practical studies, collecting data, and interpreting results for other farmers. This role of the farmer is distinguished from that played in other on-farm research such as variety testing, where multiple locations involve farmers but where they provide mainly field operations within their normal farming operation, with researchers planting experiments and collecting all the data. The nonprofit, farmer-owned Organic Crop Improvement Association (O.C.I.A.) International, headquartered in Lincoln, NE, has recently established an administratively separate Research and Education Committee to pursue an agenda that is closely linked to what farmers today perceive as the critical questions facing them in organic systems.

These cases represent only three of the many excellent programs now under way. They make the best possible use of available research funding and farmer contributions, while putting emphasis on building human capital. Some of the characteristics that are found in successful cooperative programs and which will guide their further success include:

- A shared agenda by researchers and farmers, including selection of priority questions
- An emphasis on solving practical constraints in organic farming
- Full participation of farmers as members of the research team
- Location of much of the research on farmer fields in organic production systems
- Use of multiple locations to extend the applicability of research results
- Development of practical recommendations based on sound research
- Explicit focus on outreach and education through field days, tours, and demonstrations

An increase in numbers of these cooperative programs, exemplified by close farmer–university cooperation, demonstrates the success of this emerging model for research and education. To build a cadre of young people with appreciation of and skills in organic farming will also require the development of educational programs within our public and private colleges and universities, another current growth area. Ultimately the sooner these programs begin, the better they will help develop a society with greater awareness of the importance of food and how it is grown. This strategy is exemplified by the Edible Schoolyard in Berkeley, CA (see http://www.edibleschoolyard.org/, verified 23 July 2009), a program of the Chez Panisse Foundation founded by chef Alice Waters, that includes both a school garden and school kitchen, where students learn to grow and prepare nutritious organic foods. Appleton, WI has pioneered efforts to remove junk food from their schools and provide organic meals that are made from fresh, healthy, local foods, and their observations of improved behavior and learning are drawing attention from across the country (Boyd, 2005). The "Good, Fresh, Local" food initiative at University of Nebraska (2009) brings food in season from local farmers to students in the cafeterias on campus. Creative alternatives to the massive fast food culture are in their infancy, but this movement portends a bright future for an enlightened approach to food and nutrition in the United States.

Conclusions

On the basis of the recent growth of both research and education on organic farming practices, increasing focus on integrated systems, and continuing growth of the organic food sector, we foresee a bright future for an improvement in availability of nutritious food in the United States and elsewhere. The idealism of a small number of organic and biodynamic farmers in Europe and the United States has been transformed into a growth industry that now attracts a wide array of followers, both in production and in the marketplace. Organic farming and food systems include ideas whose time has come.

There are many unresolved issues in organic farming in terms of how it will continue to exist side-by-side with a much larger conventional food industry. For example, the ubiquitous spread of pollen from transgenic, cross-pollinated crops such as maize, sunflower (*Helianthus annuus* L.), and canola (*Brassica napus* L.) represents a challenge to the purity and integrity of an organic food product free of this type of genetic material. The other side of this coin is the still unanswered question of whether some types of transgenic crops should eventually be accepted as part of the organic farming strategy, especially to manage insects and pathogens in what could be considered yet another method of biological control. Issues of how to provide sufficient essential nutrients to crop plants in the appropriate form for uptake and in relation to the stage of plant development also need to be resolved. The plant does not recognize nitrate from chemical fertilizers as any different from nitrate from manure or compost, and cold soils limit nitrification of ammonia and other organic sources of nitrogen. Emphasis perhaps should be placed on where these nutrients come from and how they are processed and brought to the farm rather than relying solely on the absolute prohibition of synthetic ingredients in organic systems. It is likely that there are larger issues to be resolved to ensure the long-term integrity of a sound and sustainable organic food system.

For example, there are large challenges coming from the continued growth and credibility of the organic sector as part of a globalized food system. As described in other chapters, there is growing involvement of large-scale, industrial model farms and multinational food conglomerates in the organic food business. While this was once a local activity, with consumers familiar with the farmers who grew and marketed their produce, organics is now a part of the industrial food complex. There has been an erosion of the social concerns and principles of fair treatment of labor that were once integral to organic farming. The singular focus by the U.S. consumer on the least expensive source of food will continue to undermine this principle of the original practitioners of organic farming. Future success will depend on re-establishing the linkages of farmers and consumers and the credibility of a system that depends on trust and knowledge rather than regulation and control to rediscover the goals of organic food systems that can provide both nutrition and food security at the local level. The ultimate system will no doubt be an extension of today's food system and will continue to be a combination of local and imported food, of organic and conventional sources, and of small and large farms. Yet the change in balance to local, organic, and socially equitable systems will depend on the motivations of consumers and the willingness of organic farmers to persevere in an often uncertain and dynamic industry.

One unanswered question in agriculture today is how much impact the organic sector is having on mainstream conventional farming operations. Given the broad concerns about the impacts of farming on the immediate and the future environment and the growing set of regulations under which all farming must operate, we believe, as described in Chapter 2 (Drinkwater, 2009, this publication), that more farming in the future will be designed to follow ecological principles, whether it is labeled or certified organic or not.

In Sweden, the national goal is to reach 20% organic food in the national diet in less than a decade. In fact, they currently have reached 10% certified food, and there is another estimated 10% that is produced under organic conditions but not certified (Rebecca Milsted, SLU, Uppsala, Sweden, personal communication, 2008). This food is sold to local consumers, who draw confidence from their knowledge of where and how the food is grown. There is trust in the system that makes an official certification unnecessary. The system functions well and brings the consumer quality food from local sources with the assurance of knowing where and how it is produced. Perhaps this is another model that will prove successful in other countries or localities. One of us (C. Francis) recalls a visit to the island of Gotland, Sweden, where there are currently more than 100 organic vegetable farms. On visits to two of these, we found a nice array of produce, a certified scale, a list of prices, and a cash box in which to place our Swedish kroner for the purchase. The farmers were not present, but rather were in the fields continuing their farming activities while trusting consumers to do their part to make the system honest and sustainable. We could hope for a future where this type of organic farming and food system can be implemented in the United States and elsewhere.

Discussion Questions

1. In what ways can the study of food systems be considered a study in the field of human ecology? Why are food systems considered *human activity systems*? What does this imply for innovation?

2. What are the major shortcomings of current global food systems in terms of reaching all people with adequate nutrition? What are the implications of seriously considering *food as a basic human right*?

3. What is the current role of science in the informing of public opinion and the determination of food policy in the United States and in other countries?

4. How important are food quality and food safety in the U.S. food system? How does this compare with E.U. members and other countries?

5. Describe the alternatives of increased efficiency, substitution, and system redesign as methods of increasing production and profits in agriculture. Provide specific examples of each.

6. Describe the current prohibition of using GMOs in organic cropping systems, and discuss the rationale for this rule. What do you consider the most important issues in the future with regard to use of GMO technology?

7. What are the most profitable marketing alternatives used today by organic farmers? What marketing methods are likely to become more important in the future?

8. What have been the impacts of industrial organic production on the organic food supply and prices? How will this impact the organic sector in the future?

9. What are the options for creating a certification process that goes beyond the current organic rules to include more emphasis on treatment of labor and other issues related to distribution of benefits?

10. What are the relative differences in food safety in organic and conventional foods? What are the quality differences related to how food is produced in different systems?

11. Discuss the current food policy of the United States, and how this could be modified to better attain food safety and food security.

12. What are the current and future potential roles of farmers in the research process to seek improved organic farming systems? How can farmer involvement be coordinated with university research programs?

References

Allen, P., and H. Melcarek. 2009. Organic agriculture and food security: Saving the environment, feeding the world? p. 235–252. *In* C. Francis (ed.) Organic farming: The ecological system. Agron. Monogr. 54. ASA, CSSA, and SSSA, Madison, WI. (This volume.)

Baker, B.P., C.M. Benbrook, E. Groth III, and K.L. Benbrook. 2002. Pesticide residues in conventional, IPM-grown and organic foods: Insights from three U.S. data sets. Food Addit. Contam. 19:427–446.

Boyd, C. 2005. Several Minnesota & Wisconsin schools move toward healthy & organic lunches. Pioneer Press, St. Paul, Minnesota, February 17, 2005. Available at http://www.organicconsumers.org/school/hopkins21705.cfm%20 (verified 23 July 2009).

Burros, M. 2009. Obamas to plant White House vegetable garden. New York Times. 19 March. Available at http://www.nytimes.com/2009/03/19/dining/19garden-web.html?_r=1&hp (verified 23 July 2009).

California Certified Organic Farmers. 2005. Genetic engineering: The dangers of genetically engineered crops. Available at http://www.ccof.org/ge_mr.php (verified 23 July 2009). CCOF, Santa Cruz, CA.

Carson, R. 1962. Silent spring. Houghton Mifflin Publ., Boston, MA.

Center for Disease Control. 2009. Infectious disease information: Food-related diseases. Available at http://www.cdc.gov/ncidod/diseases/food/ (accessed 5 Mar. 2009, verified 23 July 2009). National Center for Infectious Diseases, CDC, Atlanta, GA.

Clark, E.A. 2009. Forages in organic crop–livestock systems. p. 85–112. *In* C. Francis (ed.) Organic farming: The ecological system. Agron. Monogr. 54. ASA, CSSA, and SSSA, Madison, WI. (This volume.)

Cochran, W.W. 2003. The curse of American agricultural abundance: A sustainable solution. Univ. Nebraska Press, Lincoln.

Community Food Security Coalition's North American Urban Agriculture Committee. 2003. Urban agriculture and community food security in the United States: Farming from the city center to the urban fringe. Available at http://www.foodsecurity.org/PrimerCFSCUAC.pdf (verified 23 July 2009).

Cooper, J., C. Leifert, and U. Nigli (ed.) 2007. Handbook of organic food safety and quality. FiBL, Research Institute of Organic Agriculture, Frick, Switzerland, and Woodhead Publ., Cambridge, UK.

Center for Sustainable Agriculture and Food Systems. 2009. Center for Sustainable Agriculture and Food Systems, U.C. Santa Cruz. Available at http://casfs.ucsc.edu/ (verified 23 July 2009).

Dangour, A.D., S.K. Dodhia, A. Hayter, E. Allen, K. Lock, and R. Uauy. 2009. Nutritional quality of foods: A systematic review. Available at http://www.organicfqhresearch.org/downloads/homepage/nut_qual_organic_foods_ajcn_09.pdf (verified 13 Aug. 2009). Am. J. Clin. Nutr. doi:10.3945/ajcn.2009.28041.

Delate, K. 2009. Organic grains, oilseeds, and other specialty crops. p. 113–136. *In* C. Francis (ed.) Organic farming: The ecological system. Agron. Monogr. 54. ASA, CSSA, and SSSA, Madison, WI. (This volume.)

Drinkwater, L.E. 2009. Ecological knowledge: Foundation for sustainable organic agriculture. p. 19–48. *In* C. Francis (ed.) Organic farming: The ecological system. Agron. Monogr. 54. ASA, CSSA, and SSSA, Madison, WI. (This volume.)

Entz, M.H., and J.R. Thiessen Martens. 2009. Organic crop–livestock systems. p. 69–84. *In* C. Francis (ed.) Organic farming: The ecological system. Agron. Monogr. 54. ASA, CSSA, and SSSA, Madison, WI. (This volume.)

Farm to Folk (F2F). 2009. Farm to folk. Ames, Iowa CSA. Available at http://www.farmtofolk.com/ (verified 23 July 2009). F2F, Ames, IA.

Francis, C.A. (ed.). 1986. Multiple cropping systems. Macmillan Publ., New York.

Francis, C. 2009. Education in organic farming and food systems. p. 283–300. *In* C. Francis (ed.) Organic farming: The ecological system. Agron. Monogr. 54. ASA, CSSA, and SSSA, Madison, WI. (This volume.)

Francis, C., and J. Van Wart. 2009. History of organic farming and certification. p. 3–18. *In* C. Francis (ed.) Organic farming: The ecological system. Agron. Monogr. 54. ASA, CSSA, and SSSA, Madison, WI. (This volume.)

Guardian Staff. 2000. Post, banks, food supply now at risk. The economy: Bread and milk rationing as businesses lose £250m a day. The Guardian. 14 Sept. Available at http://www.guardian.co.uk/uk/2000/sep/14/oil.business7 (verified 23 July 2009).

Harker, F.R. 2003. Organic food claims cannot be substantiated through testing of samples intercepted in the marketplace: A horticulturalist's opinion. Food Qual. Prefer. 15:91–95.

Hawken, P., A. Lovins, and L.H. Lovins. 1999. Natural capitalism: Creating the next industrial revolution. Little and Co., Boston.

Heckman, J., J. Weil, and F. Magdoff. 2009. Practical steps to soil fertility for organic agriculture. p. 139–172. *In* C. Francis (ed.) Organic farming: The ecological system. Agron. Monogr. 54. ASA, CSSA, and SSSA, Madison, WI. (This volume.)

Japan Times. 2000. Rice self-sufficiency to stay flat around 96% in 2010. Friday, 11 Feb.

King, F.H. 1948. Formers of forty centuries: Permanent agriculture in China, Korea, and Japan. Organic Gardening Press, Emmaus, PA.

Kirschenmann, F. 2009. Farming in the middle: An ethical imperative. p. 325–342. *In* C. Francis (ed.) Organic farming: The ecological system. Agron. Monogr. 54. ASA, CSSA, and SSSA, Madison, WI. (This volume.)

Kloppenburg, J., Jr., J. Hendrickson, and G.W. Stevenson. 1996. Coming in to the foodshed. Agric. Human Values 13:33–42.

Lerman, Z., C. Csaki, and G. Feder. 2004. Agriculture in transition: Land policies and evolving farm structures in post-Soviet countries. Lexington Books, Lanham, MD.

Levins, R.A. 2000. Willard Cochran and the American family farm. Univ. Nebraska Press, Lincoln.

Liebman, M., and A.S. Davis. 2009. Managing weeds in organic farming systems: An ecological approach. p. 173–196. In C. Francis (ed.) Organic farming: The ecological system. Agron. Monogr. 54. ASA, CSSA, and SSSA, Madison, WI. (This volume.)

MacRae, R.J., S.B. Hill, G.R. Mehuys, and J. Henning. 1990. Farm-scale agronomic and economic conversion from conventional to sustainable agriculture. Adv. Agron. 43:155–198.

McAllister, J.C. 1983. A practical guide to novel soil amendments. Rodale Institute, Kutztown, PA.

Mogi, C. 2009. Japan must aim to be rice exporter. Available at http://www.reuters.com/article/FoodandAgriculture09/idUSTRE52H2J420090318 (verified 23 July 2009). Reuters.

Ordóñez-Santos, L.E., E. Arbones-Maciñeira, J. Fernández-Perejón, M. Lombardero-Fernández, L. Vázquez-Odériz, and A. Romero-Rodríguez. 2009. Comparison of physicochemical, microscopio and sensory characteristics of ecologically and conventionally grown crops of two cultivars of tomato (Lycopersicon esclulentum Mill.). J. Sci. Food Agric. 89:743–749.

Organic Center. 2008. State of science: Nutritional quality. Available at http://www.organic-center.org/science.nutri.php (verified 23 July 2009). Organic Center, Boulder, CO.

Organic Eprints. 2009. About Organic Eprints. Available at http://orgprints.org/about.html (verified 31 Mar. 2009).

Organic Materials Review Institute. 2009. The OMRI products list. Available at http://www.omri.org/OMRI_about_list.html (accessed 19 Mar. 2009, verified 23 July 2009).

Porter, P. 2009. Crop rotations in organic production systems. p. 51–68. In C. Francis (ed.) Organic farming: The ecological system. Agron. Monogr. 54. ASA, CSSA, and SSSA, Madison, WI. (This volume.)

Rzewnicki, P.E., R. Thompson, G.W. Lesoing, R.W. Elmore, C.A. Francis, A.M. Parkhurst, and R.S. Moomaw. 1988. On-farm experiment designs and implications for locating research sites. Am. J. Altern. Agric. 3:168–173.

Sanford, W. 2009. The future of food. J. Agric. Environ. Ethics 22:181–190.

Smith, M.E., and C.A. Francis. 1986. Breeding for multiple cropping systems. p. 219–249. In C.A. Francis (ed.) Multiple cropping systems. Macmillan Publ. Co., New York.

Steiner, R. 1958. Agriculture: A course of eight lectures by Rudolf Steiner. Bio-Dynamic Agric. Assoc., London.

Suppan, S. 2008. Import food safety in the twilight of the Bush Administration. Available at http://www.iatp.org/iatp/publications.cfm?accountID=451&refID=102786 (verified 23 July 2009). Intl. Agric. Trade Inst., Minneapolis, MN.

University of Nebraska. 2009. The GFL (Good, Fresh, Local) University of Nebraska—Lincoln Sustainable Food Project. Available at http://housing.unl.edu/dining/gfl.shtml (verified 23 July 2009). Univ. of Nebraska, Lincoln.

USDA-ERS. 2009. U.S. farm income data. Available at http://www.ers.usda.gov/Data/FarmIncome/Finfidmu.htm (accessed 31 Mar. 2009, verified 23 July 2009). USDA-ERS, Washington, DC.

USDA-NOP. 2002. USDA's National Organic Program (NOP). Available at www.ams.usda.gov/nop/ (verified 23 July 2009). USDA-NOP, Washington, DC.

Victory Garden. 2009. Revive the victory garden: Think global, grow local. Available at http://www.revivevictorygarden.org/ (verified 23 July 2009).

Wezel, A., S. Bellon, T. Dore, C. Francis, D. Vallod, and C. David. 2009. Agroecology as a science, a movement or a practice. Agron. Sustain. Devel. doi:10.1051/agro/2009004.

World Vision. 2009. Hunger and food aid. Available at http://www.worldvision.org/content.nsf/about/press-development-food?open&lpos=day_txt_hunger-hot-button (verified 23 July 2009). World Vision, Federal Way, WA.

Worthington, V. 2001. Nutritional quality of organic versus conventional fruits, vegetables, and grains. J. Altern. Complement. Med. 7:161–173.

15

Farming in the Middle: An Ethical Imperative

Frederick Kirschenmann
Leopold Center for Sustainable Agriculture, Iowa State University, Ames,
and Stone Barns Center for Food and Agriculture, Pocantico Hills, New York

> There is a limit beyond which machines and chemicals cannot replace peo-
> ple: there is a limit beyond which mechanical or economic efficiency cannot
> replace care.—Wendell Berry, *Another Turn of the Crank*

Back in 1945, Aldo Leopold observed that "it was inevitable and no doubt
desirable that the tremendous momentum of industrialization should have
spread to farm life" (Leopold, 1999b). He was right, of course. Industrialization
appeared to be the answer to almost every human constraint. It enabled us to
clothe, house, transport, and protect ourselves from harm more efficiently than
any prior innovation. Feeding ourselves by the same paradigm was simply too
seductive to ignore.

But Leopold also recognized, as we now must, that industrial agriculture
had its darker side. He went on to write:

> It is clear to me, however, that it has overshot the mark, in the sense
> that it is generating new insecurities, economic and ecological, in place
> of those it was meant to abolish. In its extreme form, it is humanly des-
> olate and economically unstable. These extremes will some day die of
> their own too-much, not because they are bad for wildlife, but because
> they are bad for the farmers. When that day comes, the farmer will be
> asking us how to enrich the wildlife of his community. Stranger things
> have happened. Meanwhile we must do the best we can on the ecological
> leavings. (Leopold, 1999b)

This concluding chapter in a book on organic agriculture contains many
practical recommendations, including those currently practiced on organic and
biodynamic farms. These alternatives provide useful and necessary steps toward
a future, sustainable agricultural and food system imperative, but they are not
sufficient for its success. We must pay attention to the limits of industrial agriculture that are becoming more apparent each day and understand how fully
current agriculture depends on a declining natural resource base. From this discussion emerge several ethical imperatives, including an ecological conscience as
well as a utilitarian ethic that will appeal to a wide range of thoughtful people.
Central to these imperatives is the disappearance of family farms in the middle
of the farm-size spectrum, those that have sustained U.S. and other cultures for
centuries, and the consequences of this ownership and demographic change to

rural communities. We find that this time, technology alone is not the answer, although there are components of technology that can be carefully evaluated and thoughtfully applied to help solve the challenges if considered in a whole-systems context. What emerges from this ethical and practical discussion is a proposal for an essential cultural shift in the United States and elsewhere, one that respects the land and our agroecosystems as part of a larger and interconnected regional and global ecosystem. All of these issues are addressed in the sections that follow.

Limits of Industrial Agriculture

As we enter the 21st century, we can begin to appreciate Leopold's prescience. While the industrialization of agriculture has been incredibly successful in achieving its twofold goal—maximizing production and short-term return—it is now clear that it has wrought many unintended consequences that today imperil its sustainability. This is especially apparent as we face new production obstacles on the horizon.

Applying the industrial principles of specialization, simplification, and consolidation to agriculture enabled us to achieve unprecedented yields per unit of land. Yet the principle also undermined our future productive capacity by degrading the quality of our soils, destabilizing our environment, depleting our water and energy resources, and contributing to the increase in greenhouse gases that now threatens to destabilize our climate.

Industrial agriculture's success was grounded in these same abundant resources—cheap energy, fresh water, virgin soils, and stable climates. Since all of these resources are now in steep decline or are undergoing radical change, it is unlikely that the industrial model can function very far into the future. And continued population growth and persistent poverty will make the challenge of feeding the human population even more daunting.

Industrial Agriculture Dependent on Vital, Declining Resources

Peak global oil production either already has been reached or will be reached before the end of this decade. The end of cheap oil promises to fundamentally change our world (Heinberg, 2005). The end of cheap energy will be especially devastating to our industrial food business, a massive energy-intensive system. Since fossil energy drives almost every aspect of industrial production agriculture, costs will spiral upward for almost everything it uses: fertilizers, pesticides, farm equipment, and traction fuel. Those increases will make industrial agriculture cost prohibitive.

While the production sector of our industrial food system is energy intensive, it pales in comparison to food processing. Ernest Schusky (1989, p. xii–xiii) cites one example, pointing out that it takes "about 2200 calories of fossil energy to produce a one-calorie can of diet soda." which he suggests is "downright embarrassing to human intelligence."

Climate change is another 21st-century phenomenon that is poised to disrupt our industrial production sensation. Scientists now are in virtual agreement that due to excessive greenhouse gas emissions, the climate could change dramatically in the decades ahead. Ironically, some of these troublesome greenhouse gases are being produced by the same industrial agriculture that spawned our vast production.

Furthermore, climate change likely will be in our future whether or not greenhouse gas emissions initiate it. Scientists have warned us for some time that the unusual, stable climate of the last century simply is not normal. The National Academy of Sciences (NAS) Panel on Climatic Variation reported in 1975 that "our present climate is in fact highly *abnormal*," that "the earth's climates have always been changing, and the magnitude of . . . the changes can be catastrophic" (NRC, 1975).

The report called attention to the fact that "the global patterns of food production and population that have evolved are *implicitly dependent* on the climate of the present century" (NRC, 1975). In other words, the industrial agriculture miracle of the past century is at least as much due to unusually favorable climate conditions as it is to modern production technologies. The NAS panel then pointed out that this anticipated "normal" climate change might be exacerbated further because "we may be producing climatic changes as a result of our own activities" (NRC, 1975). In other words, according to the NAS, it is this combination of "normal" climate variation plus the changes that spring from our own industrial economies that will have a significant impact on the future of agricultural productivity.

The impact of such climate changes is likely to be especially volatile for industrial farming systems. Every farmer knows that highly specialized production systems require relatively stable climates to perform well. When just two crops, maize (*Zea mays* L.) and soybean [*Glycine max* (L.) Merr.], occupy 92% of Iowa's cultivated land, Iowa farmers rely on a climate that is consistently favorable to these two commodities to maximize their production.

Of course, as Cynthia Rosenzweig and Daniel Hillel acknowledged, it is impossible to foretell exactly how climate change will affect agricultural production (Rosenzweig and Hillel, 1995). The impact on any given ecosystem will be determined by a complex set of factors such as the severity of temperature changes, precipitation patterns, and enriched carbon dioxide in the atmosphere. These factors and our inability to predict how complex natural systems will evolve under new circumstances make it impossible to offer precise predictions. Nevertheless, as Rosenzweig and her colleagues advise, we need to understand what is at stake and "prepare for change wisely" (Rosenzweig et al., 2001).

Despite that uncertainty, we can reasonably anticipate some of the short- and long-term challenges that climate change may pose for production agriculture. In the short term (2020–2080), we can anticipate greater climate fluctuations— "extremes of precipitation, both droughts and floods" (Rosenzweig et al., 2001). Such instability can be especially devastating for highly specialized, genetically uniform, monocropping systems, so characteristic of industrial agriculture. The long-term (2080 and beyond) consequences of climate change could be grim. In a review of three prominent climate change books and one film in the 13 July 2006 *New York Times Review of Books*, Jim Hansen (2006) made a telling observation about the impact that climate change may have on production agriculture in the long term: "If human beings follow a business-as-usual course, . . . the eventual effects on climate and life may be comparable to those at the time of mass extinctions." How does agriculture remain productive in a world of dramatically reduced biodiversity? Will we still have pollinators?

The impact that increased droughts stemming from climate change will have on production agriculture will be exacerbated by the fact that industrial agriculture is using up fresh water resources at an unsustainable rate. Lester Brown points out that while we each require four liters of water per day to survive, our modern industrial production systems consume 2000 L per day to produce each of our daily food requirements. Agricultural irrigation alone consumes 70% of our global fresh water resources. Today we use twice the water for agricultural irrigation that we did in the 1960s. Consequently, we have been drawing down our fresh water resources at an unsustainable rate.

Water depletion is especially troubling in China, where 80% of grain production is dependent on irrigation, and in India, where 60% requires irrigation. In some parts of China, aquifers are dropping at the rate of 3 m (10 feet) per year and in India by 6 m (20 feet) per year. Some Chinese farmers already are pumping irrigation water from 305 m (1000 feet) deep and in India farmers are tapping water from 914 m (3000 feet) (Brown, 2006).

China and India are the most populous nations in the world, and significantly reduced crop production due to water depletion in these areas would have major global food supply consequences, creating unprecedented global ethical dilemmas.

Water tables in the western Ogallala Aquifer in the High Plains of the United States, which supplies one of every two irrigated hectare in the United States, are being overdrawn at the rate of 12,000 million m^3 (3.1 trillion gallons) per year (http://news.bbc.co.uk/hi/english/static/in_depth/world/2000/world_water_crisis/default.stm [verified 28 July 2009]), and according to some reports, this fossil water bank is now half depleted. A few farmers on the edge of the aquifer already have had to abandon irrigation due to water depletion.

Reduced snow packs in mountainous regions due to climate change have decreased spring runoff, a primary source of irrigation water in many parts of the world, further reducing our food production capacity.

Water, climate, and energy are tightly coupled in the real world. Efforts to alleviate one problem often intensify another. For example, one response to the impending energy crisis has been the development of maize-based ethanol as an alternative fuel. But ethanol processing requires a significant amount of water, which is likely to further deplete the Ogallala. Longer and more frequent droughts due to climate change will likely force more farmers to install center-pivot irrigation systems, especially in the Corn Belt. Land rent and other costs have spiraled upward due to higher maize prices spurred by the increased demand for maize to supply the ethanol plants. Farmers cannot afford drought-related crop failures when they incur higher production costs. Four-dollar maize is of no economic benefit to farmers when they lose their crop to drought.

Devoting a significant percentage of our land to producing energy instead of food, feed, and fiber will likely have additional negative ripple effects. Increased demand for maize will tempt farmers to switch more of their land to continuous maize production, planting fence-row to fence-row, and applying maximum nitrogen to ensure high yields. Higher energy costs and land rent will leave them little choice. The outcome may be even greater ecological degradation and therefore reduced resilience—the ultimate basis for sustainable productivity. Furthermore, as global populations increase and water resources diminish, competition for land to produce food versus land to produce fuel could create an unprecedented moral predicament.

Ethical Imperatives

While all of these events will present us with countless ethical challenges, perhaps the most pressing ethical imperative implicit in our emerging food system will be designing a resilient food system that can feed our human population sustainably under these new circumstances. That suggests a practical, utilitarian ethic.

However, implicit throughout this chapter is a twofold ethical imperative. On the one hand, our postindustrial understanding of the world—that it is a complex, highly interdependent biotic community replete with emergent properties—suggests an ethical imperative similar to Aldo Leopold's "ecological conscience," which embraces the value of the entire biotic community. On the other hand, given the practical necessity of conserving our soil, water, climate, human, and social resources to feed our human population under challenging circumstances suggests a utilitarian–consequentialist ethic. I think both ethical perspectives are valid.

The depletion of our human and social capital—perhaps the worst toll exacted by our industrial agriculture—is often ignored as a practical necessity. Industrialization of our farming systems has systematically eliminated the very farmers who were most closely connected to their land. Market forces in our industrial economy favor centralized farm management of large, consolidated operations that can reduce the transaction costs of transferring raw materials to large manufacturing firms. But our culture still seems to be largely oblivious to the impact that this erosion of indigenous human capital may have on our ability to address the challenges ahead. Here an appeal to a consequentialist ethic may be the most compelling.

Wendell Berry has perhaps articulated the connection between human and social capital and our ability to maintain our productive capacity most clearly and succinctly. The utilitarian moral imperative implied in his analysis is obvious:

> [I]f agriculture is to remain productive it must preserve the land, and the fertility and ecological health of the land; the land, that is, must be used well. A further requirement, therefore, is that if the land is to be used well, the people who use it must know it well, must be highly motivated to use it well, must know how to use it well, must have time to use it well, and must be able to afford to use it well. Nothing that has happened in the agricultural revolution of the past fifty years has disproved or invalidated these requirements, though everything that has happened has ignored or defied them. (Berry, 1990, p. 206–207)

Berry reminds us that we cannot reasonably expect ecological or agroecological systems to be managed well without people living in those ecologies long enough and intimately enough to know how to manage them well. And he correctly asserts that we need social, cultural, and economic support systems in place to sustain such wise management. Proper land management, in other words, is a practical ethical imperative not provided for in industrial economies, which are solely focused on maximum production and short-term returns.

The NAS seems to agree. Over a decade ago, the NAS asserted that "soil degradation is a complex phenomenon driven by strong interactions among socioeconomic and biophysical factors." The NAS recognized that proper soil management is a key factor in improving soil quality and that healthy soils provide the opportunity to "simultaneously improve profitability and environmental performance" (NRC, 1993). Long-term profitability, in other words, is not a simple business arrangement but is grounded in social and cultural factors that attend to the long-term care of the soil. Sustainable profitability on the farm is linked tightly to social, cultural, and ethical commitments that safeguard the health of the land.

Specializing in one or two crops with little or no biological diversity, and reducing production management practices to the use of one or two single-tactic inputs, which is the core strategy of industrial farming systems, has yielded production systems that are extremely labor efficient but attend to none of these broader ethical imperatives.

Another hallmark of this industrial system has been the systematic elimination of the very farmers with the ecological and cultural wisdom and commitment required to restore the physical and biological health of our soils. They are the farmers who owned their land, lived on their land, were intimately related to their land, and planned to pass it on to future family members—all factors that nurtured a culture of caring for the land.

Fortunately, in the wake of this loss of human capital, some research is still being done to demonstrate the broad principles we must apply to restore soil health. *Science* magazine reported on a research project in Switzerland that traced the biological and physical properties of soils using both industrial and organic management principles over a 21-year period. The researchers found that the organically managed soils, using complex green manure and livestock manure to replenish soil nutrients, showed remarkably higher soil quality including "greater biological activity" and "10 to 60% higher soil aggregate stability" than the industrially managed soils (Mäder et al., 2002).

Such information suggests a critical ethical imperative. Since we have been able to conceal the decline in productive capacity due to the loss of soil health over the past half-century by applying cheap fossil fuel–based ingredients to the soil, we have not confronted the fact that ultimately, soil health is crucial to maintaining productivity. The NAS study reminds us that "soil degradation may have significant effects on the ability of the United States to sustain a productive agricultural system" (NRC, 1993). That statement takes on new significance in light of the depletion of the very resources that have allowed us to ignore the importance of the health of our soil—cheap energy, surplus water, and stable climates. So one could argue that there is now a compelling, practical imperative for exploring nature's ways of restoring soil health and employing the cultural, social and economic incentives to put people on the land who know the land well and know how to use it wisely. But since this imperative is not widely recognized, it may be more effective to nurture an "ecological conscience."

The Disappearing Middle

Nevertheless, it is especially worrisome as we enter an agricultural era that will require more complex thinking and ecological management skills, combined with the intimate knowledge of local landscapes, that our industrial food system, based on cheap labor and raw materials, has systematically depleted the very human capital essential for such management.

Over the past several decades, America's food system has morphed into two structural tiers. On the one hand, small-scale, direct-market enterprises have developed market structures that enable farmers to sell directly to consumers through local market outlets. While these markets have grown rapidly over the past few decades, they are performed with a very small amount of the farmland and so have little impact on the ecological health of the land. On the other hand, large-scale, bulk commodity production farms, increasingly integrated into consolidated supply chains, provide giant food and fiber companies with the raw materials required to produce products for the global market. Farmers who manage these operations are likely to rent rather than own the land and often are not intimately connected to the land they manage.

This pattern has had a disastrous effect on the nation's "independent family farmers"—the farmers who have been part of a long family farm lineage wherein land is largely owned by the farmers who manage the land, and farms are passed from one generation to another, along with the collective land-care wisdom acquired over many generations. In our recent two-tiered food system, these farmers are at a comparative disadvantage. They are too large and too commoditized to sell on direct markets and too small to supply the huge, consolidated markets with an adequate quantity of cheap raw materials. The bulk of these farms record annual gross sales of $100,000 to $250,000, a group called "farming-occupation farms" and "large family farms" according to the USDA Economic Research Service (2000), and we are losing them at an unprecedented rate.

Iowa serves as a dramatic, although not unique, example. In the decade from 1987 to 1997, Iowa experienced an 18% sales increase among farms that are 0.4 to 40 ha (1–100 acres) in size and a 71% increase in sales among farms of more than 400 ha (1000 acres). At the same time, farms between 105 and 202 ha (260 and 500 acres) in size experienced a 29% decrease in sales. We are now referring to this phenomenon as the "disappearing middle." (For a more detailed analysis of the "disappearing middle," see Fred Kirschenmann et al. [2008].)

Addressing this loss of human capital is not a matter of "saving the family farm." It is an ethical imperative. How do we nurture the human and social capital necessary to meet the challenge of sustaining a food system that can provide adequate amounts of food for an increasing human population in the face of peak global oil production, degraded soils, depleted fresh water supplies, and more unstable climates?

Technology to the Rescue?

The majority of people in the U.S. agricultural establishment probably will still argue that this ethical imperative can be more effectively addressed through the development of a new generation of technology—the next industrial silver bullet— than it can through the development of human, social, and ecological capital.

But the question we face as we develop an agriculture that can meet our future challenges is not whether we will use technology to shape this future. Clearly we will. Nor is the question what kind of technology we will use. We likely will use any technology that promises to develop an agriculture that meets the challenges confronting us. The more pertinent question is: How will we use the technologies we decide to deploy?

Throughout the industrial era, we have tended to use technologies almost exclusively to perform one-dimensional, single-tactic functions. We manufacture and apply a pesticide to get rid of a pest. We manufacture and apply a fertilizer to replace a nutrient. We manufacture and inject an antibiotic to fight a disease. It is an approach that Joe Lewis, formerly with the Insect Biology and Population Management Research Laboratories at the USDA Agricultural Research Service, and his colleagues call "therapeutic intervention" (Lewis et al., 1997).

Using a broad-spectrum pesticide as a therapeutic intervention tool to get rid of a pest provides a telling example of how this use of technology has failed to achieve sustainable results. As we all know, when we apply a pesticide to get rid of a pest, we not only kill the target pest, we also kill many beneficial organisms that previously kept other pests in check, thereby creating new pest problems. Furthermore, we never kill all of the target pests, and those that survive become resistant to the pesticide, creating a new level of pest problems. The failure to deal with the true source of the pest problem, plus the beneficial insect vacuum left by the pesticide application, invites pest resurgence. At the same time, we fail to explore, for example, the connections between proper soil quality, nutrition, and plant protection, an approach that could lead to more resilient pest control. As Joe Lewis suggested, we design pest control technology beginning with the wrong question. We ask "how do I get rid of the pest?" while an ecological, natural systems approach would begin by asking "why is the pest a pest?"

Attempting to solve a nutrient deficiency problem by injecting a nutrient into the soil leads to similar results. Healthy soil provides a range of benefits, including more efficient water use, improved water quality, and pest suppression. Applying a single nutrient to solve the problem of nutrient deficiency deprives the farmer of the free ecosystem services that good soil quality can provide. That in turn leads to the intensified use of single-tactic technologies that often are detrimental to the environment and to the restoration of natural resources that are the foundation of any productive agriculture (see, e.g., Baskin, 1997). There are inherent, renewable mechanisms within agricultural ecosystems that can be accessed to the benefit of both the environment and production agriculture (Lewis et al., 1997).

All of this makes it highly unlikely that introducing a new generation of industrial technologies, without altering the accompanying paradigms, will meet the challenges ahead, especially given the end of cheap energy that has made it possible to invent and deploy many of those technologies.

The Economic Plight of Farmers and Rural Communities

The therapeutic intervention approach to using technologies in agriculture not only ignores ecological and social sustainability, but it also fails to provide economic sustainability for farmers. A study conducted by Mike Duffy, agricultural economist at Iowa State University, provides a poignant story. Duffy's research showed that while farmers have been successful in increasing their gross income 13-fold between 1950 and 1998, they did so at a cost of total expenses that increased at the same rate, leaving their net income flat. His study further revealed that Iowa net farm income as a percentage of expenses declined from 80% in 1950 to 12% in 1998 (Duffy, 2005). It is self-evident that when the use of a technology compels farmers to use more and more of that technology, it erodes their net income.

Using technology for therapeutic intervention also fails to encourage sustainable communities. Using therapeutic intervention technologies to increase the yields of a few commodity crops has led to the transfer of resources in and out of rural communities. Communities that specialize in the production of wheat (*Triticum aestivum* L.), for example, have to export that commodity to find sufficient markets. Since most of the community's resources are tied up producing wheat as a raw material for export out of the community, it has to import the value-added products it consumes. This market paradigm makes it difficult for the community to retain either the value inherent in the production of its raw material, with the value being added elsewhere, or the value of its earned income as a multiplier effect within the community. Earned income is sent out of the community to purchase needed value-added products, and the value of raw materials is sent out of the community to have value added elsewhere. These market attributes have long been recognized as the core components of a colonial economy.

Using technologies for therapeutic intervention will produce essentially the same results regardless of the type of technology used. Whether the predominant technology is a toxic chemical, a mechanical device, a transgenic organism, or a biological control substance, the overall questionable effects relative to the development of sustainable communities will be essentially the same.

But there is another way to use technologies to meet agricultural challenges. That approach would seek to understand and appreciate the interactive, synergistic relationships within ecosystems and social settings and then manage those systems to access the maximum benefits from the energy exchanges inherent in the system to optimize production and restore the ecological health of the land. Such an approach requires a shift in our thinking and research that includes ecological and social contexts (Waltner-Toews and Lang, 2000).

This suggests that if we want to move toward a more sustainable agriculture in the future, we need to begin putting more of our research resources into understanding the local ecologies and social dynamics in which we farm and accessing the free ecosystem services available in those ecologies. Teaching farmers how to access those services through ecologically based management practices could become a vital task that extension services can provide (Warner, 2007).

Sustainable Agriculture in Resource-Poor Communities

As it turns out, teaching farmers how to access free ecosystem services through ecologically based management practices may also prove to be the most practical way to achieve food sovereignty in communities plagued by persistent poverty. In *World Watch* magazine, Brian Halweil relayed a story from Africa that can serve as an example of this alternative agriculture in a resource-poor area of the world (Halweil, 2001). One of the pernicious problems facing many African farmers is a parasitic weed, *Striga hermonthica* (Delile) Benth. It sucks the life out of East African maize by attaching itself to the roots of maize plants, robbing them of both water and nutrients. It is even more severe on grain sorghum [*Sorghum bicolor* (L.) Moench].

The therapeutic interventionist paradigm would suggest that an herbicide-resistant maize variety should be introduced to African farmers so that farmers could kill the weeds without damaging their maize crop. But that approach comes with several problems. Most African farmers—at least the smaller ones who raise most of the maize that feeds local villagers—would be unable to afford to buy the herbicide-resistant seed every year. One also has to take into account that in the not-too-distant future, the weed would become resistant to the herbicide, ratcheting up the problem (and the cost) another notch for the farmers, intensifying as energy costs rise. Furthermore, introducing this silver bullet approach to the problem fails to address the question of why the weed became a problem in the first place.

It turns out, according to Halweil's story, that *"Striga* is only a problem in overused and depleted soils." *Striga* is "what happens *after* soil health declines" (Halweil, 2001). But achieving adequate soil fertility with fertilizers again raises the problem of cost. Taking land out of production to restore soil health with leguminous cover crops also is problematic because increasing human populations require that all land be in production. Application of livestock manure also presents difficulties because animals are grazed in open fields, making it difficult to collect manure to apply to cornfields.

Some African farmers have discovered another approach. They plant local, fast-growing, leguminous trees during the dry period from February to April when not much else will grow. The trees fix nitrogen but do not grow very tall, allowing farmers to pull them out or top them off in time to plant the corn. This method seems to reduce *Striga* infestations by more than 90%. Evidently, it is not just the added nitrogen that does the trick. The trees, it seems, "have co-evolved with *Striga*; their evolutionary defenses to the parasite apparently include chemicals that they exude into the soil, and that disrupts the *Striga* lifecycle" (Halweil, 2001). We simply do not know what similar free ecosystem services are available to farmers in various local ecological and social settings because almost none of our research has focused on this approach.

This is not primarily a story about eliminating the need for a transgenic technology with a local ecological practice. One could imagine a genetic technology that might be used to uncover similar, ecologically elegant solutions to production problems by helping us to better understand how ecosystems function, especially at the genetic level. This would help us access free ecosystem services to improve production agriculture while restoring natural resources. Again, it is not a matter of which technology we use, but how we use it to meet the agricultural challenges of the 21st century. As our cheap energy era comes to an end, farmers and researchers everywhere may need to imitate this approach.

From Fantasy to Reality

Throughout the industrial era, agriculture has used cheap energy in the form of fossil fuels to mask the drawdown of our ecological capital, putting us in a highly precarious situation. Once cheap energy is no longer available, we will be unable to substitute oil for ecological health. Cheap, stored, concentrated energy has enabled us to live in a kind of fantasy world of our own creation. As the last reserves of those energy stores are depleted, we will have the difficult task of transitioning to our real, ecological world, which is based on current energy and complex energy exchanges among an incredibly diverse range of species in a dynamic set of interdependent relationships. The challenge for agriculture will not be the development of new technologies, important as those may be. It will be a test of our ability to mimic nature and to develop an agriculture based in similar biological synergies.

Such a transition will require a passage from an energy-intensive to a knowledge-intensive agriculture. That in turn will require some of the most skilled, creative, innovative farmers we have ever had. And the best resource pool of such human capital lies in the agriculture of the middle, where the culture of ecologically based agriculture has not yet entirely eroded. It is these farmers of the middle who still manage the majority of our farmland (Duffy, 2005).

While direct evidence to substantiate whether synergy and synchrony can replace fossil fuel inputs is scarce (Power, 1999), recent studies suggest that research into this area could be the most fruitful avenue to future productivity. The results of numerous studies by David Tilman and his colleagues certainly suggest that possibility (e.g., Tilman and Downing, 1994) Furthermore, farmers who have explored such systems are finding them highly productive and profitable. Farmers Takao Furuno (2001) and Joel Salatin (1998) have developed highly integrated, enormously productive, and profitable farming operations by replacing fossil fuels inputs with systems that rely largely on species interaction and interdependence to enhance productivity at reduced costs. As farmers in many parts of the world discover the benefits of these systems and learn how to manage them, they appear to adopt them (http://www.agroeco.org/fatalharvest/web_pages/developing_world.html [verified 30 July 2009]).

A Cultural Shift

This paradigm shift, however, faces several challenges. Throughout most of the fossil fuel–based agricultural era, farmers have viewed biological diversity as a constraint to be overcome. Fossil fuel–based systems sought to eliminate all species from the landscape except the one species being cultivated for production. Leopold (1999a) noted almost 70 years ago that any farmer who did not have "slick and clean" fields was considered a "sloven." Consequently, as Shiyomi and Koizumi (2001, p. 2) observed, "little attention has been paid to the complex networks of biological interactions" in contemporary agriculture. As a result, it is now difficult for us to understand "the complex effects operating between organisms themselves or the organisms and the environment." There simply has been very little effort to understand, let alone adopt, biological diversity to increase productivity or to consider complex ecosocial systems (Waltner-Toews et al., 2003).

Furthermore, the concept of ecological restoration may still be new to proponents of sustainable agriculture. Much of our focus has been on "ecological soundness," on "conservation," and on "stabilization." Yet the need to understand dynamic, adaptive behavior within complex ecosystems is critical to achieving resilience (Fiksel, 2006).

Given the state of environmental deterioration and the increasing impact of human populations on the environment, ecological restoration and resilience must now become an integral part of any strategy for making agriculture durable. A 2002 *Proceedings of the National Academy of Sciences* study indicates that human demands on the planet now exceed Earth's regenerative capacity by at least 20% (Wackernagel et al., 2002). Agricultural production is a key component of that disparity in regenerative capacity. This suggests that if we are to avoid drifting toward an inevitable and increasing state of decline, we have to attend to the task of understanding and restoring ecological health from an ecosocial and ethical context. In the meantime, we are indeed left with doing the "best we can on the ecological leavings."

Ecological restoration becomes especially urgent for agriculture as we enter the era of fossil fuel depletion. Much of the soil degradation caused by our production systems in the last century is now being masked by heavy inputs of fertilizers that are largely fossil fuel dependent. As these inputs become prohibitively costly, we will have to rely more on soil quality to maintain productivity. That in turn means redesigning our farming systems to maintain the capacity of the soil to renew itself. Ironically, this aspect of farm management was a key component in the original precepts of organic agriculture but seems to be increasingly ignored on many contemporary organic farms. It was central to the teaching of Sir Albert Howard, Lady Eve Balfour, J.I. Rodale, F. H. King, and other organic luminaries. But as Wendell Berry noted in his introduction to the republication of Howard's *The Soil and Health*, "Howard's thought, as understood by the 'organic movement' was seriously oversimplified" (Berry, 2006).

In this regard, we need to pay much closer attention to the web of life that exists and how it functions in nature. A feature article in a 1997 issue of *Nature* provides a rich example. Researchers had discovered that photosynthate from healthy forest trees that grow in full sunlight travels down and across mycorrhizal fungi, which serve as bridges, to bolster the nutrition of weaker, shaded trees deep in the forest (Simard et al., 1997).

Shortly thereafter, biologists at the University of York (UK) reported that modern, intensive agriculture specifically disrupts this incredible web (Helgasson et al., 1998). We simply must pay more attention to these undiscovered synergistic and symbiotic relationships, learn how they function, and determine how to use them in our efforts to produce food in a more sustainable manner.

Rethinking Agricultural Economics

We also need to rethink our predominant economic paradigm. Perhaps it goes without saying that an agriculture system must be economically viable to be sustainable. But there is an assumption, deeply rooted in current economic philosophy, that contends that economic viability is largely limited to economic *efficiency*. Amartya Sen, Nobel Prize–winning economist, calls this the "engineering-based" approach to economics. It is an approach that concerns itself only with the "logistic and engineering problems within economics" instead of the economic wealth and well-being of society. While the engineering-based approach "predicts" that such societal well-being will automatically be served, that assumption, according to Sen, rests more on theory than on empirical verification (Sen, 1987). As Melvin W. Reder, professor at the University of Chicago Business School put it, part of the "crisis" within economics is whether it is a science or has become a "disguised ideology" (Reder, 1999).

Classical economists, such as Adam Smith, insisted that economic *freedom* and economic *power* were as important to economic performance as economic *efficiency* (Sen, 1987). As our food and agriculture systems become increasingly consolidated, there is little freedom to move in and out of most segments of the agricultural economy. Economic power in our food and agriculture enterprises is now so heavily concentrated that neither free market competition nor efficiency is evident. Such concentration ultimately fails to serve the best interests of either producers or consumers. Farmers increasingly are forced to provide bulk commodities below the cost of production, and the potential benefits of market efficiencies are no longer passed on to consumers. This scenario hardly lends itself to a future that is economically viable or sustainable, or that supports local communities.

The three-legged stool of sustainability is generally described as an enterprise that is economically viable, ecologically sound, and socially responsible. Our current economic philosophy also has made it difficult for us to address the third component of the sustainability formula—social responsiveness. Our laissez faire economic ideology regards any interference in the free market to achieve social goals as "social engineering" and therefore suspect. But it has long been recognized that it is impossible to achieve the economic, social, or environmental goals of agriculture in any community without the "proper functioning of those social institutions which are essential to satisfactory farm life" (Hanson, 1939). To ensure a durable, economically healthy society, civil society and the state must be equal partners with free markets. As Aldo Leopold reminded us, the "economic parts of the biotic clock" will not function well without the "uneconomic parts" (Leopold, 1949). This, once again, suggests an ethical imperative.

A New Land Ethic

This leaves us with a final question. Can we achieve agricultural sustainability without an underlying ethic to direct our agricultural activities? More than 50 years ago, Aldo Leopold argued that we could not. His reasoning is perhaps more telling today than it was even when he made his case.

Leopold observed that we usually rely solely on economic motives to stimulate sustainable behavior. The difficulty with that proposition is that most members of the biotic community (many of them essential to a healthy ecology) have no immediate economic value. Consequently, any system designed to achieve sustainability that is "based solely on economic self-interest is hopelessly lopsided. It tends to ignore, and thus eventually to eliminate, many elements in the land community that lack commercial value, but are (as far as we know) essential to its healthy functioning." Our tendency, then, is to "relegate to government many functions eventually too large, too complex, or too widely dispersed to be performed by government" (Leopold, 1949).

Leopold's insight truly was profound. We know more fully now than we did 50 years ago that the entire biotic world is indeed a "community." And we know that local ecologies are highly site specific and do not respond well to ecological management from centralized bureaucracies or corporations. This is why a consequentialist–utilitarian ethic, no matter how compelling, must ultimately be reinforced with an "ecological conscience."

Furthermore, modern biology suggests that Leopold's conclusions regarding the biotic community were on target. Harvard geneticist Richard Lewontin outlined four facets concerning organism and environmental interactions that are consistent with Leopold's ethic (Lewontin, 2000).

First, each organism determines which aspects of the environment are relevant to it and accordingly selects a habitat suitable to it. Each organism in the environment finds a "special and temporal juxtaposition of bits and pieces of the world that produces a surrounding for the organism that is relevant to it." Second, each organism actively "constructs" a world around itself, thereby creating the environment. Third, each organism is in a "constant process of altering the environment." And fourth, organisms adjust some of the properties in their environment to adapt to fluctuations that could threaten the organism's survival. Plants, for example, store energy in underground tubers so the next generation can begin from internally stored energy. In other words, without the activity of organisms within the environment, many of which have no immediate economic value, there would be no environment. And there would be no agriculture.

These dynamic interactions in the biotic community suggest how we might appropriately relate to our world in the interest of sustainability. We cannot "save the environment," nor can we "stop extinctions," nor can we maintain some kind of presumed "balance" in nature. The dynamic, complex, interdependent activities taking place in the biotic community renders such control management impossible. "What we can do," writes Lewontin (2000, p. 51–57), "is to try to affect the rate of extinction and direction of environmental change in such a way as to make a decent life for human beings possible. What we cannot do is to keep things as they are."

These observations are consistent with Leopold's land ethic. Leopold suggested that the image of the "balance of nature" was not sufficient to our understanding of how nature worked. The "biotic pyramid," he suggested, was a much "truer image" since it recognized that "each species, including ourselves, is a link in many chains."

Historically we have, of course, adopted numerous ethical positions with respect to nature. At one point, we assumed that nature was the enemy—something evil that had to be tamed. Cotton Mather (1702), the 17th-century American theologian, described wilderness as the "devil's playground." He was convinced that God had sent the Puritans to America to "tame the wilderness" and "build the Kingdom of God" in this "new land." There are still those among us who regard nature as an adversary that we must "tame" if we are going to have a healthy economy. But the day has arrived when farmers must consider how they can, in the words of Aldo Leopold (1999b), "enrich the wildlife of [their] community."

Through most of the industrial era, we regarded nature as a collection of objects that functioned in accordance with mechanical laws. It became our role as humans to engineer those objects into a functioning whole for the sole benefit of the human species. Today we realize that nature is a "community of subjects" (Swimme and Berry, 1992). Until recently, we also regarded nature as a stable system that had achieved a state of equilibrium through a long process of evolution. Our responsibility as a human species, it was then assumed, was to exploit nature for the sole benefit of the human species. Today we know that nature is a dynamic, constantly changing community replete with emergent properties. And we now understand our role as one of *adaptive* management.

How Can We Make Agriculture More Sustainable?

If the above observations are valid, we cannot reduce our goal of making agriculture more sustainable to some kind of universal prescription for changing our farming practices—switching from chemical to biological inputs, for example. Nor can we condense it to a simple formula for increasing the yields of a few commodities to "feed the world." In broad terms, what we can do is to redesign our food and agriculture system so that its functions are more consistent with our best understanding of how the biotic community works and adapt agriculture to it. We can seek to provide adequate amounts of food by nurturing the potential for increased productivity inherent in such redesigned multispecies systems. And we must begin paying attention to the place and density of the human species in relation to the rest of the biotic community.

With respect to agriculture, it seems imperative to pursue three objectives in preparing for our new future. First, we should begin immediately to refocus our public research agenda. Properly refocused, this would help us better understand the synergies and synchronies of the diverse species in each agricultural watershed, and determine how they can be used to increase our agricultural productivity while simultaneously enhancing the capacity for self-renewal of local ecologies. To that end, we should explore ways that allow the disciplines of ecology, evolutionary biology, and sociology to interface more fully with agriculture. This would mean, among other things, that we would begin using ecological and social screens to determine what technologies to use in agriculture and how to manage them to achieve these larger objectives. This would include exploring the potential synergies and synchronies of multispecies production systems.

Simultaneously, we should expand our research agendas to investigate and design new food marketing relationships that would allow farmers to produce more value on their farms and retain a larger share of that value in the economy of the farm and the local community. There can be no sustainable future for an agriculture that only requires farmers to produce undifferentiated raw materials as cheaply as possible, with all of the value of that production accruing to distant shareholders. The USDA Sustainable Agriculture Research and Education (SARE) program might well be expanded to include such total food systems research.

Second, we should look at new policy options at both federal and local levels that give these new production and marketing systems a competitive advantage and that encourage farmers to transition out of the unsustainable systems of the past. If the health of economy, ecology, and community must be achieved in concert, then our public policies must be redesigned to achieve that larger, integrated goal rather than continuing to support the production of a few bulk commodities using unsustainable production practices and selling at untenable prices. In the face of declining fossil fuel resources, ecological restoration must be a centerpiece of the new policies. As Leopold argued, such policies should be geared to promoting smaller enterprises and creativity rather than consolidation and regulation. Sound ecological management can be performed only by people with an "ecological conscience" living in local ecologies long enough and intimately enough to learn how to manage them well.

Finally, we need to launch a nationwide education program to foster a national ecological conscience. As Leopold argued, "Obligations have no meaning without conscience, and the problem we face is the extension of the social conscience from people to land." Our ethical imperative, in other words, must now be broadened from one limited to human-to-human relationships to one that encompasses the entire biotic community (Leopold, 1949). As Leopold noted, "The Land Ethic simply enlarges the boundaries of the community to include soils, waters, plants, and animals, or collectively: the land."

At the heart of our mission to achieve a sustainable agriculture, then, is a social, cultural, and spiritual mission to develop a land ethic among land users. It is at the core of any effort to put a viable, functional agriculture on the landscape that can function well under the circumstances that will evolve in the decades ahead. Leopold, once again, described our mission best: "A land ethic, then, reflects the existence of an ecological conscience, and this in turn reflects a conviction of individual responsibility for the health of the land. Health is the capacity of the land for self-renewal. Conservation is our effort to understand and preserve this capacity" (Leopold, 1949).

It is the farmers of the middle who are in the best position to adopt that ethic and put it to work on a scale that can have a significant impact on the ecological, social, and human health of the planet. One of their current options is organic farming, producing crops in accordance with many of nature's principles, and marketing healthy food to consumers. And civic society has a moral obligation to make sure that they are motivated to do so, have time to do so, and can afford to do so. It is our common ethical imperative.

Discussion Questions

1. What are the current driving forces that contribute to concentration of farmland into large, industrial farming and ranching operations?

2. Describe and discuss some of the major limits of industrial agriculture, and why the current course of development in food systems will not be sustainable for the long term.

3. In what ways can technology solve the problems of providing greater food production and making this available to all global citizens, and in what ways does this singular approach fall short of achieving broad food system objectives of supply and equity?

4. Describe and discuss the current global natural resource situation and how this impacts agricultural production. What are the consequences of continuing in the current industrial food production model?

5. What is the potential impact of global climate change on agricultural production systems and geographic distribution of prime food production areas, and how will this be impacted by our decisions on farm size and structure of the agricultural sector?

6. What impact will current consumption of water in agriculture have on future potentials for food production, and in what ways are ownership and allocation of water important in the future structuring of a sustainable global agricultural system?

7. What are the ethical imperatives connected with current industrial agriculture, and what options are most likely to result in greater equity of food availability for all people in the future? In what ways is human capital one of the most important factors for the future?

8. What are the reasons for the disappearance of the small- and moderate-sized family farms in the United States, and what steps are needed to reverse this trend?

9. In what direct ways are rural communities tied to farm size in the surrounding landscape, and how does structure of farming contribute to community infrastructure and economic viability? What are the solutions for farms and for rural communities in resource-poor regions?

10. What are the alternatives to evaluating agricultural systems in current conventional economic terms? In what ways does such an analysis serve us well, and in what ways does it not adequately assess the food, nutrition, and hunger issues in society?

11. In what ways is the Aldo Leopold land ethic relevant today as we search for strategies to confront global hunger and equity in food availability?

12. What are some concrete steps that can be taken to achieve a sustainable future agricultural system, and what role can organic farming play in this strategy? What is the role of education as a part of this plan?

References

Baskin, Y. 1997. The work of nature: How the diversity of life sustains us. Island Press, Washington, DC.

Berry, W. 1990. What are people for. North Point Press, San Francisco, CA.

Berry, W. 2006. New introduction. p. xiv. In The soil and health, by A. Howard. Reprint. Univ. of Kentucky Press, Lexington.

Brown, L.R. 2006. Plan B 2.0. W.W. Norton, New York.

Duffy, M. 2005. Profits: Weather–profits–clouds. Available at http://www.econ.iastate.edu/faculty/duffy/pages/powerpoint/profitsorincome.ppt (verified 28 July 2009). Iowa State Univ., Ames.

Fiksel, J. 2006. Sustainability and resilience: Toward a systems approach. Sustainability Sci. Practice Policy 2(2):14–21.

Furuno, T. 2001. The power of duck. Tagari, Sisters Creek, Tasmania, Australia.

Halweil, B. 2001. Biotech, African corn, and the vampire weed. World Watch 14(5).

Hansen, J. 2006. The threat to the planet. New York Review of Books, 13 July.

Hanson, H.C. 1939. Ecology in agriculture. Ecology 20(2):111–117.

Heinberg, R. 2005. The party's over: Oil, war, and the fate of industrial societies. 2nd ed. Clairview Press, East Sussex, UK.

Helgasson, T., T.J. Daniell, R. Husband, A.H. Fitter, and J.P.W. Young. 1998. Ploughing up the wood-wide web? Nature 394:431.

Kirschenmann, F., G.W. Stevenson, F. Buttel, T.A. Lyson, and M. Duffy. 2008. Why worry about the agriculture of the middle? p. 3–22. In T.A. Lyson, G.W. Stevenson, and R. Welsh (ed.) Food and the mid-level farm: Renewing an agriculture of the middle. MIT Press, Cambridge, MA.

Leopold, A. 1949. A Sand County almanac. Oxford Univ. Press, New York.

Leopold, A. 1999a. Be your own emperor. p. 78. In J.B. Callicott and E.T. Freyfogle (ed.) For the health of the land. Island Press, Washington, DC.

Leopold, A. 1999b. The outlook for farm wildlife. p. 218. In J.B. Callicott and E.T. Freyfogle (ed.) For the health of the land. Island Press, Washington, DC.

Lewis, W.J., J.C. van Lenteren, S.C. Phatak, and J.H. Tumlinson III. 1997. A total system approach to sustainable pest management. Proc. Natl. Acad. Sci. USA 94:12243–12248.

Lewontin, R.. 2000. The triple helix. Harvard Univ. Press, Cambridge, MA.

Mäder, P., A. Fliessbach, D. Dubois, L. Gunst, P. Fried, and U. Niggli. 2002. Soil fertility and biodiversity in organic farming. Science 296:1694–1697.

Mather, C. 1702. Magnalia Christi Americana. Book 1, Part 1, Chapter 4.

National Research Council (NRC). 1975. Understanding climate change: A program for action. National Academy of Sciences, Washington, DC.

National Research Council (NRC). 1993. Soil and water quality: An agenda for agriculture. National Academy Press, Washington, DC.

Power, A.G. 1999. Linking ecological sustainability and world food needs. Environ. Dev. Sustain. 1(3/4):185–196.

Reder, M.W. 1999. Economics: The culture of a controversial science. University of Chicago Press, Chicago, IL.

Rosenzweig, C., and D. Hillel. 1995. Potential impacts of climate change on agriculture and food supply. Consequences 1(2).

Rosenzweig, C., A. Iglesias, X.B. Yang, P.R. Epstein, and E. Chivian. 2001. Climate change and extreme weather events: Implications for food production, plant diseases and pests. Glob. Change Hum. Health 2(2):90–104.

Salatin, J. 1998. You can farm: The entrepreneur's guide to start and succeed in a farming enterprise. Polyface Enterprises, Swope, VA.

Schusky, E.L. 1989. Culture and agriculture: An ecological introduction to traditional and modern farming systems. Bergin & Garvey, New York.

Sen, A. 1987. On ethics and economics. Blackwell, Oxford, UK.

Shiyomi, M., and H. Koizumi. 2001. Structure and function in agroecosystem design and management. CRC Press, Boca Raton, FL.

Simard, S.W., D.A. Perry, M.D. Jones, D.D. Myrold, D.M. Durall, and R. Molina. 1997. Net transfer of carbon between ectomycorrhizal tree species in the field. Nature 388:579–582.

Swimme, B., and T. Berry. 1992. The universe story. Harper Collins, San Francisco, CA.

Tilman, D., and J.A. Downing. 1994. Biodiversity and stability in grasslands. Nature 367:363–365.

USDA Economic Research Service. 2000. Farm typology for diverse agriculture. ERS Information Bull. 759. USDA Economic Research Service, Washington, DC.

Wackernagel, M., N.B. Schulz, D. Deumling, A. Callejas Linares, M. Jenkins, V. Kapos, C. Monfreda, J. Loh, N. Myers, R. Norgaard, and J. Randers. 2002. Tracking the ecological overshoot of the human economy. Proc. National Acad. Sci. USA 99:9266–9271.

Waltner-Toews, D., J.J. Kay, C. Neudoerffer, and T. Gitau. 2003. Perspective changes everything: Managing ecosystems from the inside out. Frontiers Ecol. Environ. 1(1):23–30.

Waltner-Toews, D., and T. Lang. 2000. A new conceptual base for food and agricultural policy: The emerging model of links between agriculture, food, health, environment and society. Glob. Change Hum. Health 1(2):116–130.

Warner, K. 2007. Agroecology in action: Extending alternative agriculture through social Networks. MIT Press, Boston, MA.

Subject Index ◗